Analog Electronics
Analysis and Design

Other Macmillan titles of related interest

W. A. Atherton, *From Compass to Computer*
B. R. Bannister and D. G. Whitehead, *Fundamentals of Modern Digital Systems*
G. B. Clayton, *Data Converters*
G. B. Clayton, *Experiments with Operational Amplifiers*
J. C. Cluley, *Electronic Equipment Reliability*, second edition
R. F. W. Coates, *Modern Communication Systems*, second edition
A. R. Daniels, *Introduction to Electrical Machines*
C. W. Davidson, *Transmission Lines for Communication*
J. D. Edwards, *Electrical Machines—An Introduction to Principles and Characteristics*
M. E. Goodge, *Semiconductor Device Technology*
B. A. Gregory, *An Introduction to Electrical Instrumentation and Measurement Systems*, second edition
L. F. Lind and J. C. C. Nelson, *Analysis and Design of Sequential Digital Systems*
Paul A. Lynn, *An Introduction to the Analysis and Processing of Signals*, second edition
S. A. Marshall, *Introduction to Control Theory*
A. G. Martin and F. W. Stephenson, *Linear Microelectronic Systems*
J. E. Parton, S. J. T. Owen and M. S. Raven, *Applied Electromagnetics*, second edition
M. Ramamoorty, *An Introduction to Thyristors and their Applications*
Douglas A. Ross, *Optoelectronic Devices and Optical Imaging Techniques*
Trevor J. Terrell, *Introduction to Digital Filters*
B. W. Williams, *Power Electronics—Devices, Drivers and Applications*
G. Williams, *An Introduction to Electrical Circuit Theory*

Analog Electronics Analysis and Design

Malcolm Goodge

BSc (Hons), MPhil, CEng, MIEE
Senior Lecturer
School of Computer Science and Electronic Systems
University of Kingston

First published 1990 by
MACMILLAN PRESS LTD
Houndmills, Basingstoke, Hampshire RG21 6XS
and London
Companies and representatives
throughout the world

ISBN 0-333-48838-5 hardcover
ISBN 0-333-48839-3 paperback

A catalogue record for this book is available
from the British Library.

10 9 8 7 6 5 4 3 2
03 02 01 00 99 98 97 96 95

Printed in Malaysia

Contents

Preface

Analog Electronics is an undergraduate main course text dealing with the analysis and design of continuous-signal electronic hardware. No previous experience in the subject is assumed. Treatment throughout is at device/component level with sufficient explanation to enable the reader develop both an understanding of the principles involved and a proficiency in basic design.

The material covers the analog electronics syllabuses of the first 2 years of MEng, BEng and BSc courses in Electronics and related subjects, providing a sound foundation for more specialised work in final-year options and post-graduate studies. The book will also be useful to students of Higher Diploma courses in Electronics.

Each chapter begins by listing the coverage so that the reader can see at a glance the direction of the work. Over 50 worked examples are included in the text and more than 120 further graduated tutorial questions, with answers, provide readers with the opportunity to test their developing understanding and design ability. Although devoted mainly to analog electronics, pulse circuits are also included since this material is not normally covered in complementary texts devoted to digital electronics.

The introductory chapter is concerned with basics including essential terminology, circuit analysis techniques applicable to electronic circuits and the operation of the basic transistor–load–power supply circuit in the linear and switching modes.

Chapter 2 is devoted to the various electronic devices and components: transistors, diodes, resistors, capacitors, inductors and transformers. The material included is limited to that required as foundation to the use of these circuit elements in subsequent work, the emphasis being on practical details. Brief explanation of device operation is included for completeness; the reader is referred to the author's text *Semiconductor Device Technology* for more detailed information where necessary. The chapter concludes with an outline of component and manufacturing costs.

For convenience, the major topic of amplification is subdivided into small-signal amplifiers, operational amplifiers and power amplifiers, with separate chapters devoted to frequency response and feedback. Chapter 3 covers the fundamentals of linear circuit performance and design: biasing, dc stability, load line analysis and ac performance at mid-frequencies, together with comparison of the performance of the various configurations of both BJT and FET single-stage circuits.

The topic of frequency response is considered in chapter 4 with the effects of series and shunt capacitance on the gain and phase response of linear circuits being examined initially, leading to treatment of amplifier response at low and high frequencies, including the effect of stray capacitance. The significance of limited frequency response as far as distortion is concerned is included here, and the chapter concludes with consideration of the pulse response of analog circuits.

Chapter 5 introduces feedback and investigates its effect on gain, bandwidth, stability, input and output resistance, distortion and noise before considering the practical implementation of the various feedback arrangements.

More advanced aspects of small-signal amplifiers are described in chapter 6, notably bootstrapping, biasing by current mirror and the use of active loads. The chapter continues with consideration of differential, Darlington and complementary stages together with treatment of the cascode arrangement, the effect of cascading amplifier stages and the performance of tuned amplifiers.

Operational amplifiers are dealt with in chapter 7. After consideration of general aspects, a typical commercially-available op-amp is used as a vehicle for performance analysis, providing a useful example of the application of some of the techniques discussed previously. The concept of the hypothetical ideal op-amp is introduced and the circumstances discussed under which a practical op-amp may be considered as ideal, thereby greatly simplifying the analysis of circuits employing this type of amplifier; a range of linear and switching applications is then investigated using this simplification. The latter part of the chapter deals with the significance of the imperfections of the practical op-amp, such as finite parameters, offsets, output loading, slew rate limiting and stability; compensation for closed-loop stability is considered in detail.

Chapter 8 on power amplifiers considers the special aspects associated with higher power stages, notably power efficiency and distortion, and examines classes A, B and AB performance and implementation. Special-purpose class C operation and switched-mode power stages, classes D and E, are also discussed briefly.

Developing from previous work on feedback, linear oscillators are considered in chapter 9 in the context of analog signal generation; the work covers the theory and practical aspects of the various *CR*, *LC* and crystal types. The second half of this chapter is devoted to various aspects of analog signal processing. Signal limiting, clamping and precision rectification are covered initially followed by sections on filtering, based mainly on the popular Sallen and Key active filter, shaping using piecewise-linear techniques together with an introduction to modulation and demodulation.

Both discrete-component and op-amp based pulse circuits are considered in chapter 10. After an introductory section concerned with the various aspects of the use of transistors as switches, the operation and design of discrete-component bistable, monostable and astable circuits are examined. Then, extending the work on the use of op-amps in switching applications in chapter 7, sections are included on op-amp based astable and monostable circuits, illustrating the relatively simple design procedures involved.

The final chapter on power supplies considers the various stages of ac–dc, dc–ac and dc–dc supplies, and includes a section on batteries. The concept of power is introduced initially together with the significance and determination of the average and root-mean-square values of a time-varying quantity. Based on the linear ac–dc supply, transformation and rectification are then considered, followed by detailed coverage of the various types of smoothing filter, with performance and component selection being considered in each case. The operation and design of linear regulators is then included with further sections on current limiting and protection. Switched-mode techniques for ac–dc supplies, inverters and step-up converters are then introduced, but the reader is referred to texts devoted to power electronics for detailed consideration of these specialist topics. The section on batteries is concerned mainly with the designation and performance of the popular disposable and rechargeable types. Battery performance parameters are listed and the factors affecting battery selection considered.

Each chapter includes a detailed list of reference material to assist the reader in further work. Additional material on the Fourier representation of non-sinusoidal waveshapes, the performance of tuned circuits, component coding, ranges of preferred component values and manufacturers' data sheets for a range of typical devices and ICs is included as appendixes.

Malcolm Goodge

Acknowledgements

I should like to thank several members of the School of Computer Science and Electronic Systems at Kingston Polytechnic for their support and encouragement during the preparation of this text, in particular, Professor Peter Barnwell, Jerry Ingham, Gordon Shaw and David Lush, also Dr John Coekin, the former Head of School, and Dr Don Pedder, now with ERA plc. In addition I am grateful to the many MEng, BEng and formerly BSc students of Electronic Systems at Kingston who have tested the material, particularly the tutorial questions, over several years.

I thank Philips Components Limited, Siliconix Limited and Texas Instruments Limited for allowing me to incorporate their published data sheets on selected devices; and also Philips, formerly Mullard, for permission to use the heatsink selection chart in chapter 11.

However, most thanks are due to my wife Judith for her continued encouragement during the preparation of this text and for typing the manuscript.

1 Introductory Topics

Coverage

- Essential concepts and terminology: signals, analog and digital systems, discrete-component and integrated systems, active devices and passive components, current–voltage performance characteristic, data sheet, static and dynamic operation, linearity, small-signal and large-signal operation.
- Comparison of the analysis techniques applicable to linear and non-linear circuits.
- Analysis of non-linear circuits by graphical techniques: quiescent operating point, load line.
- Analysis of non-linear circuits using a network model; the concept of piecewise-linear modelling.
- Small-signal analysis of non-linear circuits.
- The basic transistor–load–power supply circuit: analog and digital operation.

1.1 Basic concepts and terminology

Electronic *hardware* uses the basic circuit elements such as transistors, diodes and resistors to control the flow of electrical energy for purposes of communication, computation or automatic control. In each case the energy flow, *current*, or the disturbance causing, or caused by, the flow (*voltage*) is used to convey information – it is termed a *signal*. Systems in which the signal voltage or current can change smoothly over a range of values are termed *analog* systems while those in which the electrical *variable* can have only certain predefined values are described as *digital*. The basic analog electronic circuit is the *amplifier* while in digital systems the basic circuit is the electronic *switch*.

Systems constructed using individual circuit elements such as transistors and resistors, usually inconnected via copper tracks on a printed-circuit board (pcb) are termed *discrete-component circuits* while those formed using integrated circuit 'building blocks' are referred to as *integrated systems*. A feature of most digital systems is that they are formed from what is a relatively small number of circuit arrangements such as gates, counters, multiplexers and memory cells, but the system requires a large number of each circuit type and for this reason digital systems are almost totally integrated. Such repetition does not occur in analog systems and as a result discrete-component technology is far more widespread in this branch of electronics. This text concentrates mostly on analog circuit design using discrete components.

Transistors, which have a control terminal in addition to the main energy input and output terminals, are described as *active devices* because the control feature enables them to provide signal amplification and switching. Two-terminal elements such as diodes and resistors are termed *passive components* since they do not permit such control, the current flow being dependent only on the voltage across the component.

The relationship between current and voltage is the fundamental performance *characteristic* of a device or component. Such characteristics are given either graphically, as in the device *specification* supplied by the manufacturer, often called the *data sheet*, or as a mathematical equation as in the case of Ohm's law for a resistor. Where the characteristic refers to the relationship between constant current and constant voltage it is described as the *static characteristic* while for time-varying current and voltage the relationship is described as the *dynamic characteristic*; in the latter case the corresponding *frequency* of the varying current and voltage is also quoted. In the same way, *static* (direct current, dc) operation of an electronic device or component refers to operation under constant current and constant voltage conditions while *dynamic* (alternating current, ac) operation describes use under time-varying current and voltage conditions. The most significant difference between these two modes of operation is that in the dynamic case the energy storage properties of devices and components can have a major effect on their performance, resulting in limited high frequency use of analog systems, usually described in terms of *bandwidth*, and in limited switching rate in digital systems.

Another important aspect of circuit element performance regards *linearity*. Resistors, capacitors and wound components are described as *linear* over limited operating ranges because the associated variables exhibit proportionality, namely voltage is proportional to current for a resistor, charge is proportional to voltage for a capacitor and magnetic flux is proportional to current for an inductor (section 2.4). In contrast, transistors and diodes are described as *non-linear* since the current and voltage are not proportional. Linearity is particularly significant in the analysis of circuit performance as discussed in section 1.2. Linear circuits obey the principle of *superposition*, that is, if a voltage v applied to a linear circuit causes a current i in a branch of the circuit, and if in terms of values v_1 results in i_1 and v_2 in i_2, then if $(v_1 + v_2)$ was to be applied the corresponding current would be $(i_1 + i_2)$. In the case of non-linear circuits, superposition does not apply, owing to the non-linear relationship between voltage and current; for example, a doubling of the voltage does not, in general, cause a doubling of the current.

A consequence of non-linear performance is that in the case of dynamic operation where the voltage and current vary with time, the performance of the circuit depends on the extent of the fluctuation. When the *amplitudes* of the variations are relatively low, the system operation is described as *small-signal* and the analog performance of a non-linear circuit under these conditions is different from the case of wide fluctuations, termed *large-signal* operation.

1.2 **Circuit analysis**

Analysis refers to the prediction of voltages and currents in a circuit in response to an input stimulus. In *static* (dc) analysis the stimulus, such as the power source used to energise the circuit, does not vary with time and the voltage and current levels in the circuit will be constant values. In most applications however it is the variation of voltages and currents with time or frequency that is of main interest, termed the *time-domain response* and *frequency-domain response* respectively; determination of these responses is described as *dynamic* (ac) analysis.

1.2.1 ***Linear circuit analysis***

Circuits comprising entirely linear elements, that is, resistors, capacitors and wound components, can be solved mathematically to determine both the static and dynamic performance.

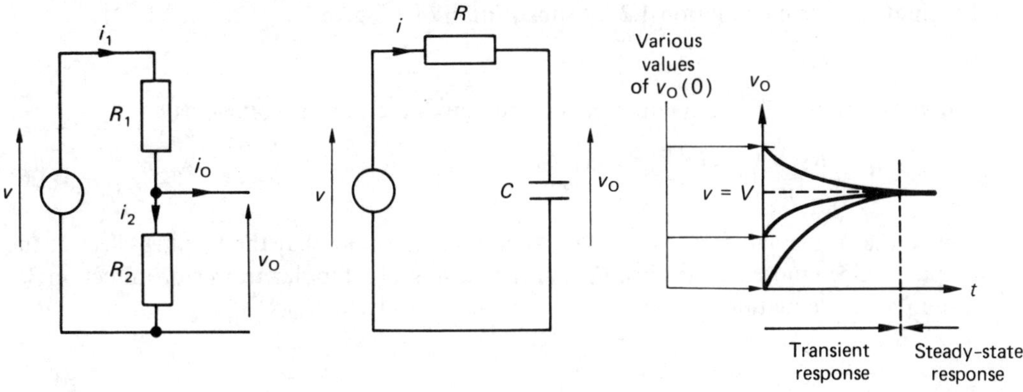

Figure 1.1 Linear circuits

In the case of circuits comprising only one type of element such as the potential divider of figure 1.1a, the circuit equations are *algebraic* and solution involves substitution/elimination of the set of simultaneous equations to obtain the required variables in terms of the known variables. In the potential divider of example 1.1 the required variables are the current i_1 and output voltage v_O and the known variable is the applied voltage v; if applicable, the output loading i_O would also need to be known.

Example 1.1: Analysis examples of networks comprising only one type of linear element – the resistive potential divider

(a) Determine the current drawn from the source v and the output voltage v_O for the basic potential divider of figure 1.1a.

(b) If $R_1 = 8.2\ \text{k}\Omega$ and $R_2 = 1.8\ \text{k}\Omega$, what is the maximum allowable current loading i_O, as a percentage of the main current i_1, if the potential divider ratio v_O/v must be within 2 per cent of its unloaded value?

(a) If the *loading* on the output of the circuit causes a current i_O to be drawn, the current through R_2 is $i_1 - i_O$ thus

$$i_2 = i_1 - i_O \tag{1.1}$$

Summing the voltages around the loop (Kirchhoff's voltage law)

$$v = R_1 i_1 + R_2 i_2 \tag{1.2}$$

The output voltage v_O is given by Ohm's law as

$$v_O = R_2 i_2 \tag{1.3}$$

Eliminating i_2 from equation 1.2 by substitution from 1.1 gives

$$v = R_1 i_1 + R_2(i_1 - i_O) \tag{1.4}$$

from which the current drawn from the source is

$$i_1 = \frac{v}{R_1 + R_2} + \left(\frac{R_2}{R_1 + R_2}\right) i_O \tag{1.5}$$

Eliminating i_2 from equation 1.2 by substitution of 1.3 gives

$$v_O = v - R_1 i_1$$

and substitution of i_1 from equation 1.5 then gives the output voltage as

$$v_O = \left(\frac{R_2}{R_1 + R_2}\right)v - \left(\frac{R_1 R_2}{R_1 + R_2}\right)i_O \quad (1.6)$$

Notice that if the value of $(R_1 + R_2)$ is such that $i_1 \gg i_O$ so that the loading effect at the output can be ignored, as for example in the biasing of a bipolar transistor in section 3.1 (example 3.3), equations 1.5 and 1.6 reduce respectively to

$$i_1 = \frac{v}{R_1 + R_2} \quad (1.7)$$

and

$$v_O = \left(\frac{R_2}{R_1 + R_2}\right)v \quad (1.8)$$

which are the *ideal* or *unloaded* potential divider relations.
If the source voltage v is known, either a constant voltage V or a time-varying voltage $v(t)$, the values of i_1 and v_O can be calculated.

(b) Comparing the loaded (finite i_O) and unloaded ($i_O = 0$) situations, equations 1.6 and 1.8 respectively, the reduction in the potential divider ratio v_O/v caused by the loading is $\left(\frac{R_1 R_2}{R_1 + R_2}\right)\frac{i_O}{v}$. In this particular case, the maximum allowable load i_O max corresponds to the reduction $\left(\frac{R_1 R_2}{R_1 + R_2}\right)\frac{i_O \max}{v}$ being 2 per cent of the unloaded ratio $\left(\frac{R_2}{R_1 + R_2}\right)$ from which

$$\left(\frac{R_1 R_2}{R_1 + R_2}\right)\frac{i_O \max}{v} = \frac{2}{100}\left(\frac{R_2}{R_1 + R_2}\right)$$

or

$$\frac{v}{i_O \max} = 50R_1 \quad (1.9)$$

However the requirement is to determine i_O max as a percentage of i_1 for this condition and so it is necessary to write v in equation 1.9 in terms of i_1.
Substituting for v from equation 1.4, relation 1.9 becomes

$$\frac{(R_1 + R_2)i_1 - R_2 i_O \max}{i_O \max} = 50R_1$$

from which

$$\frac{i_O \max}{i_1} = \frac{R_1 + R_2}{50R_1 + R_2} \quad (1.10)$$

For $R_1 = 8.2\ \text{k}\Omega$ and $R_2 = 1.8\ \text{k}\Omega$, the maximum loading condition corresponding to a 2 per cent reduction in potential divider output is

$$\frac{i_O \max}{i_1} = \frac{8.2\ \text{k}\Omega + 1.8\ \text{k}\Omega}{50(8.2\ \text{k}\Omega) + 1.8\ \text{k}\Omega} = \frac{10\ \text{k}\Omega}{411.8\ \text{k}\Omega} = 0.024 \text{ or } 2.4 \text{ per cent.}$$

For a circuit involving different types of linear element such as *CR*, *LR* and *LCR* circuits, the resulting equations describing the performance are *differential* as shown in example 1.2 and although more complex, these can be solved using standard mathematical techniques as in the algebraic case. Example 1.2 illustrates a feature of the time-domain response of networks containing different types of linear element, namely that the overall response can be divided into *transient* and *steady-state* responses which correspond, in mathematical terms, to the complementary function and particular integral components of the solution of a differential equation [1a]. The transient response results from the redistribution of energy within the system when the stimulus is applied and in the case of a *CR* network the controlling feature is the *time constant* $\tau = CR$ of the circuit. Eventually, depending on the value of τ, the response settles down to a 'steady' response provided the stimulus remains unchanged. Notice that the steady-state response is actually a constant value only if the stimulus is constant, as in example 1.2; if v was time varying, the steady-state response would also be time varying.

Example 1.2: Analysis example of a circuit comprising different types of linear element – a CR network

(a) For the circuit of figure 1.1b determine the voltage across the capacitor v_O as a function of time if the applied voltage v is a constant value V and the initial value of the capacitor voltage is $v_O(0)$.
(b) Calculate the capacitor voltage v_O as a percentage of the steady-state value V when $t = \tau$ and when $t = 5\tau$ assuming the capacitor is uncharged at $t = 0$.

(a) Summing the voltages around the loop

$$v = iR + v_O \tag{1.11}$$

The current–voltage relationship for the capacitor (equation 2.24) is

$$i = C\frac{dv_O}{dt} \tag{1.12}$$

Substituting for i from equation 1.12 into 1.11 gives

$$CR\frac{dv_O}{dt} + v_O = v \tag{1.13}$$

Solution of this first-order differential equation using standard mathematical techniques such as D-operator or Laplace transform as explained in mathematics texts such as references [1b] and [2], for v = constant V, gives

$$v_O = V + (v_O(0) - V)\exp(-t/CR) \tag{1.14}$$

The corresponding response of v_O as a function of time for various values of $v_O(0)$ is shown in figure 1.1b.

For the special case of the capacitor being uncharged when V is applied, $v_O(0) = 0$, and the solution becomes

$$v_O = V[1 - \exp(-t/CR)]$$
$$= V[1 - \exp(-t/\tau)] \quad (1.15)$$

where CR is the time constant τ.

(b) From equation 1.15

$$\frac{v_O}{V} = 1 - \exp\left(-\frac{t}{\tau}\right)$$

When $t = \tau$, $\frac{v_O}{v} = 1 - \exp(-1) = 0.632$ or 63.2 per cent

when $t = 5\tau$, $\frac{v_O}{v} = 1 - \exp(-5) = 0.993$ or 99.3 per cent

indicating that after charging for a time equal to the time constant, the capacitor voltage has risen to 63.2 per cent of its final value while after a time of 5τ the voltage is within 0.7 per cent of its steady-state value.

Although examples 1.1 and 1.2 show that linear networks can be solved by establishing a set of simultaneous equations that represent the performance of the circuit and which can be solved by standard mathematical techniques, it should be noted that if a large number of loops are involved, hand calculation is tedious and computer circuit analysis programs can be usefully employed.

1.2.2 *Non-linear circuit analysis using graphical techniques*

Most practical electronic circuits are non-linear because they contain diodes and transistors which have non-linear characteristics. Although approximate mathematical representation of such characteristics is possible (section 2.3), often other techniques are more convenient.

Manufacturers normally provide the $I-V$ characteristics of diodes and transistors in graphical form (appendix E) and it is therefore convenient to use graphical techniques for analysis. Consider the network of figure 1.2a in which the non-linear device has a static characteristic $I = f(V_D)$ where V_D is the voltage across the device and I is the corresponding current flowing through it. Using Kirchhoff's voltage law together with the relationship $V_R = RI$ for the series resistor, the network equation is

$$V_S - RI - V_D = 0 \quad (1.16)$$

This equation cannot be solved without knowledge of the relationship between I and V_D for the non-linear device, namely

$$I = f(V_D) \quad (1.17)$$

Determination of the static operating conditions for the network, that is the values I, V_D and V_R, requires the simultaneous solution of equations 1.16 and 1.17. As it is assumed that equation 1.17 is not known in precise mathematical terms, direct mathematical solution is not possible but solution can be obtained graphically by superimposing equation 1.16 on the

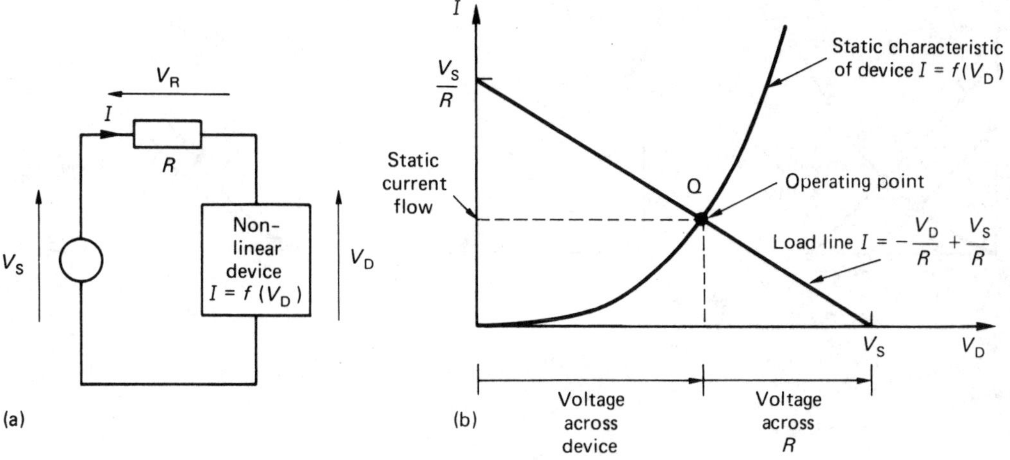

Figure 1.2 Graphical analysis

device characteristic (figure 1.2b); the point of intersection of the two graphs then giving the operating condition of the device.

Rearranging equation 1.16 in the form $I = f(V_D)$ to enable superposition on the same axes $(I-V_D)$ as the device characteristic gives

$$I = -\left(\frac{1}{R}\right)V_D + \frac{V_S}{R} \tag{1.18}$$

indicating a straight line (compare with the general form $y = mx + c$) of gradient $-1/R$ and intercept $+V_S/R$ on the I-axis.

The point of intersection of the two graphs then gives the *operating point* of the circuit, from which the current flow through the circuit and the voltages across the components can be obtained as shown in figure 1.2b. This is a *static* operating point as the source voltage V_S is constant and the term *quiescent* (*no signal*) *point* or *Q-point* is often used.

The graph of equation 1.18 is commonly described as a *load line* as the resistor R can be considered as the load on the device. A convenient method of drawing the load line, knowing it to be straight as R is constant, is to simply draw a straight line through the intercept points on the axes which are $I = +V_S/R$ when $V_D = 0$ and $V_D = V_S$ when $I = 0$ from equation 1.18.

This graphical technique is useful not only because of its simplicity and the fact that the device characteristic is normally provided in graphical form but also because the technique readily shows the change in operating conditions if the source voltage varies, provided the rate of change of voltage is sufficiently low that the static characteristic still represents the current–voltage performance of the device with reasonable accuracy. Figure 1.3a shows the shift in load line due solely to a change in source voltage and the corresponding change in the operating conditions of the device can clearly be obtained from the shift of the operating point. If V_S remains fixed but the load R is altered, the corresponding change is shown in figure 1.3b while the change in operating conditions caused by a shift in device characteristic, either due to a change of device or to a change of environment such as temperature, is illustrated in figure 1.3c. Such techniques are useful in assessing the possible range of operating conditions caused by a combination of effects (figure 1.3d) such as for example the *spread* of characteristics for a particular type number of device, the *spread* due to an operating

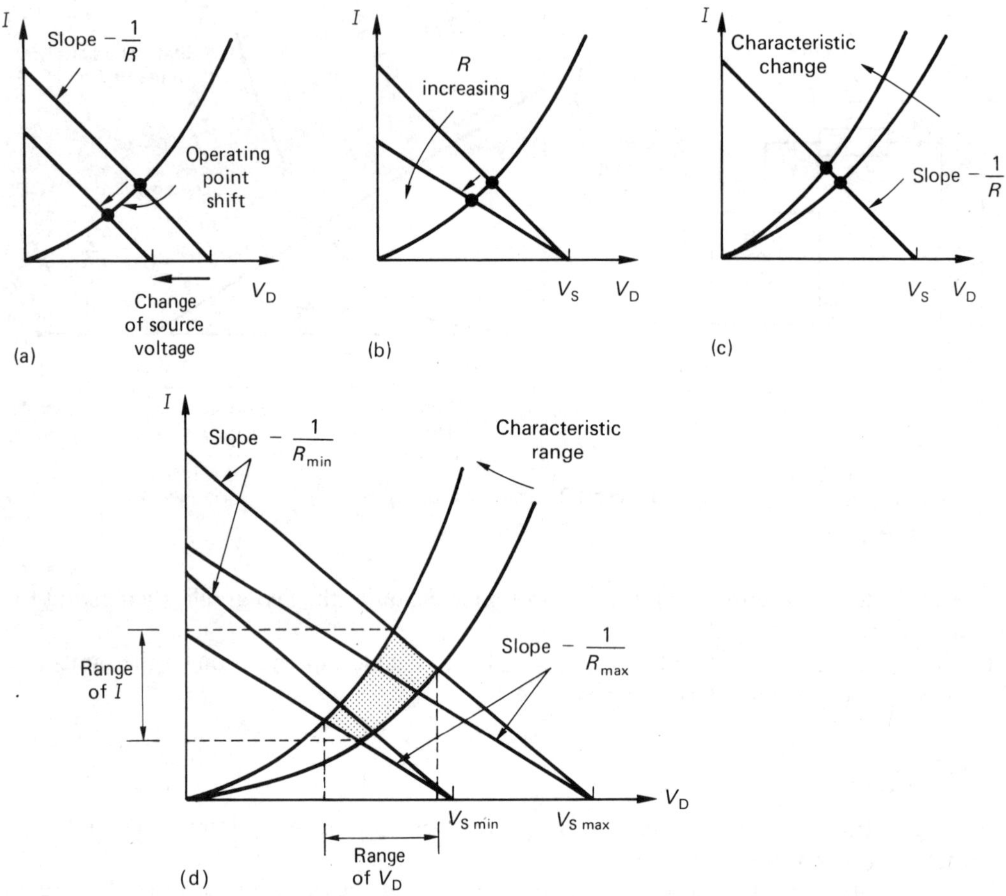

Figure 1.3 Use of graphical techniques to investigate changing conditions

temperature range or component tolerance ($R \pm x$ per cent) and a specified fluctuation of source voltage. For such investigations, graphical techniques are invaluable.

One criticism of graphical techniques is the possible poor accuracy of the results compared with mathematical precision. It must be appreciated however that in practical electronic design, apart from some specialised areas such as high-accuracy signal processing and instrumentation, extreme accuracy is not required, and indeed is of little practical use, as the final product will be constructed in most cases from preferred-value components (appendix D) and active devices that are not individually selected to have precisely known parameters and characteristics. It should be noted that the characteristics provided by the device manufacturer are for a *typical* device, often with information of *spread* (max–min range), and so the precise characteristic of a particular device is not known unless individual tests are carried out.

Example 1.3: Non-linear circuit analysis using graphical techniques

The non-linear device in the circuit of figure 1.2a is a diode having the current–voltage characteristic shown in figure 1.4.

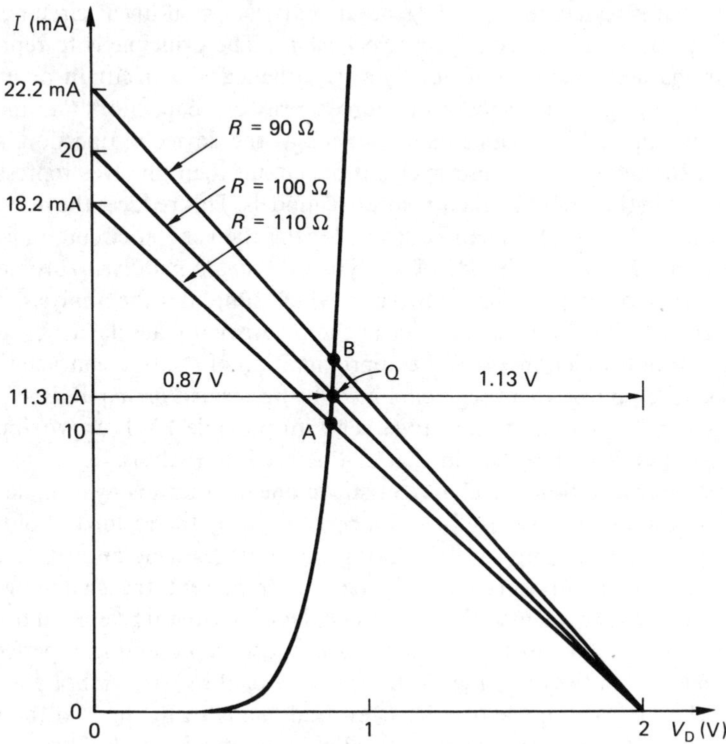

Figure 1.4 Diode characteristic for example 1.3

(a) If V_S is 2 V with polarity such that the diode conducts and $R = 100\,\Omega$, determine graphically the Q-point of the diode. What is the voltage across R under these conditions?
(b) If R has a tolerance range of ± 10 per cent, estimate from the graph the range over which the Q-point may vary for resistors from a given batch.

(a) Construct the load line on figure 1.4 for $R = 100\,\Omega$ and $V_S = 2$ V, that is, corresponding to figure 1.2b between coordinates $V_D = 0$, $I = 2\text{ V}/100\,\Omega = 20$ mA and $V_D = 2$ V, $I = 0$. The intercept with the diode characteristic gives the operating (Q) point of the diode which is $V_D = 0.87$ V, $I = 11.3$ mA.
The voltage across R can be read from the graph as 1.13 V or calculated from $V_S - V_D = 2\text{ V} - 0.87\text{ V} = 1.13$ V.
(b) If the circuit resistance has a tolerance of ± 10 per cent, the resistance can have any value in the range $100\,\Omega - 10$ per cent to $100\,\Omega + 10$ per cent, that is, $90\,\Omega$ to $110\,\Omega$. Construction of corresponding load lines for these two extremes shows that the Q-point will be between points A and B on the characteristic which gives the Q-point range as approximately (0.86 V, 10.3 mA) to (0.88 V, 12.5 mA).

1.2.3 *Non-linear circuit analysis using piecewise-linear modelling*

For most practical purposes, graphical techniques are restricted to analysis of static operation and investigation of the change of static operating point as conditions slowly change.

A technique that is widely used in the general analysis of non-linear circuits, for both static and dynamic operation, is the use of a *network model.* The principle is to represent or *model* the non-linear characteristic of a device by a hypothetical linear circuit or *network* of ideal circuit elements (voltage sources, current sources, resistors, capacitors and inductors) which would have approximately the same characteristic as the device in question. Analysis of the performance of the practical non-linear electronic circuit then involves representation of the non-linear devices in the circuit by their respective models. This reduces the non-linear problem to a *set* of linear problems which can be tackled using the general circuit analysis techniques set out in section 1.2.1. The difficulty of analysis of a *single non-linear* problem is therefore traded for a *number* of simpler *linear* problems which simplifies the analysis task.

The first step is to linearise the non-linear characteristic of the device by *piecewise-linear* (PWL) representation which involves the approximation of the true characteristic by a set of linear *segments*; the points where segments meet being termed *breakpoints.* Figure 1.5 shows various non-linear $I-V$ characteristics together with possible PWL approximations and the corresponding network representation that can be used in analysis.

The simplest representation of a characteristic in one quadrant is by a single linear segment (figure 1.5a) corresponding to a fixed resistance as given by the reciprocal of the slope of the segment. Accuracy can be improved by using multiple segment approximations although complications are then introduced by the need to represent the switching action at the breakpoint between the segments. The hypothetical ideal switch represented by the unblanked diode symbol in figure 1.5 can be used for this purpose, representing a perfect short circuit (s/c) for current flow in the direction of the arrow formed by the symbol and a perfect open circuit (o/c) when the voltage across it is reversed. Thus in figure 1.5b the switch is open circuit for applied voltages V less than the fixed breakpoint voltage V_1 and so for $V \leqslant V_1$ there is no current flow. For $V > V_1$ the switch is short circuit and the current increases with voltage according to the value r corresponding to the second segment in the linearised characteristic. When operating in this region the current flow I is given, from the model, as

$$\begin{aligned} I &= \frac{V - V_1}{r} \\ &= \left(\frac{1}{r}\right)V - \frac{V_1}{r} \end{aligned} \tag{1.19}$$

which is the equation of the second segment (figure 1.5b) having a slope $\mathrm{d}I/\mathrm{d}V = 1/r$ and an intercept on the I-axis, if projected downward, of $-V_1/r$. Use of this model in analysis to represent the non-linear characteristic of the real device results, in general, in two linear equations corresponding to operation above and below the breakpoint V_1.

Accuracy of the PWL method can be further improved by introducing more segments and breakpoints although the resulting more complex model means that analysis using the model is more complicated. This is of particular concern if hand calculation is intended but if computer analysis is to be used, the more complex model merely results in a longer execution time as the program has to deal with more equations.

1.2.4 *Small-signal analysis of non-linear circuits*

Analysis of non-linear circuits using PWL modelling as described in section 1.2.3 refers to *large-signal* analysis because the model approximates the real device performance over a wide operating range which, for a reasonably accurate representation, involves the complication

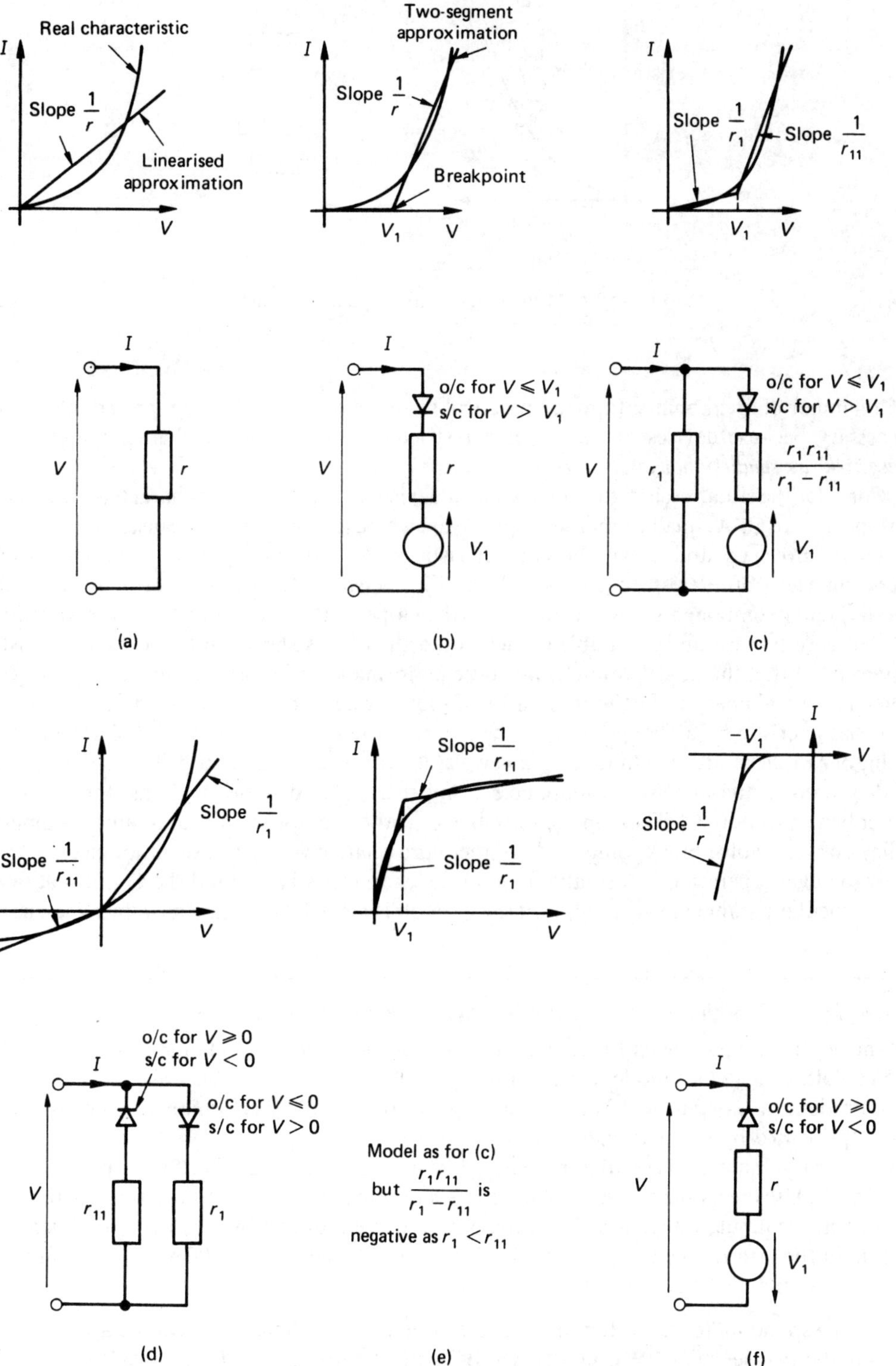

Figure 1.5 Piecewise-linear modelling

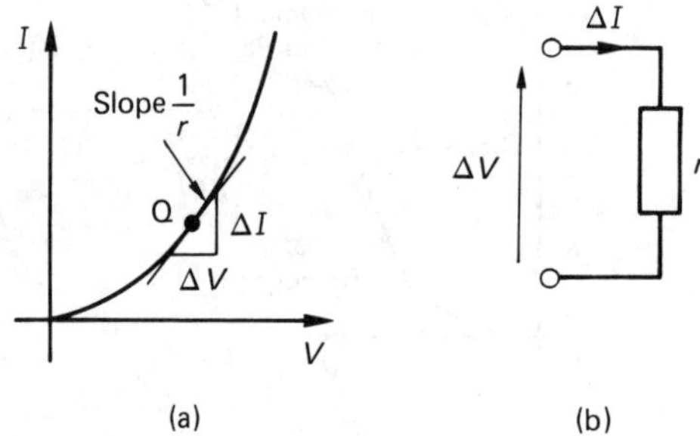

Figure 1.6 Modelling of small-signal performance

of a number of breakpoints. In many practical analog circuits such wide representation is not necessary because devices operate over a restricted portion of their characteristics; this is described as *small-signal* operation.

Consider the situation in figure 1.6a where a device with a non-linear characteristic is biased to operate at Q. A small-amplitude signal superimposed on the bias causes the operating point to move up and down the characteristic either side of Q. If only the small-signal performance is of interest, that is the relationship between ΔI and ΔV, normally referred to as the signal components i and v, it is only the slope of the characteristic in the vacinity of Q that is of interest and a suitable model would then be as shown in figure 1.6b. It must be appreciated that the model contains no static performance information and can only be used for small-signal analysis, furthermore if the Q-point were to be moved to a different place on the characteristic by a change of bias, the slope of the characteristic would change and the value of r in the model would take on a new value. This small-signal modelling is the principle widely used in the analysis of amplifiers using the h, y and hybrid-π transistor models as described in section 3.4. These models are linear as they comprise constant-value parameters. They do not involve breakpoints and are therefore relatively easy to use although they apply only to device operation in a small region of the characteristics around the Q-point at which the particular parameter values apply; if the Q-point is moved the parameter values will change.

Example 1.4: Non-linear circuit analysis using modelling techniques

Manufacturer's data (appendix E, section E.2) gives the reverse bias characteristic of a BZX79 C5V6 voltage reference diode as shown in figure 1.7a.

(a) Produce a 2-segment PWL model representing diode performance over the range represented by the characteristic.

(b) The basic shunt diode regulator of figure 1.7c incorporates a BZX79 C5V6 voltage reference diode. Use the model devised in part (a) to determine the output voltage from the regulator when the input voltage is 9 V and the output current drawn by a resistive load is 50 mA.

(c) If, in the arrangement of part (b), the 9 V input fluctuates by $\pm$ 100 mV, what will be the corresponding variation in load voltage?

(a) Corresponding to figure 1.5f, the diode characteristic of figure 1.7a can be approximated by the two-segment PWL model AB, BC with the breakpoint B at -5.6 V.
The slope resistance of segment AB is ∞ so that the diode is represented by an open circuit for applied voltages between zero and -5.6 V. For biases more negative than

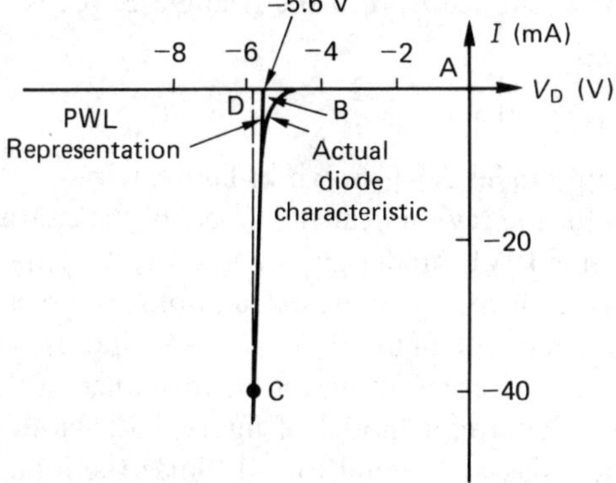

(a) BZX79 C5V6 voltage-reference diode characteristic and PWL approximation

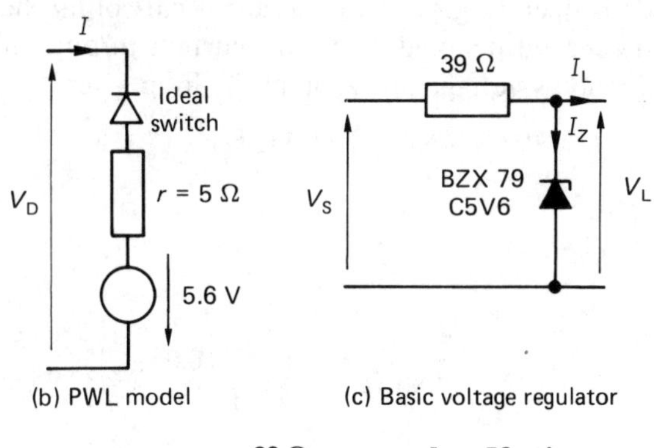

(b) PWL model

(c) Basic voltage regulator

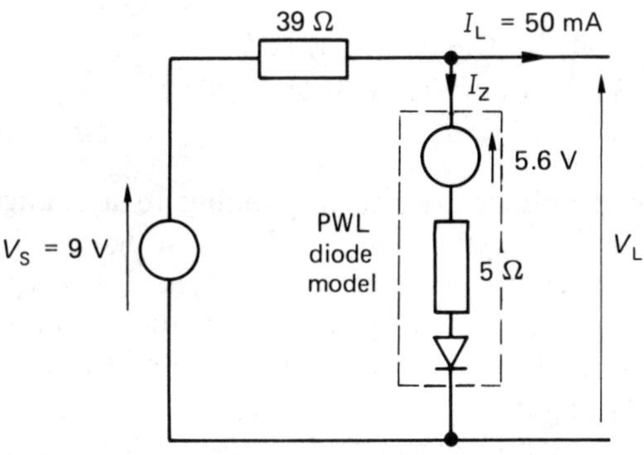

(d) Model of regulator performance

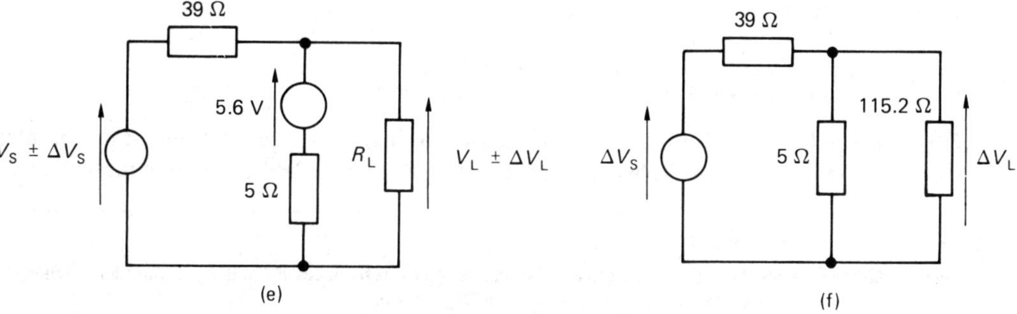

(e)

(f)

Figure 1.7 Piecewise-linear analysis (example 1.4)

-5.6 V the slope resistance r, from the triangle BDC, is

$$r = \frac{\Delta V_D}{\Delta I} = \frac{DB}{DC} = \frac{0.2\ \text{V}}{40\ \text{mA}} = 5\ \Omega$$

The corresponding model is as shown in figure 1.7b.
Note that except for the region near the 'knee' of the characteristic, $V_D = -4.8 \rightarrow -5.6$ V, $I = 0 \rightarrow -8$ mA, this PWL model gives a good representation of the diode characteristic that is sufficiently accurate for most calculations; see section 11.2.4.

(b) In the regulator circuit of figure 1.7c $V_S = 9$ V and $I_L = 50$ mA; the value of the load voltage V_L is required. Representing the performance of the diode by the PWL model of part (a) produces the circuit model of figure 1.7d. Notice that $V_L = -V_D$ and that the diode current shown as I_Z is equal to $-I$. Since the input voltage V_S is greater than the breakpoint value, the ideal switch in the model is a short circuit indicating that the voltage reference diode is operating on the breakdown part of its characteristic.
With the diode current denoted by I_Z, the current through the 39 Ω resistor is $(I_Z + I_L)$ and using Kirchhoff's voltage law around the loop gives

$$9\ \text{V} = (I_Z + I_L)(39\ \Omega) + 5.6\ \text{V} + (I_Z)(5\ \Omega)$$

from which

$$I_Z = \frac{3.4 - 39 I_L}{44}$$

But $I_L = 50\ \text{mA} = 0.05$ A and so $I_Z = \dfrac{3.4 - 39(0.05)}{44} = 32.95$ mA

Then $V_L = V_S - (I_Z + I_L)39\ \Omega$

$$= 9\ \text{V} - (32.95\ \text{mA} + 50\ \text{mA})39\ \Omega$$

$$= 5.76\ \text{V}$$

(c) The change of load voltage ΔV_L corresponding to a change of input voltage ΔV_S of 100 mV is required. The circuit model is shown in figure 1.7e where the load R_L draws 50 mA (specified) when the voltage across it is 5.76 V (part(b)), thus $R_L = 5.76\ \text{V}/50\ \text{mA} = 115.2\ \Omega$. As only small-signal performance is of interest here, the constant components (V_S, V_L and the 5.6 V breakpoint source) can be removed, resulting in the *small-signal model* of figure 1.7f.
Therefore as far as small changes are concerned, the regulator behaves as a potential divider with resistances of 39 Ω and $5\ \Omega // 115.2\ \Omega = (5\ \Omega)(115.2\ \Omega)/(5\ \Omega + 115.2\ \Omega) \simeq 4.8\ \Omega$* from which

$$\Delta V_L = \left(\frac{4.8\ \Omega}{39\ \Omega + 4.8\ \Omega}\right)\Delta V_S \simeq 0.11\ \Delta V_S$$

Thus, for $\Delta V_S = \pm 100$ mV, the fluctuation in load voltage will be approximately $0.11(\pm 100\ \text{mV}) = \pm 11$ mV. See also coverage in section 11.2.4 leading to equation 11.76.

---

* *Parallel combination of resistances.* The effective resistance R of two resistances R_1 and R_2 in parallel, often indicated as $R_1//R_2$, from $\dfrac{1}{R} = \dfrac{1}{R_1} + \dfrac{1}{R_2}$ is given by $R = \dfrac{R_1 R_2}{R_1 + R_2} = \dfrac{\text{product}}{\text{sum}}$.

1.3 The basic electronic circuit

Transistors allow control of the main current flow through the device by the voltage applied to a separate control terminal. Figure 1.8a shows the basic electronic circuit arrangement; the main current terminals XY of the transistor are connected in series with a resistive *load* R and a constant voltage power supply V_S. Note that although the transistor symbol shown in figure 1.8a refers to a particular type of transistor (section 2.3.3) this is for convenience; the following discusssion of this circuit arrangement is general and refers to all types of transistors.

The operating point of the transistor in such an arrangement can be determined graphically in a similar way to that described in section 1.2.2. It will be noted that the only essential difference between the basic transistor circuit of figure 1.8a and the general network of figure 1.2a is that the transistor has three terminals while the latter network involves a two-terminal non-linear device. Three-terminal devices have a set or 'family' of output characteristics, a different characteristic for each value of input control voltage V_C. Figure 1.8b shows five typical *output* characteristics of a transistor corresponding to five specific values of V_C. The term *output* characteristic is used because these are plots of output current I against the voltage V across the output terminals XY of the transistor; which of the set of characteristics applies in an analysis depends on the value of control voltage applied to the transistor. The load line corresponding to V_S and R can be drawn on the output characteristics as shown in figure 1.8b using the method described in section 1.2.2. The Q-point is then given by the point of intersection of the load line with the characteristic corresponding to the particular value of V_C applied to the input of the transistor as represented by the heavy line in the figure.

An important property of transistors is that in normal operation they have an appreciable output resistance, that is the effective resistance across the output terminals XY, and so a substantial load resistance can be connected in series with the output terminals of the device, as in figure 1.8a, without the main current being reduced appreciably. This is an important property in the use of transistors in analog amplification.

When used as an amplifier, the *signal* v to be amplified is superimposed on the fixed *bias* V_C causing the operating point to move up and down the load line about Q causing a

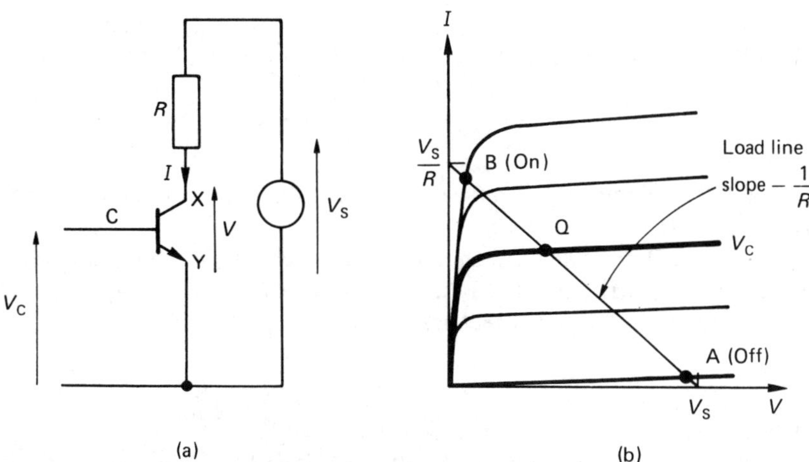

Figure 1.8 Use of a transistor as an amplifier or a switch

corresponding variation in the main current. With V_S and R constant, the main current is approximately proportional to the total input (control) voltage. This fluctuating current is forced through the load resistor R creating a proportional fluctuating voltage across R. Because R can be large, the ratio of fluctuating voltage across R to the input signal v can be large; the signal voltage is *amplified*. The circuit also provides power amplification as well as voltage amplification because the signal power developed in R is greater than the input power drawn from the signal source. This is achieved by converting some of the power from the V_S supply into signal form by causing the current to fluctuate; overall, taking account of signal *and* bias components, there is an electrical power *loss* as some electrical power is dissipated as heat in the transistor.

The same basic electronic circuit operates as a switch if the input control voltage is varied over a sufficiently wide range to cause the transistor to switch fully ON and OFF. If the input voltage is low enough, the operating point moves down the load line to point A (figure 1.8b) and the transistor is said to be OFF. The current is then almost zero so there is only a very small voltage across R and most of the power supply voltage therefore falls across the transistor. Alternatively if the input voltage is high, the operating point can be made to move up to point B when the transistor is fully ON. In this condition, the voltage across the transistor is at its minimum value and almost all of V_S appears across R.

The series connection of an active device, a resistive load and a dc power supply therefore may be considered as *the basic electronic circuit*. If the transistor is biased to operate at some mid-point on the load line the circuit forms the basis of *analog* (continuous signal) circuits whereas if the transistor is switched from ON to OFF the same circuit forms the basis of *digital* (discrete signal) and *power switching* circuits.

References and further reading

Solution of differential equations

1. K.A. Stroud, *Engineering Mathematics*, 2nd edition (Macmillan, 1985)
   (a) programme 25, frame 23,
   (b) programme 26
2. K.A. Stroud, *Further Engineering Mathematics*, programme 7 (Macmillan, 1986)

General circuit analysis

3. W.H. Hayt and J.E. Kemmerly, *Engineering Circuit Analysis*, 4th edition, chapters 2–11 (McGraw-Hill, 1987)
4. R.J. Smith, *Circuits, Devices and Systems*, 4th edition, chapters 1–8 (Wiley, 1984)
5. C.H. Durney, L.D. Harris and C.L. Alley, *Electric Circuits: Theory and Engineering Applications*, chapters 2–6 (Holt, Rinehart and Winston, 1982)

Device modelling

6. M.E. Goodge, *Semiconductor Device Technology*, sections 1.8, 2.2.26, 2.3.9 and appendix A (Macmillan, 1985)

Tutorial questions

Linear circuit analysis

1.1 Show that the current i_1 flowing through R_1 in the current divider of figure 1.9 is given by $i\left(\dfrac{R_2}{R_1 + R_2}\right)$. If the main current i is to be split into two components in the ratio 1:2, what must be the resistance ratio?

[Answer: 1:2]

1.2 Two voltage sources v_1 and v_2 having output resistances R_1 and R_2 are connected as shown in figure 1.10, what is the voltage v across the points of connection?

$$\left[\text{Answer: } \frac{v_1 R_2 + v_2 R_1}{R_1 + R_2}\right]$$

1.3 In the circuit of figure 1.1b the applied voltage v is a constant value V_1 and the circuit is at steady state. If the applied voltage is suddenly switched to a new value V_2, derive an expression giving the capacitor voltage v_O as a function of time from the switching instant. Note the analysis procedure shown in example 1.2.

If $R = 10\,\text{k}\Omega$, $C = 100\,\text{nF}$, $V_1 = 10\,\text{V}$ and $V_2 = 2\,\text{V}$, determine the time taken for the capacitor voltage to fall to the mean value of V_1 and V_2.

[Answers: $v_O = V_2 + (V_1 - V_2)\exp(-t/CR)$, 693 μs]

1.4 A coil having inductance L and resistance R is connected across a constant voltage source V. Derive an expression for the current drawn from the source as a function of time from the instant of connection. Note that the differential equation describing the performance of the circuit has the same *form* as that of equation 1.13 in example 1.2 and so the solution can be deduced from equation 1.14.

If $L = 100\,\text{mH}$, $R = 200\,\Omega$ and a 5 V source is connected, what is the steady-state current flow and how long does it take for the current to rise to half the steady-state value?

$$\left[\text{Answers: } i = \frac{V}{R}\left[1 - \exp\left(-t\Big/\frac{L}{R}\right)\right],\ 25\text{ mA},\ 347\ \mu\text{s}\right]$$

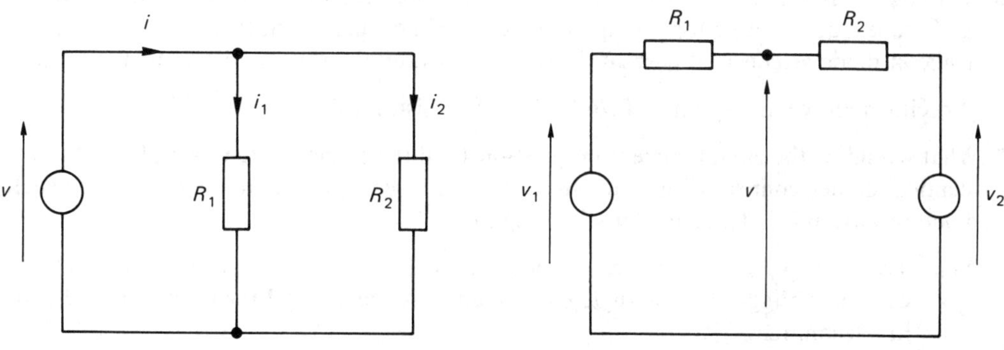

Figure 1.9 **Figure 1.10**

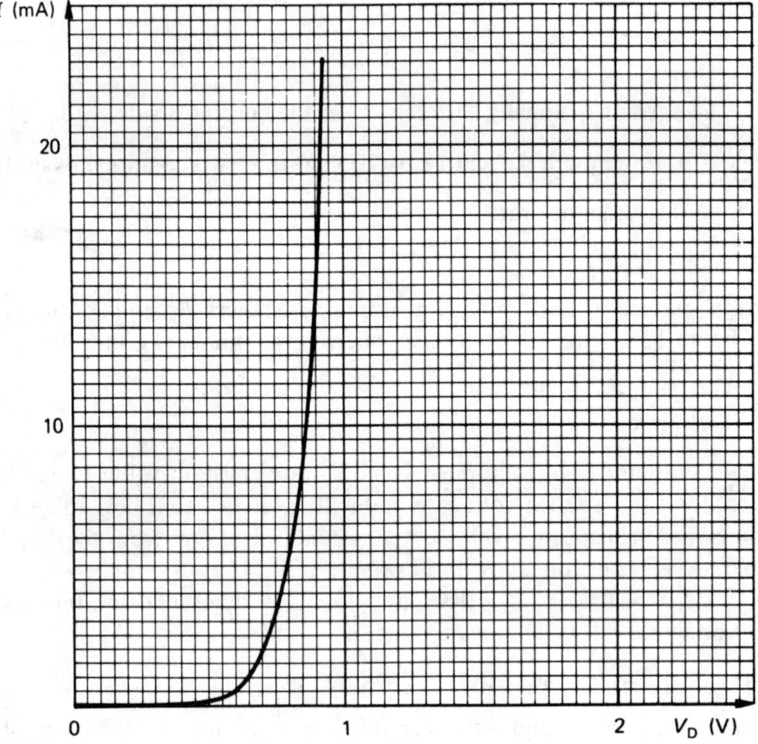

Figure 1.11 Silicon diode characteristic

Non-linear circuit analysis using graphical techniques

1.5 A 1.5 V battery is used to forward-bias a silicon diode with a current-limiting 75 Ω resistor connected in series; the circuit arrangement corresponds to that of figure 1.2a. The current–voltage characteristic of the diode is given in figure 1.11. Using the graphical load line technique, determine the Q-point of the diode and the voltage across the resistor.

[Specimen answers: Q-point is 0.85 V, 8.7 mA; resistor voltage is 0.65 V]

1.6 Assuming that the diode characteristic of figure 1.11 corresponds to a temperature of 25 °C, repeat question 1.5 for a temperature of 75 °C noting that the forward voltage across a silicon diode at constant current decreases at a rate of 2 mV/°C rise in temperature.

[Specimen answers: Q-point is 0.76 V, 9.8 mA; resistor voltage is 0.74 V]

1.7 What would be the circuit current in question 1.5 if the single diode was replaced by two identical diodes connected in series such that they were both conducting? Assume each diode to have the I–V_D characteristic of figure 1.11.

Note: Treat the two series-connected diodes as a single composite device. First sketch the current–voltage characteristic of the composite device and then use standard load line techniques.

[Answer: 1.75 mA]

Non-linear circuit analysis using PWL modelling techniques

1.8 Figure 1.11 shows the current–voltage conduction characteristic of a silicon junction diode. Produce a two-segment PWL model representing this performance. Use the model to solve question 1.5 analytically and compare the results with those of the graphical solution.

[Specimen answers: two segments between coordinates 0, 0; 0.75 V, 0 and 0.90 V, 20 mA result in the model of figure 1.5b with $V_1 = 0.75$ V and $r = 7.5\ \Omega$. Use of this model to solve question 1.5 analytically gives the diode Q-point as approximately 0.82 V, 9.09 mA and the resistor voltage as 0.68 V]

1.9 In the circuit of figure 1.1b the capacitance is 10 nF, the voltage source has a constant value of 5 V and the resistor is replaced by a diode having the current–voltage characteristic shown in figure 1.11. Assuming the relative polarity of the source and the diode are such that the diode conducts and that the capacitor is uncharged when the 5 V source is connected, use the PWL model developed in question 1.8 to determine the time taken for the capacitor voltage to rise to 1 V.

Note: After representation of the diode by its PWL model the problem becomes linear and may be solved using the technique illustrated in example 1.2.

[Specimen answer: 20.1 ns]

2 Electronic Devices and Components

Coverage

- Consideration of the general limitations to electronic device operation: temperature and voltage. Discussion of power dissipation, thermal resistance, derating, breakdown.
- Brief treatment of semiconductor material and the physical operation of the junction diode; contact potential, forward and reverse bias, leakage, $I-V$ characteristic, effects of temperature variation.
- Explanation of the operation of the various types of transistor: bipolar, junction FET, MOST with corresponding static equations and characteristics.
- Types and performance of passive components: resistors, capacitors, inductors and transformers with particular reference to manufacturers' specifications.

Electronic systems rely on the performance of transistors, diodes, resistors, capacitors, inductors and transformers. This chapter considers the performance of these components and examines the fundamental limitations of *temperature* and *voltage* that apply to their use.

2.1 Temperature limitation

Device manufacturers quote a maximum internal operating temperature for their products which is chosen to ensure that devices operate within specification, as given on the device *data sheet*, as well as providing reasonable reliability in terms of working life.

In operation the internal temperature of a device rises because of the resistance to current flow through the material; *power* is said to be *dissipated*. If v is the voltage across the device and i the current flowing through it, the *instantaneous* power dissipated (equation 11.4) is

$$p = vi \tag{2.1}$$

There is a time lag however between the power being dissipated and the temperature of the material rising, the device is said to have *thermal capacity*, and as a consequence *average* power dissipated over a time interval P_{AV} is of more interest than instantaneous power. Average power is given by

$$P_{AV} = \frac{1}{\Delta t} \int_{\Delta t} vi \, dt \tag{2.2}$$

where Δt is the time interval.
The corresponding rise in temperature of the device above its surroundings, known as the

ambient, depends on how easily heat can flow away from the material. This heat flow is described in terms of *thermal resistance* R_{th} given by

$$R_{th} = \frac{T - T_{amb}}{P_{AV}} \tag{2.3}$$

where, at steady state, for an ambient temperature T_{amb}, an average power dissipation of P_{AV} results in an internal device temperature of T. The maximum level of average power dissipation $P_{AV}\max$ corresponding to the maximum allowable internal device temperature T_{max} is therefore given by

$$P_{AV}\max = \frac{T_{max} - T_{amb}}{R_{th}} \tag{2.4}$$

Example 2.1: Allowable power dissipation for a diode

A diode specification quotes
Maximum junction temperature, $T_j\max = 200\,°C$
Thermal resistance from junction to ambient, $R_{th(j-amb)} = 0.6\,°C/mW$.
What is the maximum allowable average power dissipation in the diode when the ambient temperature is 25°C?

Corresponding to equation 2.4, $P_{AV}\max = \dfrac{T_j\max - T_{amb}}{R_{th(j-amb)}}$

$$= \frac{200\,°C - 25\,°C}{0.6\,°C/mW} = 291.7\ mW$$

Usually the maximum power dissipation capability of a device, $P_{AV}\max$, is quoted for ambient temperatures up to a specific value, often 25°C for semiconductor devices, 70°C for resistors. For ambient temperatures above this value, value $P_{AV}\max$ must be reduced so that the maximum internal temperature is not exceeded; the device must be *derated*. The sloping section of figure 2.1 is a typical derating graph; it is a plot of $P_{AV}\max$ against T_{amb} as given by equation 2.4 and therefore has a slope of $-1/R_{th}$. The power dissipation capability of the device falls from the quoted value at, for example, 25°C to zero at $T_{amb} = T_{max}$; notice that if the temperature of the device surroundings, T_{amb}, were raised to the maximum allowable

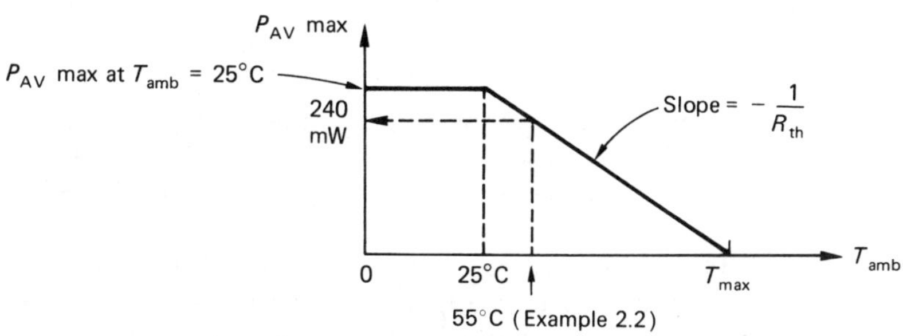

Figure 2.1 Derating of device power capability

device temperature then no power could be dissipated in the device without the limit being exceeded. The term *derating factor* is sometimes used to describe the reduction in $P_{AV}\max$ that must be made for high ambient temperatures, for example, for $P_{AV}\max$ quoted at 25 °C,

$$\text{derating factor} = \frac{P_{AV}\max}{T_{max} - 25\,°\mathrm{C}} = \frac{1}{R_{th}} \tag{2.5}$$

This factor has units of W/°C and gives the amount by which the power rating of the device must be reduced for every 1 °C that the ambient temperature exceeds 25 °C (see example 2.2).

Example 2.2: Allowable power dissipation for a transistor – derating for operation at elevated temperature

A transistor has a maximum power rating of 300 mW for $T_{amb} \leqslant 25\,°\mathrm{C}$. If the maximum allowable junction temperature is 175 °C, what is the thermal resistance from junction to ambient and the derating factor? What would be the power rating of this transistor in an ambient of 55 °C?

From equation 2.4, $R_{th(j\text{-}amb)} = \dfrac{T_j\max - T_{amb}}{P_{AV}\max}$

$$= \frac{175\,°\mathrm{C} - 25\,°\mathrm{C}}{300\,\mathrm{mW\ at\ }25\,°\mathrm{C}} = 0.5\,°\mathrm{C/mW}$$

From equation 2.5, Derating factor $= \dfrac{1}{R_{th(j\text{-}amb)}} = 2\,\mathrm{mW/°C}$

From equation 2.4, $P_{AV}\max$ at $T_{amb} = 55\,°\mathrm{C}$ is $\dfrac{175\,°\mathrm{C} - 55\,°\mathrm{C}}{0.5\,°\mathrm{C/mW}} = 240\,\mathrm{mW}$

Alternatively, in terms of derating factor:

$$\begin{aligned} P_{AV}\max\,(T_{amb} = 55\,°\mathrm{C}) &= P_{AV}\max\,(T_{amb} = 25\,°\mathrm{C}) - \text{Derating factor}\,(55\,°\mathrm{C} - 25\,°\mathrm{C}) \\ &= 300\,\mathrm{mW} - (2\,\mathrm{mW/°C})(30\,°\mathrm{C}) \\ &= 240\,\mathrm{mW} \end{aligned}$$

2.2 Voltage limitation

In addition to premature failure due to excessive temperature rise, devices can also fail due to overvoltage. An applied voltage imposes a stress on insulating materials which, if excessive, causes *breakdown* resulting in a sudden current surge and damage to the material. Manufacturers quote a maximum working voltage for devices so that breakdown can be avoided. It should be noted that *insulation breakdown* is a different phenomenon from *junction breakdown* in semiconductor devices. In the latter case the breakdown mechanism is not damaging in itself provided the resultant current flow is restricted so that the power dissipation rating of the device is not exceeded.

2.3 Performance of semiconductor devices: diodes and transistors

2.3.1 *Semiconductor material*

The electrical conductivity of a semiconductor such as silicon is increased enormously by the addition of a dopant element. Depending on the element used, the resulting doped semiconductor has either an excess of mobile *p*ositive charge (holes) or an excess of mobile *n*egative charge (electrons), termed p-type and n-type semiconductors respectively.

As well as introducing additional mobile charge, the dopant atoms also introduce fixed ions; negative ions in p-type material and positive ions in n-type material. These ions are what remains of the dopant atoms after they have lost part of their charge to the material.

The charge content ot the two types of semiconductor is therefore

p-type: High density of mobile positive holes provided by the dopant atoms, often termed *majority (charge) carriers.*

High density of fixed negative ions.

Low density of mobile negative electrons provided by the host material such as silicon (minority carriers).

n-type: High density of mobile negative electrons (majorities).

High density of fixed positive ions.

Low density of mobile positive holes (minorities).

In both types of semiconductor the densities of positive and negative charges are equal so that the material is electrically neutral at equilibrium.

2.3.2 *Junction diode*

A semiconductor junction diode comprises a *chip* of semiconductor that is mostly n-type (the cathode region) with a p-type *anode* region introduced into one face. The interface between the p and n regions is the *junction* as shown in figure 2.2a.

Figure 2.2b shows the charge content of the p and n regions. With a high density of one type of mobile carrier on each side of the junction and a corresponding low density on the other side, there is a tendency for holes to *diffuse* from p to n and electrons to diffuse from n to p. This leaves the region either side of the junction devoid of mobile charge; a *depletion layer* is formed containing fixed positive ions on one side of the junction and fixed negative ions on the other. These ions create an electric field which imposes a force on the mobile charge carriers balancing the tendency to diffuse. At equilibrium, with no externally applied voltage ($V=0$, figure 2.2b), a depletion layer of finite width exists across which there is a voltage called the *contact potential* or *potential barrier*, ψ, due to the fixed ions. For a silicon diode, ψ is approximately 0.7 V.

When an external *bias* voltage is applied such that the anode is positive with respect to the cathode (figure 2.2b), the bias and the contact potential are in opposition and there is negligible current flow until the bias exceeds the contact potential beyond which current increases rapidly with increasing voltage (figure 2.2c). Current and voltage may be allowed to increase until the power rating P_{max} is reached. In this *forward bias* or ON condition, the depletion region has disappeared and mobile carriers diffuse across the junction in either direction. Note that forward current flow through the diode is in the direction of the arrow in the diode symbol (figure 2.2a).

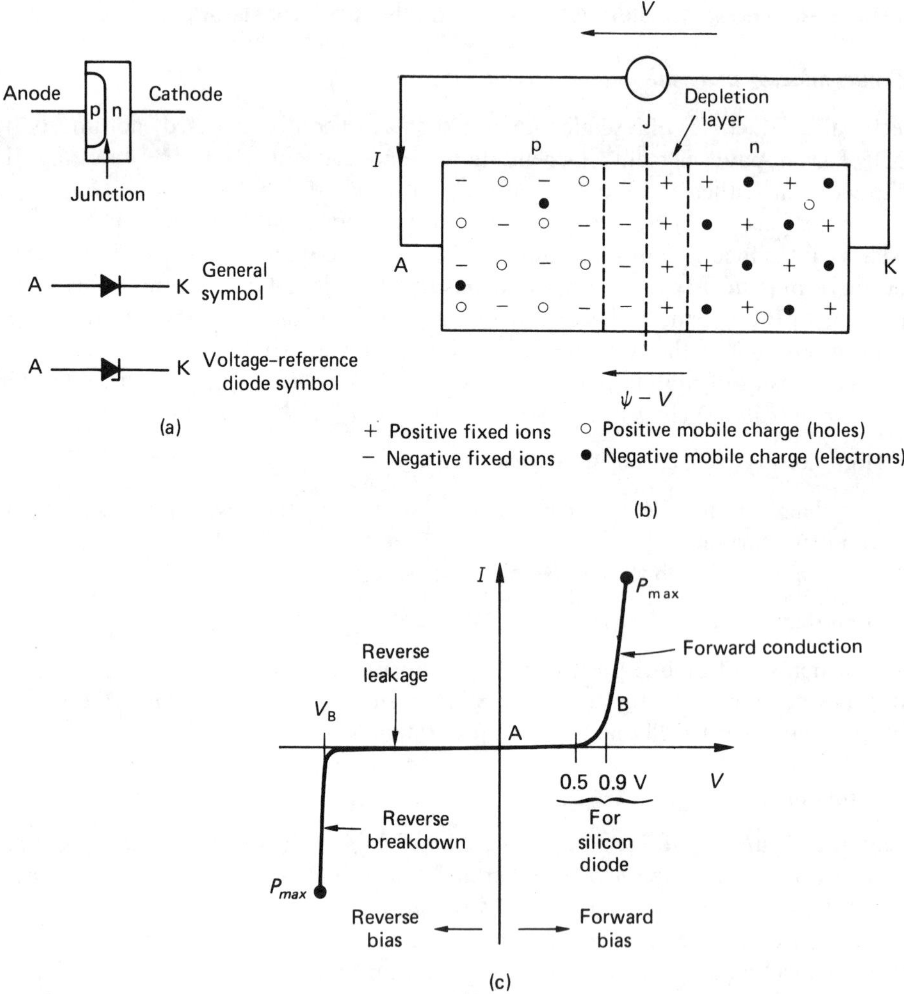

Figure 2.2 Semiconductor junction diode

With the applied bias reversed, that is the cathode positive with respect to the anode (V negative in figure 2.2b), the bias augments the contact potential and the depletion layer widens. The barrier to hole diffusion from p to n and electron diffusion from n to p is therefore increased so that these components are reduced. However there remains the *drift* of minority carriers (electrons from p to n and holes from n to p) across the junction in the electric field and these components are responsible for a small *reverse leakage* current typically in the range 2–40 nA for a low-power silicon diode at room temperature. This is the reverse bias or OFF state of the diode. If the reverse bias is progressively increased, junction breakdown eventually occurs (at V_B figure 2.2c) beyond which the reverse current increases sharply. Provided the maximum power condition P_{max} is not exceeded, this breakdown condition does not damage the diode and in fact a range of diodes is produced with values of V_B as low as 2.4 V that are intended to be used as *voltage references* making use of the almost constant voltage nature of the breakdown characteristic (see section 11.2.4). In most diode applications however, such as rectification or signal switching, the diode must remain non-conducting when reverse biased and so operation is kept well below breakdown. The special symbol for a voltage-reference diode, often termed a *zener* diode, is shown in figure 2.2a.

Temperature variation has a marked effect on the properties of semiconductor devices because the energy imparted to the material thermally alters both the densities of mobile carriers in the material and their energy, which in turn alters the components of current flow across the junction. Theoretical analysis [1] shows that the forward characteristic of a junction diode at low current levels (section AB, figure 2.2c) can be represented by the *theoretical diode equation*

$$I \simeq I_0 \exp\left(\frac{eV_F}{kT}\right) \tag{2.6}$$

where V_F is the applied forward bias voltage, I_0 is the *theoretical* reverse saturation current, e is the magnitude of electronic charge, k is Boltzmann's constant (the link between thermal energy and temperature) and T is absolute temperature. Note that I_0 is a theoretical value of reverse current, it is *not* the reverse leakage value referred to on the diode characteristic of figure 2.2c; the symbol I_R is used for the actual reverse leakage current of the diode.

At 25°C (298 K) the term kT/e has a value of approximately 26 mV and so the diode equation can be written

$$I \simeq I_0 \exp\left(\frac{V_F}{0.026}\right) \tag{2.7}$$

at this temperature.

At current levels above point B (figure 2.2c) equation 2.6 is invalid because of the dominance of the resistance of the bulk p and n regions which results in an approximately linear characteristic at higher current levels.

From equation 2.6 the voltage across the forward biased diode is

$$V_F \simeq \frac{kT}{e} \ln\left(\frac{I}{I_0}\right) \tag{2.8}$$

indicating that V_F changes with temperature. Theoretical analysis [1] shows that at constant forward current I, the change of V_F is of the order of -2 mV/°C at low current levels ($\leqslant 10$ mA) changing to typically $+2$ mV/°C at 100 mA. This change of forward voltage with temperature causes the forward I–V characteristic to shift along the voltage axis as the internal device temperature changes which is particularly significant in establishing a stable operating point for a bipolar transistor (section 3.1).

Consideration of the nature of reverse leakage I_R for a pn junction [1] leads to a relationship between the values of leakage current at two temperatures in the region of 25°C:

$$I_R(T_2) \simeq I_R(T_1) \exp[0.06(T_2 - T_1)] \tag{2.9}$$

indicating that I_R *approximately doubles per 8°C rise in temperature* for operation near 25°C. At higher temperatures the rate of increase reduces so that in the region of 150°C, I_R doubles per 20°C rise in temperature. For a low-power silicon diode, reverse leakage is typically in the range 1–40 μA at 150°C.

Note that in most applications of silicon junction devices, the change of forward voltage V_F with temperature has far more significance than reverse leakage effects. At normal operating temperatures (< 50°C) and current levels (> 1 μA), reverse leakage of a silicon junction diode can be ignored in most applications.

Example 2.3: Change of forward voltage drop and reverse leakage of a junction diode with temperature

A silicon junction diode has a forward voltage drop of 700 mV and reverse leakage of 5 nA at 25 °C. What would be the percentage changes in these values for a 20 °C rise in temperature?

Assuming forward conduction of < 10 mA, $\frac{\partial V_F}{\partial T}$ may be taken as -2 mV/°C, thus a 20°C rise in temperature results in a 40 mV *fall* in V_F corresponding to a $\frac{-40 \text{ mV}}{700 \text{ mV}} \times 100$ per cent $= -5.7$ per cent change.
From equation 2.9:

$$
\begin{aligned}
I_R(45\,°\text{C}) &= I_R(25\,°\text{C}) \exp[0.06(45\,°\text{C} - 25\,°\text{C})] \\
&= (5\text{nA}) \exp[1.2] \\
&= 16.6 \text{ nA}
\end{aligned}
$$

Thus the rise in I_R is 16.6 nA $-$ 5 nA $=$ 11.6 nA which constitutes a $+\frac{11.6 \text{ nA}}{5 \text{ nA}} \times 100$ per cent $= +232$ per cent change.

Note: Although I_R is more sensitive to temperature than V_F, its low value compared with typical operating current levels ($> 1\ \mu$A) makes its change less important than that of V_F.

2.3.3 *Bipolar junction transistor (BJT)*

A BJT comprises two pn junctions formed back-to-back in a single semiconductor chip. Operation relies on the two junctions being extremely close, typically less than 1 μm apart, and as both types of charge carrier, electrons and holes, feature in the operation it is termed *bipolar*.

Both npn and pnp structures are produced although the npn version is more popular because of its superior performance which stems from the higher energy and hence faster movement of mobile electrons compared with holes. The two types operate in a similar manner, the only differences being that, internally, the roles of electrons and holes are interchanged and, externally, voltage polarities and current directions are reversed. Figure 2.3a shows the basic structures and circuit symbols of the two types. Note that the direction of the emitter arrow indicates the direction of the emitter current in each case.

The main current flow through a BJT, between *collector* and *emitter*, is controlled by the potential applied to the *base*. Figure 2.3b shows the components of charge movement within an npn BJT; normal operation being described by the processes of *injection, diffusion* and *collection.* If external voltage sources are connected to bias the two junctions as shown and V_{BE} is increased to about $+0.7$ V (for a silicon BJT), the emitter–base junction conducts as described above for the basic diode. This results in electrons (majorities in the n-type emitter) being injected into the base and holes being injected from base to emitter.

Figure 2.3 BJT operation and characteristics

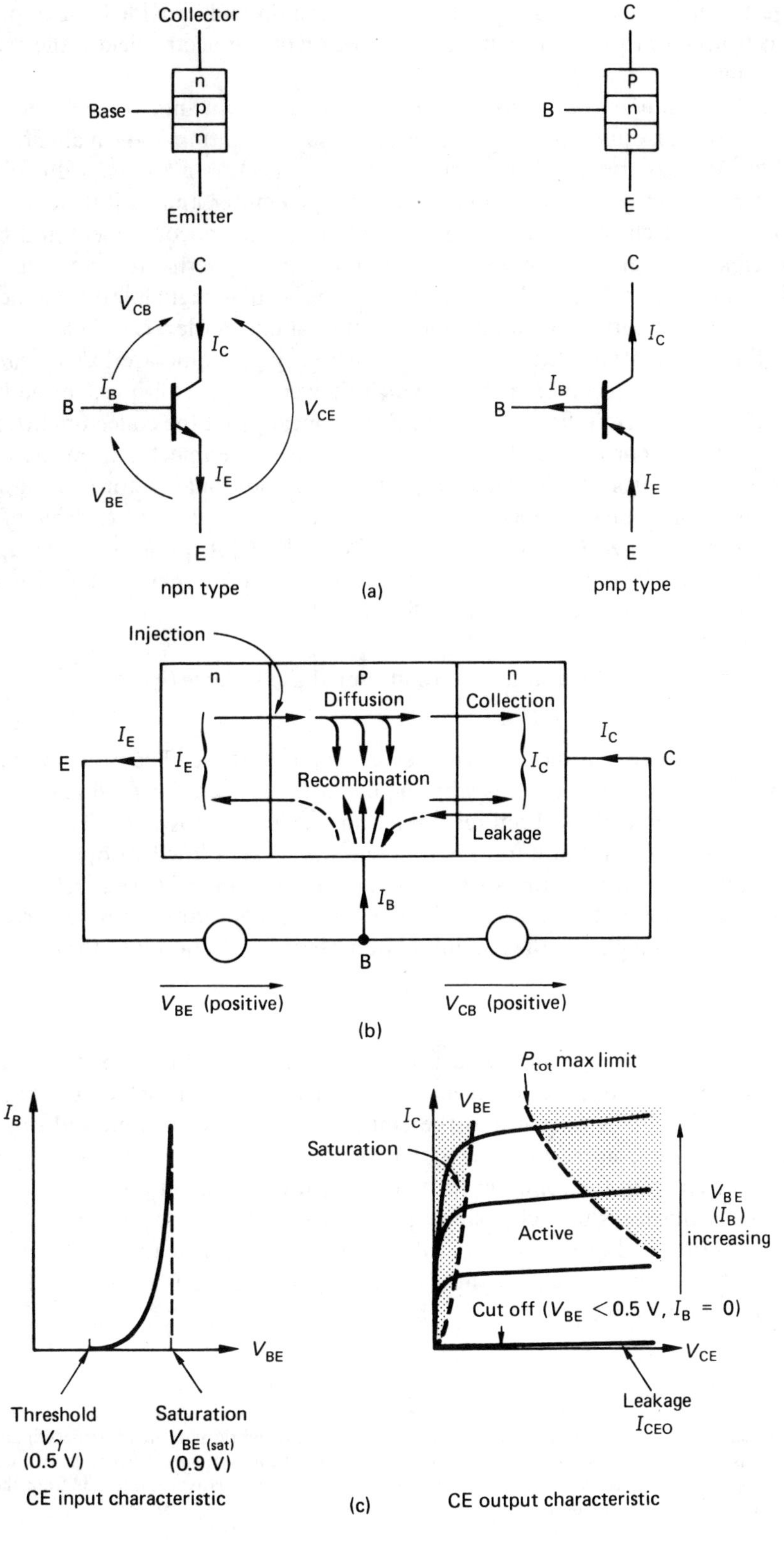
Collector
Base
n
p
n
Emitter
C
B
P
n
p
E
C
V_{CB}
I_C
I_B
B
V_{CE}
I_E
V_{BE}
E
npn type
(a)
C
I_C
I_B
B
I_E
E
pnp type
Injection
n
P
Diffusion
n
Collection
I_E
E
I_E
Recombination
I_C
I_C
C
Leakage
I_B
B
V_{BE} (positive)
V_{CB} (positive)
(b)
I_B
V_{BE}
Threshold
V_γ
(0.5 V)
Saturation
$V_{BE\ (sat)}$
(0.9 V)
CE input characteristic
P_{tot} max limit
I_C
V_{BE}
Saturation
Active
V_{BE}
(I_B)
increasing
Cut off (V_{BE} <0.5 V, I_B = 0)
V_{CE}
Leakage
I_{CEO}
(c)
CE output characteristic

The injected electrons diffuse out into the base region and provided V_{CB} is positive, most of these electrons are attracted into the collector region by the electric field at the collector–base junction, forming the collector current.

The fact that V_{CB} must be positive to attract electrons out into the collector also means that the collector–base junction is reverse-biased. Thus in addition to the main flow of electrons from the base, there is also a leakage current between *c*ollector and *b*ase I_{CB} due to the resident minority carriers. In the absence of injection from the emitter, that is if the emitter was open circuit, the collector current would comprise only this leakage component and therefore the leakage current is given the symbol I_{CBO}; the O in the subscript representing *o*pen circuit emitter. In practice, for silicon BJTs, this leakage component is negligible during the conduction (*active*) mode in comparison with normal operational current levels.

During the diffusion of electrons across the base region, some are lost as *mobile* carriers by a process known as recombination in which they combine with holes in the base and are annihilated as far as current flow is concerned. This means that the collector current is slightly less than the emitter current. Additionally the holes that are injected from the base into the emitter do not come from the collector and this is an additional factor causing $I_C < I_E$. The ratio of I_C to I_E for *static* (dc) operation is termed the *static (dc) current gain of the BJT for common base (CB) operation* and has the symbol $-h_{FB}$* (also referred to as α_{dc}); the term common-base refers to the fact that, in this configuration, the base terminal is common to the input and output circuits of the BJT (figure 2.3b).

From figure 2.3b:

$$I_C = \text{(current from the emitter)} + \text{(collector–base leakage)}$$

$$= -h_{FB}I_E + I_{CBO} \tag{2.10}$$

A typical value of h_{FB} for a modern low-power BJT is -0.996. The need to make the gain as near to unity as possible explains why the distance between the *E–B* and *C–B* junctions must be very small, namely to keep recombination as low as possible. The other factor that degrades the gain, hole injection from base to emitter, is kept low by doping the base region only lightly relative to the emitter so that the hole density in the base is relatively low.

The difference between the emitter and collector currents forms the base current I_B which replaces carriers taking part in the recombination process, injection into the emitter and *C–B* leakage:

$$I_E = I_C + I_B \tag{2.11}$$

In practice, although the common-base configuration is useful in certain circumstances (section 3.5), the most popular arrangement is *common emitter* in which the base is used as the input, the collector as output and the emitter is common to input and output circuits. The popularity of the common-emitter (CE) configuration stems from the fact that because $I_B \ll I_E$, the current gain for common emitter (I_C/I_B) is very much greater than for common base (I_C/I_E) and this leads to higher *power* gain in application. For the CE configuration, the link between output and input currents is between I_C and I_B instead of between I_C and I_E in the CB case. To obtain the relationship between I_C and I_B, I_E is eliminated from equation 2.10 by substitution from equation 2.11, thus

$$I_C = -h_{FB}(I_C + I_B) + I_{CBO}$$

---

* *Symbol terminology*: A popular form of BJT representation uses the hybrid parameter model (figure 3.9d). The gain symbol *h* used here indicates a *h*ybrid parameter. Suffix FB indicates *f*orward current gain (output/input) for common-*b*ase operation. Upper case suffixes indicate dc operation. The negative sign results from the convention used for current directions in the model.

from which $I_C = \left(\frac{-h_{FB}}{1+h_{FB}}\right) I_B + \frac{I_{CBO}}{1+h_{FB}}$

$$= h_{FE} I_B + I_{CEO} \tag{2.12}$$

where $h_{FE} = \frac{-h_{FB}}{1+h_{FB}}$ = static (dc) current gain of the BJT in the common-emitter configuration (2.13)

(also referred to as β_{dc})

and $I_{CEO} = \frac{I_{CBO}}{1+h_{FB}}$ = leakage current from collector to emitter with the base open circuit (2.14)

Example 2.4: Calculation of static currents for a BJT

In a silicon BJT the static collector current in active mode operation is 99.5 per cent of the static emitter current. What are the values of dc common-base and common-emitter current gains? If the same BJT has collector–base leakage of 10 nA at 25°C, what would be the collector–emitter leakage at the same temperature?

$$I_C = 0.995\ I_E$$

from which the common-base static current gain $h_{FB} = \frac{-I_C}{I_E} = -0.995$

From equation 2.13:

Common-emitter static current gain, $\frac{I_C}{I_B} = h_{FE} = \frac{-h_{FB}}{1+h_{FB}} = \frac{0.995}{1-0.995} = 199$

From equation 2.14:

Common-emitter leakage, $I_{CEO} = \frac{I_{CBO}}{1+h_{FB}} = \frac{10\ \text{nA}}{1-0.995} = 2\ \mu\text{A}$

Static performance of the BJT for the CE configuration is given by the *input* (I_B against V_{BE}) and *output* (I_C against V_{CE}) characteristics as shown in figure 2.3c.

The input characteristic is similar to the $I-V$ characteristic of a junction diode (figure 2.2c). With V_{BE} less than the conduction threshold of about 0.5 V for a silicon device, negligible injection occurs and only leakage I_{CEO} flows between collector and emitter; the BJT is said to be *cut off* or in the OFF state. As V_{BE} increases above 0.5 V, injection increases and correspondingly I_C increases; this region of operation is termed the *active* or *normal* region and it is in this mode that the BJT can be used as an amplifier (section 1.3 and chapter 3). V_{BE} limits at about 0.9 V for a low-power silicon BJT; this limiting value is termed the saturation value $V_{BE(sat)}$. A suitable mid-range value of V_{BE} for bias calculation purposes (section 3.1) is 0.6 V.

The output characteristic is the relation between output current I_C and output voltage, which, for the CE configuration, is the voltage between collector and emitter V_{CE}. Notice that this is the voltage across two junctions $V_{CB} + V_{BE}$ and so for active region operation, for which

V_{CB} must be positive (for an npn BJT) to ensure collection of electrons, V_{CE} must be greater than V_{BE} which corresponds to the area to the right of the V_{BE} locus on the output characteristics of figure 2.3c. If V_{CE} is less than V_{BE} (the shaded area to the left of the V_{BE} locus), V_{CB} is negative and both junctions are forward-biased; the BJT is then in a state of *saturation*, the fully ON state. In this mode the value of V_{CE} is at a minimum value, $V_{CE(sat)}$, which is less than 0.5 V for a low-power silicon BJT.

In the active mode of operation it should be noted that I_C is almost independent of V_{CE} and therefore the BJT may be considered to operate approximately as a controlled current source, the control being provided by I_B (and hence V_{BE}). This property is particularly significant in the use of a BJT as an amplifier (section 1.3 and chapter 3).

In application, the power, voltage and current ratings of the BJT must not be violated. Power dissipation in a BJT occurs mainly at the junctions where the main voltage drops exist. Thus, for static operation, the total power dissipation is

$$\begin{aligned} P_{tot} &= V_{CB}I_C + V_{BE}I_E \\ &= V_{CB}I_C + V_{BE}(I_C + I_B) \\ &= V_{CE}I_C + V_{BE}I_B \end{aligned} \tag{2.15}$$

But for active region operation $V_{CE} \gg V_{BE}$ and $I_C \gg I_B$, and therefore

$$P_{tot} \simeq V_{CE}I_C \tag{2.16}$$

indicating that the locus of BJT operation at constant power dissipation forms a hyperbola on the CE output characteristic of I_C against V_{CE}. The maximum allowable dissipation P_{tot}max forms a boundary to the active region of operation as shown in figure 2.3c. Voltage limits V_{CB}max, V_{EB}max (and hence V_{CE}max) are set by the breakdown properties of the junctions. The limiting value of collector current $I_C$max may correspond to maximum power dissipation (noting that V_{CE} cannot fall below the limiting value $V_{CE(sat)}$) or more likely, because BJT current gain is a function of collector current, the manufacturer may quote a value of $I_C$max which ensures that the gain is not less than the quoted minimum value.

Reference [1] gives more comprehensive details of the manufacture, structure, operation and performance of BJTs.

2.3.4 *Field-effect transistors* (FETs)

FETs are of two types: the *junction* FET (JFET) and the *insulated-gate* FET. The latter commonly has a *m*etal–*o*xide–*s*emiconductor structure and is usually described as a MOSFET or MOST.

In each type the current flow through the semiconductor *channel* between the *drain* and *source* terminals depends on the potential applied to the *gate* control terminal. In a JFET, control is by variation of the cross-section of the channel by the depth of penetration of the depletion layer formed at the reverse-biased gate–channel junction. In a MOST, conductivity control is provided by an electric field induced capacitively across a thin insulating layer between the gate electrode and the channel. Two types of MOST are available: the *depletion* type (d-MOST) which conducts between drain and source when the gate-source voltage V_{GS} is zero and the *enhancement* type (e-MOST) which does not conduct for $V_{GS} = 0$. All three types, JFET, d-MOST and e-MOST, are produced in n-channel and p-channel forms;

n-channel versions are the more popular because of their superior performance, resulting from the higher energy and hence faster movement of mobile electrons compared with holes.

All FETs have a very high input resistance (typically $> 10^8\,\Omega$ for JFETs, $> 10^{12}\,\Omega$ for MOSTs) and so the gate current I_G is negligible for most applications at dc and low frequency. This is an important property because it means that FETs are totally voltage controlled; they do not draw current from the circuit driving them, unlike BJTs for which the base current cannot be taken as negligible.

JFETs

The basic structure and circuit symbol of an n-channel JFET is shown in figure 2.4a. With no applied voltage between gate and source ($V_{GS} = 0$), the gate–channel depletion layer is uniform and penetrates the channel region to a finite depth, exactly similar to conditions in a pn junction diode for zero applied bias.

If the voltage V_{DS} across the channel is then progressively increased, the drain current I_D increases; the channel behaves like a resistor and the JFET is said to be in the *ohmic* region of operation. Because of the voltage drop along the length of the channel, the voltage across the gate–channel junction is greater at the drain end than at the source end and the depletion layer width becomes non-uniform. Continuing increase in V_{DS} causes the depletion region to extend almost entirely across the channel (referred to as *pinch-off*) causing the value of I_D to limit; the JFET is then said to be operating in the *saturation* region or the *region beyond pinch-off* and the drain current is denoted by $I_{D(sat)}$. The corresponding output characteristic is as shown in figure 2.4b where P is the pinch-off point; the value of drain current at pinch-off for $V_{GS} = 0$ is designated I_{DSS}, that is, the current from drain to source with the gate shorted to the source ($V_{GS} = 0$) as indicated by the final S in the subscript.

If instead of V_{GS} being zero it is made negative before V_{DS} is increased, then the initial penetration of the depletion layer into the channel is deeper and pinch-off then occurs at a lower value of V_{DS}, the value of $I_{D(sat)}$ attained also being reduced. A set of output characteristics therefore exists (figure 2.4b) for a range of negative values of V_{GS}. If V_{GS} is made sufficiently negative, the channel is pinched-off by virtue of V_{GS} and there is no current flow through the channel as V_{DS} is increased. The value of V_{GS} to cause pinch-off when V_{DS} is zero is termed the pinch-off voltage V_P which is often designated $V_{GS(off)}$ on manufacturers' device data sheets.

Notice that although operation of a JFET is entirely different from that of a BJT, the resulting output characteristics have a similar form.

As the gate current of a JFET for normal operation (gate–channel junction reverse-biased) is approximately zero, the input characteristic (I_G against V_{GS}) is of no use. However the *transfer* characteristic showing how the output current *in the saturation region* $I_{D(sat)}$ varies with input voltage V_{GS} is useful in circuit design (section 3.2). It is approximately parabolic ($I_{D(sat)} \propto V_{GS}^2$ for $V_{GS} > V_P$) as shown in figure 2.4b; the relationship [1] is approximately

$$I_{D(sat)} \simeq I_{DSS}\left(1 - \frac{V_{GS}}{V_P}\right)^2 \tag{2.17}$$

The symbol for an n-channel JFET is shown in figure 2.4a; the gate arrow shows the direction that gate current *would* flow if the gate–channel junction was to be forward-biased, even though this is not a normal operating condition; for a p-channel device the gate arrow would be reversed. The above explanation of operation also applies to the p-channel version except current flow would be via holes instead of electrons and the voltage polarities and current directions would be reversed.

d-MOSTs

The mechanism of operation and resulting characteristics of a d-MOST are similar to those of a JFET even though the device structures are different. A d-MOST has a sandwich structure (figure 2.4a) comprising a thin n-type channel layer on a p-type *substrate*; the gate is separated from the channel by a thin insulating layer. A depletion layer exists at the channel–substrate pn junction. If $V_{GS} = 0$, progressive increase of V_{DS} causes pinch-off to occur at the drain end and a saturating output characteristic results (figure 2.4b) as for a JFET. If V_{GS} is made

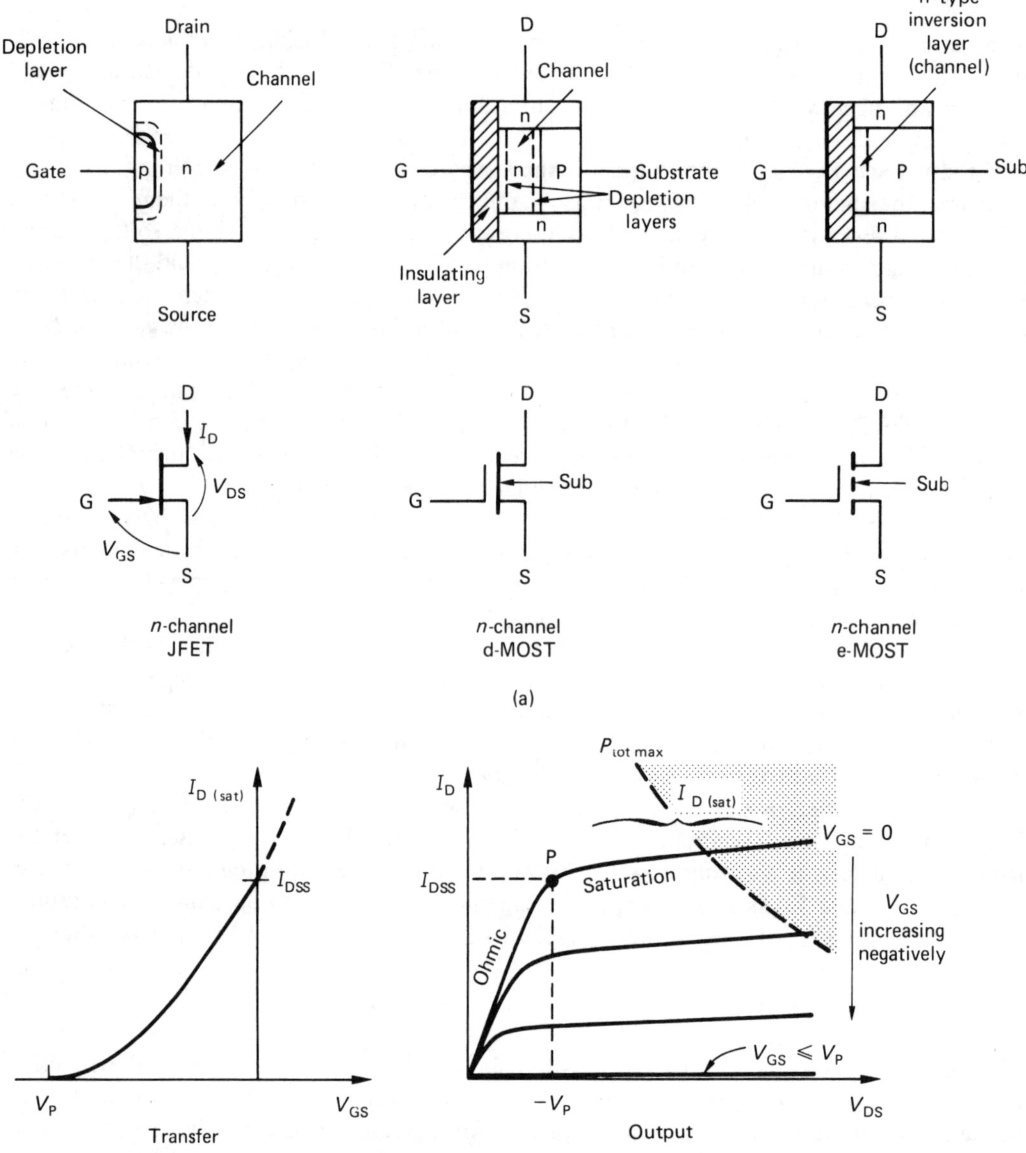

Figure 2.4 FET operation and characteristics

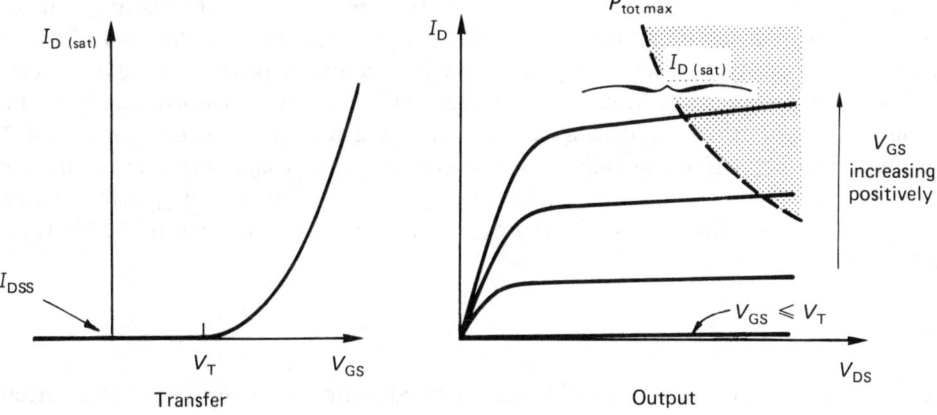

(c) e-MOST characteristics (*n*-channel)

Figure 2.4 *continued*

negative, electrons are repelled from the channel surface just under the insulating layer, resulting in a second depletion region. As with the JFET, subsequent increase of V_{DS} results in pinch-off at a lower value of V_{DS} and a set of output characteristics results for $0 > V_{GS} > V_P$. If $V_{GS} < V_P$, the channel is completely pinched off and only leakage current flows when V_{DS} is increased.

The only significant difference between the d-MOST and the JFET, apart from the structural difference and the corresponding different values of input resistance, is that the d-MOST can be operated with both polarities of V_{GS}. If V_{GS} is made positive for an n-channel d-MOST, electrons are attracted to the channel region, lessening the effect of the channel–substrate depletion layer so that pinch-off occurs at a higher value of V_{DS}. Positive V_{GS} cannot be applied to an n-channel JFET because the gate–channel junction would become forward-biased, gate current would flow, the input resistance would fall to a low value and the entire operation of the device would change. The transfer characteristic of the d-MOST is the same as that for a JFET, figure 2.4b, except the dashed portion for V_{GS} positive is valid for a d-MOST. The same parabolic relationship between $I_{D(sat)}$ and V_{GS}, equation 2.17, applies to the d-MOST [1] as for the JFET.

The symbol for an n-channel d-MOST shows the gate electrode insulated from the channel (heavy line) and the channel type is shown by the direction of the substrate arrow which indicates the direction of current flow across the substrate–channel junction if it was to be forward-biased, even though this is not a normal operating condition. Usually the substrate is internally shorted to the source, producing a three-terminal device.

For a p-channel d-MOST current flow through the channel is by holes, the voltage polarities and current directions are opposite to those for the n-channel device and the arrow on the circuit symbol is reversed.

e-MOSTs

The enhancement type MOST is similar in structure to the d-MOST except that no channel layer is formed during manufacture (figure 2.4a). Thus with $V_{GS} = 0$, current flow between drain and source is blocked by a reverse-biased pn junction and I_{DSS} is therefore only leakage current.

For an n-channel device, if V_{GS} is made positive, electrons are attracted to the surface of the p-type substrate directly under the insulating layer and similarly holes are repelled away from the surface. At a particular value of V_{GS}, termed the threshold voltage V_T (often $V_{GS(th)}$ on manufacturers' device data sheets), the density of electrons becomes just greater than the density of holes in this surface layer and an n-type *inversion* layer is formed. Once this channel region has been formed, subsequent increase in V_{DS} eventually results in pinch-off and a saturating output characteristic (figure 2.4c) similar to that for a d-MOST. Notice that the only significant difference between the output characteristics of n-channel e- and d-MOSTs (figures 2.4b and c) is the different range of values of V_{GS} in the two cases.

Analysis [1] shows that the transfer characteristic is approximately parabolic for $V_{GS} > V_T$ given by

$$I_{D(sat)} \simeq K\left(\frac{V_{GS}}{V_T} - 1\right)^2 \tag{2.18}$$

where K is a current parameter for the device obtained using the value of $I_{D(sat)}$ at a particular value of $V_{GS}(> V_T)$.

For all types of FET, current flow through the resistive channel results in power dissipation and temperature rise. Under static operating conditions the total power dissipation is

$$P_{tot} = V_{DS}I_D \tag{2.19}$$

and the hyperbola $V_{DS}I_D = P_{tot}\text{max}$ plotted on the static output characteristics, figure 2.4b and c, sets a boundary to the safe operating area of the device in an exactly similar way to that for a BJT. The drain current rating, $I_D\text{max}$, for a particular value of V_{GS} is set by the intercept of that particular output characteristic with the $P_{tot}\text{max}$ hyperbola. Voltage ratings are set by breakdown; $V_{DS}\text{max}$ by breakdown of the gate–channel or substrate–channel junctions, $V_{GS}\text{max}$ by breakdown of the reverse-biased gate–channel junction in a JFET and breakdown of the gate–channel insulating layer in a MOST. Often maximum voltages for FETs are specified as breakdown voltages BV, thus $V_{DS}\text{max}$ is given as BV_{DSS}, the *b*reakdown *v*oltage between D and S with the gate shorted to the source; similarly $V_{GS}\text{max}$ is given as BV_{GSS}.

More comprehensive details of the manufacture, structure, operation and performance of FETs can be found in reference [1].

Example 2.5: Calculation of drain current and allowable power dissipation for a JFET

The specification of a JFET states that $V_{GS(off)} = -4$ V, $I_{DSS} = 10$ mA, $P_{tot}\text{max} = 300$ mW and $V_{DS}\text{max} = 60$ V. Estimate the drain current when $V_{GS} = -1$ V and determine the maximum value of V_{DS} that can be allowed under these conditions.

Pinch-off voltage $V_P = V_{GS(off)} = -4$ V

From equation 2.17, $I_{D(sat)} \simeq I_{DSS}\left(1 - \dfrac{V_{GS}}{V_P}\right)^2$

$$= 10\text{ mA}\left(1 - \frac{V_{GS}}{(-4\text{ V})}\right)^2$$

Thus, when $V_{GS} = -1$ V, $I_{D(sat)} \simeq 10\text{ mA}\left(1 - \dfrac{(-1\text{ V})}{(-4\text{ V})}\right)^2$

$$= 10(0.75)^2 = 5.63\text{ mA}$$

The maximum value of V_{DS} that can be allowed is limited by either the breakdown rating of

60 V or the power dissipation rating of 300 mW. In terms of power dissipation, the maximum value of V_{DS} that can be allowed at $I_D = 5.63$ mA is, from equation 2.19:

$$V_{DS}\max = \frac{P_{tot}\max}{I_D} \simeq \frac{300\text{ mW}}{5.63\text{ mA}} = 53.3\text{ V}$$

As this limiting value of V_{DS} is less than the breakdown limit of 60 V, it can be concluded that for this operating condition ($V_{GS} = -1$ V), V_{DS} must not exceed 53.3 V; the limit is set by power dissipation rather than breakdown.

2.4 **Performance of passive components: resistors, capacitors and wound components**

2.4.1 ***Resistors***

The current flow through a resistor is proportional to the voltage across it as given by Ohm's law

$$v = Ri \tag{2.20}$$

where R is the *resistance* measured in ohms (Ω).

General-purpose discrete resistors are manufactured as a carbon, metal or metal oxide film deposited on a ceramic rod. This film is formed into a track of suitable length to provide the required resistance by cutting a helical groove in the film. End caps make contact to the film and carry the external connection leads. Figure 2.5a shows the circuit symbol for a resistor and the typical operational details given in a resistor specification are listed in table 2.1. Such resistors are manufactured according to a series of preferred *nominal* values, the E-series (appendix D), with an associated percentage tolerance. The *actual* resistance of a particular resistor is then guaranteed to lie within the tolerance band spanning the nominal value *provided* the power and voltage ratings are not exceeded. Colour coding (appendix C) is normally used to indicate the nominal value and tolerance on the resistor body although some low resistance types ($R < 10\,\Omega$) and high-power types ($P > 2$ W) have the resistance and tolerance details printed on the component. The power rating is limited by the body temperature which for the hypothetical, though typical, type referred to in table 2.1 is 250 mW at an ambient of 70°C. If in a particular application the ambient is likely to exceed 70°C then the resistor must be derated (example 2.6) in a similar way to the transistor in example 2.2. Discrete resistors are manufactured with power ratings of 0.125, 0.25, 0.5, 1 and 2 W together with higher ratings, usually in wirewound form, for special-purpose applications.

Corresponding to equation 2.1, the *static* power dissipated in a resistor is

$$P = VI = \frac{V^2}{R} = I^2R \tag{2.21}$$

using $V = RI$; upper case symbols are used for constant values of voltage and current. If the voltage, and hence current, are time varying the average power dissipated is given by equation 2.2 which, *by definition* of *root-mean-square* values V_{RMS} and I_{RMS} (equations 11.6 to 11.9), may be written

$$P_{AV} = V_{RMS}I_{RMS} = \frac{V_{RMS}^2}{R} = I_{RMS}^2R \tag{2.22}$$

v

i R

General symbol

$v = Ri$

(a) Resistor

v q

i C

General symbol

+

Polarised (electrolytic) type

$$i = C\frac{dv}{dt}$$

(b) Capacitor

v N turns

i L ϕ

General symbol

$$v = N\frac{d\phi}{dt} = L\frac{di}{dt}$$

(c) Inductor

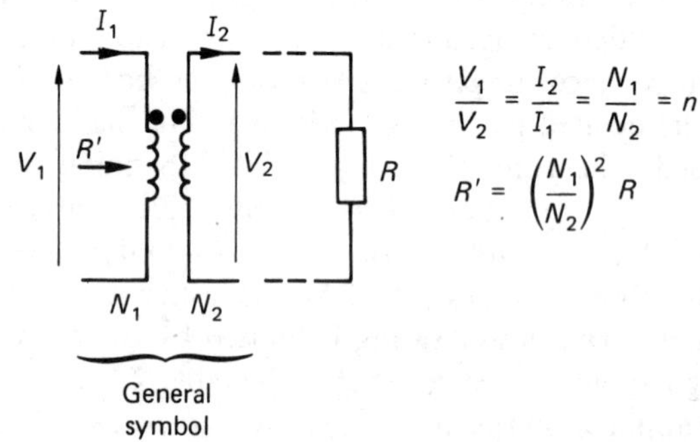

$$\frac{V_1}{V_2} = \frac{I_2}{I_1} = \frac{N_1}{N_2} = n$$

$$R' = \left(\frac{N_1}{N_2}\right)^2 R$$

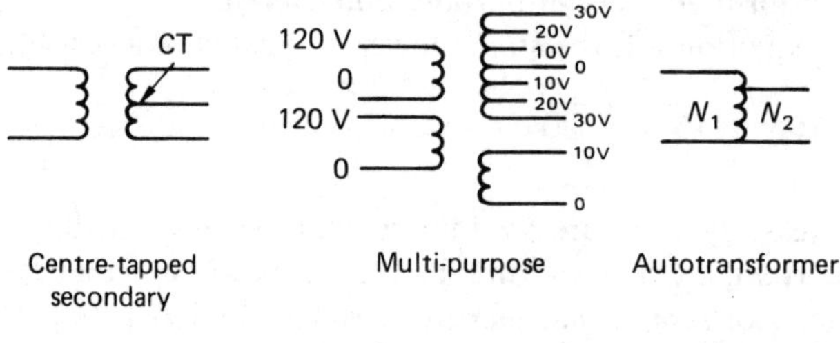

Centre-tapped secondary

Multi-purpose

Autotransformer

(d) Transformer

Figure 2.5 Passive electronic components

Table 2.1 Passive component specifications

Typical general-purpose resistor	
Resistance range 10 Ω to 10 MΩ in E12 series (BS2488: 1966)	
Resistance tolerance	±5 per cent
Maximum power dissipation at $T_{amb} = 70°C$	0.25 W
Maximum body temperature	155°C
Voltage rating	350 V
Temperature coefficient	−250 ppm/°C
Stability	<0.5 per cent
Maximum noise	<0.5 μV/V
Typical wet aluminium electrolytic capacitor	
Capacitance range	1 to 4700 μF (E6 series)
Capacitance tolerance	±20 per cent
Rated voltage (*see note 1*)	10 to 450 V dc
Static leakage current (*see note 2*)	<0.01 μA/μFV
Loss factor (tan δ) at 100 Hz	<0.15
Temperature range	−40 to +85°C
Life	>10^5 h at $T_{amb} = 40°C$ >10^4 h at 70°C
Note 1: Available rated voltages are 10 V, 25 V, 63 V, 100 V, 450 V.	
Note 2: At steady state at $T_{amb} = 20°C$.	
Typical general-purpose metallised polyester film capacitor	
Capacitance range	0.01 to 2.2 μF (E6 series)
Capacitance tolerance	±10 per cent
Rated voltage	250 V dc, 160 V ac (rms)
Loss factor (tan δ) at 1 kHz	<0.015
Temperature range	−40 to +100°C
Temperature coefficient	+200 ppm/°C
Stability	<5 per cent

Even though the power rating imposes a limit to the voltage that may be applied to a resistor of value R (from equation 2.21 for static operation, equation 2.22 for the dynamic case), an overriding voltage limit is also imposed to avoid breakdown (see example 2.6). The temperature coefficient, which may be positive or negative depending on the resistive film material, indicates the typical drift of resistance value as the resistor temperature increases; this coefficient is normally quoted in parts-per-million (ppm)/°C rise in temperature (see example 2.6). Stability refers to the typical change in resistance value after continuous operation for a period of time (often 1000 h) at a particular power level and ambient temperature (often maximum allowable dissipation at $T_{amb} = 70°C$). The figure of < 0.5 per cent quoted in table 2.1 indicates that after continuous operation at 250 mW for 1000 h at $T_{amb} = 70°C$, the resistance value will typically remain within 0.5 per cent of its initial value (see example 2.6). Because of the random movement of charge carriers through the material, a random voltage termed a noise voltage appears across a resistor even for constant current flow. The reference to maximum noise < 0.5 μV/V in the specification of table 2.1 indicates that, for this type of resistor, the rms noise voltage across the resistor is < 0.5 μV for every 1 V applied externally.

Example 2.6: Properties of a typical resistor

Consider the properties of a 470 kΩ resistor having the specification given in table 2.1.

470 kΩ ±5 per cent, that is $(470 \times 10^3)\,\Omega$ ±5 per cent; multiplier k is $\times 10^3$ (appendix C).
Colour code (appendix C):
yellow (4), violet (7), yellow (multiplier $\times 10^4\,\Omega$), gold (tolerance ±5 per cent) BS 1852: 1967

written code (appendix C):

470 kΩ ± 5 per cent is written 470 KJ (K = × 10^3 Ω, J = ± 5 per cent)

The actual resistance value is within the range 470 kΩ − 5 per cent to 470 kΩ + 5 per cent, that is, between 446.5 kΩ and 493.5 kΩ.
Power rating at $T_{amb} = 70°C$: 250 mW provided the voltage across the resistor does not exceed 350 V from consideration of breakdown. For $R = 470$ kΩ the static voltage across the resistor corresponding to maximum dissipation is (equation 2.21) $\sqrt{PR} = \sqrt{(0.25\ \text{W})(470 \times 10^3\ \Omega)} =$ 342.8 V which is less than the 350 V limit and therefore the 0.25 W power limit applies. Note that for a larger value of resistance the voltage limit is reached before the power limit, for example, for a 1 MΩ resistor, power dissipation at the 350 V limit is V^2/R (equation 2.21) which is only 122.5 mW. Therefore, for a 1 MΩ resistor in this range, the maximum power dissipation at $T_{amb} = 70°\text{C}$ is limited by breakdown to only 122.5 mW.

For ambient temperatures higher than 70°C the power rating must be derated. The thermal resistance of the type considered here is, from the information in table 2.1 and using equation 2.4:

$$R_{th} = \frac{T_{max} - T_{amb}}{P_{max} \text{ at } T_{amb} = 70°\text{C}} = \frac{155°\text{C} - 70°\text{C}}{250\ \text{mW}} = 0.34°\text{C/mW}$$

Then, the power rating at, for example, $T_{amb} = 90°\text{C}$ is

$$\frac{155°\text{C} - 90°\text{C}}{0.34°\text{C/mW}} = 191.2\ \text{mW}$$

The temperature coefficient of − 250 ppm/°C shows that the resistance value of the nominal 470 kΩ resistor will drift at a typical rate of $\frac{-250}{10^6} \times 470\ \text{k}\Omega/°\text{C} \simeq -120\ \Omega/°\text{C}$ temperature rise and so for a 10°C rise, the resistance could be expected to *reduce* by about 1.2 kΩ.

The stability factor of *better than* 0.5 per cent indicates that for long term operation at constant temperature, the resistance can be expected to remain within 0.5 per cent, that is, $\frac{0.5}{100} \times 470\ \text{k}\Omega = 2.35\ \text{k}\Omega$, of the initial value.

2.4.2 *Capacitors*

Capacitors comprise a thin insulator, termed the dielectric, with electrodes on either side. When a voltage is applied across the electrodes, a stress is established in the dielectric which is represented in terms of *charge q* in *coulombs*. The charge is proportional to the applied voltage

$$q = Cv \tag{2.23}$$

the proportionality parameter being the *capacitance C* measured in *farads* (F).

As current is given by the rate of flow of charge, the current flow through a capacitor is proportional to the time rate of change of the applied voltage

$$i = \frac{dq}{dt} = C\frac{dv}{dt} \tag{2.24}$$

using equation 2.23. Thus the faster the voltage changes the greater the current flow, while for constant voltage ($dv/dt = 0$) the current flow is zero. This property provides the important use of a capacitor in blocking constant current while allowing time-varying components to pass as in the use as a coupling capacitor between the stages of an ac amplifier (section 3.3).

Because, by Fourier representation (appendix A), any time variation can be represented by a series of sinusoidal variations, the response of a capacitor to sinusoidal excitation is of particular interest. If a sinusoidally varying voltage $v = V_m \sin \omega t$ is applied to an *ideal* capacitor, the resulting current flow is given (equation 2.24) by

$$\begin{aligned} i &= C \frac{d}{dt}(V_m \sin \omega t) \\ &= \omega C V_m \cos \omega t \\ &= \omega C V_m \sin(\omega t + \pi/2) \end{aligned} \tag{2.25}$$

where $\omega = 2\pi f$ is the angular frequency of the variation in radians/s; f is the frequency in hertz.

The current variation therefore *leads* the voltage variation by $\pi/2$ radians (a quarter cycle) and the maximum value of current, from equation 2.25, is $\omega C V_m$. Thus the ratio of maximum voltage to maximum current, which is also equal to the ratio of rms voltage to rms current (rms value = maximum value/$\sqrt{2}$ for a sinusoidal variation, see note 11.1 in chapter 11), is

$$\frac{V_m}{I_m} = \frac{V_{rms}}{I_{rms}} = \frac{1}{\omega C} = X_C \tag{2.26}$$

where X_C, termed *capacitive reactance*, describes the capacitor's 'opposition' to alternating (sinusoidal) current flow. In describing the relationship between voltage and current, X_C for a capacitor is analogous to R for a resistor and, like resistance, reactance is measured in ohms. It should be noted however that whereas resistance is a general property of a resistor, reactance describes the response of a capacitor *only* for the special case of sinusoidal variation of voltage and current. Furthermore, because the phase relation between v and i for a capacitor is different from that for a resistor, the properties reactance and resistance *cannot* be added directly (see below) even though they are both measured in ohms. Notice from equation 2.26 that for constant current, $\omega = 0$, $X_C = \infty$, indicating the dc blocking properties of an ideal capacitor.

Equation 2.26 relates only the 'values' of voltage and current, the phase relationship is not represented. The mathematical operator j has the property of advancing a sinusoidally varying quantity by a quarter cycle, thus a waveform jv leads v by a quarter cycle; v is a voltage that is varying sinusoidally with time. From equation 2.25, a voltage $v = V_m \sin \omega t$ causes a current $i = \omega C V_m \sin(\omega t + \pi/2)$ which, using j-notation, may be written $i = \omega C(jv)$. The voltage–current ratio for the capacitor may therefore be written

$$\frac{v}{i} = \frac{v}{\omega C(jv)} = \frac{1}{j\omega C} = \frac{X_C}{j} = -jX_C \tag{2.27}$$

which provides both magnitude and phase representation, noting that $j^2 = -1$. The term $-jX_C$ may be termed the *operational reactance* of a capacitor and as it includes phase information it may be combined directly with resistance so that a series capacitor–resistor combination has an *operational impedance* $R - jX_C$ and a parallel combination (product divided by sum, corresponding to the footnote in example 1.4) $R(-jX_C)/(R - jX_C)$.

Returning to the voltage and current relationships for an ideal capacitor (equation 2.25), $v = V_m \sin \omega t$ and $i = \omega C V_m \sin(\omega t + \pi/2)$, the average power dissipated in the device, from equation 2.2, is

$$P_{AV} = \frac{1}{\Delta t} \int_{\Delta t} \omega C V_m^2 \sin \omega t \sin(\omega t + \pi/2)\, dt \tag{2.28}$$

By making the time interval Δt an integral number of periods and simplifying the sine product using the identity $2\sin A \sin B = \cos(A - B) - \cos(A + B)$, the average power dissipated in an ideal capacitor is found to be zero. In practice however there is a degree of leakage through a real capacitor so that absolute dc blocking does not occur. The real capacitor therefore performs as though it were an ideal capacitor shunted (in parallel with) by a large-value *leakage* resistance which degrades its performance. In consequence the phase angle between current and voltage is slightly less than a quarter cycle and some power is dissipated in the device.

The capacitance of the electrode–dielectric–electrode structure can be found by considering the electric field within the dielectric. A static voltage V across the dielectric layer of thickness d results in an electric field (potential gradient) within the layer of $E = V/d$. If, under these conditions, the static charge in the layer is Q then an electric flux density $D = Q/A$ exists within the dielectric as, by definition, one unit of flux originates and terminates on one unit of charge, A being the electrode area. The link between flux and field is the fundamental electrostatic equation

$$D = \varepsilon E \tag{2.29}$$

where ε is the *permittivity* of the dielectric material. Substituting $D = Q/A$ and $E = V/d$ in equation 2.29 gives

$$\frac{Q}{A} = \varepsilon \frac{V}{d}$$

from which capacitance C, from the static charge–voltage relationship corresponding to equation 2.23, is

$$C = \frac{Q}{V} = \varepsilon \frac{A}{d} \tag{2.30}$$

Capacitance is therefore determined by the choice of dielectric material, the electrode area and the thickness of the dielectric. High-value capacitors therefore require a high permittivity dielectric, a high electrode area and/or a thin dielectric. Many capacitors, those having a flexible dielectric, use a tubular structure in which the electrode–dielectric–electrode sandwich is rolled to provide a relatively large electrode area in a compact shape. The minimum dielectric thickness is limited by breakdown taking account of the required working voltage of the device.

Capacitors are manufactured in ranges of preferred nominal values as for resistors but the ranges are more restricted. High-value and general-purpose types are usually available in E6 values (appendix D), although often some values are omitted; low-value, close-tolerance types used in precision applications such as filters are usually available in the E12 range but again not all values in the range may be available. The most widely used types are the polarised *electrolytic* variety and the non-polarised *plastic film* type; the corresponding circuit symbols are shown in figure 2.5b. The former provides values of capacitance upwards of about 1 μF (10^{-6} F), the largest widely-available value being of the order of 220 000 μF, at rated voltages from 6.3 V up to typically 400 V; the larger capacitance values are available only at the lower values of rated voltage. To maintain the dielectric layer which is formed as an oxide layer in either a liquid or solid electrolyte, termed *wet* and *solid* types respectively, the anode terminal must be kept positive relative to the cathode in use. The plastic film type, being non-polarised, can be used in ac applications; values are available from as low as 10 pF (10×10^{-12} F) up to 10 μF with working voltages from typically 63 V to 1500 V dc (45 to 450 V ac rms) depending on the film material.

The widely-used film plastics are polyester (Mylar), polycarbonate, polypropylene and polystryrene. The *polyester* range is intended for general-purpose use providing capacitances typically up to 2.2 μF with a tolerance of ± 10 or ± 20 per cent. *Polycarbonate* types are marketed as better quality general-purpose capacitors offering improvements in leakage and stability with values up to 10 μF ± 5 per cent. *Polypropylene* capacitors are often specified for high voltage/high frequency applications because of their low loss properties; values are available up to typically 0.47 μF with a ± 20 per cent tolerance, although values below about 100 nF (100×10^{-9} F) are available with tolerances of ± 2 or ± 5 per cent. *Polystyrene* types are characterised by very low loss and excellent stability. Values up to 33 nF are widely available at a tolerance of ± 1 per cent; this type has a lower high temperature limit (typically $+70$°C) than other plastic types ($+100$°C) because of softening of the polystyrene dielectric film. Other capacitor types in limited use are *disc ceramics* and *silvered mica* types. For most types of capacitor, the capacitance value and tolerance are printed on the body, but for some tantalum and polyester-film resin-dipped types, colour coded bands are used (appendix C).

Table 2.1 gives the specification of a typical range of wet aluminium capacitors. The important points to note are the wide tolerance and poor leakage properties which limit use to non-precise applications in low impedance circuits such as smoothing in ac–dc power supplies (section 11.2.3) and bypass in ac amplifiers (section 3.3). The static leakage current is proportional to the capacitance–rated voltage (CV) product and the quoted value of < 0.01 μA/μF V indicates that the worst-case static leakage current for a 100 μF, 63 V device is $0.01 \times 100 \times 63 = 63$ μA. This value normally refers to steady-state operation after the dielectric oxide layer has stabilised; before stabilisation is reached, leakage is likely to be considerably greater than this value. Because the physical size of a capacitor increases with CV-product, usually the higher capacitance versions in a range are available at only the lower rated voltage levels.

The *loss factor*, also known as dissipation factor and power factor, is the tangent of the loss angle δ where the phase angle between i and v is $(\pi/2 - \delta)$. Because of leakage resistance, a practical capacitor behaves as a parallel CR circuit with the result that the phase angle between i and v is slightly less than $\pi/2$ (90°). Analysis of the parallel CR model shows that $\tan\delta = 1/2\pi fCR$ which is used as a figure-of-merit for a capacitor; ideally the leakage resistance is infinite, $\tan\delta = 0$, $\delta = 0$ and i leads v by 90°. The value of < 0.15 at 100 Hz quoted in table 2.1 shows that the leakage resistance $R\ (= 1/2\pi fC \tan\delta)$ of a 100 μF capacitor of this type, at 100 Hz, is

$$> 1/[2\pi \times 100\ \text{Hz} \times (100 \times 10^{-6})\ \text{F} \times 0.15] \simeq 106\ \Omega$$

Notice that although this is a relatively low value, the corresponding reactance of a 100 μF capacitor at 100 Hz is only 16 Ω (equation 2.26). As a point of clarification it should be noted that the leakage properties of this type of capacitor have been referred to in terms of *static* leakage, related to CV-product, and in terms of loss factor at a particular frequency. Static leakage refers to the situation where the voltage across the capacitor is constant. Although electrolytic capacitors are polarised, so that the applied voltage must not be reversed, in many applications the voltage across the capacitor fluctuates as in a smoothing circuit (section 11.2.3). In such situations the applied voltage effectively comprises a moderate average value, which maintains the required polarity, with a superimposed fluctuating component which is often termed *ripple* in a smoothing circuit or the *signal* component in an amplifier. It is the frequency of this ripple component that is referred to above in relation to loss factor.

The temperature range of wet electrolytic capacitors is limited to typically -40 to $+85\,^\circ$C by the properties of the electrolyte which is normally impregnated into a carrier such as paper. Gradual evaporation of the electrolyte eventually leads to device failure although improvements in container design have enabled lifetimes in excess of 10^5 h (>11 years' continuous usage) to be attained at modest operating temperatures. Notice from the specification how the life is shortened drastically by operation at elevated temperature. Solid electrolyte construction based on either aluminium or tantalum gives improved performance in terms of shelf life, reliability and temperature range but at increased cost.

Table 2.1 also gives a typical specification for a range of metallised polyester film capacitors. The tolerance of ± 10 per cent is typical for general-purpose capacitors up to about 1 μF. Being non-polarised this type of capacitor is suitable for both dc and ac applications. The constant voltage rating of 250 V relates to dielectric breakdown taking into account operating temperature and acceptable life (often taken as one failure in 10^5 operating hours). The alternating voltage rating, usually quoted in terms of rms value assuming a sinusoidal waveshape, is set to avoid breakdown and refers to operation at 'low' frequencies up to the order of 100 kHz. At higher frequencies, dielectric heating becomes the limiting factor and the voltage rating must be derated accordingly. The loss factor for a polyester capacitor is the same figure-of-merit referred to above in relation to electrolytic types. Notice that the value of tan δ for the polyester type is one-tenth the value quoted for a typical electrolytic type, indicating that the ac leakage resistance of the polyester type is considerably larger, that is, the polyester capacitor approximates more closely to an ideal capacitor than does an electrolytic type. The quoted value of <0.015 at 1 kHz shows that the leakage resistance of a 0.1 μF polyester capacitor at 1 kHz is typically

$$>1/[2\pi \times 1\ \text{kHz} \times (0.1 \times 10^{-6})\ \text{F} \times 0.015] \simeq 106\ \text{k}\Omega$$

Notice however that the capacitance value provided is *very* much smaller than that of the electrolytic type previously considered. The information given in the specification as to the variation of capacitance with temperature and time, temperature coefficient and stability, is used in exactly the same way as for a resistor (example 2.6). Notice that such information is not given for electrolytic capacitors because the applications in which they are used, such as smoothing, coupling and bypass, do not require precise values.

2.4.3 *Wound components: inductors and transformers*

An influence exists in the region around a current-carrying wire that is commonly referred to as a magnetic field. If such a field *links with* or *cuts* a conductor, by virtue of the field moving as a result of a changing current or by the conductor moving in the field, a current is *induced* in the conductor. Components utilising this effect comprise a coil, or coils, of insulated wire wound on a magnetic core and are often termed generally as *wound components.*

The basic component of this type is an *inductor* which consists of a single coil on a ferromagnetic (steel or iron alloy) or ferrite (iron oxide base) core. If a current i flows through the coil, a proportional magnetic flux ϕ is established and, if the coil has N turns, this results in a *flux linkage* ψ of

$$\psi = N\phi \tag{2.31}$$

If the current varies with time, ψ varies and a voltage v is induced across the coil where

$$v = \frac{d\psi}{dt} = N\frac{d\phi}{dt} \tag{2.32}$$

using equation 2.31.
As the flux ϕ is proportional to the current i, $d\phi/dt$ is proportional to di/dt and from equation 2.32 the voltage across the coil is therefore proportional to the rate of change of current:

$$v = L\frac{di}{dt} \tag{2.33}$$

where the proportionality parameter L is the *inductance* of the coil measured in *henrys* (H). Comparison of equations 2.32 and 2.33 shows that

$$L = N\frac{d\phi}{di} \tag{2.34}$$

Magnetic flux ϕ and 'magnetising' current i are linked by the fundamental electrodynamic (magnetic) equation

$$B = \mu H \tag{2.35}$$

for the core material containing the flux, where B is the magnetic flux density, H is the magnetising force and μ is the *permeability* of the core material. If a cylindrical inductor has cross-sectional area A, axial length l and the coil has N turns, then $B = \phi/A$ and $H = Ni/l$. Substituting these relations into equation 2.35 gives

$$\frac{\phi}{A} = \mu\frac{Ni}{l}$$

from which

$$\frac{d\phi}{di} = \mu\frac{NA}{l}$$

and using equation 2.34, the coil inductance is

$$L = \mu N^2\frac{A}{l} \tag{2.36}$$

The link between current, flux and induced voltage gives an inductor the property of opposing change of current. If an attempt is made to change the current rapidly, di/dt instantaneously has a high value, resulting in a high induced voltage (equation 2.33). This induced voltage opposes the externally applied voltage that is responsible for changing the current with the overall effect that the rate of increase of current is limited to a value dependent on the inductance of the coil. The alternative name for an inductor, a *choke*, originated from the property of this component to restrict or choke a change of current. If however the current is constant, di/dt is zero, the induced opposing voltage is zero (equation 2.33) and there is no *induced* opposition to current flow. Note however that a coil still provides resistive opposition to current flow by virtue of the resistance of the wire. Inductance is described as the *dual* of capacitance in that an inductor allows constant current to pass while time-varying current is opposed. The circuit symbol of an inductor is shown in figure 2.5c.

As with capacitors, the response of an inductor to sinusoidal excitation is of interest because any waveshape can be represented in terms of a series of sinusoidal variations using Fourier representation (appendix A). If a sinusoidally varying voltage $v = V_m \sin \omega t$ is applied to an *ideal* inductor, that is one having zero resistance, the corresponding current flow, from equation 2.33, is

$$\begin{aligned} i &= \frac{1}{L}\int v \, dt \\ &= \frac{1}{L}\int V_m \sin \omega t \, dt \\ &= \frac{V_m}{\omega L}(-\cos \omega t) \\ &= \frac{V_m}{\omega L}\sin(\omega t - \pi/2) \end{aligned} \tag{2.37}$$

The opposition of the inductor to sinusoidal current flow, termed *inductive reactance* X_L, measured in ohms, is given by the ratio

$$X_L = \frac{V_m}{I_m} = \frac{V_{rms}}{I_{rms}} = \omega L \tag{2.38}$$

where the maximum value of current, I_m, is $V_m/\omega L$ from equation 2.37. From $v = V_m \sin \omega t$ and $i = (V_m/\omega L)\sin(\omega t - \pi/2)$ it can be seen that the current variation *lags* the voltage variation by $\pi/2$ radians and that, in terms of j-notation, the current can be written $-jv/\omega L$; the variation $-jv$ lags v by $\pi/2$ radians (90° or a quarter cycle) by virtue of the property of the operator j. Thus the voltage–current ratio for an ideal inductor may be written

$$\frac{v}{i} = \frac{v}{-jv/\omega L} = \frac{\omega L}{-j} = j\omega L \tag{2.39}$$

since $j^2 = -1$. The term $j\omega L$ is the *operational reactance* of an inductor.

For constant current flow $\omega = 0$ and so $X_L = 0$ (equation 2.38), indicating that an ideal inductor does not oppose the flow of constant current. As the frequency of alternating current increases so does X_L, corresponding to increased opposition.

From the voltage and current expressions for sinusoidal excitation, $v = V_m \sin \omega t$ and $i = (V_m/\omega L)\sin(\omega t - \pi/2)$, the average power dissipated in an ideal inductor is (equation 2.2)

$$P_{AV} = \frac{1}{\Delta t}\int_{\Delta t} \frac{V_m^2}{\omega L} \sin \omega t \sin(\omega t - \pi/2) \, dt \tag{2.40}$$

Integration over an integral number of periods shows that no power is dissipated in an ideal inductor. In practice the coil has a finite resistance R so that the *operational impedance* is $R + j\omega L$, the phase angle between v and i being $\tan^{-1}(\omega L/R)$ which is less than 90°. Some power is dissipated in a practical inductor as a consequence of the resistance; in this respect, the practical inductor behaves as a resistor.

A figure-of-merit for a practical inductor at a particular operating frequency is given by the ratio of its inductive to resistive properties which can be represented in terms of the energy stored to energy dissipated. This parameter is the *quality factor* (Q-factor) of the coil and is given (appendix B, section B.1) by

$$Q_L = \frac{\text{reactance}}{\text{resistance}} = \frac{\omega L}{R} \tag{2.41}$$

The *Q*-factor of a coil is particularly significant in the performance of tuned (resonant) circuits as incorporated in a tuned amplifier (section 6.9). Care must be taken not to confuse the *Q*-factor of a *coil* (Q_L) with the *Q*-factor of the parallel inductor–capacitor tuned *circuit* which is usually denoted simply as *Q* (appendix B, section B.3).

Unlike resistors and capacitors, inductors are *not* widely available as off-the-shelf general-purpose items because of their somewhat specialised and limited use. Traditional applications have been in filters, tuned circuits and as RF chokes. Only the latter type, which are used to provide dc coupling while providing high impedance to radio frequency signals, as in the class E power amplifier of section 8.7, is available as standard items, usually in E6-range inductance values up to 1 mH. The specification of such chokes also quotes the maximum allowable steady current flow, which is linked to wire gauge and maximum allowable temperature, resistance and *Q*-factor at a typical operating frequency. Inductors required for filters, both high-current types as used for smoothing in ac–dc power supplies (section 11.2.3) and low-current types used in signal filtering and resonant circuits, are available either as special-order items designed for the particular application concerned or can be wound by the user from information supplied by the core manufacturer. Power losses occur in wound components because of both dissipation in the winding, often termed *copper loss*, and dissipation in the core due to induced circulating currents (eddy currents) which is normally described as the *core loss*. Components intended for use at high frequency normally use ferrite cores which, having low electrical conductivity, restrict eddy currents and therefore have a low core loss. Lower operating frequency components such as high-current inductors for ac–dc power supply smoothing filters normally use a ferromagnetic (metal) core which is constructed from laminations that are electrically insulated from one another to reduce eddy current flow. In either case, design of an inductor involves the selection of an appropriate core, both in terms of material and physical size, that can accommodate the required number of turns using an adequate gauge of wire taking account of the current flow and/or maximum allowable coil resistance (minimum allowable *Q*-factor) specified.

Wound components are generally bulky and costly and, if possible, are avoided in circuit design. High-current smoothing circuits are often replaced by solid-state regulators (section 11.2.4) avoiding the use of high-current, high inductance chokes while inductive properties (increase of reactance with frequency, equation 2.38) required in signal filters and tuned circuits are frequently simulated using an op-amp (section 9.2.2 and figure 9.26).

An important extension of the use of the link between current, magnetic flux and induction is the *transformer* in which the varying current in one coil, the *primary*, induces a varying voltage across a second coil, the *secondary*. The general circuit symbol for a transformer is shown in figure 2.5d; V_1, V_2 and I_1, I_2 are the rms primary and secondary voltages and currents respectively, and N_1, N_2 are the number of turns on the primary and secondary windings. The changing flux due to the primary current links with the secondary winding and, ignoring the small leakage flux, the voltage induced in each turn (V_t) of the two windings is the same, thus

$$V_1 = V_t N_1 \text{ and } V_2 = V_t N_2$$

from which

$$\frac{V_1}{V_2} = \frac{N_1}{N_2} \tag{2.42}$$

The relationship between primary and secondary currents for the transformer *on load*, that is, with a current I_2 drawn from the secondary, can be established from the ampere-turns balance between the two windings. If the magnetising component of the input current, that component which establishes the working flux, is small and losses (winding and core) are negligible, the ampere-turns product NI for each winding must be the same. This product is termed the magnetomotive force (mmf) and is analogous to emf in an electrical circuit. Thus

$$N_1 I_1 = N_2 I_2 \tag{2.43}$$

which, when combined with equation 2.42, gives the fundamental relationship for a transformer

$$\frac{V_1}{V_2} = \frac{I_2}{I_1} = \frac{N_1}{N_2} = n \tag{2.44}$$

n being the primary-to-secondary *turns ratio.*

As well as providing voltage step-up or step-down (transformation), transformers are also used to transform impedance (resistance at low frequencies) levels. From the loaded transformer in figure 2.5d, the effective resistance across the primary terminals R' is V_1/I_1 while the actual load resistance R is V_2/I_2, thus

$$\frac{R'}{R} = \frac{V_1/I_1}{V_2/I_2} = \left(\frac{V_1}{V_2}\right)\left(\frac{I_2}{I_1}\right) = \left(\frac{N_1}{N_2}\right)^2 = n^2 \tag{2.45}$$

using equation 2.44 and so

$$R' = n^2 R \tag{2.46}$$

This transformation of impedance (resistance) levels can be useful in *matching* one circuit to another (section 8.2).

The application of a transformer normally enables the primary and secondary voltages and the secondary current to be specified. From this information the minimum allowable VA rating of the core can be calculated as the product of secondary rms voltage and secondary rms current, which indicates the minimum core size. Manufacturers produce cores with quoted VA ratings such as 1, 5, 10, 20, 50, 100, 200, 500 and 1000 VA. The VA rating indicates the allowable power throughput of the transformer which is limited by temperature rise; the voltage–ampere product is quoted instead of 'true' power in watts, which depends on the phase relationship between voltage and current, to allow for the fact that v and i may not be in phase. Knowledge of I_2, and subsequent calculation of I_1 using equation 2.44, enables suitable wire gauges for the primary and secondary windings to be selected from standard wire tables.

At this stage, the turns ratio is known from the voltage ratio (equation 2.44) but actual values of N_1 and N_2 have not yet been calculated. The technique is to calculate N_1 from knowledge of the maximum allowable flux in the core, noting that the core material must not be allowed to saturate otherwise the flux would not change linearly with current and severe distortion would result.

Assuming a sinusoidal variation of core flux with time

$$\phi = \phi_{\mathrm{m}} \sin 2\pi f t \tag{2.47}$$

and the instantaneous primary voltage v_1, from equation 2.32, is

$$\begin{aligned} v_1 &= N_1 \frac{\mathrm{d}\phi}{\mathrm{d}t} \\ &= 2\pi f N_1 \phi_{\mathrm{m}} \cos 2\pi f t \end{aligned} \tag{2.48}$$

from which the rms primary voltage V_1, $\sqrt{2}$ of the peak value for a sinusoidal variation, see note 11.1, chapter 11, is

$$V_1 = \frac{2\pi f N_1 \phi_m}{\sqrt{2}} = (\sqrt{2})\pi f N_1 \phi_m$$

giving

$$N_1 = \frac{V_1}{(\sqrt{2})\pi f \phi_m} \tag{2.49}$$

Having already provisionally selected a core on the basis of VA rating, the manufacturer's data provides information of the maximum permitted flux density $B_m(=\phi_m/A)$ for the material to ensure linearity, where A is the cross-sectional area of the core, from which

$$N_1 = \frac{V_1}{(\sqrt{2})\pi f B_m A} \tag{2.50}$$

Knowledge of the required turns ratio then allows N_2 to be determined and the only remaining calculation is to check if the physical cross-sectional size of the windings, having N_1 and N_2 turns of appropriate gauge wire corresponding to the current ratings, is such that the selected core can accommodate the windings. If not, a larger core must be selected and the number of turns recalculated bearing in mind that the core cross-section A will then be different.

Figure 2.5d also shows other transformer arrangements including a secondary with a *centre tap* as required with a two-diode rectifier (figure 11.7a) and a multi-purpose *mains* or *line* transformer where two primary windings can be connected either in parallel for a 120 V input or in series for 240 V operation, with a range of secondary tappings to meet a variety of applications. A feature of the standard transformer is the electrical *isolation* provided between the primary and secondary windings which is an important safety aspect. A simpler and cheaper type of transformer termed an *autotransformer* is basically a tapped inductor and does not provide isolation between input and output.

2.5 Manufacturing costs

As in all engineering work the financial aspect of electronic equipment manufacture is of fundamental importance in the development of a successful product. Assessment of overall costs taking account of market research, design and development, production, distribution and overheads is a complex subject; this section is intended only to outline the factors involved.

Table 2.2 sets out typical component costs at the time of writing for both small quantity and high volume purchase, the latter being typically 40–60 per cent of the small quantity cost. The prices quoted should be treated as only approximate since many factors other than the manufacturing cost influence the pricing level adopted by a manufacturer, such as competition from other manufacturers, demand, state of development and, in some cases, world exchange rates. Also included in table 2.2 are typical costs involved in the production of printed circuit boards and hardware assembly.

Example 2.7 gives a cost analysis for the manufacture of a basic item of electronic equipment.

Table 2.2 Typical costs associated with electronic hardware

	Low volume (<10)	*High volume* (>1000)
Discrete components		
Low-power switching diode (5 ns, 50 V)	4 p (7c)	2p (3c)
Medium-power rectification diode (3 A, 200 V)	15p (26c)	9p (15c)
Low-power voltage reference diode (400 mW)	9p (15c)	5p (9c)
Low-power BJT (100 mA, 45 V, 300 mW)	20p (34c)	12p (20c)
High-power BJT (10 A, 60 V, 80 W)	£1 ($1.70)	65p ($1.10)
Low-power JFET (10 mA, 25 V, 300 mW)	35p (60c)	16p (27c)
High-power VMOST (2 A, 60 V, 15 W)	£1.20 ($2)	80p ($1.40)
Low-power general-purpose resistor (250 mW, ±1 per cent)	3p (5c)	2p (3c)
Medium-power general-purpose resistor (2 W, ±2 per cent)	5p (9c)	3p (5c)
General-purpose polyester capacitor (100 nF, 250 V)	10p (17c)	5p (9c)
Medium CV-product wet aluminium capacitor (100 μF, 25 V)	16p (27c)	8p (14c)
Medium CV-product tantalum capacitor (100 μF, 16 V)	90p ($1.50)	75p ($1.30)
High CV-product wet aluminium capacitor (6800 μF, 40 V)	£5 ($8.50)	£3 ($5)
High-value low-frequency inductor (100 mH, 500 mA)	£4 ($6.80)	£3 ($5)
Low-value high-frequency inductor (100 μH, 250 mA, $Q = 60$ at 1 MHz)	80p ($1.40)	60p ($1)
Miniature ferrite core assembly for high-frequency inductor/pulse transformer	£1.50 ($2.55)	£1.20 ($2)
General-purpose mains/line transformer (100 VA; 240/120 V: 50; 50 V, 1 A)	£13 ($22)	£8 ($14)
Medium-power audio frequency output transformer (3 W, 8 Ω)	£5 ($8.50)	£3 ($5)
Integrated components		
Silicon bridge rectifier (2 A, 400 V)	38p (65c)	26p (44c)
Voltage regulator (fixed, 15 V, 500 mA)	60p ($1)	35p (60c)
General-purpose internally compensated op-amp (741)	45p (77c)	20p (34c)
High slew rate op-amp (531, 35 V/μs)	£1.80 ($3)	85p ($1.45)
General-purpose comparator (311)	60p ($1)	32p (54c)
General-purpose timer (555)	40p (68c)	17p (29c)
Small-scale digital IC (such as quad 2-input TTL NAND gates)	28p (48c)	12p (20c)
Medium-scale digital IC (such as 4-bit full adder)	90p ($1.50)	50p (85c)
Large-scale digital IC (such as 6809 8-bit microprocessor)	£7 ($12)	£3 ($5)
Very large-scale digital IC (such as 1 Mb dynamic random access memory)	£28 ($48)	£16 ($27)
Printed circuit boards (including layout design; tinned and drilled ready for assembly)		
Small size, basic quality, low density, single sided (100 mm × 80 mm, 200–300 holes)	£18 ($46)	£3 ($8)
Large size, high quality, high density, double sided (300 mm × 200 mm, 1500–2000 holes)	£45 ($115)	£13 ($33)
Assembly costs (placement and soldering of components, inspection, and test; including 30 per cent manufacturing overheads)		
Small-size pcb (100 mm × 80 mm, 10–25 components)	£3 ($7)	60p ($1)
Large-size pcb (300 mm × 200 mm, 80–200 components)	£20 ($40)	£4 ($6.80)

Market research is of fundamental importance in assessing the likely market of the intended product and in fact such research is often crucial in development of the specification of the equipment to ensure that it meets a known demand. This research necessarily involves prediction of the likely sales volume (number of units/year) and the life of the product, that is, the time for which the product is likely to attract reasonable sales before a redesign is necessary.

Development involves the electronic and mechanical design of the product including ergonomic and artistic factors such as layout of controls and external colour/finish which affect the appeal of the product to a potential customer.

The total capital outlay on market research, development and prototype production is assessed in terms of the number of man-hours involved and takes account of labour costs and manufacturing overheads. It is planned that this capital outlay together with associated

Example 2.7: Cost analysis of the manufacture of an ac–dc bench power supply required to provide a variable output up to 30 V, 1 A

	Unit cost £	Unit cost $
Market research leading to specification and sales prediction. Development, prototype assembly and testing	30	50
Total component cost including metal case	40	68
Assembly and testing	15	25
Ex-factory cost	85	143
Manufacturer's gross profit margin	20	34
Ex-factory price	105	177
Sales and distribution costs together with distributor's profit margin	35	60
Pre-tax selling profit	140	237

loan charges will be recovered over a certain period which, linked to the predicted sales volume, allows a unit figure to be estimated to cover this part of the manufacturing cost.

Once the design has been finalised the unit component cost can be established based on high volume purchasing. The equipment case may be a 'bought-in' item from another manufacturer or it may be produced 'in house' in which case a unit cost must be estimated taking account of manufacturing costs. For high volume production as would be applicable to this example, automatic assembly and test equipment would be employed to reduce production costs.

The total unit cost, covering pre-production (market research and development), components, production and testing, results in a unit manufacturing cost termed the ex-factory cost. To this must be added the manufacturer's required profit margin to give the price the manufacturer would expect to receive, which is termed the ex-factory price. The ultimate price to the customer must also cover sales and distribution costs and, in cases where the manufacturer does not sell directly to the customer, the costs and profit margin of the distributor or retailer.

The manufacturer naturally takes account of the pricing levels of competitors in the market and adjusts the pricing level accordingly. Additionally the manufacturer is likely to allow a discount for volume sales since distribution costs are then slightly lower.

It should be noted that although this example is useful in illustrating some features of manufacturing costs such as, in this case, that component costs amount to only about 30 per cent of the selling price, this breakdown cannot be applied universally to all electronic equipment because different criteria apply in different areas of the market. In state-of-the-art equipment, research and development costs are likely to be large whereas innovation in basic equipment such as power supplies is likely to be low. Different rules apply to the fiercely competitive domestic market where the product selling life may be very short while in the production of equipment for aerospace, military and some medical applications, reliability considerations are likely to be paramount and costs are affected accordingly.

References and further reading

Semiconductor devices

1. M.E. Goodge, *Semiconductor Device Technology*, chapters 1 and 2 (Macmillan, 1985)
2. A. Bar-Lev, *Semiconductors and Electronic Devices*, chapters 2, 8, 9, 12 and 14 (Prentice-Hall, 1979)
3. J. Seymour, *Electronic Devices and Components*, chapters 3, 4 and 6 (Pitman, 1981)
4. B.G. Streetman, *Solid-State Electronic Devices*, 2nd edition, chapters 3 and 5–8 (Prentice-Hall, 1980)
5. J.J. Sparkes, *Semiconductor Devices*, chapters 1–4 (Van Nostrand Reinhold Tutorial Guide 12, 1987)

Passive components

6. S.J. Sangwine, *Electronic Components and Technology*, chapters 3 and 5 (Van Nostrand Reinhold Tutorial Guide 13, 1987)
7. J. Seymour, *Electronic Devices and Components*, chapters 10 and 11 (Pitman, 1981)

Tutorial questions

Ratings

2.1 A 1 kΩ resistor carries a steady current of 10 mA. If the thermal resistance between the resistor and ambient is 0.5°C/mW, what would be the steady-state temperature of the resistor in an ambient of 20°C?

[Answer: 70°C]

2.2 The specification for a diode states that the maximum allowable junction temperature is 175°C and that the maximum average power dissipation at an ambient temperature of 25°C is 500 mW. What is the thermal resistance of the diode between junction and ambient? What is the derating factor for $T_{amb} > 25$°C?

[Answers: 0.3°C/mW, 3.33 mW/°C]

2.3 A transistor has a maximum power dissipation limit of 300 mW for ambient temperatures up to 25°C. If the maximum allowable junction temperature is 150°C, what is the power dissipation limit of the device in an ambient of 80°C?

[Answer: 168 mW]

2.4 The thermal resistance between junction and *case* of the transistor in question **2.3** is 0.2°C/mW. If a heatsink of thermal resistance 10°C/W is connected between the transistor case and ambient, what is the maximum allowable dissipation of the transistor at an ambient temperature of (a) 25°C, (b) 80°C?

Note: The thermal resistance between junction and ambient is made up of the thermal resistance between the junction and the device package, usually termed the *case*, in series with the thermal resistance from case to ambient. When a heatsink is connected, its thermal resistance is effectively in parallel with the case-to-ambient value for the device. For simplicity, in this question, assume that the case-to-ambient thermal resistance of the *transistor* is sufficiently high, compared with that of the heatsink, to be ignored.

[Answers: 595.2 mW, 333.3 mW]

Semiconductor device performance

2.5 A low-power junction diode has a forward voltage of 700 mV for low current levels at an ambient temperature of 25°C and under reverse-bias conditions the leakage current is 10 nA at the same temperature. Estimate the values of forward voltage and reverse leakage at an ambient temperature of 45°C.

[Answers: 660 mV, 33.2 nA]

2.6 The static current gain of a BJT for active mode operation in the common-emitter configuration is specified as 250. What is the value of static emitter current when the collector current is 1 mA? Calculate the static current gain h_{FB} for common-base operation.
If the reverse leakage between collector and base is 15 nA, what is the leakage current between collector and emitter? Calculate the proportion of leakage in the collector current of 1 mA and hence comment on its significance.

[Answers: 1.004 mA, -0.996, 3.75 μA, 0.375 per cent, negligible]

2.7 The static characteristic of an n-channel JFET shows that the drain–source current at pinch-off, with $V_{GS}=0$, is 20 mA. If measurements show that $I_{D(sat)}$ is 10 mA when $V_{GS}=-2$ V, estimate the pinch-off voltage for the device. If the JFET has a maximum power rating of 400 mW, what is the maximum (negative) value of V_{GS} that can be allowed if V_{DS} is 50 V?

[Answers: -6.83 V, -2.51 V]

Passive device performance

2.8 A 100 kΩ resistor has the specification given in table 2.1. Determine
(a) the maximum static current flow that can be allowed,
(b) the change of resistance value corresponding to a 30°C rise in temperature,
(c) the maximum long-term drift in resistance.

[Answers: 1.58 mA, -25 Ω, 500 Ω]

2.9 Calculation of resistance values for a circuit leads to the following requirements
(a) a resistor of 400 Ω that carries a constant current of 30 mA,
(b) a resistor of 1660 Ω that has a sinusoidal voltage of amplitude 20 V across it,
(c) a resistor required to develop a voltage of the order of 10 V when carrying a constant current of 2 μA.

In each case, select the most suitable preferred-value resistor from the E12 series assuming power ratings of 0.125, 0.25, 0.5, 1 and 2 W are available. For each resistor, quote the resistance value using the BS 1852: 1967 written code (appendix C) assuming 2 per cent tolerance components are to be specified throughout.

[Answers: 390RG, 0.5 W; 1K8G, 0.125 W; 4M7G, 0.125 W]

2.10 A 1 μF polyester film capacitor has a loss factor of 0.01 at 1 kHz. Calculate the leakage resistance of the capacitor at this frequency and hence represent the performance of the capacitor by a circuit model. What is the operational impedance of the device at this frequency? Calculate the phase relationship between capacitor voltage and current at 1 kHz assuming sinusoidal excitation.

[Answers: 15.9 kΩ, parallel combination of an ideal 1 μF capacitor and an ideal 15.9 kΩ resistor, $(1.59 - j159)\,\Omega$, current leads voltage by 89.4°]

2.11 The specification of an inductor gives $L = 100\ \mu$H and $Q = 40$ at 1 MHz. Calculate
(a) the coil resistance,
(b) the operational impedance of the coil at 1 MHz,
(c) the phase relationship between the current through the coil and the voltage across it at 500 kHz assuming sinusoidal excitation.

[Answers: 15.7 Ω, $(15.7 + j628.3)\,\Omega$, voltage leads current by 87.1°]

3 Small-signal Amplifiers: Basics

Coverage

- Explanation of how transistors provide signal amplification.
- The need for biasing and the factors involved in choosing the bias (Q) point.
- Significance of bias stability and the use of dc negative feedback to provide adequate dc stability.
- Use of capacitors to provide ac coupling and ac bypass.
- Component selection.
- Small-signal analysis to determine circuit performance for mid-frequency operation.
- Comparison of the basic amplifier configurations with regard to performance and applications.

The basic transistor–load–dc power supply circuit of section 1.3 forms the basis of an electronic amplifier. Signal voltage, current or power amplification is achieved by using the transistor as a linear modulator whereby the current flow through the load from the high-power dc supply is modulated (varied) in proportion to the input signal voltage or current. The varying current through the load generates a corresponding varying voltage across the load. In this way a relatively high-power output signal can be generated from a relatively low-power input signal. Low distortion amplification requires good proportionality between the variation of the load current and the variation of the controlling input current or voltage, that is, the operation of the circuit must be *linear*.

Figure 3.1 shows basic amplifier circuits based on bipolar and field-effect transistors with the corresponding load line constructions (section 1.3). In each case, to establish operation of the transistor in its linear region a constant *bias* is applied, V_{BE} (or I_B) in the case of a BJT, V_{GS} for a FET; upper case symbols and suffixes are used to indicate constant values. The effect of the bias is to establish the *static operating point*, also termed the *quiescent* (Q) *point*, at a mid-range level of conduction so that when the signal to be amplified is superimposed, the load current can fluctuate about this quiescent (no signal) value.

The need for a bias for analog (linear) operation is easily demonstrated by considering the effect of applying the alternating signal directly to the input of a transistor in the absence of a constant biasing component. Using the BJT case as an example, the characteristics of figure 2.3 show that the transistor conducts only when the base-emitter voltage is positive (for an npn type) and greater than the threshold value of 0.5 V. Thus without the biasing component, the BJT would conduct only while the input signal was positive and greater than 0.5 V, during negative excursions the transistor would remain at cut off resulting in severe distortion. The bias ensures that as the signal fluctuates the transistor remains in its linear conducting region.

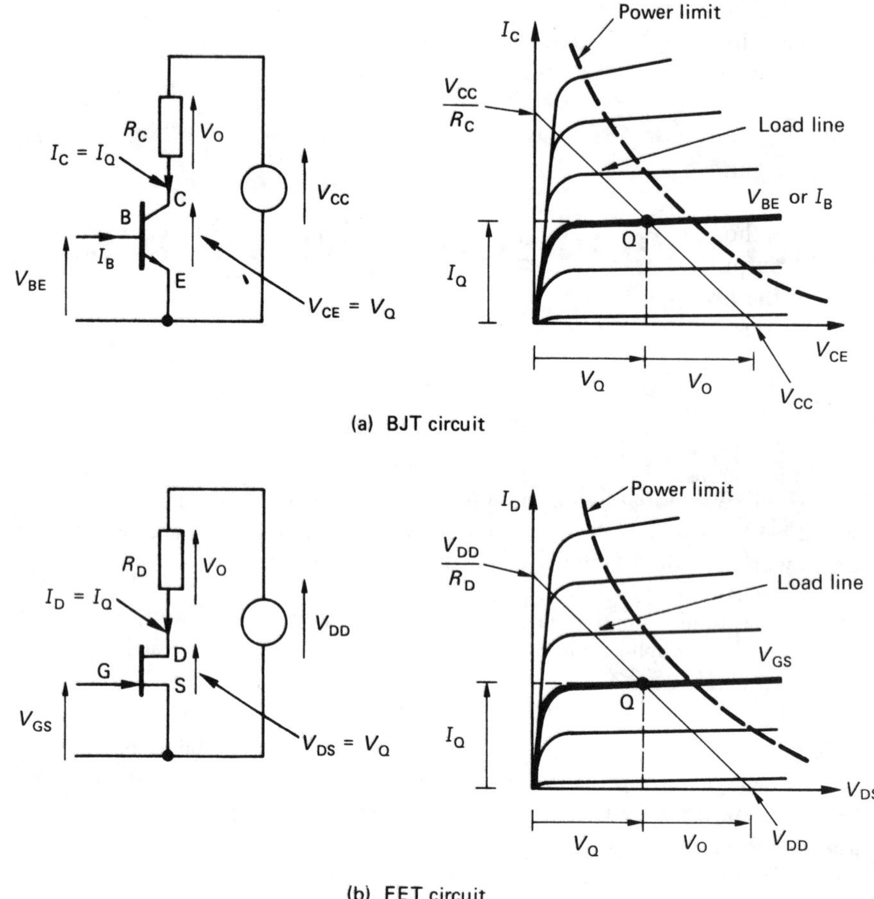

Figure 3.1 Basic amplifiers: static operation

The choice of the position of the dc load line and the Q-point depends on

(1) power dissipation,
(2) linearity of the transistor characteristics,
(3) ac gain of the transistor, which is a function of static current flow, and hence the required gain of the circuit, and
(4) required output signal amplitude.

The stability of the Q-point, that is, the dependence of the Q-point position on transistor parameters and temperature, is an important aspect in the design of an amplifier. Manufacturing tolerances cause the properties of transistors of a particular type number to have a spread of values and also transistor properties vary with temperature. Commercial manufacture of electronic amplifiers requires that they function satisfactorily over a specified temperature range using transistors that have not been individually selected to have precise parameter values, and this means that the bias circuit must provide a reasonably stable Q-point (V_Q, I_Q) for a range of values of transistor parameters. If the Q-point were to vary significantly either with temperature, transistor parameters or with the input signal, amplifier performance could not be guaranteed and significant distortion would be likely to occur. Different biasing arrangements give different degrees of dc stability and so the choice of circuit is fundamental in good amplifier design.

3.1 BJT bias circuits

The most basic method of biasing a BJT is to supply a constant base current I_B corresponding to the particular output characteristic on which the Q-point is required to reside as represented, for example, by the heavy line in figure 3.1a. This base current can be drawn from the V_{CC} supply using a series resistor R_B to control its value as in figure 3.2a, from which

$$I_B = \frac{V_{CC} - V_{BE}}{R_B} \tag{3.1}$$

where V_{BE} is the static voltage required between the base and emitter terminals of the BJT for active region operation. From Figure 2.3c this value of V_{BE} is between 0.5 V and 0.9 V; a value of about 0.6 V is usually taken for purposes of calculation.

Substituting for I_B from equation 3.1 in equation 2.12, the corresponding static collector current I_C, which is the quiescent value I_Q, is

$$I_C = I_Q = h_{FE}\left(\frac{V_{CC} - V_{BE}}{R_B}\right) + I_{CEO} \tag{3.2}$$

where h_{FE} is the static (common-emitter) current gain of the BJT and I_{CEO} is the collector–emitter leakage current. Notice that I_C is independent of R_C which is a consequence of the approximate constant-current nature of the BJT for active region operation whereby I_C is almost independent of V_{CE} for constant I_B (figure 3.1a).

The corresponding quiescent collector-emitter voltage V_Q is

$$V_Q = V_{CC} - I_Q R_C \tag{3.3}$$

Component selection for this arrangement for a particular value of V_{CC} first involves choice of I_Q bearing in mind the linearity of the output characteristics along the load line for change

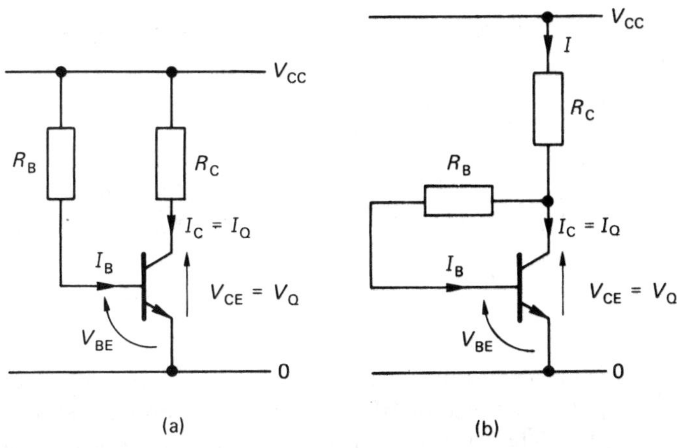

Figure 3.2 Basic BJT bias circuits

of I_B, power dissipation $V_Q I_Q$ (from equation 2.16) which must not exceed the P_{tot}max rating for the BJT and the dependence of small-signal current gain h_{fe} on I_C [1a]. Having selected I_Q, resistor R_B can be calculated from equation 3.2 knowing the static gain h_{FE} of the BJT, taking $V_{BE} \simeq 0.6$ V for active region operation and noting that leakage I_{CEO} is normally negligible for silicon BJTs operating at typical current and temperature levels. The collector load R_C determines the static voltage drop $I_Q R_C$ and hence fixes V_Q (equation 3.3), but also R_C fixes the small-signal gain of the circuit for ac operation (section 3.4.3). At this stage, in the absence of information as to the required gain of the circuit, it is usual to position the Q-point approximately midway along the load line so allowing equal amplitude swings about Q during subsequent ac operation. A mid-range Q-point for this circuit requires

$$V_Q = V_O = \frac{V_{CC}}{2} \tag{3.4}$$

Example 3.1: Design of a basic BJT bias circuit

Select suitable E12 resistance values for the circuit of figure 3.2a if V_{CC} is 15 V, the quiescent collector current is to be approximately 1 mA and the static gain of the BJT at 1 mA is 200.

$V_{CC} = 15$ V
$I_Q = 1$ mA
h_{FE} at 1 mA = 200

Assuming negligible leakage (I_{CEO}), $I_B = \dfrac{I_C}{h_{FE}} = \dfrac{1 \text{ mA}}{200} = 5\ \mu\text{A}$ using equation 2.12.

Taking $V_{BE} = 0.6$ V for active region operation

$$R_B = \frac{V_{CC} - V_{BE}}{I_B} = \frac{15 \text{ V} - 0.6 \text{ V}}{5\ \mu\text{A}} = 2.88 \text{ M}\Omega$$

from equation 3.1.

A value of 2.7 MΩ is therefore selected for R_B, being the nearest preferred value in the E12 series (appendix D) to the calculated value of 2.88 MΩ. Recalculation of I_B (equation 3.1) using $R_B = 2.7$ MΩ gives a value of approximately 5.3 μA and hence the collector current will be approximately 200 × 5.3 μA = 1.06 mA.

To position the Q-point approximately midway along the load line, the voltage drop across R_C must be $V_{CC}/2$ at $I_Q = 1.06$ mA, thus

$$I_Q R_C = \frac{V_{CC}}{2} = \frac{15 \text{ V}}{2} = 7.5 \text{ V}$$

requiring $R_C = 7.5 \text{ V}/1.06 \text{ mA} = 7.08$ kΩ. The nearest E12 value of 6.8 kΩ would therefore be chosen, resulting in $I_Q R_C = (1.06 \text{ mA})(6.8 \text{ k}\Omega) \simeq 7.2$ V being dropped across R_C with 15 V − 7.2 V = 7.8 V across the BJT.

The stability of the basic biasing arrangement of figure 3.2a is poor because of the wide spread of values of h_{FE} for a particular type of BJT, typically from about 100 to 400 at $I_C = 1$ mA for a BC107 (appendix E5). The linear relationship between I_Q and h_{FE} in equation 3.2 shows that the spread of h_{FE} will be reflected proportionally in I_Q giving, for example, a range of I_Q

from 0.5 mA to 2 mA for the circuit of example 3.1. Such a wide spread of Q-point would be unsatisfactory for most practical applications.

Adequate bias stability requires the introduction of *dc negative feedback* whereby if a change of transistor property such as gain tends to cause I_Q to be different from the design value, the circuit automatically compensates to greatly lessen the effect. One such arrangement is shown in figure 3.2b, the base current being supplied from the collector of the BJT instead of from the constant voltage power supply. Such an arrangement provides dc stabilization because if I_Q tends to be larger than the required value owing for example, to the use of a higher gain BJT or to a rise in temperature, the increased collector current causes a larger voltage drop across R_C so reducing V_{CE}. With V_{CE} reduced, the base current supplied to the BJT also reduces which correspondingly reduces the collector current so tending to offset the original rise.

Analysis of the circuit of figure 3.2b is similar to that for the basic circuit, except the current through the collector load R_C is now the sum of the collector and base currents:

$$I = I_C + I_B = I_Q + I_B \tag{3.5}$$

The base current is

$$I_B = \frac{V_{CE} - V_{BE}}{R_B} = \frac{V_Q - V_{BE}}{R_B} \tag{3.6}$$

and

$$V_{CE} = V_Q = V_{CC} - IR_C \tag{3.7}$$

Together with the basic current relationship for the BJT, assuming negligible leakage, $I_C = I_Q = h_{FE} I_B$ from equation 2.12, the quiescent collector current is given by

$$I_Q = \frac{h_{FE}(V_{CC} - V_{BE})}{R_B + (h_{FE} + 1)R_C} \tag{3.8}$$

which, for $h_{FE} \gg 1$, gives

$$I_Q \simeq h_{FE}\left(\frac{V_{CC} - V_{BE}}{R_B + h_{FE} R_C}\right) \tag{3.9}$$

Example 3.2: Design of a basic BJT bias circuit incorporating dc feedback for improved stability

Select suitable E12 resistance values for the bias circuit of figure 3.2b for $V_{CC} = 15$ V, $V_{BE} = 0.6$ V, $I_Q \simeq 1$ mA and $h_{FE} = 200$.

For the chosen component values calculate the spread of I_Q corresponding to a spread of h_{FE} from 100 to 400.

For mid-range positioning of the Q-point on the load line as in example 3.1, V_Q is required to be approximately $V_{CC}/2$, that is, 7.5 V.

Also, for $I_Q \simeq 1$ mA, I_B is required to be $I_Q/h_{FE} \simeq 1\ \text{mA}/200 = 5\ \mu\text{A}$. Thus, from equation 3.6

$$R_B = \frac{V_Q - V_{BE}}{I_B} = \frac{7.5\ \text{V} - 0.6\ \text{V}}{5\ \mu\text{A}} = 1.38\ \text{M}\Omega$$

The corresponding nearest E12 value (appendix D) is 1.2 MΩ which corresponds to a base current of 5.7 μA from equation 3.6. Combining equations 3.5 and 3.7

$$R_C = \frac{V_{CC} - V_Q}{I_Q + I_B} = \frac{15\ \text{V} - 7.5\ \text{V}}{1\ \text{mA} + 5.7\ \mu\text{A}} = 7.46\ \text{k}\Omega$$

from which the E12 value 6.8 kΩ can be selected.

Note: Although R_C carries both the collector and base currents in this circuit compared with only the collector current in the basic circuit of example 3.1, $I_B \ll I_C$ because of the high value of h_{FE}, so that the current through R_C is approximately the same in the two examples, resulting in the same selected value for R_C.

From equation 3.9, with $V_{CC} = 15$ V, $V_{BE} = 0.6$ V, $R_B = 1.2$ MΩ and $R_C = 6.8$ kΩ, the spread of I_Q for values of h_{FE} from 100 to 400 is from 0.77 mA to 1.47 mA.

Example 3.2 shows that for the selected values of components, a spread of BJT gain h_{FE} from 100 to 400 would result in a range of Q-point collector current from 0.77 mA to 1.47 mA which is considerably less than the corresponding range of 0.5 mA to 2 mA previously quoted for the basic bias circuit without feedback. This improved stability of the Q-point position on the load line for change of transistor parameters is due to the effect of the dc negative feedback which can be seen analytically by comparing equations 3.2 and 3.9. Without feedback (equation 3.2) a change in h_{FE} produces a proportional change in I_Q but with feedback (equation 3.9), the $h_{FE}R_C$ term in the denominator partly compensates for the change of value of h_{FE} in the numerator so reducing the change of I_Q.

Further improvement in bias stability can be achieved using a combination of *fixed* and *self bias* as provided in the circuit of figure 3.3a. This circuit concentrates on applying a base–emitter voltage V_{BE} to the BJT rather than establishing a certain value of base current I_B, although V_{BE} and I_B are related via the input characteristic of the BJT (figure 2.3c). Provided the current I_1 is much larger than the base current I_B, the potential divider formed by R_1 and R_2 applies a fixed bias potential V_B to the base of the BJT. The main current flow through the BJT establishes a voltage V_E across the resistor R_E in series with the emitter, and the resultant value of V_{BE} applied to the BJT is the difference between V_B and V_E. The voltage V_E is termed *self bias* because it is the current through the BJT that establishes V_E.

If an increase in gain tends to cause the quiescent collector current I_Q to rise, the emitter current I_E also tends to rise and correspondingly V_E rises. With V_B fixed, the rise in V_E causes V_{BE} to fall, hence reducing the base current I_B which in turn causes I_Q to fall so compensating for its original tendency to rise. Thus R_E introduces *dc negative feedback* into the circuit whereby the current at the *output* of the BJT I_Q, and hence I_E, has a controlling effect on the *input* current I_B.

For analysis purposes it is convenient to redraw the circuit as in figure 3.3b and to simplify the network to that of figure 3.3c using Thévenin reduction (note 3.1) of the section to the left of XX, whereby

$$V_{BB} = V_{CC}\left(\frac{R_2}{R_1 + R_2}\right) \tag{3.10}$$

and

$$R_B = R_1 /\!/ R_2 = \frac{R_1 R_2}{R_1 + R_2} \tag{3.11}$$

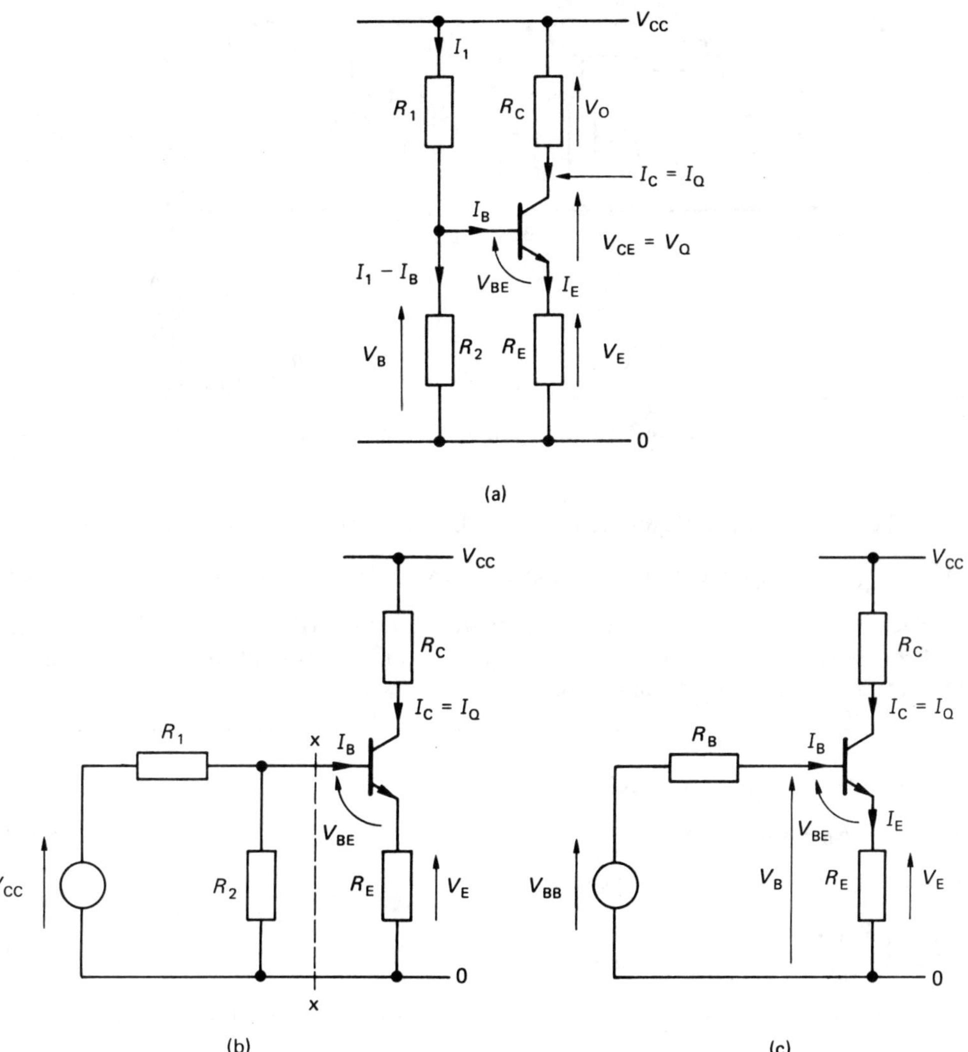

Figure 3.3 Combined fixed and self bias for a BJT

Note 3.1: Thévenin reduction

Thévenin's theorem: Any linear two-terminal network can be represented, as far as external circuitry connected across the network is concerned, as a single voltage v_T in series with an impedance Z_T.

The voltage source v_T is the open-circuit voltage across the terminals, that is, the voltage across the terminals with no *external* circuitry connected. The series impedance Z_T is the effective impedance between the terminals when the internal sources are made passive, that is, ideal voltage sources are replaced by short circuits and ideal current sources by open circuits.

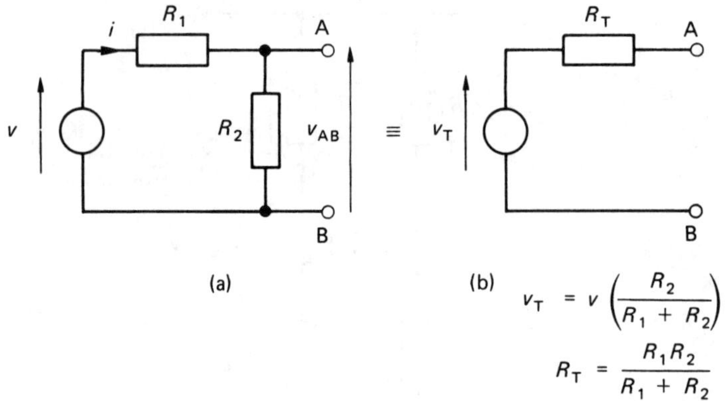

Figure 3.4 Illustration of Thévenin reduction

In the resistive example of figure 3.4a, the open-circuit voltage v_{AB} is given by $v\left(\frac{R_2}{R_1+R_2}\right)$ corresponding to equation 1.8 in example 1.1, while with source v passive (replaced by a short circuit) the effective resistance across AB is R_1 in parallel with R_2. Lower case symbols are used for voltage and current in this example because Thévenin's theorem applies to both dc and ac operation.

From the input loop of figure 3.3c

$$V_{BB} = I_B R_B + V_{BE} + I_E R_E \tag{3.12}$$

which, noting that $I_E = I_C + I_B$, leads to

$$I_B = \left(\frac{V_{BB} - V_{BE}}{R_B + R_E}\right) - I_C\left(\frac{R_E}{R_B + R_E}\right) \tag{3.13}$$

Substituting this expression for I_B in equation 2.12 gives the quiescent collector current I_Q as

$$I_C = I_Q = \left[\frac{(V_{BB} - V_{BE})h_{FE}}{R_B + R_E(h_{FE}+1)}\right] + I_{CEO}\left[\frac{R_B + R_E}{R_B + R_E(h_{FE}+1)}\right] \tag{3.14}$$

For a practical BJT, $h_{FE} \gg 1$ so that $(h_{FE}+1) \simeq h_{FE}$. Also, collector–emitter leakage I_{CEO} is approximately equal to $h_{FE} I_{CBO}$ where I_{CBO} is collector–base leakage since from equation 2.14 $I_{CEO} = \frac{I_{CBO}}{1 + h_{FB}}$ and $(1 + h_{FB}) = \frac{1}{h_{FE}+1}$ using equation 2.13.
These relationships enable equation 3.14 to be simplified to

$$I_C = I_Q \simeq \left(\frac{V_{BB} - V_{BE}}{\frac{R_B}{h_{FE}} + R_E}\right) + I_{CBO}\left(\frac{R_B + R_E}{\frac{R_B}{h_{FE}} + R_E}\right) \tag{3.15}$$

If resistances R_1 and R_2 are chosen so that

$$\frac{R_B}{h_{FE}} \ll R_E \tag{3.16}$$

where $R_B = R_1 /\!/ R_2$, then equation 3.15 reduces to

$$I_C = I_Q \simeq \left(\frac{V_{BB} - V_{BE}}{R_E}\right) + I_{CBO}\left(\frac{R_B + R_E}{R_E}\right) \tag{3.17}$$

which is *independent of* h_{FE} provided the value of h_{FE} is sufficiently high to ensure that relation 3.16 is valid. This means that Q-point stability with respect to change of h_{FE} will be extremely good. Adequate stability is usually provided if the R_B/h_{FE} term is no more than 10 per cent of R_E, giving the condition for good bias stability for change of h_{FE} as

$$R_B \leqslant \frac{h_{FE} R_E}{10} \tag{3.18}$$

Notice that this link between the values of R_B ($= R_1 /\!/ R_2$) and R_E for good dc stability with respect to change of transistor gain corresponds to establishing the potential divider current I_1 much greater than the base current I_B so that the base potential V_B is almost independent of I_B; compare with example 1.1.

The value of the voltage V_E across R_E is an important aspect as regards the dc stability of the circuit. The larger R_E, and hence the larger V_E, the greater is the negative feedback effect (in terms of the feedback fraction β, section 5.8) and hence the greater the speed of correction for changes in I_Q due to variation of transistor parameters. However, the greater the proportion of the power supply voltage V_{CC} dropped across R_E, the less voltage can be dropped across the collector load R_C and the transistor which limits the maximum amplitude of the output voltage when the circuit is operating as an amplifier (section 3.4.3). A reasonable compromise is to arrange for V_E to be between 10 and 20 per cent of V_{CC}.

The design sequence for this fixed/self bias BJT circuit is

(1) Select I_Q.

(2) Select R_E to make $V_E \simeq 10-20$ per cent of V_{CC} noting that for a high gain (h_{FE}) BJT, $I_E \simeq I_Q$.

(3) Having fixed V_E, the required base voltage V_B is known since $V_B = V_E + V_{BE}$ and for active region operation V_{BE} must be of the order of 0.6 V for a low-power silicon BJT operating with a collector current of about 1 mA.

(4) For good stability, the potential divider current I_1 must be $\geqslant 10 I_B$ so that the R_1, R_2 potential divider provides an essentially constant base bias voltage V_B even though the base current I_B depends on h_{FE} of the transistor.
Knowledge of h_{FE} min of the BJT, allows I_B max to be calculated from

$$I_B \max = \frac{I_Q}{h_{FE} \min} \tag{3.19}$$

The value of I_1 can then be chosen to be $\geqslant 10 I_B$ max and then

$$R_1 + R_2 = \frac{V_{CC}}{I_1} \tag{3.20}$$

(5) With $I_1 \gg I_B$ by design, the R_1, R_2 bias circuit operates as an ideal potential divider (example 1.1) and therefore

$$V_B = V_{CC}\left(\frac{R_2}{R_1 + R_2}\right) \tag{3.21}$$

corresponding to equation 1.8.

(6) Combination of equations 3.20 and 3.21 allows the values of R_1 and R_2 to be selected.

(7) Having selected R_1 and R_2 to make $I_1 \gg I_B$, the stability of the Q-point against h_{FE} spread can be checked using equation 3.18 where R_B is the parallel combination of R_1 and R_2, that is, $R_B = R_1 /\!/ R_2 = \dfrac{R_1 R_2}{R_1 + R_2}$.

(8) With voltage V_E dropped across R_E, there remains $(V_{CC} - V_E)$ to be dropped across R_C and the CE terminals of the BJT. As with the basic bias arrangements considered previously, in the absence of information as to the small-signal gain required for ac operation (section 3.4.3), it is usual to select R_C to divide the voltage $(V_{CC} - V_E)$ equally between R_C and the transistor so as to approximately centralise the Q-point on the load line and thereby maximise the allowable swing of collector potential for ac operation. Dividing $(V_{CC} - V_E)$ equally between R_C and the transistor requires

$$V_O = I_Q R_C = \frac{V_{CC} - V_E}{2} \tag{3.22}$$

from which

$$R_C = \frac{V_{CC} - V_E}{2I_Q} \tag{3.23}$$

Example 3.3: BJT fixed/self bias circuit design

In the fixed/self bias BJT circuit of figure 3.3a, V_{CC} is 15 V and the typical gain h_{FE} of the BJT is 200. Select suitable E12 resistance values for the circuit if the quiescent collector current is to be of the order of 1 mA.

Following the above design procedure, V_E should be chosen between 10 and 20 per cent of 15 V, that is, between 1.5 V and 3 V.
With high gain, $I_E \simeq I_Q \simeq 1$ mA from which

$$R_E = \frac{V_E}{I_E} = \frac{1.5 \text{ V to } 3 \text{ V}}{1 \text{ mA}} = 1.5 \text{ k}\Omega \text{ to } 3 \text{ k}\Omega$$

An E12 value (appendix D) of 2.2 kΩ is chosen as being near the centre of this range; at $I_E = 1$ mA, the actual value of V_E will be 2.2 V. Allowing for $V_{BE} = 0.6$ V to ensure active region operation of the BJT, the base voltage V_B is required to be

$$V_B = V_E + V_{BE} = 2.2 \text{ V} + 0.6 \text{ V} = 2.8 \text{ V}$$

For $h_{FE} = 200$, the base current corresponding to $I_Q = 1$ mA is

$$I_B = \frac{I_Q}{h_{FE}} = \frac{1 \text{ mA}}{200} = 5\ \mu\text{A}$$

If information of the spread of values of h_{FE} for the BJT had been given, the minimum value would have been used here to obtain the maximum value of I_B.

The potential divider current I_1 is taken as $\geqslant 10 I_B\text{max}$, but as only typical gain information is given here, I_1 will be taken as $20 I_B$, that is, $20 \times 5\ \mu\text{A} = 100\ \mu\text{A}$, to allow a margin of safety.

With $V_{CC} = 15$ V and $I_1 = 100\ \mu$A, equation 3.20 gives

$$R_1 + R_2 = \frac{V_{CC}}{I_1} = \frac{15\text{ V}}{100\ \mu\text{A}} = 150\text{ k}\Omega$$

Also, using equation 3.21, to obtain the required base voltage V_B of 2.8 V, taking $R_1 + R_2 = 150$ kΩ from above:

$$R_2 = \frac{V_B}{V_{CC}}(R_1 + R_2) = \frac{2.8\text{ V}}{15\text{ V}}(150\text{ k}\Omega) = 28\text{ k}\Omega$$

The nearest E12 value of 27 kΩ is therefore chosen for R_2 and the corresponding value of R_1 is then given by

$$\frac{V_{CC}}{V_B} = \frac{R_1 + R_2}{R_2} = \frac{R_1}{R_2} + 1$$

from which $R_1 = R_2\left(\frac{V_{CC}}{V_B} - 1\right)$

$$= 27\text{ k}\Omega\left(\frac{1.5\text{ V}}{2.8\text{ V}} - 1\right) = 117.6\text{ k}\Omega$$

allowing an E12 value of 120 kΩ to be selected.

Note that with $R_1 = 120$ kΩ and $R_2 = 27$ kΩ, $R_B = 120\text{ k}\Omega /\!/ 27\text{ k}\Omega =$

$$\frac{(120\text{ k}\Omega)(27\text{ k}\Omega)}{120\text{ k}\Omega + 27\text{ k}\Omega} \simeq 22\text{ k}\Omega$$

This design therefore provides adequate dc stability against change of h_{FE} which requires $R_B \leqslant 44$ kΩ from condition 3.18, h_{FE} being 200 and R_E selected as 2.2 kΩ.

Having chosen R_E to provide $V_E = 2.2$ V at $I_E \simeq I_C = 1$ mA, the required value of collector load to split the remaining voltage $(V_{CC} - V_E)$ approximately equally between R_C and the BJT is given by equation 3.23 as

$$R_C = \frac{V_{CC} - V_E}{2I_Q} = \frac{15\text{ V} - 2.2\text{ V}}{2(1\text{ mA})} = 6.4\text{ k}\Omega$$

allowing the nearest E12 value 6.8 kΩ to be selected.

For any BJT circuit, Q-point stability can be assessed by differentiating the equation for quiescent collector current I_Q with respect to the various factors that can cause a change in I_Q, namely the gain h_{FE}, input voltage V_{BE} and leakage I_{CBO} (all associated with the BJT) together with the power supply V_{CC} (and hence V_{BB} from equation 3.10) and the circuit resistance values.

For the fixed/self bias circuit of figure 3.3a, the quiescent collector current is given by equation 3.15. The stability of I_Q for change of, for example, V_{BE} is given by $\partial I_Q / \partial V_{BE}$ which, from equation 3.15, is

$$\frac{\partial I_Q}{\partial V_{BE}} \simeq -\frac{1}{\dfrac{R_B}{h_{FE}} + R_E} \simeq -\frac{1}{R_E} \tag{3.24}$$

provided $R_B/h_{FE} \ll R_E$.

This shows that as far as changes in V_{BE} are concerned, the stability of I_Q depends almost entirely on the value of R_E. A larger value of R_E results in improved stability in this respect since, for a certain change of V_{BE}, the corresponding change in I_Q will be reduced. This differential coefficient is termed the *stability factor* for the circuit for *change of* V_{BE} and is given the symbol $S_{V_{BE}}$; the smaller the value of stability factor, the better the dc stability of the circuit.

Example 3.4: Use of stability factor
For the fixed/self bias circuit designed in example 3.3, use the stability factor $S_{V_{BE}}$ to determine the shift in quiescent current I_Q due to a 20°C rise in temperature.

V_{BE} is the forward voltage across the base–emitter junction of the BJT and, from equation 2.8, the forward junction voltage at low current levels changes with temperature at typically -2 mV/°C, thus

$$\frac{\partial V_{BE}}{\partial T} \simeq -2\text{ mV/°C} = -(2 \times 10^{-3})\text{ V/°C}$$

From equation 3.24, a change in V_{BE} in the fixed/self bias circuit causes a change in I_Q given by

$$S_{V_{BE}} = \frac{\partial I_Q}{\partial V_{BE}} \simeq -\frac{1}{R_E} = -\frac{1}{(2.2 \times 10^3)\,\Omega}$$

in this case ($R_E = 2.2$ kΩ).
The change of I_Q with temperature T is given by

$$\frac{\partial I_Q}{\partial T} = \left(\frac{\partial I_Q}{\partial V_{BE}}\right)\left(\frac{\partial V_{BE}}{\partial T}\right)$$

$$= \left(-\frac{1}{2.2 \times 10^3\,\Omega}\right)(-2 \times 10^3\text{ V/°C})$$

$$\simeq +0.91\ \mu\text{A/°C}$$

For a 20°C *rise* in temperature, $\Delta T = +20$°C and so the corresponding change in I_Q is

$$\Delta I_Q = \left(\frac{\partial I_Q}{\partial T}\right)\Delta T \simeq (+0.91\ \mu\text{A/°C})(+20\text{°C}) = +18.2\ \mu\text{A}$$

Notice that this is a small change (<2 per cent) compared with the actual quiescent collector current of about 1 mA, indicating that this bias circuit provides good stability against change of V_{BE}.

Differentiation of equation 3.15 gives other stability factors as

$$S_{h_{FE}} = \frac{\partial I_Q}{\partial h_{FE}} \simeq \frac{R_E}{h_{FE}^2 R_E^2}(V_{BB} - V_{BE}) \tag{3.25}$$

$$S_{I_{CBO}} = \frac{\partial I_Q}{\partial I_{CBO}} \simeq \frac{R_B + R_E}{R_E} \tag{3.26}$$

and $$S_{V_{CC}} = \frac{\partial I_Q}{\partial V_{CC}} = \left(\frac{\partial I_Q}{\partial V_{BB}}\right)\left(\frac{\partial V_{BB}}{\partial V_{CC}}\right) \simeq \frac{R_2}{R_E(R_1+R_2)} \tag{3.27}$$

for the fixed/self bias circuit using the practical simplification $R_B/h_{FE} \ll R_E$. Equation 3.27, which incorporates $\partial V_{BB}/\partial V_{CC}$ from equation 3.10, shows the sensitivity to variation of power supply voltage.

The values of the dc stability factors for a circuit are useful because they provide a simple method of assessing the Q-point range corresponding to component tolerances and temperature variations. Taking account of all possible variations for the fixed/self bias circuit, the change of quiescent collector current ΔI_Q due to changes ΔV_{BE}, Δh_{FE}, ΔI_{CBO}, ΔV_{CC}, ΔR_B and ΔR_E, from equation 3.15, is given by

$$\Delta I_Q = \left(\frac{\partial I_Q}{\partial V_{BE}}\right)\Delta V_{BE} + \left(\frac{\partial I_Q}{\partial h_{FE}}\right)\Delta h_{FE} + \left(\frac{\partial I_Q}{\partial I_{CBO}}\right)\Delta I_{CBO}$$

$$+ \left(\frac{\partial I_Q}{\partial V_{CC}}\right)\Delta V_{CC} + \left(\frac{\partial I_Q}{\partial R_B}\right)\Delta R_B + \left(\frac{\partial I_Q}{\partial R_E}\right)\Delta R_E$$

$$= S_{V_{BE}}\Delta V_{BE} + S_{h_{FE}}\Delta h_{FE} + S_{I_{CBO}}\Delta I_{CBO} + S_{V_{CC}}\Delta V_{CC} + S_{R_B}\Delta R_B + S_{R_E}\Delta R_E \tag{3.28}$$

3.2 FET bias circuits

As in the BJT case, the biasing of a FET is to establish a stable quiescent operating point at a suitable position on the characteristics to enable linear operation when an ac signal is superimposed on the bias. There are however several differences between FETs and BJTs that are significant in this respect, namely

(1) As the dc gate current of a FET I_G is essentially zero, it is only realistic to refer to a *voltage* bias V_{GS}.
(2) For some types of FET the required bias voltage V_{GS} is of opposite polarity to the power supply voltage V_{DD}.
(3) The main stability problem in the case of FETs is the wide spread of characteristics for a batch of devices having the same type number; temperature variation is less significant than for BJTs.

Using an *n*-channel JFET as an example, the bias arrangement must apply a value of V_{GS} to position the Q-point at a suitable position on the output characteristics (figure 3.1b). In the case of a BJT the required value of bias voltage V_{BE} must be approximately 0.6 V for a low-power silicon BJT. With a FET no such 'universal' bias value can be quoted and the transfer characteristic of the particular device must be used to select the required value of V_{GS} corresponding to the selected quiescent drain current. However, the transfer characteristic of a particular type of JFET usually has a wide spread with values of pinch-off voltage V_P and drain current for zero V_{GS} (I_{DSS}) typically having a relative range of one to four (figure 3.5c). The design is therefore based on a mid-range characteristic using a 'typical' Q-point V_{GS}typ, $I_D$typ.

The value of V_{GS} for an *n*-channel JFET is required to be negative (figure 2.4b) and therefore V_{GS} cannot be derived directly from the V_{DD} power supply which, for an *n*-channel FET, is positive. The most basic arrangement therefore uses self bias whereby a resistor R_S in series

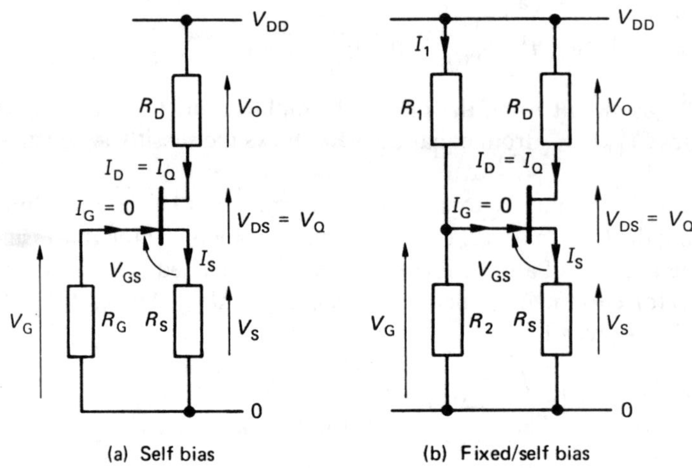

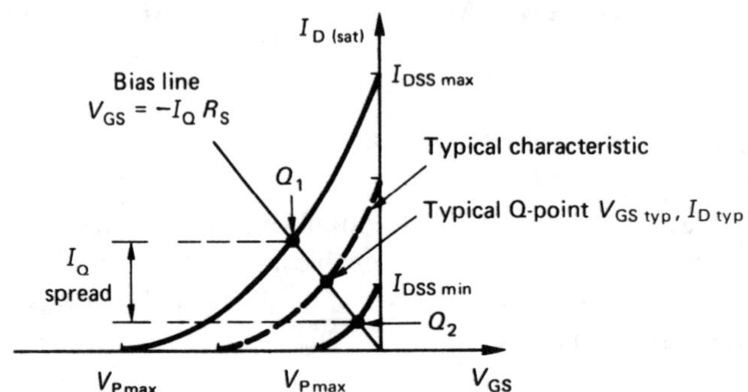

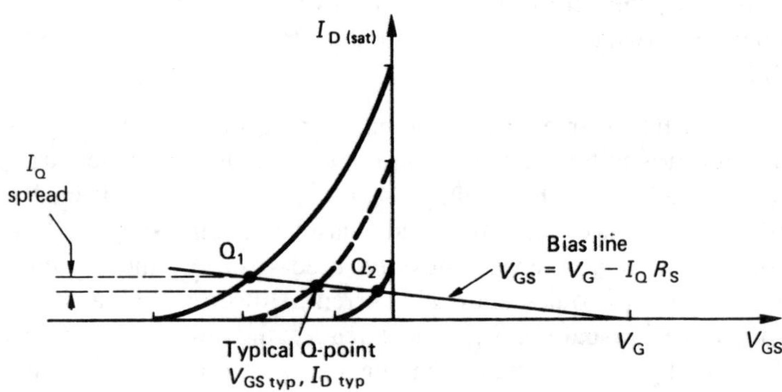

Figure 3.5 FET biasing

with the source terminal* is used to make the potential of the source higher than that of the gate, so making V_{GS} negative.

In the self bias circuit of figure 3.5a, the gate is grounded via R_G; with very low gate current (typically <1 nA) due to the high gate–source resistance of the JFET (section 2.3.4), the gate voltage V_G is also very low (<1 mV). Notice that as far as dc operation is concerned, R_G could be omitted and the gate connected directly to ground. However subsequent use of the circuit as an amplifier requires a signal to be superimposed on the gate bias and the inclusion of R_G allows the gate potential to fluctuate in response to the signal. Normally a high value of resistance ($\geqslant 1$ MΩ) is selected for R_G so that the circuit presents a high resistance to the signal source.

With $V_G = 0$:

$$V_{GS} = V_G - V_S = -V_S = -I_S R_S \simeq -I_D R_S = -I_Q R_S \tag{3.29}$$

since, with $I_G = 0$, $I_S = I_D$ and the quiescent drain current is denoted by I_Q.

The Q-point range corresponding to the characteristic spread can be found by superimposing the *bias line* (equation 3.29) on the *transfer* characteristics as shown in figure 3.5c. Clearly this self bias technique does not provide good dc stability, the Q-point being anywhere on the bias line between Q_1 and Q_2 depending on the characteristic of the particular FET being used.

Having selected R_S (using equation 3.29) to provide the required value of V_{GS} corresponding to the selected 'typical' Q-point on the mid-range characteristic, there remains the selection of R_D to position the Q-point on the *load line* which is superimposed on the *output* characteristics (figure 3.1b). As in the BJT case, in the absence of information regarding the required small-signal gain of the circuit (section 3.4.3), it is usual to make V_O and V_{DS} (figure 3.5a) approximately equal so maximising the allowable swing about Q during subsequent ac operation. Now

$$V_{DS} + V_O = V_{DD} - V_S = V_{DD} - (-V_{GS}) \tag{3.30}$$

as $V_S = -V_{GS}$ from equation 3.29, V_G being zero.

For $V_{DS} = V_O$ to centralise the Q-point:

$$V_O = \frac{V_{DD} + V_{GS}}{2}$$

which must be equal to $I_Q R_D$ (figure 3.5a) giving

$$R_D = \frac{V_{DD} + V_{GS}}{2I_Q} \tag{3.31}$$

Having selected R_D on the basis of the mid-range value of quiescent drain current $I_D$typ, the wide characteristic spread will result in a wide variation of Q-point position on the load line (figure 3.1b). Such a wide variation cannot be tolerated for most applications as the allowable swing in drain potential before the onset of distortion would vary considerably among circuits manufactured using FETs from a batch of the same type number.

The spread can be reduced considerably by using a combination of fixed and self bias (figure 3.5b), which corresponds directly to the BJT circuit of figure 3.3a. The R_1, R_2 potential

---

* Care must be taken not to confuse the term *source* referring here to the terminal of the FET with a *signal source* used in subsequent work to represent the ac input signal to an amplifier.

divider provides a fixed bias V_G from which

$$V_{GS} = V_G - V_S = V_G - I_S R_S \simeq V_G - I_D R_S \text{ (as } I_G \simeq 0) = V_G - I_Q R_S \tag{3.32}$$

The effect of V_G on the bias line is shown in figure 3.5d whereby, with the greatly reduced slope (R_S being considerably larger than for the self bias circuit of figure 3.5a), the Q-point current range is greatly reduced.

The gate bias V_G provided by the R_1, R_2 potential divider is given by

$$V_G = V_{DD}\left(\frac{R_2}{R_1 + R_2}\right) \tag{3.33}$$

corresponding to equation 1.8 in example 1.1. Notice that with $I_G \simeq 0$ there is negligible loading on the divider circuit, enabling a low value to be selected for I_1, so reducing power consumption. This results in high values for R_1 and R_2, so providing a high input resistance for ac operation (section 3.4.3). Notice that this is a simplification compared with the corresponding work for the BJT circuit of figure 3.3a where it was necessary to ensure $I_1 \gg I_B$max for satisfactory operation.

Selection of the actual value of V_G is a compromise. The larger V_G, the lower the slope of the corresponding bias line in figure 3.5d and the smaller the spread of I_Q. However, the larger V_G, the larger the voltage $I_Q R_S$ across R_S to provide the required value of V_{GS} (equation 3.32) which reduces the proportion of V_{DD} that remains to be divided between R_D and the drain-source terminals of the FET and leads to a restricted output signal amplitude in subsequent ac operation. A satisfactory compromise is to make V_G of the order of 20 per cent of V_{DD}.

The design procedure is therefore to choose a suitable value for V_G, typically $V_{DD}/5$, and after constructing the bias line as in figure 3.5d, select suitable values for a mid-range Q-point, V_{GS}typ and $I_D$typ ($= I_Q$). Using these values, R_S can be calculated from equation 3.32. The resistance ratio R_2/R_1 can be calculated from equation 3.33 since V_G has been selected and V_{DD} is known. Determination of individual values for R_1 and R_2 requires the current level I_1 to be fixed. With static gate currents for FETs less than 1 nA at room temperature, a choice of I_1 of $\geqslant 100$ nA should be more than adequate to ensure that a stable gate bias voltage V_G is obtained. Having selected the value of I_1, $(R_1 + R_2)$ can be calculated from

$$R_1 + R_2 = \frac{V_{DD}}{I_1} \tag{3.34}$$

Use of equation 3.34 together with the previously calculated ratio R_2/R_1 enables suitable values to be selected for R_1 and R_2.

Finally there remains the choice of the drain load R_D. As with other biasing arrangements, with no information given as to the required small-signal gain of the circuit, which would influence the choice of R_D (section 3.4.3), it is usual to split the voltage ($V_{DD} - V_S$) approximately equally between R_D and the FET so as to maximise the allowable swing of drain potential for ac operation. From equation 3.32:

$$V_S = V_G - V_{GS}$$

and so

$$V_{DD} - V_S = V_{DD} - V_G + V_{GS} \tag{3.35}$$

Equal division of this voltage between R_D and the transistor requires

$$V_O = \frac{V_{DD} - V_G + V_{GS}}{2} = I_Q R_D$$

from which

$$R_D = \frac{V_{DD} - V_G + V_{GS}}{2I_Q} \tag{3.36}$$

Example 3.5: FET fixed/self bias circuit design

Select suitable E12 resistance values for the fixed/self bias FET circuit of figure 3.5b. The drain supply V_{DD} is 15 V and a suitable mid-range Q-point V_{GS}typ, $I_D$typ has been selected from the transfer characteristics as -1.5 V, 2 mA.

Select V_G as 20 per cent of V_{DD} to provide reasonable stability against change of transfer characteristic without significant limitation of V_O and V_{DS}, giving

$$V_G = 0.2(15\text{ V}) = 3\text{ V}$$

From equation 3.32, for $V_G = 3$ V, the value of R_S required for $V_{GS} = V_{GS}\text{typ} = -1.5$ V and $I_Q = I_D\text{typ} = 2$ mA is

$$R_S = \frac{V_G - V_{GS}}{I_Q} = \frac{3\text{ V} - (-1.5\text{ V})}{2\text{ mA}} = 2.25\text{ k}\Omega$$

enabling the E12 value 2.2 kΩ (appendix D) to be selected.
For the R_1, R_2 potential divider to provide $V_G = 3$ V from the 15 V supply

$$\frac{R_1 + R_2}{R_2} = \frac{V_{DD}}{V_G} = \frac{15\text{ V}}{3\text{ V}} = 5$$

from equation 3.33, which requires $R_1 = 4R_2$.
The low gate current enables satisfactory operation to be obtained at room temperature with a divider current I_1 as low as 100 nA. To allow an adequate margin for the increase of gate current with temperature, a value of I_1 and 1 μA will be selected here giving

$$R_1 + R_2 = \frac{V_{DD}}{I_1} = \frac{15\text{ V}}{1\ \mu\text{A}} = 15\text{ M}\Omega$$

using equation 3.34.
Combination of $R_1 + R_2 = 15$ MΩ and $R_1 = 4R_2$ to give the required value of V_G leads to $R_1 = 12$ MΩ and $R_2 = 3$ MΩ.
The 12 MΩ value is available in the E12 range but a series combination of 2.7 MΩ and 270 kΩ is necessary to obtain approximately 3 MΩ, although a value of 3 MΩ is available in the E24 series.

At $I_Q = 2$ mA, the voltage across the 2.2 kΩ source resistor is 4.4 V leaving $V_{DD} - V_S =$ 15 V $-$ 4.4 V = 10.6 V to be dropped across the drain load R_D and the transistor. To position the Q-point near the middle of the load line, this voltage should be split equally between R_D and the transistor, thus R_D is selected to make

$$V_O = \frac{V_{DD} - V_S}{2} = \frac{10.6\text{ V}}{2} = 5.3\text{ V}$$

At $I_D \doteq I_Q = 2\,\text{mA}$, the required value of drain load is

$$R_D = \frac{V_O}{I_Q} = \frac{5.3\,\text{V}}{2\,\text{mA}} = 2.65\,\text{k}\Omega$$

allowing an E12 value of 2.7 kΩ to be selected.

3.3 AC operation: bypassing and coupling

Bypassing

In sections 3.1 and 3.2 it is explained that self biasing using an emitter resistor R_E in the BJT case or a source resistor R_S for an FET stabilises the Q-point by providing dc negative feedback. If the load current tends to rise, the self bias voltage V_E (or V_S) also rises, causing the input voltage to the transistor V_{BE} or V_{GS} to change and thereby causing the load current to fall, so compensating for the original tendency to rise. Although this mechanism is desirable for dc stability, the same effect causes the ac gain of the circuit to be reduced (section 5.1) which is undesirable if high signal gain is required. What is required is to retain the feedback effect provided by R_E (R_S) for *static* components to provide Q-point stability while removing the effect for *signal* components so as to permit high ac gain. This can be achieved by shunting R_E (R_S) with a capacitor C_B as shown in figure 3.6a for the BJT case. Provided the reactance of C_B (equation 2.26) is very much less than R_E (R_S) at the signal frequency, the impedance in the emitter (source) branch of the circuit is greatly reduced *as far as signal components are concerned*, thereby reducing the ac negative feedback. C_B therefore provides a low impedance path for signal current to bypass R_E (R_S) and in this role it is therefore termed a *bypass capacitor*. As a capacitor does not allow constant current to pass (except for leakage, section 2.4.2), the addition of C_B does not alter the dc conditions for the circuit and dc negative feedback is maintained.

To calculate a suitable value for C_B, consider the circuit of figure 3.6a in which the lower case symbols refer to signal currents and voltages. The ac voltage gain of the circuit is the ratio v_o/v_i where

$$v_o = i_c R_C \tag{3.37}$$

In this instance it is the ratio of the *amplitudes* of v_o and v_i, that is the modulus $|v_o/v_i|$, that is of main interest rather than the phase relationship.

Consider the two extreme cases of the effect of C_B: *total bypass* where the reactance of C_B is so low at the frequency of v_i that ac negative feedback is completely removed giving maximum voltage gain, and *no bypass* (C_B removed) where maximum negative feedback occurs and the voltage gain is a minimum.

For total bypass, C_B is an ac short circuit, $v_e = 0$, $v_i = v_{be}$ and by combination with equation 3.37

$$\text{ac voltage}\left|\frac{v_o}{v_i}\right| = \left|\frac{i_c R_C}{v_{be}}\right| = |g_{fe} R_C| \tag{3.38}$$

where g_{fe} ($= i_c/v_{be}$) is a gain parameter of the BJT termed the forward transconductance (section 3.4.2).

With no bypass (C_B removed), $v_i = v_{be} + v_e = v_{be} + i_e R_E$. For a high gain BJT, $i_c \simeq i_e$ and

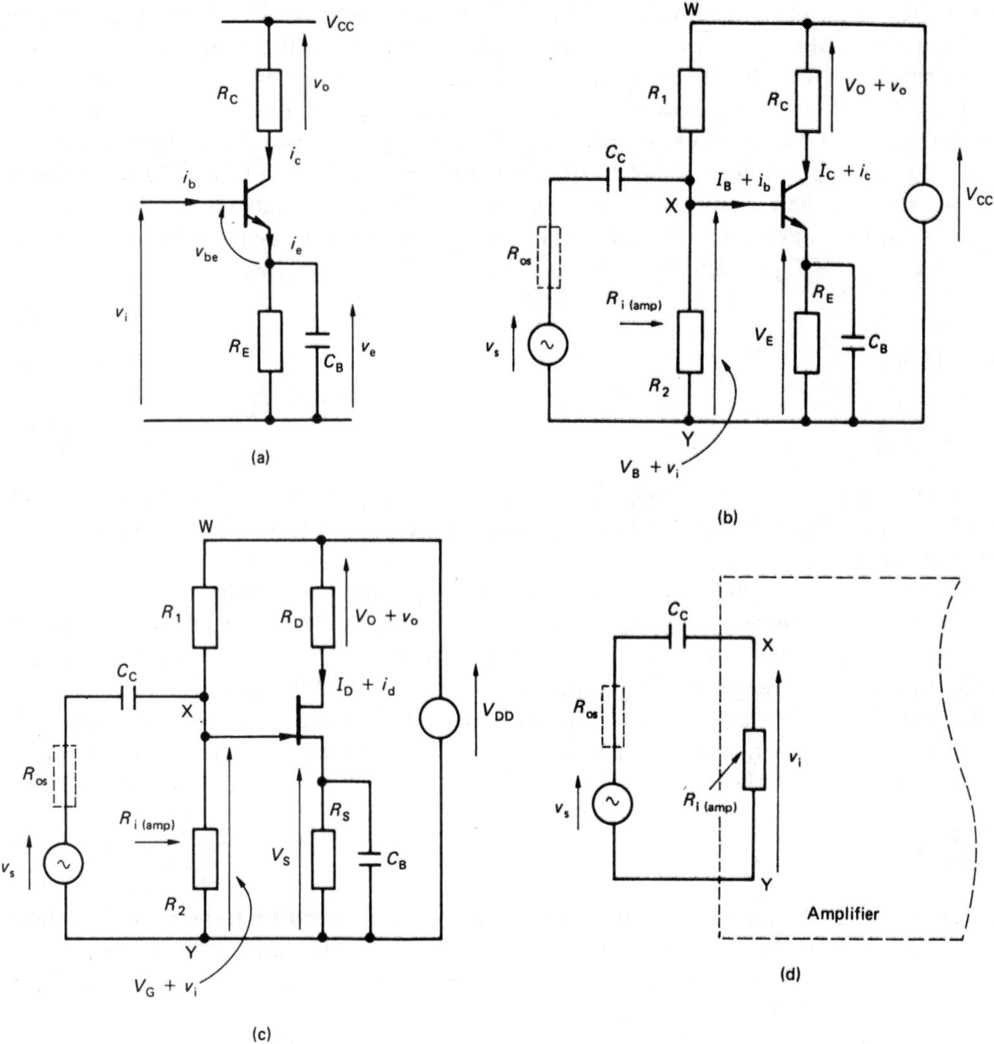

Figure 3.6 AC bypass and coupling

for typical values of i_c and R_E, $i_c R_E > v_{be}$ from which $v_i \simeq i_c R_E$. Combination with equation 3.37 gives the voltage gain for this condition as

$$\text{ac voltage gain}\left|\frac{v_o}{v_i}\right| \simeq \frac{i_c R_C}{i_c R_E} = \frac{R_C}{R_E} \tag{3.39}$$

Notice that for typical circuit values, $R_C = 6.8\ \text{k}\Omega$ and $R_E = 2.2\ \text{k}\Omega$ in example 3.3, the voltage gain with C_B removed is very low, approximately 3 for these values.

If the value of C_B shunting R_E is such that $X_{C_B} \ll R_E$ then, corresponding to equation 3.39, the

$$\text{ac voltage gain}\left|\frac{v_o}{v_i}\right| \simeq \frac{R_C}{X_{C_B}} = 2\pi f C_B R_C \tag{3.40}$$

since the reactance of C_B then replaces R_E. If C_B is progressively increased, the gain increases (equation 3.40) until it reaches the maximum value $g_{fe}R_C$ for total bypass (equation 3.38).

In normal operation the input signal v_i comprises a wide range of frequency components and for low distortion amplification the circuit is required to amplify each component by the same amount. Thus a flat (constant) gain response is required down to a certain minimum signal frequency f_{min}, and therefore C_B is selected so that at f_{min} (at which the reactance of C_B is a maximum and therefore the ac negative feedback also a maximum), the gain from equation 3.40 has not reduced below the maximum (flat response) value given by equation 3.38. A suitable value of C_B is therefore given by

$$2\pi f_{min} C_B R_C = g_{fe} R_C \qquad (3.41)$$

from which

$$C_B \geqslant \frac{g_{fe}}{2\pi f_{min}} \qquad (3.42)$$

Note that C_B must not be less than the value given by equation 3.41 but a larger value will extend the 'flat response' band below f_{min} which provides a safety margin with regard to component tolerance.

The value of g_{fe} for a BJT, also referred to as mutual conductance g_m, is approximately equal to $40I_C$ at low current levels (equation 3.63 and reference [1b]) where I_C is the quiescent collector current, so that at $I_C = 1$ mA, $g_{fe} \simeq 40$ mS where S denotes the unit of conductance (siemen) which is the reciprocal of ohms and sometimes termed 'mhos'.

The above work applies equally to the selection of C_B for the FET circuit of figure 3.6c except that the transconductance gain term for an FET is denoted by g_{fs}, thus, corresponding to equation 3.42 for a BJT:

$$C_B \geqslant \frac{g_{fs}}{2\pi f_{min}} \qquad (3.43)$$

The value of g_{fs} at the particular Q-point involved can be obtained from the FET data sheet. For a type 2N5457JFET, g_{fs}max at $V_{GS} = -1.5$ V (example 3.5) is about 3500 μmho (= 3.5 mS) at 25°C. The maximum value of g_{fs} is used in calculation to ensure that C_B is sufficiently large in the worst-case situation.

Note that the value of C_B will typically be several microfarads, often up to 100 μF or more if f_{min} is low, requiring use of a polarity-conscious electrolytic type (section 2.4.2). For circuits involving npn BJTs or *n*-channel FETs, the power supply V_{CC} or V_{DD} is positive and so C_B must be connected with its positive terminal connected to the transistor.

Example 3.6: Calculation of bypass capacitor value

Select suitable values for bypass capacitor C_B from the E6 series for use in

(a) the BJT circuit of example 3.3 required to amplify signals of minimum frequency 50 Hz,
(b) the FET circuit of example 3.5 with $g_{fs} = 5$ mS and $f_{min} = 20$ Hz.

In each the capacitors are available with working voltage ratings of 10 V, 25 V, 35 V, 63 V and 100 V.

(a) The quiescent collector current for the circuit in example 3.3 is 1 mA and so g_{fe} for the

BJT is approximately 40 mS (equation 3.63). Using equation 3.42, with $f_{min} = 50$ Hz:

$$C_B \geqslant \frac{g_{fe}}{2\pi f_{min}} = \frac{(40 \times 10^{-3})\,\text{S}}{2\pi(50\,\text{Hz})} = 127\,\mu\text{F}$$

so that a value of 150 μF can be chosen from the E6 range (appendix D).
The static voltage across C_B in this circuit is the same as the static voltage across R_E, that is, V_E which is 2.2 V. Therefore a capacitor with the minimum voltage rating of 10 V will be suitable.

Selection: $C_B = 150\,\mu$F, 10 V

(b) For a FET with $g_{fs} = 5$ mS and $f_{min} = 20$ Hz, the value of C_B for the circuit of example 3.5, from equation 3.43, is

$$C_B \geqslant \frac{g_{fs}}{2\pi f_{min}} = \frac{(5 \times 10^{-3})\,\text{S}}{2\pi(20\,\text{Hz})} \simeq 40\,\mu\text{F}$$

allowing an E6 value of 47 μF to be selected.
The static voltage across C_B in this circuit is V_S (across R_S) $= V_G - V_{GS}$ (equation 3.32) $=$ 3 V $-$ ($-$1.5 V) $=$ 4.5 V and so a minimum rating component of 10 V will be adequate.

Selection: $C_B = 47\,\mu$F, 10 V

Coupling

To use the BJT and FET circuits of figures 3.3a and 3.5b as small-signal amplifiers, the input signal v_i must be superimposed on the input bias V_B (BJT), V_G (FET) so as to vary the degree of conduction of the transistor and so develop an output signal voltage across the load.

As the dc component (average value) of the signal waveform is invariably different from the dc level of the BJT base or FET gate, it is necessary to provide *dc isolation* between them so that connection of the input signal source does not upset the biasing of the transistor. Although dc isolation is required, the connection (coupling) between the signal source and the transistor must allow the ac component of the waveform to pass so as to influence transistor conduction. Such a requirement is provided by a *coupling capacitor* C_C (section 2.4.2) as shown in figures 3.6b,c where the signal current and voltage components are denoted by lower case symbols, added to the dc (bias) components (upper case symbols). C_C is often termed a *dc blocking* or *ac coupling* capacitor.

The value of C_C is chosen in relation to the other circuit component values taking account of the frequency of the signal. As far as the ac signal is concerned, the input XY of the amplifier may be represented by its input impedance which, at the frequency of interest here, is mainly resistive as represented by $R_{i(amp)}$ in figures 3.6b,c. C_C and $R_{i(amp)}$ thus form a frequency-dependent potential divider (figure 3.6d) so that the signal voltage at the input of the transistor v_i is less than that provided by the source v_s. To prevent excessive attenuation and reduced overall ac voltage gain (v_o/v_s), the reactance of C_C (X_{C_C}, equation 2.26) must be small compared with $R_{i(amp)}$ at the frequency of v_s:

$$X_{C_C} = \frac{1}{2\pi f C_C} \ll R_{i(amp)} \tag{3.44}$$

In most applications the input signal v_i is a complex waveform having a range of frequency components. Since capacitive reactance increases as the frequency is reduced (equation 2.26), it is the value of X_{C_C} at the lowest frequency component of v_i (f_{min}) that is most relevant. As a compromise between reduced gain due to $R_{i(amp)}$, C_C potential division and an unnecessarily large value of C_C, with corresponding increased cost, size and leakage (section 2.4.2), it is usually adequate to choose C_C so that its reactance at f_{min} does not exceed 10 per cent of $R_{i(amp)}$, that is:

$$C_C \geqslant \frac{1}{2\pi f_{min}\left(\frac{R_{i(amp)}}{10}\right)} \tag{3.45}$$

Note that if the input signal source providing v_i has an ac output resistance R_{os} (shown dashed in figures 3.6b, c, d and sometimes termed the signal *source* resistance), $R_{i(amp)}$ in equation 3.45 must be replaced by $(R_{i(amp)} + R_{os})$.

One of the most fundamental points to appreciate about the ac performance of such circuits is that *as far as the ac signal is concerned, the dc power supply* (V_{CC}, V_{DD}) *acts as an ac short circuit*. Since the power supply voltage is *constant* there is no ac component between nodes W and Y (figures 3.6b, c) and so these points are at the same potential as far as the *signal* is concerned. Thus, in terms of the ac performance of the circuit, it is as if the bias resistors are in parallel across the input terminals XY.

Assuming that C_B provides total bypass of R_E (R_S), the ac input resistance $R_{i(amp)}$ is the parallel combination of R_1, R_2 and the input resistance R_i between base and emitter (gate and source) of the transistor. In the FET case, R_i is very high ($>10^8\ \Omega$) and so

$$R_{i(amp)} = R_1 /\!/ R_2 \tag{3.46}$$

R_i having negligible influence on $R_{i(amp)}$. For the BJT circuit, however, the input resistance of the transistor is typically in the range 1–10 kΩ and must be taken into account. The input resistance of a BJT is denoted by the parameter h_{ie} (section 3.4.2), the value of which is given on the data sheet. For a type BC107 BJT (appendix E, section E.5) the value of h_{ie} at $I_C = 1$ mA has a typical value of 6.5 kΩ with a spread from 4.8 kΩ to 8.5 kΩ.

With $R_i = h_{ie}$ for a BJT, the input resistance of the BJT amplifier (figure 3.6b) is

$$R_{i(amp)} = R_1 /\!/ R_2 /\!/ h_{ie} = R_B /\!/ h_{ie} \tag{3.47}$$

where $R_B = R_1 /\!/ R_2$.

Example 3.7: Calculation of coupling capacitor value

The small-signal amplifiers of figures 3.6b, c incorporate resistance values calculated in examples 3.3 and 3.5 respectively. For the same values of minimum frequency used in example 3.6, select suitable E6 values for the coupling capacitors in each case.

(a) Circuit of figure 3.6b with $R_1 = 120$ kΩ, $R_2 = 27$ kΩ ($R_B = 120\ \text{k}\Omega /\!/ 27\ \text{k}\Omega \simeq 22$ kΩ) from example 3.3.

Taking h_{ie} for the BJT at $I_C = 1$ mA as the typical value of 6.5 kΩ quoted above for a BC107 and using equation 3.47:

$$R_{i(amp)} = R_B /\!/ h_{ie} \simeq 22\ \text{k}\Omega /\!/ 6.5\ \text{k}\Omega = \frac{(22\ \text{k}\Omega)(6.5\ \text{k}\Omega)}{(22\ \text{k}\Omega) + (6.5\ \text{k}\Omega)} \simeq 5\ \text{k}\Omega$$

Notice that because $h_{ie} \ll R_B$ it is h_{ie} that dominates the value of $R_{i(amp)}$.

Then, using equation 3.45, for $f_{\min} = 50$ Hz (example 3.6a):

$$C_C \geqslant \frac{1}{2\pi(50\ \text{Hz})\left(\dfrac{5\ \text{k}\Omega}{10}\right)} \simeq 6.4\ \mu\text{F}$$

allowing choice of the E6 value 6.8 μF, or 10 μF allowing for component tolerance.

(b) For the FET circuit of figure 3.6c with $R_1 = 12$ MΩ and $R_2 = 2.7$ MΩ + 270 kΩ = 2.97 MΩ from example 3.5, the input resistance $R_{i(amp)}$ is given (equation 3.46) by

$$R_{i(amp)} = R_1 /\!/ R_2 = 2.97\ \text{M}\Omega /\!/ 12\ \text{M}\Omega = \frac{(2.97\ \text{M}\Omega)(12\ \text{M}\Omega)}{(2.97\ \text{M}\Omega) + (12\ \text{M}\Omega)} \simeq 2.4\ \text{M}\Omega$$

Then, from equation 3.45, for $f_{\min} = 20$ Hz (example 3.6b):

$$C_C \geqslant \frac{1}{2\pi(20\ \text{Hz})\left(\dfrac{2.4\ \text{M}\Omega}{10}\right)} \simeq 33\ \text{nF}$$

Although a value of 33 nF is available in the E6 series, the next higher value (47 nF) is chosen to allow for component tolerance.

This section has been concerned with the need for bypassing and coupling capacitors to enable the basic BJT and FET amplifier stages to function satisfactorily as small-signal amplifiers together with basic methods of estimating the component values required. More detailed consideration of the effect of these capacitors on amplifier response can be found in chapters 4 and 5.

3.4 AC performance

3.4.1 *Gain, input impedance, output impedance*

Figure 3.7 gives a general representation of an amplifying arrangement where the basic amplifier, represented by the dashed rectangle, has input signal voltage and current v_i, i_i and corresponding output signal levels v_o and i_o. The small-signal voltage and current gains of the amplifier are defined as

$$A_{v(amp)} = \frac{v_o}{v_i} \tag{3.48}$$

and

$$A_{i(amp)} = \frac{i_o}{i_i} \tag{3.49}$$

with corresponding signal power gain of

$$A_{p(amp)} = \frac{-v_o i_o}{v_i i_i} = -A_{v(amp)} A_{i(amp)} \tag{3.50}$$

The negative sign in equation 3.50 arises because of the defined direction for i_o; numerical

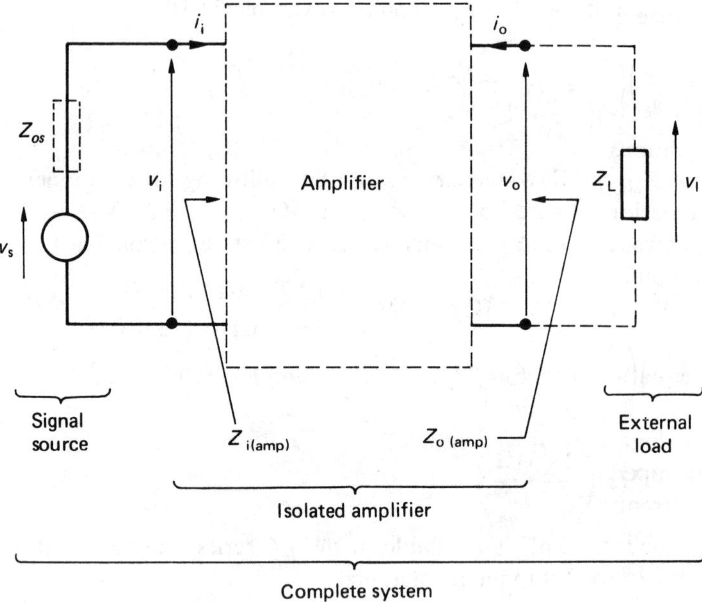

Figure 3.7 General amplifying arrangement

calculation results in a positive value for $A_{p(amp)}$. The basic amplifier cannot be used in isolation; the input signal is provided either by another circuit or by a transducer while the output may be required to drive an *external* load Z_L which may be the input impedance of another circuit. When connected to a source, the input impedance of the basic amplifier

$$Z_{i(amp)} = \frac{v_i}{i_i} \tag{3.51}$$

is significant because the relative values of $Z_{i(amp)}$ and the output impedance of the source Z_{os} determine the proportion of the available source signal v_s that has effect at the input of the amplifier. By potential division within the input loop of figure 3.7:

$$v_i = v_s\left(\frac{Z_{i(amp)}}{Z_{i(amp)} + Z_{os}}\right) \tag{3.52}$$

Similarly the relative value of the output impedance of the amplifier

$$Z_{o(amp)} = \frac{v_o}{i_o} \tag{3.53}$$

in comparison with the external load Z_L is important because this determines the proportion of the amplified signal v_o that is developed across the external load since by potential division at the output:

$$v_l = v_o\left(\frac{Z_L}{Z_L + Z_{o(amp)}}\right) \tag{3.54}$$

where v_o is the output voltage from the amplifier with no external load connected.

The overall voltage gain of the arrangement, termed the *system* gain, $A_{v(sys)}$ is then

$$A_{v(sys)} = \frac{v_l}{v_s} = \left(\frac{v_o}{v_i}\right)\left(\frac{v_i}{v_s}\right)\left(\frac{v_l}{v_o}\right) = A_{v(amp)}\left[\frac{Z_{i(amp)}}{Z_{i(amp)} + Z_{os}}\right]\left[\frac{Z_L}{Z_L + Z_{o(amp)}}\right] \quad (3.55)$$

by combining equations 3.48, 3.52 and 3.54. To avoid severe voltage gain reduction, $Z_{i(amp)}$ must be $\gg Z_{os}$ and $Z_{o(amp)}$ must be $\ll Z_L$.

Similar representation of a signal *current* amplifier system where the signal source can be represented by a current source i_s in *parallel* with its output impedance Z_{os}, termed a Norton model, with the amplifier output represented by a current source i_o shunted by $Z_{o(amp)}$, shows that

$$A_{i(sys)} = \frac{i_l}{i_s} = \left(\frac{i_o}{i_i}\right)\left(\frac{i_i}{i_s}\right)\left(\frac{i_l}{i_o}\right) = A_{i(amp)}\left[\frac{Z_{os}}{Z_{os} + Z_{i(amp)}}\right]\left[\frac{Z_{o(amp)}}{Z_{o(amp)} + Z_L}\right] \quad (3.56)$$

indicating that for high overall current gain $Z_{i(amp)}$ must be $\ll Z_{os}$ and $Z_{o(amp)} \gg Z_L$. Notice that the required impedance conditions for high overall voltage gain are opposite to those for high overall current gain.

Except for operation at very high frequency, the reactive components of $Z_{i(amp)}$, $Z_{o(amp)}$, Z_{os} and Z_L are often negligible and these impedances can be considered simply as resistances $R_{i(amp)}$, $R_{o(amp)}$, R_{os} and R_L.

Example 3.8: Effect of amplifier input and output resistance on overall voltage gain

An amplifier has a voltage gain of 200 with input and output resistances of 5 kΩ. What would be the overall voltage gain obtained when it is driven from a source of output resistance R_{os} and it drives an external load R_L where

(a) $R_{os} = 1$ kΩ, $R_L = 1$ kΩ, (b) $R_{os} = 1$ kΩ, $R_L = 100$ kΩ, (c) $R_{os} = 100$ kΩ, $R_L = 1$ kΩ, (d) $R_{os} = 100$ kΩ, $R_L = 100$ kΩ?

From equation 3.55, the overall voltage gain $A_{v(sys)}$ is

$$A_{v(amp)}\left[\frac{R_{i(amp)}}{R_{i(amp)} + R_{os}}\right]\left[\frac{R_L}{R_L + R_{o(amp)}}\right]$$

(a) $$A_{v(sys)} = 200\left(\frac{5\text{ k}\Omega}{5\text{ k}\Omega + 1\text{ k}\Omega}\right)\left(\frac{1\text{ k}\Omega}{1\text{ k}\Omega + 5\text{ k}\Omega}\right) \simeq 28$$

(b) $$A_{v(sys)} = 200\left(\frac{5\text{ k}\Omega}{5\text{ k}\Omega + 1\text{ k}\Omega}\right)\left(\frac{100\text{ k}\Omega}{100\text{ k}\Omega + 5\text{ k}\Omega}\right) \simeq 159$$

(c) $$A_{v(sys)} = 200\left(\frac{5\text{ k}\Omega}{5\text{ k}\Omega + 100\text{ k}\Omega}\right)\left(\frac{1\text{ k}\Omega}{1\text{ k}\Omega + 5\text{ k}\Omega}\right) \simeq 1.6$$

(d) $$A_{v(sys)} = 200\left(\frac{5\text{ k}\Omega}{5\text{ k}\Omega + 100\text{ k}\Omega}\right)\left(\frac{100\text{ k}\Omega}{100\text{ k}\Omega + 5\text{ k}\Omega}\right) \simeq 9$$

Note that the highest overall voltage gain is obtained for the low R_{os} and high R_L combination.

3.4.2 *AC modelling*

To analyse the performance of an amplifier, it is necessary to represent the performance of the transistor: sections 1.2.2 and 1.2.3 consider general techniques. Because ac analysis involves time-varying currents and voltages, graphical techniques are of little use, being limited mainly to illustrative consideration. Representation of transistor performance by a network model is far more productive and further, since small-signal operation of an amplifier involves transistor operation only in the vicinity of the Q-point, the simplifications outlined in section 1.2.4 can be applied.

A further general problem is that amplifiers comprise more than one type of circuit element; in addition to the bias resistors there are coupling and bypass *circuit* capacitors as well as capacitances within the transistor. Thus although small-signal operation of the amplifier can be represented by a linear model, the model contains both resistances and capacitances resulting in time-dependent solutions as outlined in section 1.2.1. In most cases however there is a wide range of operation termed the *mid-frequency band* over which the effect of both circuit capacitors and transistor capacitances is negligible. Over this range of frequencies the small-signal performance of an amplifier can be represented by a linear model involving only one type of linear element which simplifies analysis considerably. This section is concerned only with operation in this mid-frequency band; chapter 4, concerned with frequency response, considers the effect of capacitance.

AC model of the amplifier circuit

Using a BJT amplifier as an example, figure 3.8a shows the complete *practical* circuit; bias voltages and currents are represented by upper case symbols with signal components by lower case. Note that the collector signal current i_c is the output signal current i_o.

For signals in the mid-frequency range the reactances of the coupling and bypass capacitors are sufficiently low that, *as far as the signal is concerned*, they can be considered as short circuits. The dc power supply V_{CC} also acts as a very low impedance path to the ac signal and it also can be represented by an ac short circuit. The *ac performance* of the amplifier can therefore be represented by the *model* of figure 3.8b which further reduces to that of figure 3.8c, R_1 and R_2 being *effectively* in parallel ($R_B = R_1 /\!/ R_2$) as far as the signal is concerned. Note that in making the reduction from figure 3.8b to c the direction of the output signal voltage v_o has been redefined. This is because in practical application the output voltage is normally taken as the variation of collector potential *with respect to ground* which simplifies consideration when circuits are cascaded (interconnected output-to-input) to form multistage circuits. Note that it is this definition of v_o that causes this amplifier to exhibit phase inversion between input and output at mid frequencies (equation 3.65 and section 4.5).

From figure 3.8c the ac performance of the circuit can be represented as in figure 3.8d which applies equally to the FET amplifier of figure 3.6c except that the collector resistor R_C then becomes the drain resistor R_D. R_i and R_o represent the input and output resistances of the transistor, from which

$$R_{i(amp)} = R_i /\!/ R_B \tag{3.57}$$

and

$$R_{o(amp)} = R_o /\!/ R_C \tag{3.58}$$

Note that the dashed rectangle in figure 3.7 represents the model of figure 3.8d.

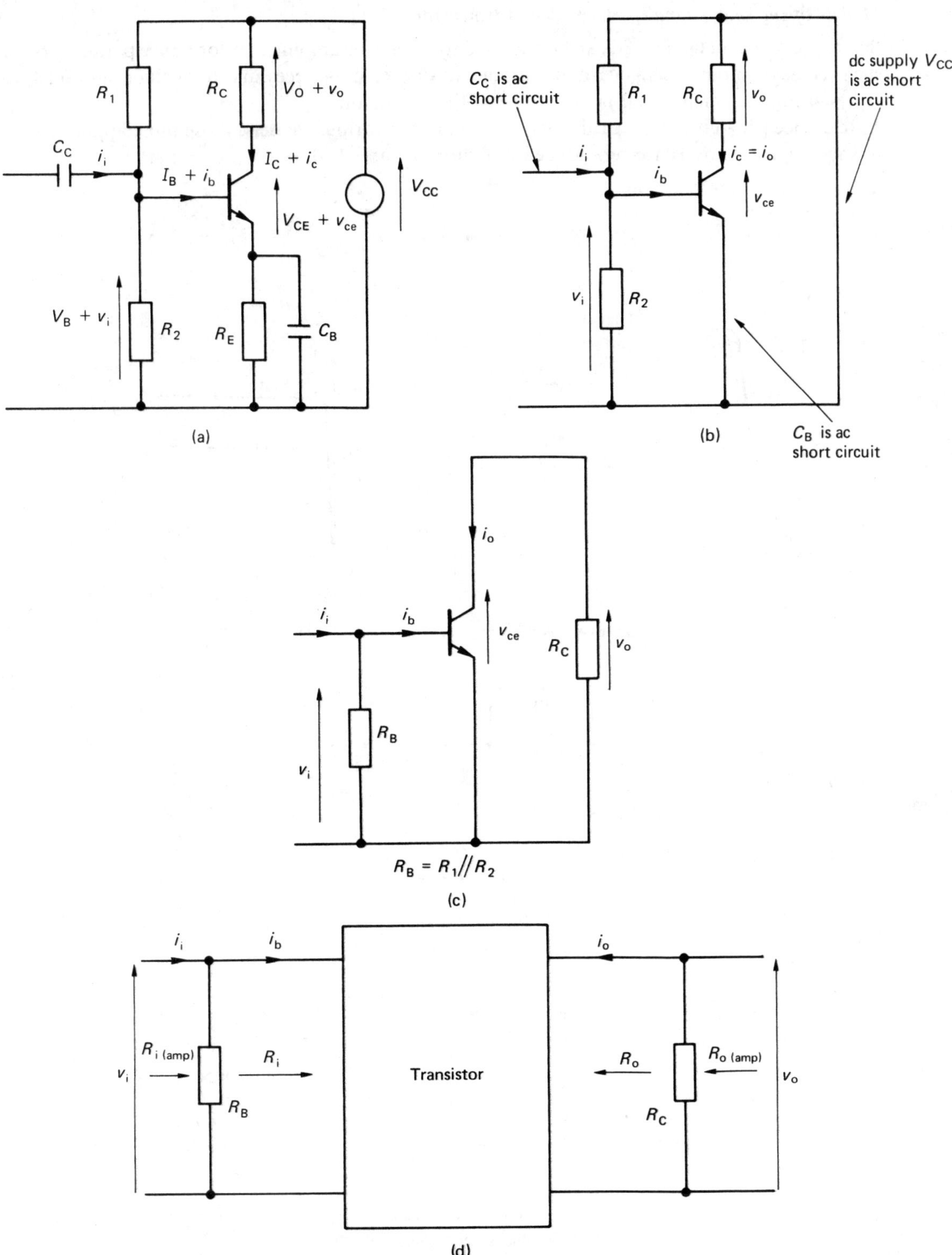

Figure 3.8 Derivation of the ac circuit model for mid-frequency operation

Models of the small-signal performance of transistors

Before the model of figure 3.8d can be analysed to determine amplifier performance parameters such as gain, input resistance and output resistance, it is necessary to include a model representing the small-signal performance of the transistor.

Reference [1c] gives a detailed consideration of the various models; those most applicable to small-signal analysis are reproduced in figures 3.9 and 3.10.

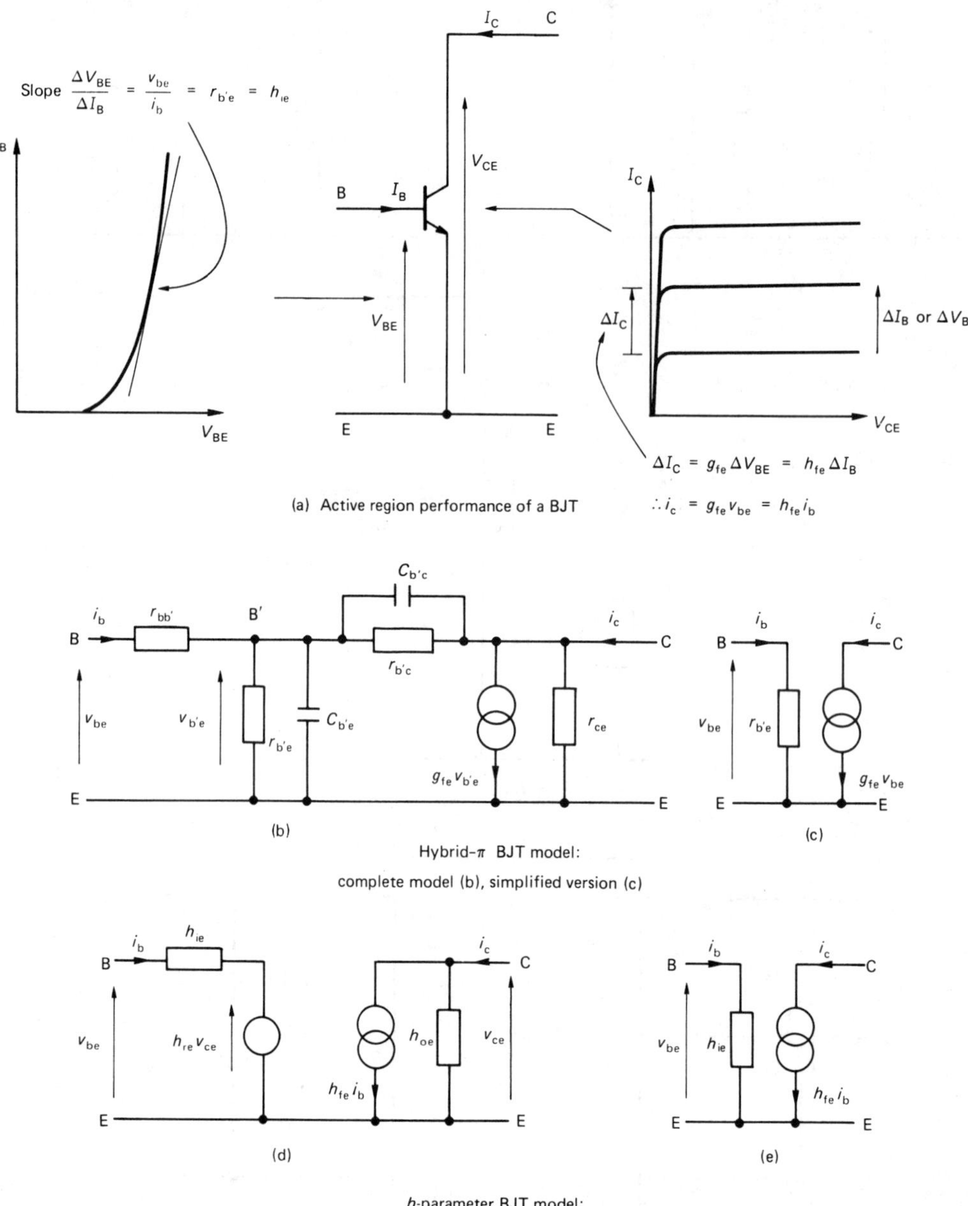

Figure 3.9 Representation of the small-signal performance of a BJT by a network model

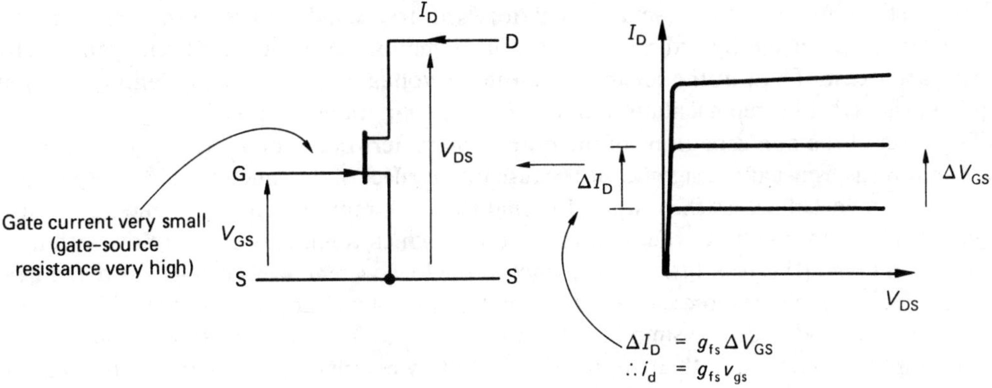

(a) Saturation region performance of a FET

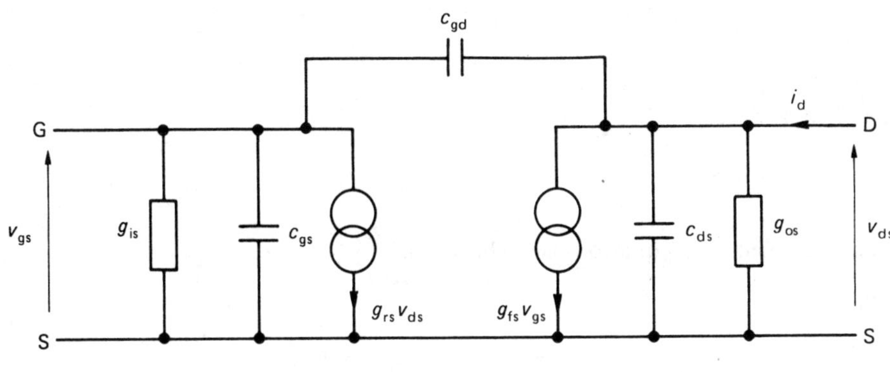

(b) Complete conductance parameter model

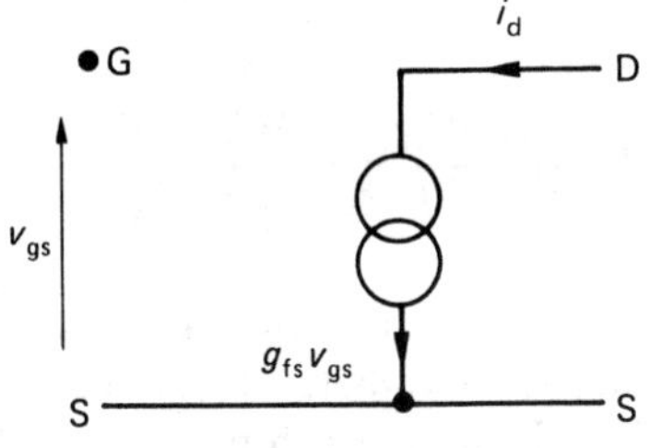

(c) Simplified version

Figure 3.10 Representation of the small-signal performance of a FET by a network model

For a BJT, both the hybrid-π and h-parameter models are widely used, the former being particularly popular for use at high frequencies where h-parameters are difficult to measure. The two complete models are given in figures 3.9b and d. As far as basic BJT behaviour is concerned, the most important relationships are between v_{be} and i_b at the input and how the output current i_c depends on v_{be} or i_b. The relationship between v_{be} and i_b at low- and mid-frequencies is given by the *slope resistance* (section 1.2.4) of the input characteristic which is represented by $r_{b'e}$ in the hybrid-π model and by h_{ie} in the h-parameter model. For ideal output characteristics the collector current is proportional to v_{be} and i_b, the constant of proportionality being g_{fe} (small-signal forward transconductance, also called mutual conductance g_m) in the hybrid-π model and h_{fe} (small-signal forward current gain) in the h-parameter case. Thus, in the ideal case, an input voltage v_{be} results in a collector current $g_{fe}v_{be}$ in the hybrid-π representation and $h_{fe}i_b$ in the h-parameter model.

The effect of the non-zero slope of the output characteristics, represented by r_{ce} and h_{oe} in the two models, is usually insignificant because of the effect of the much lower value collector resistance connected across the output. Internal feedback represented by $r_{b'c}$ and $h_{re}i_b$ is also of minor importance in first-order analysis and $r_{bb'}$, which represents current flow within the base region of the BJT, is of little consequence at the low current levels being considered here. The high-frequency effects represented by $C_{b'e}$ and $C_{b'c}$ are not relevant at low- and mid-frequencies and so the two models can be simplified to those of figures 3.9c and e for subsequent analysis. Being simplified versions, both are approximate, but by comparison it can be established that

$$r_{b'e} \simeq h_{ie} \tag{3.59}$$

and

$$g_{fe}v_{be} \simeq h_{fe}i_b \tag{3.60}$$

From figure 3.9e however:

$$i_b = \frac{v_{be}}{h_{ie}} \tag{3.61}$$

which, when combined with equation 3.60, shows that

$$g_{fe} \simeq \frac{h_{fe}}{h_{ie}} \tag{3.62}$$

Further, since at low current levels, the base–emitter junction is operating on the approximately exponential part of its characteristic, it follows from equation 2.6 for a forward biased pn junction that

$$g_{fe} = \frac{i_c}{v_{be}} \simeq \frac{\partial I_C}{\partial V_{BE}} \simeq \frac{\partial I_E}{\partial V_{BE}} = \frac{\partial}{\partial V_{BE}}\left[I_0 \exp\left(\frac{eV_{BE}}{kT}\right)\right] = \frac{eI_E}{kT} \simeq \frac{eI_C}{kT} \simeq 40I_C \tag{3.63}$$

at 25°C since $kT/e \simeq 26$ mV at this temperature (equation 2.7). This relationship is particularly useful because it enables the small-signal gain parameter (g_{fe}) to be calculated from knowledge of *static* quiescent current I_C. Note that this relationship is only valid at low current levels because the forward characteristic of a pn junction is not exponential at higher current levels (above point B, for example, in figure 2.2c).

In the case of an FET the most popular model is based on the conductance parameter model which is the low-frequency version of the general admittance (y) parameter model. The input and output conductances of the FET relative to the source terminal are represented by g_{is} and g_{os} respectively. Output current is related to input voltage via the small-signal forward transconductance of the FET, g_{fs} (also termed the mutual conductance g_m), while internal feedback is represented by the $g_{rs}v_{ds}$ current source (figure 3.10b). Performance at high frequency is dependent on internal capacitances which are represented in the model by C_{gs}, C_{gd} and C_{ds}.

At low- and mid-frequencies, the capacitive effects are negligible. Input resistance is very high so that g_{is} is insignificant compared with the effective conductance of the bias resistors connected at the input, and also internal feedback is usually sufficiently low to be ignored.

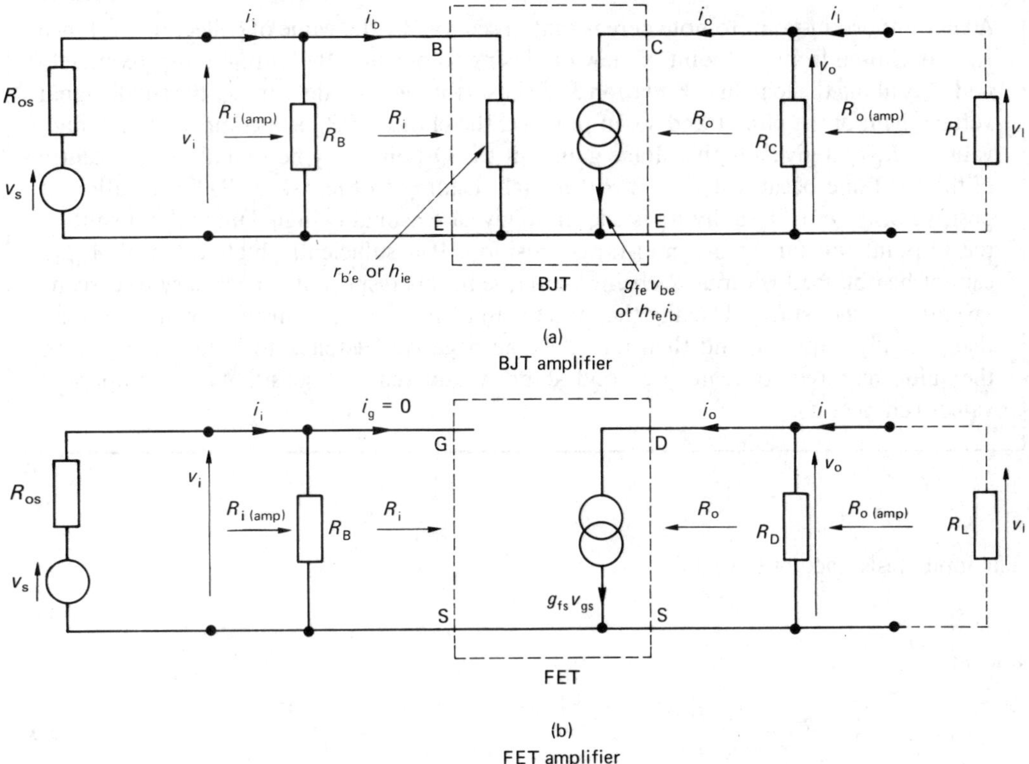

Figure 3.11 Models representing the small-signal amplifier performance

As in the BJT case, the effect of finite output characteristic slope, as represented by g_{os}, is usually negligible compared with the drain load connected across the output. These factors enable the complete model of figure 3.10b to be reduced to that of figure 3.10c for most analysis work at low and mid frequencies.

3.4.3 *AC analysis*

Gain and input, output resistances of the BJT amplifier

By combining the representations of figures 3.7, 3.8d and using either of the simplified models of BJT performance in the active region (figures 3.9c and e), the small-signal performance of the amplifier of figure 3.6b at mid-frequencies can be represented as shown in figure 3.11a. Ignoring the external load R_L initially and using hybrid-π parameters

$$v_o = -g_{fe}v_{be}R_C = -g_{fe}v_iR_C \tag{3.64}$$

since $v_{be} = v_i$, and so

$$A_{v(amp)} = \frac{v_o}{v_i} = -g_{fe}R_C \tag{3.65}$$

the negative sign indicating that v_o is inverted relative to v_i, that is, there is a phase shift of 180° (half a cycle) between v_o and v_i.

A very important point to note here is that in section 3.1 the value of collector resistance R_C was chosen from the point of view of biasing to position the Q-point approximately mid-way along the load line. Equation 3.65 shows that R_C also determines the small-signal voltage gain of the circuit and so, in practice, the choice of R_C is a compromise. A high value of R_C will give a high voltage gain, but the Q-point may be well above the centre of the load line because V_O $(=I_Q R_C)$ is high, leading to the risk of BJT saturation at positive peaks of v_i. Usually R_C is chosen to give a reasonably high gain without shifting the Q-point too far from a mid-range position. If a sufficiently high value of $A_{v(mid)}$ cannot be obtained without R_C being too large in this respect, it is necessary to cascade several amplifier stages. Usually the target is to achieve a gain considerably higher than that actually required, and then introduce ac negative feedback to reduce the gain to the value required so achieving good stability and reduced sensitivity to component values (chapter 5).

The input resistance of the BJT,

$$R_i = r_{b'e} \tag{3.66}$$

and so

$$R_{i(amp)} = r_{b'e} /\!/ R_B = \frac{r_{b'e} R_B}{r_{b'e} + R_B} \tag{3.67}$$

using equation 3.57.
Output signal current,

$$i_o = g_{fe} v_{be} = g_{fe} v_i \tag{3.68}$$

and the input signal current:

$$i_i = \frac{v_i}{R_{i(amp)}} \tag{3.69}$$

thus

$$A_{i(amp)} = \frac{i_o}{i_i} = g_{fe} R_{i(amp)} = g_{fe}(r_{b'e} /\!/ R_B) = \frac{g_{fe} r_{b'e} R_B}{r_{b'e} + R_B} \tag{3.70}$$

The output resistance of the transistor R_o is very high, theoretically infinite using the ideal BJT model (see note 3.2). With $R_o = \infty$, the output resistance of the amplifier

$$R_{o(amp)} = R_o /\!/ R_C = R_C \tag{3.71}$$

The corresponding analysis using h-parameters gives

$$v_o = -h_{fe} i_b R_C \tag{3.72}$$

and

$$i_b = \frac{v_i}{h_{ie}} \tag{3.73}$$

from which

$$A_{v(\text{amp})} = \frac{-h_{fe}}{h_{ie}} R_C \tag{3.74}$$

$$i_o = h_{fe} i_b \tag{3.75}$$

and by current division between h_{ie} and R_B at the input:

$$i_b = i_i \left(\frac{R_B}{R_B + h_{ie}} \right) \tag{3.76}$$

Combining equations 3.75 and 3.76

$$A_{i(\text{amp})} = \frac{h_{fe} R_B}{R_B + h_{ie}} \tag{3.77}$$

The BJT input resistance

$$R_i = h_{ie} \tag{3.78}$$

and so

$$R_{i(\text{amp})} = h_{ie} /\!/ R_B = \frac{h_{ie} R_B}{h_{ie} + R_B} \tag{3.79}$$

Using the low/mid-frequency equivalents of equations 3.55 and 3.56 (Z replaced by R), the overall system gains $A_{v(\text{sys})}$ and $A_{i(\text{sys})}$ taking account of the output resistance of the source and the connection of an external load, are

$$A_{v(\text{sys})} = -g_{fe} R_C \left[\frac{r_{b'e} /\!/ R_B}{(r_{b'e} /\!/ R_B) + R_{os}} \right] \left[\frac{R_L}{R_L + R_C} \right] \tag{3.80}$$

$$= \frac{-h_{fe}}{h_{ie}} R_C \left[\frac{h_{ie} /\!/ R_B}{(h_{ie} /\!/ R_B) + R_{os}} \right] \left[\frac{R_L}{R_L + R_C} \right] \tag{3.81}$$

and

$$A_{i(\text{sys})} = g_{fe} (r_{b'e} /\!/ R_B) \left[\frac{R_{os}}{R_{os} + (r_{b'e} /\!/ R_B)} \right] \left[\frac{R_C}{R_C + R_L} \right] \tag{3.82}$$

$$= \frac{h_{fe} R_B}{R_B + h_{ie}} \left[\frac{R_{os}}{R_{os} + (h_{ie} /\!/ R_B)} \right] \left[\frac{R_C}{R_C + R_L} \right] \tag{3.83}$$

Gain and input, output resistances of the FET amplifier

Analysis of the small-signal performance of the amplifier of figure 3.6c at mid-frequencies using the model of figure 3.11b follows the same pattern as that for the BJT circuit considered above except that, with the input resistance of the FET being so very high, $R_i = \infty$ simplifying the analysis.

From figure 3.11b, ignoring R_L initially,

$$v_o = -g_{fs} v_{gs} R_D = -g_{fs} v_i R_D \tag{3.84}$$

$$v_i = v_{gs} \tag{3.85}$$

$$i_o = g_{fs} v_{gs} \tag{3.86}$$

and

$$i_i = \frac{v_i}{R_{i(amp)}} = \frac{v_i}{R_B} \tag{3.87}$$

from which:

$$A_{v(amp)} = \frac{v_o}{v_i} = -g_{fs} R_D \tag{3.88}$$

$$A_{i(amp)} = \frac{i_o}{i_i} = g_{fs} R_B \tag{3.89}$$

$$R_{i(amp)} = R_B \tag{3.90}$$

$$R_{o(amp)} = R_D \tag{3.91}$$

Note that the value of drain resistance R_D features in both the static circuit operation (positioning of the Q-point, section 3.2) and the small-signal ac performance. In practice, therefore, as for the choice of R_C in the BJT case above, the value of R_D is chosen as a compromise between the requirements of high gain and reasonable positioning of the Q-point.

The corresponding system gains using equations 3.55 and 3.56 are

$$A_{v(sys)} = -g_{fs} R_D \left[\frac{R_B}{R_B + R_{os}}\right]\left[\frac{R_L}{R_L + R_D}\right] \tag{3.92}$$

and

$$A_{i(sys)} = g_{fs} R_B \left[\frac{R_{os}}{R_{os} + R_B}\right]\left[\frac{R_D}{R_L + R_D}\right] \tag{3.93}$$

Example 3.9: Analysis of the mid-frequency small-signal performance of a BJT amplifier

If the BJT in the amplifier circuit designed in example 3.3 has a small-signal current gain h_{fe} of 200, determine the small-signal voltage and current gains and the input and output resistances of the circuit for mid-frequency operation. If the circuit is driven from a 600 Ω source and feeds a 10 kΩ external load, what would be the overall voltage gain achieved?

The relevant component values selected for the circuit in example 3.3 are $R_1 = 120\,\text{k}\Omega$, $R_2 = 27\,\text{k}\Omega$ (giving $R_B = R_1 /\!/ R_2 \simeq 22\,\text{k}\Omega$) and $R_C = 6.8\,\text{k}\Omega$.
For the design value of quiescent collector current of 1 mA, the value of g_{fe} for the BJT must be $\simeq 40$ mS from equation 3.63.
Knowing $h_{fe} = 200$ and $g_{fe} \simeq 40$ mS enables the input resistance h_{ie} of the transistor to be

estimated using equation 3.62,

$$h_{ie} \simeq \frac{h_{fe}}{g_{fe}} \simeq \frac{200}{40\ \text{mS}} = 5\ \text{k}\Omega$$

Then, from equations 3.65, 3.77, 3.79 and 3.71

$$A_{v(amp)} = -g_{fe}R_C = -(40\ \text{mS})(6.8\ \text{k}\Omega) = -272$$

indicating that the amplitude of v_o is 272 times that of v_i, the negative sign indicating that v_o is inverted relative to v_i, that is, there is a phase shift of 180° (half a cycle) between v_o and v_i.

$$A_{i(amp)} = \frac{h_{fe}R_B}{R_B + h_{ie}} \simeq \frac{(200)(22\ \text{k}\Omega)}{(22\ \text{k}\Omega)+(5\ \text{k}\Omega)} = 163$$

indicating that the amplitude of i_o is 163 times that of i_i.

$$R_{i(amp)} = \frac{h_{ie}R_B}{h_{ie} + R_B} \simeq \frac{(5\ \text{k}\Omega)(22\ \text{k}\Omega)}{(5\ \text{k}\Omega)+(22\ \text{k}\Omega)} \simeq 4\ \text{k}\Omega$$

$$R_{o(amp)} = R_C = 6.8\ \text{k}\Omega$$

When driven from a 600 Ω source, there will be a potential division of $4\ \text{k}\Omega/(4\ \text{k}\Omega + 600\ \Omega) \simeq 0.87$ at the input due to R_{os}, $R_{i(amp)}$ (figure 3.11a). Similarly when the output is connected to a 10 kΩ external load, there will be a potential division of $10\ \text{k}\Omega/(10\ \text{k}\Omega + 6.8\ \text{k}\Omega) \simeq 0.6$ at the output due to $R_{o(amp)}$, R_L (figure 3.11a).
The overall gain for this arrangement is therefore

$$A_{v(sys)} \simeq (-272)(0.87)(0.6) = -142$$

Note that the overall gain is substantially less than that of the isolated amplifier because of potential division at input and output.

Graphical analysis

Determination of small-signal gain using graphical load line techniques (section 1.2.2) is not as convenient as numerical analysis using an ac model of the transistor but it does have the advantage of being more illustrative.

Figure 3.12a shows the output loop of a BJT amplifier circuit labelled with bias components (upper case symbols) and signal components (lower case) of voltage and current. As far as static (dc) operation is concerned, C_B is an open circuit and thus is omitted from the *static* model (figure 3.12b). It can be seen that the total resistance in series with the output terminals of the BJT is $(R_C + R_E)$ and so construction of the *static* (*dc*) *load line* on the output characteristics involves the coordinate $[0, V_{CC}/(R_C + R_E)]$ on the I_C-axis in place of $(0, V_{CC}/R_C)$ in the basic case of figure 3.1a. The Q-point is then at the point of intersection of the load line and the output characteristic corresponding to the applied bias I_B or V_{BE} (figure 3.12d).

In terms of the ac performance in response to an input signal v_i, except when v_i is of low frequency (sections 3.3 and 4.3), the low reactance of C_B removes the effect of R_E and so the *dynamic* model is as shown in figure 3.12c, the V_{CC} power supply being an effective short circuit to the ac signal (section 3.3). The resistance in series with the BJT as far as the ac signal is concerned is therefore simply R_C and the corresponding *dynamic* (*ac*) *load line* is then drawn through Q with a slope of $-1/R_C$ as in figure 3.12d. Application of the ac signal v_i causes the operating point of the circuit to move along the dynamic load line about Q.

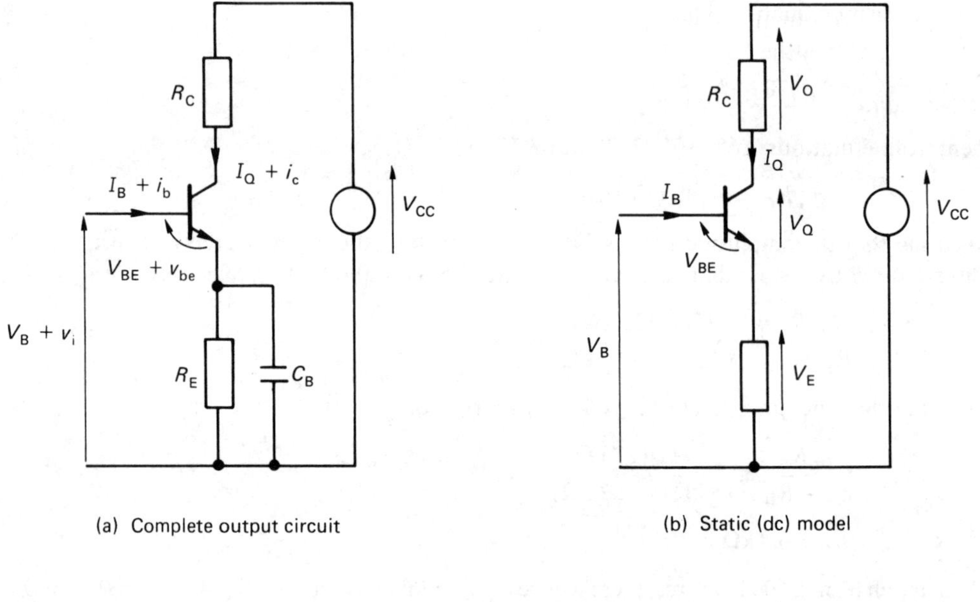

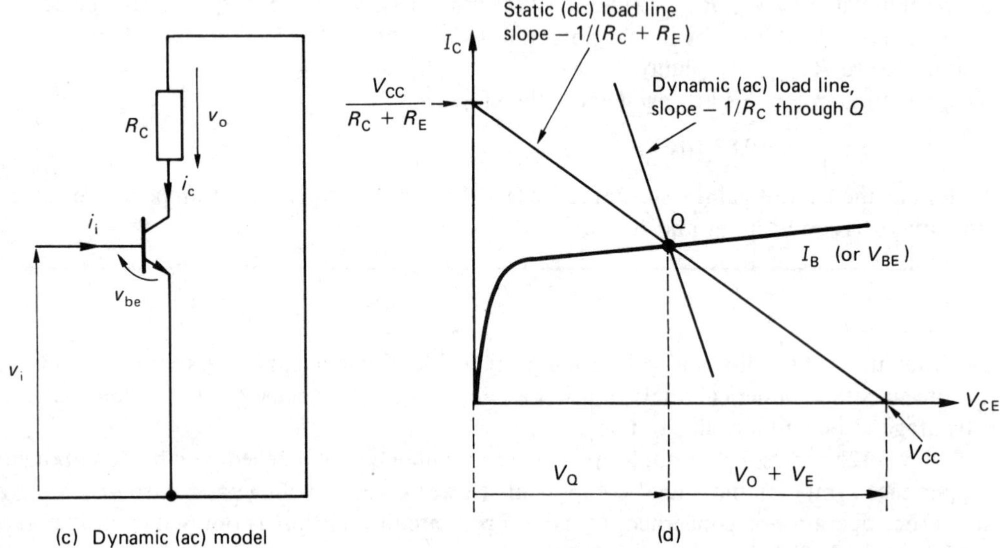

Figure 3.12 Static and dynamic load lines

Example 3.10: Use of graphical techniques to investigate the small-signal performance of an amplifier

To determine the mid-frequency voltage gain of the amplifier designed in example 3.3 using load line techniques.

Figure 3.13 shows the load line construction on the output characteristics of the BJT. For $V_{CC} = 15$ V and circuit values of $R_E = 2.2$ kΩ and $R_C = 6.8$ kΩ, the dc load line is drawn between the coordinates $V_{CC}/(R_C + R_E) = 15\ \text{V}/(6.8\ \text{k}\Omega + 2.2\ \text{k}\Omega) = 1.67\ \text{mA}$ on the I_C-axis and $V_{CC} = 15\ \text{V}$ on the V_{CE}-axis.

The Q-point is then at $V_{CE} = V_Q = 6\ \text{V}$, $I_C = I_Q = 1\ \text{mA}$ from the intersection of the dc load line with the $V_{BE} = 0.6\ \text{V}$ (base–emitter static voltage used in example 3.3) output characteristic. Having established the Q-point position, the ac load line XX of slope $-1/R_C\ (= -1/6.8\ \text{k}\Omega)$ is drawn through Q.

Consider the situation when a sinusoidal input signal of amplitude 5 mV is applied to the circuit. This will cause the operating point to move up and down the ac load line about Q between points A and B, where A is the intercept of the ac load line with the 0.6 V + 5 mV (= 605 mV) BJT characteristic and B is the corresponding intercept with the 0.6 V − 5 mV (= 595 mV) characteristic.

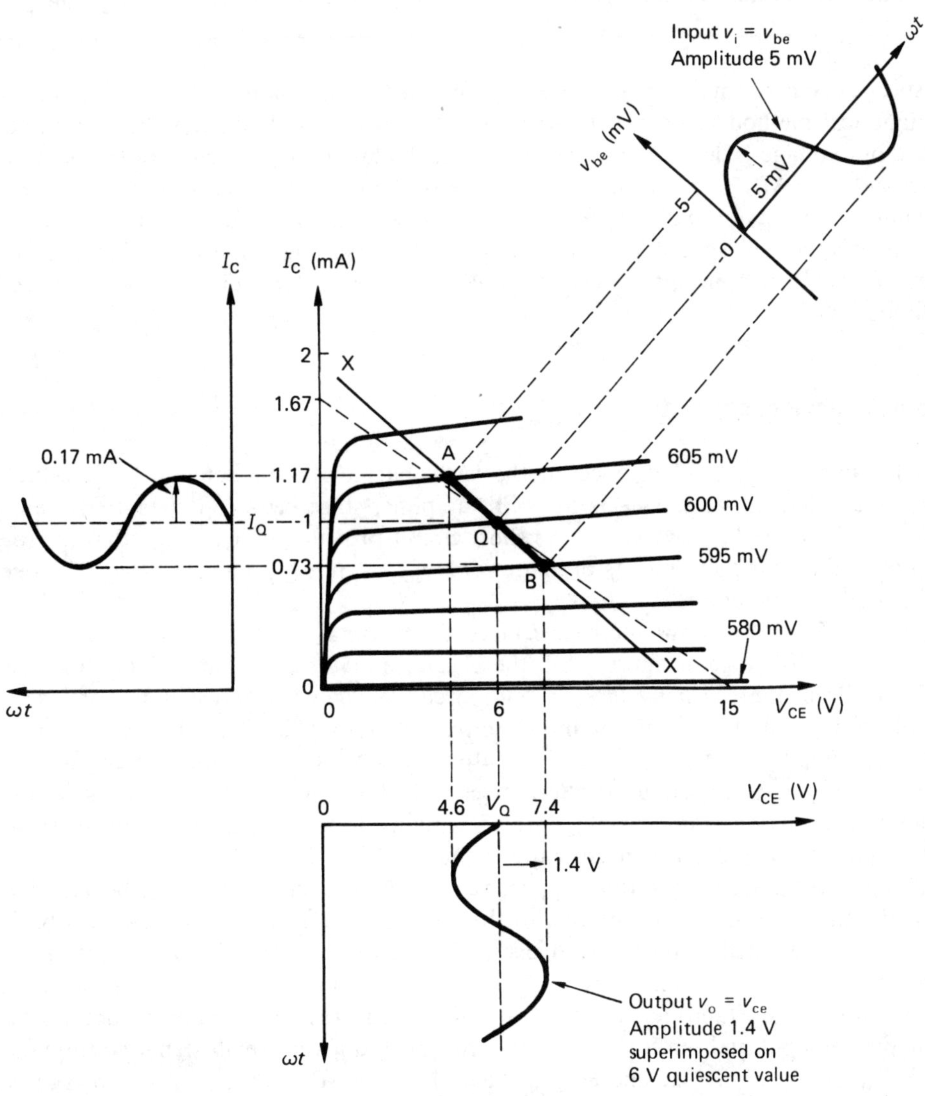

Figure 3.13 Graphical investigation of the small-signal mid-frequency voltage gain of a BJT amplifier

Projection of the range AB on to the V_{CE} and I_C axes shows that the signal component of the collector–emitter voltage v_{ce} has an amplitude of 1.4 V and the signal component of the collector current i_c has an amplitude of 170 μA.

With an output signal voltage amplitude of 1.4 V for an input signal amplitude of 5 mV:

$$\text{small-signal voltage gain} = \frac{1.4\ \text{V}}{5\ \text{mV}} = 280$$

Comparison of the input and output waveforms in figure 3.13 shows that as v_i rises, v_o falls so that there is a phase shift of half a cycle between the waveforms, that is, v_o is magnified but *inverted* compared with v_i; thus

$$A_{v(amp)} = -280$$

This value corresponds to the figure of -272 obtained by numerical techniques in example 3.9.

An aspect of ac performance that is readily illustrated using graphical techniques but not by the numerical method using a network model, is distortion. In figure 3.13 the amplitude of the input voltage is deliberately chosen so that the excursion of the operating point along the ac load line (AB) is only a small proportion of the range between saturation and cut-off as required for *small-signal* operation. In this case the BJT output characteristics are approximately equally spaced for equal changes of V_{BE} resulting in low distortion. Figure 3.14 illustrates the distortion introduced by non-linear characteristics or large input signal amplitude.

3.5 Single-stage configurations

The BJT amplifier stage developed in the early part of this chapter and reproduced in figure 3.15a is termed a *common-emitter* (CE) amplifier stage because the emitter terminal is common to input and output via the ac short circuit provided by C_B. Note that the second subscript in the BJT *h*-parameters of figure 3.9d, h_{ie}, h_{re}, h_{fe}, h_{oe}, indicates that they refer to the CE mode of operation.

Figures 3.15b and c show alternative methods of using the BJT as an amplifier. In the *common-base* (CB) stage of figure 3.15b the base terminal is common to input and output, via C_B, while in the *common-collector* (CC) circuit of figure 3.15c the collector resistor is omitted and the collector is then common to input and output via the ac short circuit provided by the V_{CC} supply. In the CC circuit the output voltage is taken from the emitter resistor *which is not bypassed*; the circuit is alternatively called an *emitter follower* because as output and input voltages differ only by V_{BE}, which remains approximately constant at 0.6 V, the output voltage *follows* changes in the input voltage.

Although the three configurations appear very different, each has the base bias established by R_1, R_2 and each has R_E in series with the emitter. The arrangements are thus basically the same as represented by figure 3.15d, except for the CC configuration $R_C = 0$, the essential difference being which terminals are designated as input and which as output. In each case the Q-point must be established in the active region to ensure linear operation but the different designation of input and output in each case results in different small-signal performance as regards $A_{v(amp)}$, $A_{i(amp)}$, $R_{i(amp)}$ and $R_{o(amp)}$. Analysis of the CB and CC stages follows the same pattern as for the CE stage considered in section 3.4.2. The ac model of the circuit is first

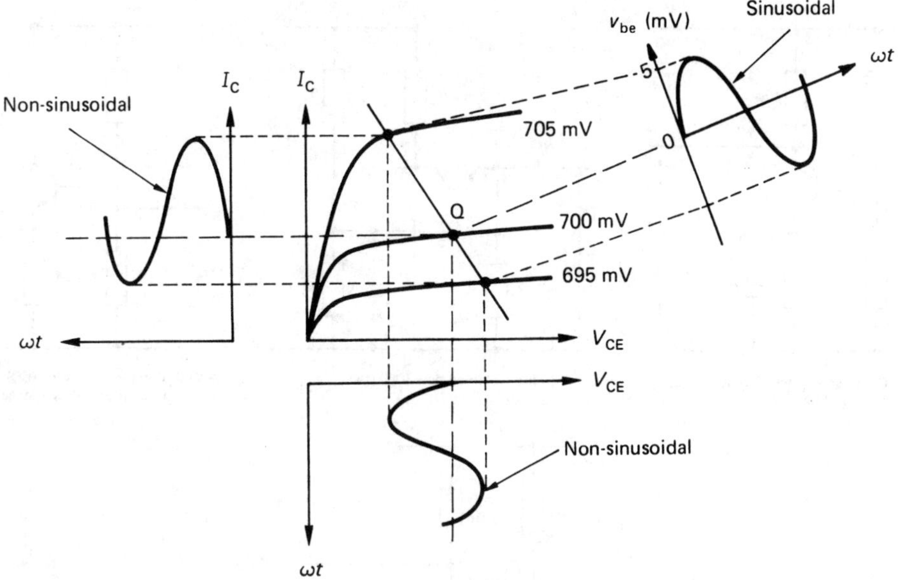

(a) Distortion caused by a non-linear relationship between I_C and V_{BE} along the load line

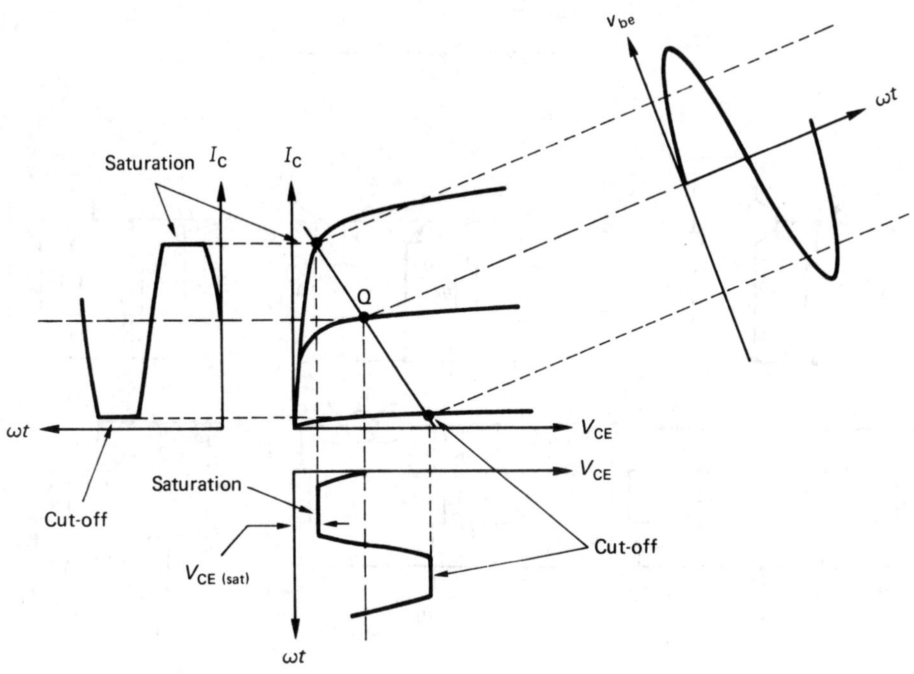

(b) Severe distortion caused by excessive input amplitude or a poorly positioned Q-point.

Figure 3.14 Graphical analysis illustrates signal distortion

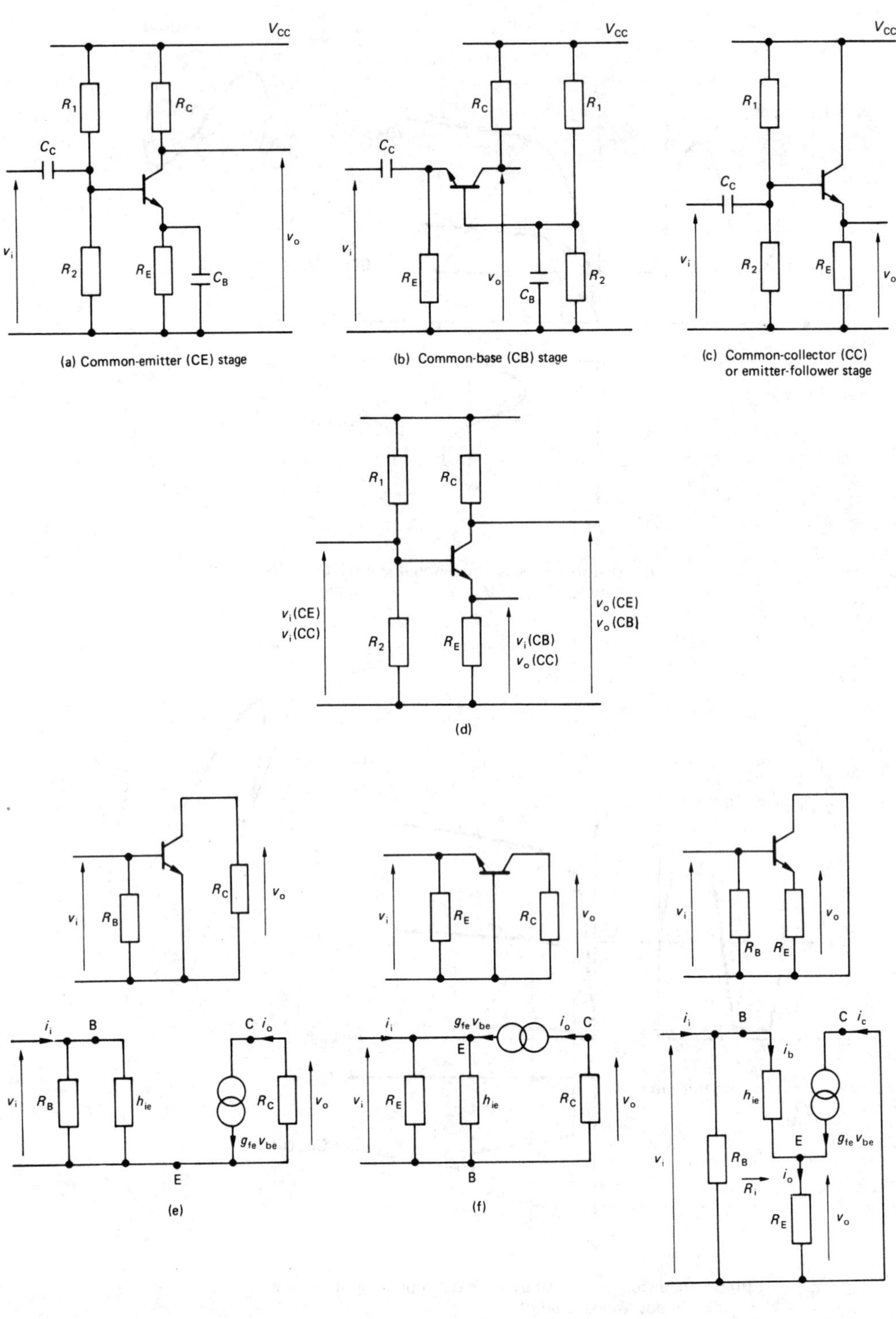

Figure 3.15 Amplifier configurations

created by treating the capacitors and the dc power supply as ac short circuits, then the BJT is represented by its small-signal model. The resulting linear model is then analysed to determine the gains and input, output resistances of the circuit. This procedure is used in sections 3.4.2 and 3.4.3 for the CE circuit, the ac model being reproduced in figure 3.15e.

Small-signal performance of the CB stage at mid frequencies

The ac model representing small-signal performance of the CB stage is developed in figure 3.15f using the simplified BJT model of figure 3.9c and noting that $r_{b'e} \simeq h_{ie}$ from equation 3.59. From figure 3.15f

$$i_o = g_{fe} v_{be} \qquad \text{where} \qquad v_{be} = -v_i \tag{3.94}$$

$$v_o = -i_o R_C \tag{3.95}$$

$$v_i = (i_i + g_{fe} v_{be})(R_E /\!/ h_{ie}) \tag{3.96}$$

from which

$$v_o = -(-g_{fe} v_i) R_C$$

giving

$$A_{v(amp)} = \frac{v_o}{v_i} = +g_{fe} R_C \tag{3.97}$$

The positive sign in equation 3.97 shows that v_o is in phase with v_i in contrast to equation 3.65 for the CE circuit.
Combining equations 3.94 and 3.96

$$v_i = (i_i - g_{fe} v_i)(R_E /\!/ h_{ie})$$

from which

$$v_i[1 + g_{fe}(R_E /\!/ h_{ie})] = i_i(R_E /\!/ h_{ie}) \tag{3.98}$$

Substituting for v_i from equation 3.98 into 3.94 gives

$$i_o = -g_{fe} v_i = -g_{fe}\left[\frac{i_i(R_E /\!/ h_{ie})}{1 + g_{fe}(R_E /\!/ h_{ie})}\right] \tag{3.99}$$

from which

$$A_{i(amp)} = \frac{i_o}{i_i} = \frac{-g_{fe}(R_E /\!/ h_{ie})}{1 + g_{fe}(R_E /\!/ h_{ie})} \simeq -1 \qquad \text{as} \qquad g_{fe}(R_E /\!/ h_{ie}) \gg 1 \tag{3.100}$$

From equation 3.98

$$R_{i(amp)} = \frac{v_i}{i_i} = \frac{(R_E /\!/ h_{ie})}{1 + g_{fe}(R_E /\!/ h_{ie})} \simeq \frac{1}{g_{fe}} \qquad \text{as} \qquad g_{fe}(R_E /\!/ h_{ie}) \gg 1 \tag{3.101}$$

Note 3.2: Determination of output resistance

The value of the small-signal output resistance of an amplifier $R_{o(amp)}$ is important when the circuit is required to drive an external load R_L as in figure 3.11 because the output voltage developed across R_L depends on the relative values of $R_{o(amp)}$ and R_L.

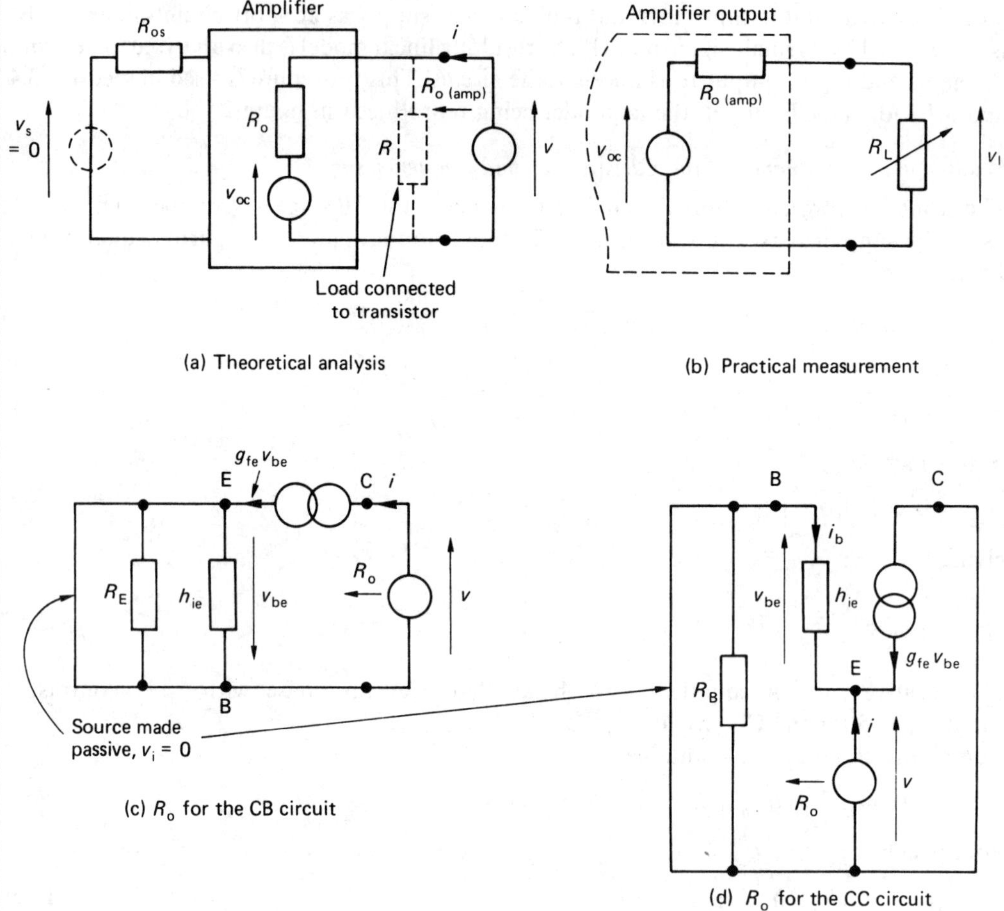

Figure 3.16 Determination of output resistance

Theoretical analysis

$R_{o(amp)}$ is made up of the output resistance of the transistor R_o and the load R connected to the transistor (figure 3.16a) where R is the collector resistor R_C in CE and CB circuits and the emitter resistor R_E in a CC circuit.

In figure 3.16a, if the source is made passive, that is, v_s is reduced to zero, the 'generated' voltage v_{oc} is also zero and $R_{o(amp)}$ is then given by the parallel combination of R_o and R.

Thus, theoretical determination of $R_{o(amp)}$ using the small-signal model of the amplifier involves

(1) making $v_s = 0$ (source resistance R_{os}, if significant, is left in the model),
(2) removing the load R on the transistor, and
(3) applying an external voltage source v to the *output*.

The output resistance of the transistor R_o is then given by the ratio v/i where i is the current *driven into the output terminals*.
$R_{o(amp)}$ is then given by $R_o /\!/ R$.

Practical measurement

The output of an amplifier may be represented by the model of figure 3.16b where v_{oc} is the open-circuit output voltage, that is, the output voltage obtained when no external load is connected.

Having measured v_{oc} using a voltmeter or oscilloscope, a variable external load is connected to the output of the amplifier and its value adjusted until v_l is a value $v_{oc}/2$ at which point

$$R_{o(amp)} = R_L$$

since $v_l = v_{oc}\left(\dfrac{R_L}{R_L + R_{o(amp)}}\right)$ by potential division.

With reference to note 3.2, R_o for the CB circuit can be determined as shown in figure 3.16c. Considering the complete small-signal model for the CB arrangement (figure 3.15f), if R_C is removed and the source made passive, v_i is zero and so $v_{be} = 0$ and in turn the current $g_{fe}v_{be}\,(=i)$ is also zero, resulting in the model of figure 3.16c. It has been assumed for simplicity here that the source resistance R_{os} is very low so that v_i can be replaced by a short circuit.

With $i = 0$:

$$R_o = \frac{v}{i} = \infty$$

and so

$$R_{o(amp)} = R_o /\!/ R_C \text{ (note 3.2)} = \infty /\!/ R_C = R_C \tag{3.102}$$

Example 3.11: Small-signal performance of the basic common-base BJT stage

For the same resistance component values as those calculated for a quiescent collector current of 1 mA in example 3.3, calculate the mid-frequency values of $A_{v(amp)}$, $A_{i(amp)}$, $R_{i(amp)}$ and $R_{o(amp)}$ if the circuit is connected in the form of a common-base amplifier (figure 3.15b). As in example 3.9, the BJT has a small-signal CE current gain h_{fe} of 200.

The relevant resistance values (example 3.3) are $R_E = 2.2\,\text{k}\Omega$ and $R_C = 6.8\,\text{k}\Omega$.
From example 3.9, with $I_C = 1$ mA and $h_{fe} = 200$, the values of g_{fe} and h_{ie} are approximately 40 mS and 5 kΩ respectively.
Then, from equation 3.97:

$$A_{v(amp)} = +g_{fe}R_C = +(40\,\text{mS})(6.8\,\text{k}\Omega) = +272$$

Note that this positive result means that, in contrast to the CE stage, v_o and v_i are in-phase for the CB circuit.
With $R_E = 2.2\,\text{k}\Omega$ and $h_{ie} = 5\,\text{k}\Omega$:

$$R_E /\!/ h_{ie} = \frac{R_E h_{ie}}{R_E + h_{ie}} = \frac{(2.2\,\text{k}\Omega)(5\,\text{k}\Omega)}{(2.2\,\text{k}\Omega) + (5\,\text{k}\Omega)} \simeq 1.5\,\text{k}\Omega$$

then, from equation 3.100:

$$A_{i(amp)} = \frac{-(40\ \text{mS})(1.5\ \text{k}\Omega)}{1+(40\ \text{mS})(1.5\ \text{k}\Omega)} = \frac{-60}{61} = -0.98$$

so that the current gain of the isolated CB amplifier is approximately unity and i_o, as defined in the model of figure 3.15f, is out-of-phase with i_i.
From equation 3.101:

$$R_{i(amp)} = \frac{1.5\ \text{k}\Omega}{1+(40\ \text{mS})(1.5\ \text{k}\Omega)} \simeq 25\ \Omega$$

while

$$R_{o(amp)} = R_C = 6.8\ \text{k}\Omega$$

Notice that $R_{i(amp)}$ for the CB circuit is very small in comparison with that for the CE circuit (4 kΩ, example 3.9) while $R_{o(amp)}$ for the two circuits have the same value.

Small-signal performance of the CC (emitter follower) stage at mid-frequencies

Figure 3.15g gives the small-signal model of emitter-follower performance at mid-frequencies using the simplified BJT model of figure 3.9c, noting that $r_{b'e} \simeq h_{ie}$ from equation 3.59. In the circuit the emitter resistor is the load on the transistor (in the absence of an external load) and so the output current i_o follows through R_E.
From figure 3.15g:

$$i_o = i_c + i_b \tag{3.103}$$

$$i_c = g_{fe} v_{be} \tag{3.104}$$

$$v_{be} = i_b h_{ie} \tag{3.105}$$

$$v_{be} = v_i - v_o \tag{3.106}$$

$$v_i = i_b h_{ie} + i_o R_E \tag{3.107}$$

$$i_i = \frac{v_i}{R_B /\!/ R_i} \quad \text{where} \quad R_i = \frac{v_i}{i_b} \tag{3.108}$$

$$v_o = i_o R_E \tag{3.109}$$

Combining equations 3.103, 3.104, 3.105, 3.106 and 3.108:

$$v_o = (i_c + i_b) R_E = \left(g_{fe} v_{be} + \frac{v_{be}}{h_{ie}} \right) R_E = (g_{fe} + 1/h_{ie}) R_E (v_i - v_o)$$

from which

$$A_{v(amp)} = \frac{v_o}{v_i} = \frac{(g_{fe} + 1/h_{ie}) R_E}{1 + (g_{fe} + 1/h_{ie}) R_E}$$

$$\simeq \frac{g_{fe} R_E}{1 + g_{fe} R_E} \quad \text{as} \quad g_{fe} \gg \frac{1}{h_{ie}}, \quad \text{that is,} \quad h_{fe} \gg 1$$

$$\simeq 1 \quad \text{as} \quad g_{fe} R_E \gg 1 \tag{3.110}$$

Notice that as the base–emitter voltage (bias V_{BE} + signal v_{be}) remains approximately constant at about 0.6 V, the signal component v_{be} must be small. This shows, from equation 3.106, that $v_o \simeq v_i$ leading to the above result for small-signal voltage gain.
From equations 3.103, 3.104, 3.105 and 3.107

$$v_i = i_b h_{ie} + [g_{fe}(i_b h_{ie}) + i_b] R_E = [R_E + (1 + g_{fe} R_E) h_{ie}] i_b$$

giving

$$R_i = \frac{v_i}{i_b} = h_{ie} + (1 + g_{fe} h_{ie}) R_E \simeq g_{fe} h_{ie} R_E = h_{fe} R_E \tag{3.111}$$

as $g_{fe} h_{ie} \gg 1$, $g_{fe} R_E \gg 1$ and $g_{fe} = h_{fe}/h_{ie}$ from equation 3.62. Then

$$R_{i(amp)} = R_i /\!/ R_B = h_{fe} R_E /\!/ R_B \tag{3.112}$$

Combining equation 3.103, 3.104 and 3.105 gives

$$i_o = g_{fe}(i_b h_{ie}) + i_b$$

from which

$$\frac{i_o}{i_b} = 1 + g_{fe} h_{ie} \simeq g_{fe} h_{ie} \qquad \text{as} \qquad g_{fe} h_{ie} \gg 1, \text{ that is, } h_{fe} \gg 1 \tag{3.113}$$

By current division between R_B and R_i at the input (figure 3.15g):

$$\frac{i_b}{i_i} = \frac{R_B}{R_B + R_i} \tag{3.114}$$

from which

$$A_{i(amp)} = \frac{i_o}{i_i} = \left(\frac{i_o}{i_b}\right)\left(\frac{i_b}{i_i}\right) \simeq g_{fe} h_{ie}\left(\frac{R_B}{R_B + R_i}\right) = h_{fe}\left(\frac{R_B}{R_B + R_i}\right) \tag{3.115}$$

where R_i is given by equation 3.111, $g_{fe} h_{ie}$ being equal to h_{fe} from equation 3.62.
The output resistance of the transistor in the CC stage can be found using the theoretical technique of note 3.2 whereby in the model of figure 3.15g, v_i is reduced to zero (replaced by a short circuit) and R_E is removed, resulting in the model of figure 3.16d, from which

$$i = -(g_{fe} v_{be} + i_b) \tag{3.116}$$

But $i_b = v_{be}/h_{ie}$ and, with v_i replaced by a short circuit on the assumption that the source resistance R_{os} is low, $v_{be} = -v$ where v is the voltage applied to the output.
Thus, from equation 3.116

$$i = -v_{be}(g_{fe} + 1/h_{ie}) = v(g_{fe} + 1/h_{ie})$$

from which

$$R_o = \frac{v}{i} = \frac{1}{g_{fe} + 1/h_{ie}} \simeq \frac{1}{g_{fe}} \tag{3.117}$$

since $g_{fe} \gg 1/h_{ie}$, that is, $h_{fe} \gg 1$.
Then $R_{o(amp)} = R_o /\!/ R_E$ (note 3.2)

$$\simeq \frac{1}{g_{fe}} /\!/ R_E \tag{3.118}$$

Example 3.12: Design and small-signal analysis of a basic common-collector (emitter follower) stage

Select suitable component values for the emitter-follower circuit of figure 3.15c for a 15 V power supply and a quiescent collector current of approximately 1 mA assuming h_{FE} for the BJT is 200. Determine the small-signal performance parameters $A_{v(amp)}$, $A_{i(amp)}$, $R_{i(amp)}$ and $R_{o(amp)}$ of the circuit assuming the small-signal CE current gain of the BJT (h_{fe}) is 220.

Static design

Selection of resistance values follows a similar procedure to that of example 3.3 for a common-emitter circuit although with no collector resistor, V_{CC} is shared approximately equally between the output of the BJT and R_E.

For a high value of h_{FE}, $I_E \simeq I_C$ and so $I_E \simeq 1$ mA, then, for a voltage of $V_{CC}/2$ across R_E

$$R_E = \frac{V_{CC}/2}{I_E} = \frac{7.5\text{ V}}{1\text{ mA}} = 7.5\text{ k}\Omega$$

enabling either 6.8 kΩ of 8.2 kΩ to be selected from the E12 series (appendix D). The higher value 8.2 kΩ is chosen to give marginally lower power dissipation; I_E will therefore be approximately 7.5 V/8.2 kΩ $\simeq$ 0.91 mA.

With the voltage across R_E approximately 7.5 V, the R_1, R_2 potential divider must provide 7.5 V + 0.6 V = 8.1 V to bias the BJT base to ensure active region operation.

For $I_C \simeq 0.91$ mA and $h_{FE} = 200$, the static base current I_B $(= I_C/h_{FE})$ is about 4.6 μA and, as in example 3.3, $(R_1 + R_2)$ is then chosen to make the current drawn by the potential divider about $20I_B$ to provide a stable bias; this results in $R_1 + R_2$ of the order of 163 kΩ.

For a base bias voltage of 8.1 V, from equation 3.21:

$$\frac{R_1}{R_2} = \frac{V_{CC}}{V_B} - 1 = \frac{15\text{ V}}{8.1\text{ V}} - 1 \simeq 0.85$$

Combining $R_1 + R_2 = 163$ kΩ and $R_1 \simeq 0.85R_2$ gives $R_1 \simeq 75$ kΩ and $R_2 \simeq 88$ kΩ, enabling E12 values 68 kΩ and 82 kΩ to be selected for R_1 and R_2 respectively.

Small-signal analysis

$R_E = 8.2$ kΩ, $R_1 = 68$ kΩ and $R_2 = 82$ kΩ.
Thus

$$R_B = R_1 /\!/ R_2 = \frac{(68\text{ k}\Omega)(82\text{ k}\Omega)}{(68\text{ k}\Omega) + (82\text{ k}\Omega)} \simeq 37.2\text{ k}\Omega$$

From equations 3.62 and 3.63, for $I_C \simeq 0.91$ mA and $h_{fe} = 220$:

$$g_{fe} = 40(I_C) \simeq 40(0.91\text{ mA}) \simeq 36\text{ mS} \qquad \text{and} \qquad h_{ie} \simeq h_{fe}/g_{fe} \simeq 220/(36\text{ mS}) \simeq 6\text{ k}\Omega$$

Then from equation 3.110

$$A_{v(amp)} = \frac{v_o}{v_i} = \frac{(g_{fe} + 1/h_{ie})R_E}{1 + (g_{fe} + 1/h_{ie})R_E} \simeq \frac{[36\text{ mS} + 1/(6\text{ k}\Omega)]8.2\text{ k}\Omega}{1 + [36\text{ mS} + 1/(6\text{ k}\Omega)]8.2\text{ k}\Omega}$$

$$= \frac{(36.17\text{ mS})(8.2\text{ k}\Omega)}{1 + (36.17\text{ mS})(8.2\text{ k}\Omega)} = \frac{296.6}{1 + 296.6} = 0.997$$

From equation 3.111, the input resistance of the transistor, that is without the bias resistors R_1, R_2, is

$$R_i \simeq h_{fe} R_E = (220)(8.2\ \text{k}\Omega) \simeq 1.8\ \text{M}\Omega$$

and then, from equation 3.112, the input resistance of the complete circuit

$$R_{i(amp)} = R_i /\!/ R_B \simeq (1.8\ \text{M}\Omega) /\!/ (37.2\ \text{k}\Omega) = \frac{(1.8\ \text{M}\Omega)(37.2\ \text{k}\Omega)}{(1.8\ \text{M}\Omega) + (37.2\ \text{k}\Omega)} \simeq 36.4\ \text{k}\Omega$$

Note that $R_{i(amp)}$ is dominated by the bias resistors and that these resistors degrade the fundamentally high input resistance of this arrangement. Section 6.1 shows how this degradation can be reduced considerably by a technique termed bootstrapping.
The small-signal current gain $A_{i(amp)}$ is given (equation 3.115) by

$$h_{fe}\left(\frac{R_B}{R_B + R_i}\right) \simeq 220\left(\frac{37.2\ \text{k}\Omega}{37.2\ \text{k}\Omega + 1.8\ \text{M}\Omega}\right) \simeq 4.5$$

Here again the effect of the bias resistors greatly degrades performance because of current division at the input between R_B and the input resistance of the transistor.
From equation 3.118, the small-signal output resistance $R_{o(amp)}$ is given approximately by

$$\frac{1}{g_{fe}} \Big/\!\!\Big/ R_E \simeq \frac{1}{36\ \text{mS}} \Big/\!\!\Big/ 8.2\ \text{k}\Omega \simeq 28\ \Omega /\!/ 8.2\ \text{k}\Omega = \frac{(28\ \Omega)(8.2\ \text{k}\Omega)}{(28\ \Omega) + (8.2\ \text{k}\Omega)} \simeq 28\ \Omega$$

Note that in contrast to the CB circuit of example 3.11, the input resistance of the emitter follower is high and its output resistance low.

Selection of the input coupling capacitor C_C depends on $R_{i(amp)}$ and the minimum frequency f_{min} at which the circuit is required to operate. If f_{min} is 50 Hz then from equation 3.45

$$C_C \geqslant \frac{1}{2\pi(50\ \text{Hz})\left(\dfrac{36.4\ \text{k}\Omega}{10}\right)} = 0.87\ \mu\text{F}$$

enabling a value of 1 μF to be selected from the E6 range.

Table 3.1 lists the approximate expressions for the small-signal performance parameters of the three basic BJT amplifier configurations for mid-frequency operation at which all capacitive effects are negligible. The bracketed numerical values are those obtained for the specific circuits analysed in examples 3.9, 3.11 and 3.12 and are listed for comparison purposes.

CE and CB circuits both provide substantial voltage amplification, the CE configuration inverting the signal while the CB arrangement provides non-inverting amplification. The CC (emitter-follower) circuit has a voltage gain of only unity and so is of no use for voltage amplification. Of the three configurations, only the CE circuit offers high voltage gain *and* high current gain and so it is this arrangement that offers the highest power gain.

The CE stage has mid-range values of input and output resistance which is a disadvantage in many cases. When used as a voltage amplifier, unless the source resistance is very low and the external load very high, there is considerable loss of overall gain $A_{v(sys)}$ because of potential division at the input and output (example 3.9). Similarly, there is loss of gain when used as a current amplifier unless R_{os} is very high and R_L very low. The emitter-follower is very useful as a *buffer* circuit to avoid substantial loss of voltage gain, making use of its high input

Table 3.1 Comparative small-signal performance of CE, CB and CC single-stage BJT amplifiers at mid-frequencies

	CE	*CB*	*CC (emitter-follower)*
Voltage gain, $A_{v(amp)}$	$-g_{fe}R_C$ (−272)	$+g_{fe}R_C$ (+272)	$\simeq +1$ (+0.997)
Current gain, $A_{i(amp)}$	$\dfrac{h_{fe}R_B}{R_B+h_{ie}}$ (+163)	$\simeq -1$ (−0.98)	$\dfrac{h_{fe}R_B}{R_B+h_{fe}R_E}$ (+4.5)
Typical power gain, $A_{p(amp)}$ (equation 3.50)	(4.4×10^4)	(267)	(4.5)
Input resistance, $R_{i(amp)}$	$h_{ie}/\!/R_B$ (4 kΩ)	$1/g_{fe}$ (25 Ω)	$h_{fe}R_E/\!/R_B$ (36.4 kΩ)
Output resistance, $R_{o(amp)}$	R_C (6.8 kΩ)	R_C (6.8 kΩ)	$(1/g_{fe})/\!/R_E$ (28 Ω)
Phase relation between v_o and v_i	$-\pi$ rad (out of phase)	0 (in phase)	0 (in phase)
Main applications	General amplification (high gains, particularly power)	Non-inverting voltage amplifier Impedance matching (low $R_{i(amp)}$, high $R_{o(amp)}$)	Current driving (low $R_{o(amp)}$) Impedance matching (high $R_{i(amp)}$, low $R_{o(amp)}$)

Note: The typical numerical values quoted above refer to the specific circuits analysed in examples 3.9, 3.11 and 3.12.

resistance and low output resistance as demonstrated in example 3.13. Correspondingly, the CB circuit is useful in maintaining overall current gain by virtue of its low input resistance and high output resistance. The CB circuit also offers considerable advantages in very high frequency applications as explained in section 4.5.

Example 3.13: Improvement of overall voltage gain using a buffer circuit

Consider the situation where the CE stage of example 3.9 is used to drive a 1 kΩ external load. Compare the overall voltage gain obtained if the CE stage drives the external load directly with that obtained if the emitter-follower of example 3.12 is included as an intermediate buffer.

From example 3.9, the CE stage has a voltage gain $A_{v(amp)}$ of −272 and an output resistance $R_{o(amp)}$ of 6.8 kΩ.
When used to drive the external load directly, the situation may be modelled as in figure 3.17a from which

$$v_o = -272 v_i \left(\frac{1\ \text{k}\Omega}{1\ \text{k}\Omega + 6.8\ \text{k}\Omega} \right)$$

giving an overall voltage gain v_o/v_i of $-272/7.8 \simeq -35$.
If the emitter-follower of example 3.12 is now included at XX as represented in figure 3.17b, the overall gain becomes

$$\frac{v_o}{v_i} = \left(\frac{v_i'}{v_i}\right)\left(\frac{v_o}{v_i'}\right) = \left[-272\left(\frac{36.4\ \text{k}\Omega}{36.4\ \text{k}\Omega + 6.8\ \text{k}\Omega}\right)\right]\left[+0.997\left(\frac{1\ \text{k}\Omega}{1\ \text{k}\Omega + 28\ \Omega}\right)\right] \simeq -222$$

Inclusion of the buffer increases the overall gain magnitude from 35 to 222. This vast improvement is due to the reduced loading on the output of the CE stage provided by the

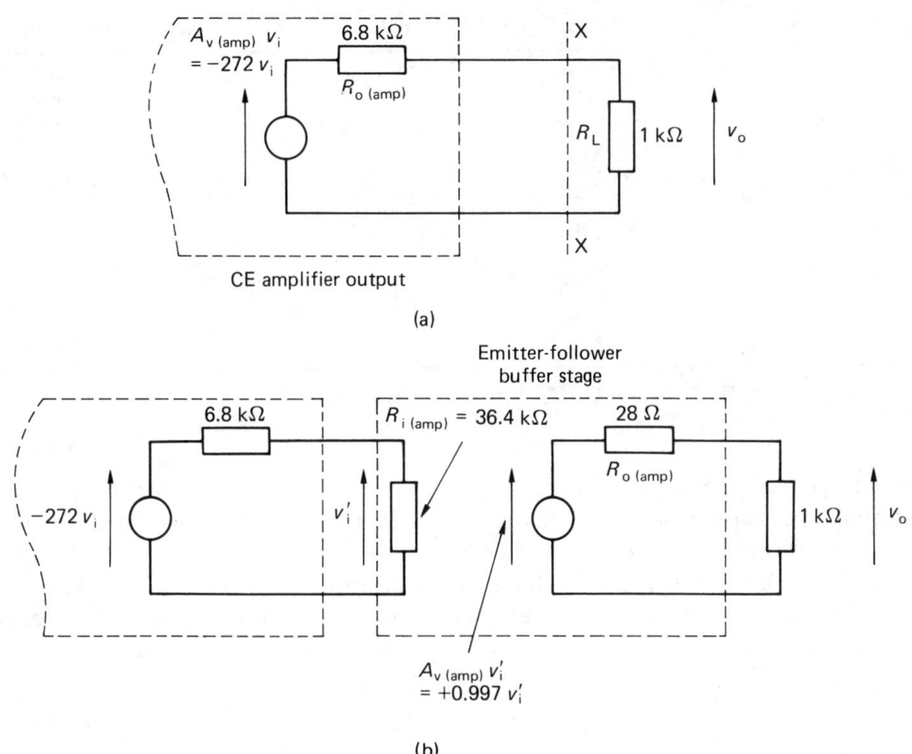

Figure 3.17 Improvement of overall gain using an emitter-follower buffer stage

relatively high input resistance of the emitter-follower, compared with the external load together with the improved current drive capability provided by the emitter-follower due to its low output resistance.

Note: The term *direct* used in this example referring to the connection of the load to the amplifier, means *without inclusion of the buffer stage.* Practical implementation would involve capacitive coupling (section 3.3) to avoid disturbing the static operation of the circuits and consequential change of performance.

Example 3.13 is an example of a *multistage* amplifying arrangement where stages are *cascaded* to provide improved overall performance.

A similar consideration to that presented above for the CE, CB and CC (emitter-follower) BJT configurations applies to the corresponding FET circuits which are termed the common-source (CS), common-gate (CG) and common-drain (CD, source-follower) arrangements. Such a consideration would follow precisely the same procedure as that adopted above for the BJT circuits. The circuits of figure 3.15 would represent the FET arrangements if the BJTs were replaced by FETs, R_C and R_E replaced by R_D and R_S respectively, and the small-signal FET model of figure 3.10c used to represent FET performance.

Subsequent analysis to determine the small-signal performance of the CS, CG and CD circuits follows the same pattern as for the BJT equivalents although in the case of $A_{i(amp)}$ and $R_{i(amp)}$ the analysis is simpler than in the BJT case because of the very high input resistance

Table 3.2 Small-signal performance of CS, CG and CD single-stage FET amplifiers at mid-frequencies

	CS	*CG*	*CD* (*source follower*)
$A_{v(\text{amp})}$	$-g_{fs}R_D$	$+g_{fs}R_D$	$\frac{+g_{fs}R_S}{1+g_{fs}R_S} \simeq +1$
$A_{i(\text{amp})}$	$g_{fs}R_B$	$\frac{-g_{fs}R_S}{1+g_{fs}R_S} \simeq -1$	$\frac{g_{fs}R_B}{1+g_{fs}R_S}$
$R_{i(\text{amp})}$	R_B	$\frac{R_S}{1+g_{fs}R_S} \simeq \frac{1}{g_{fs}}$	R_B
$R_{o(\text{amp})}$	R_D	R_D	$(1/g_{fs}) /\!/ R_S$

Note: R_B is the parallel combination of bias resistances R_1 and R_2.

of FETs. The simplified expressions for $A_{v(\text{amp})}$, $A_{i(\text{amp})}$, $R_{i(\text{amp})}$ and $R_{o(\text{amp})}$ for the three FET configurations are listed in table 3.2. As in the corresponding BJT cases, the CS and CG circuits provide inverting and non-inverting voltage amplification respectively. Only the CS arrangement provides both moderate voltage gain and moderate current gain and so it is the CS circuit that provides the highest power gain of the three arrangements. The CG circuit has low $R_{i(\text{amp})}$ and high $R_{o(\text{amp})}$ while the source-follower (CD circuit) has high $R_{i(\text{amp})}$ and low $R_{o(\text{amp})}$, making both useful for matching applications.

References and further reading

1. M.E. Goodge, *Semiconductor Device Technology* (Macmillan, 1985)
   (a) section 2.2.17,
   (b) section 2.2.26,
   (c) sections 2.2.26 and 2.3.9
2. C.J. Savant, M.S. Roden and G.L. Carpenter, *Electronic Circuit Design*, chapters 2–5 (Benjamin/Cummings, 1987)
3. T.F. Bogart, *Electronic Devices and Circuits*, chapters 4, 5 and 7–9 (Merrill, 1986)
4. F.H. Mitchell, *Introduction to Electronics Design*, chapters 7–9 (Prentice-Hall, 1988)
5. T.L. Floyd, *Electronic Devices*, 2nd edition, chapters 6–9 (Merrill, 1988)
6. C.L. Alley and K.W. Atwood, *Microelectronics*, chapters 5–9 (Prentice-Hall, 1986)
7. M.S. Ghausi, *Electronic Devices and Circuits*, chapters 2–4 (Holt-Saunders, 1985)
8. W.H. Hayt and G.W. Neudeck, *Electronic Circuit Analysis and Design*, 2nd edition, chapters 3–6 (Houghton Mifflin, 1984)
9. G.J. Ritchie, *Transistor Circuit Techniques*, 2nd edition, chapters 2–4 and 7 (Van Nostrand Reinhold, 1987)
10. A.S. Sedra and K.C. Smith, *Microelectronic Circuits*, 2nd edition, chapters 6–8 (Holt, Rinehart and Winston, 1987)
11. P.M. Chirlian, *Analysis and Design of Integrated Electronic Circuits*, 2nd edition, chapters 5, 6 and 12 (Harper and Row/Wiley, 1987)
12. R.J. Maddock and D.M. Calcutt, *Electronics: A Course for Engineers*, chapter 5 (Longman, 1988)
13. R.A. Colclaser, D.A. Neamen and C.F. Hawkins, *Electronic Circuit Analysis*, chapters 4, 10 and 11 (Wiley, 1984)

14. J. Millman and A. Grabel, *Microelectronics*, 2nd edition, chapter 10 (McGraw-Hill, 1988)
15. E.N. Lurch, *Fundamentals of Electronics*, 3rd edition, chapters 4–10 (Wiley, 1981)
16. M. Cirovic, *Basic Electronics*, 2nd edition, chapters 4, 5, 9 and 10 (Prentice-Hall, 1979)
17. C.A. Holt, *Electronic Circuits*, chapters 12, 13, 15 and 17 (Wiley, 1978)
18. S.A. Knight, *Electronics for Higher TEC*, chapters 3, 5 and 6 (Granada, 1983)
19. D.C. Green, *Electronics TEC Level IV*, chapters 1 and 3 (Pitman, 1981)

Tutorial questions

Note: Preferred (E-series) component values are given in appendix D. Answers correspond to rounding to 2 decimal places during calculation.

BJT and FET bias circuit analysis and design

3.1 The BJT in the circuit of figure 3.18 has $h_{FE} = 150$, $V_{BE} = 0.6$ V and negligible leakage; what is the Q-point of the transistor? If the 1 kΩ resistor is replaced by a short circuit, what would be the new Q-point?
[Answers: $I_Q = I_C = 2.93$ mA, $V_Q = V_{CE} = 2.65$ V; 4.27 mA, 3.60 V]

3.2 If BJTs used in the circuit of figure 3.18 have a range of h_{FE} from 100 to 200, what would be the Q-point range?
[Answers: 2.18 mA, 4.53 V to 3.54 mA, 1.13 V]

3.3 For the circuit of figure 3.19, $V_{CC} = 10$ V, $h_{FE} = 150$ and $V_{BE} = 0.6$ V; BJT leakage may be assumed negligible. Select suitable resistance values from the E12 range to establish the Q-point of the BJT at approximately 2 mA, 4 V with a voltage drop of 2 V across the emitter resistor. Check that the values selected provide adequate Q-point stability against change of h_{FE} as indicated by the requirement $R_B \leqslant h_{FE}R_E/10$ where $R_B = R_1 /\!/ R_2$.
[Specimen answers: $R_E = 1$ kΩ, $R_1 = 27$ kΩ, $R_2 = 10$ kΩ, $R_C = 1.8$ kΩ]

3.4 By analysing the static operation of the circuit of figure 3.19, show that the stability factors for change of V_{BE}, I_{CBO} and h_{FE} are, respectively

$$S_{V_{BE}} \simeq -\frac{1}{R_E}, \qquad S_{I_{CBO}} \simeq \frac{R_B}{R_E} + 1$$

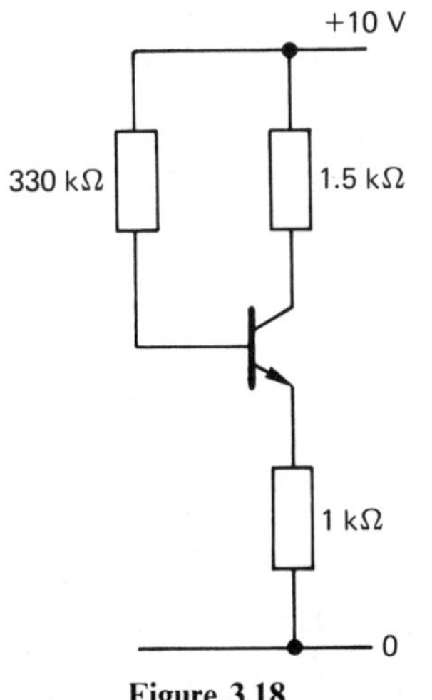

Figure 3.18

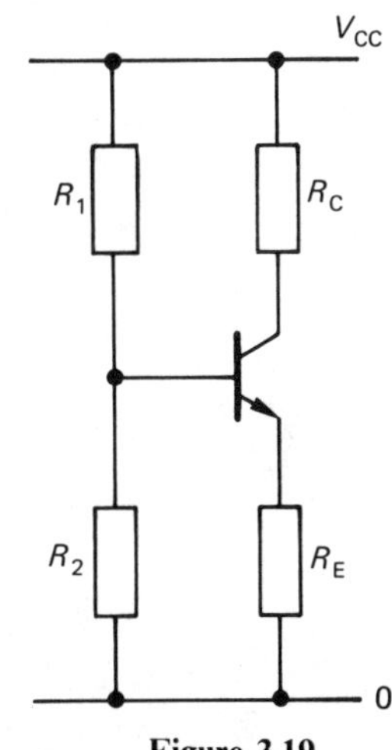

Figure 3.19

and

$$S_{h_{FE}} \simeq \frac{R_B(V_{BB} - V_{BE})}{R_E^2 h_{FE}^2}$$

assuming $R_B \ll h_{FE} R_E$, where $R_B = R_1 /\!/ R_2$. In the case of $S_{h_{FE}}$ the effect of transistor leakage is assumed negligible. Calculate the values of these stability factors for the circuit designed in question 3.3.

[Answers: $S_{V_{BE}} \simeq -1$ mS, $S_{I_{CBO}} \simeq 8.30$, $S_{h_{FE}} \simeq 0.65$ μA]

3.5 Because of a small increase in temperature, the value of V_{BE} in the circuit of question 3.3 reduces by 20 mV while transistor gain h_{FE} and leakage I_{CBO} increase by 10 and 5 nA respectively. Using the stability factor values for this circuit as calculated in question 3.4, determine the change of quiescent collector current due separately to each of these changes. Note the order of significance of the three changes and their significance relative to the value of I_Q used in the design in question 3.3.

[Answers: ΔI_Q due to ΔV_{BE}, Δh_{FE} and ΔI_{CBO} are +20 μA, +6.5 μA, +41.5 nA respectively. All changes negligible ($\leqslant 1$ per cent) compared with $I_Q = 2$ mA, indicating good bias stability]

3.6 The typical transfer characteristic of the JFET in the self bias circuit of figure 3.20 is shown dashed in figure 3.21. It is required to establish the Q-point of the transistor at approximately 2 mA, 4.5 V when V_{DD} is 12 V. Select suitable values for R_S and R_D from the E12 range. Comment on the value of R_G and select a suitable value.

[Specimen answers: 680 Ω, 3.3 kΩ, 1 MΩ]

3.7 In the circuit of figure 3.22, $R_1 = 3.9$ MΩ, $R_2 = 1$ MΩ, $R_D = 1.2$ kΩ and $R_S = 1$ kΩ; power is provided by a 9 V battery. If the transfer characteristic of the JFET is as shown dashed in figure 3.21, determine the Q-point of the transistor. The end-of-life battery voltage is specified as 7 V; what is the corresponding Q-point?

[Answers: 2.8 mA, 2.84 V at $V_{DD} = 9$ V; 2.5 mA, 1.5 V at $V_{DD} = 7$ V]

3.8 Figure 3.21 shows the range of transfer characteristic for a JFET with the typical characteristic shown dashed. This type of JFET is to be used in the circuit of figure 3.22; select suitable E12 resistance values for R_S, R_1, R_2 and R_D to establish a *typical* Q-point

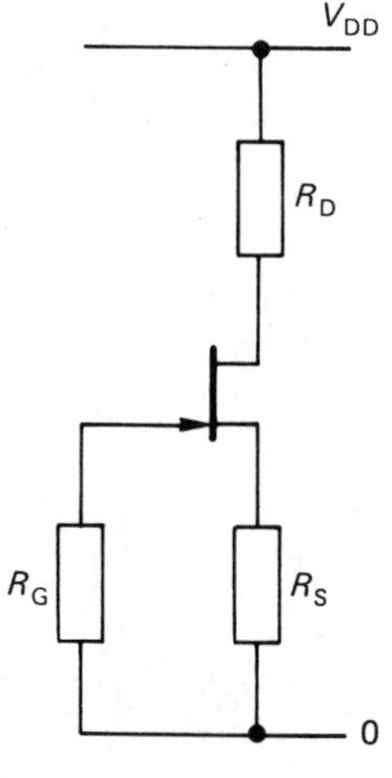

Figure 3.20

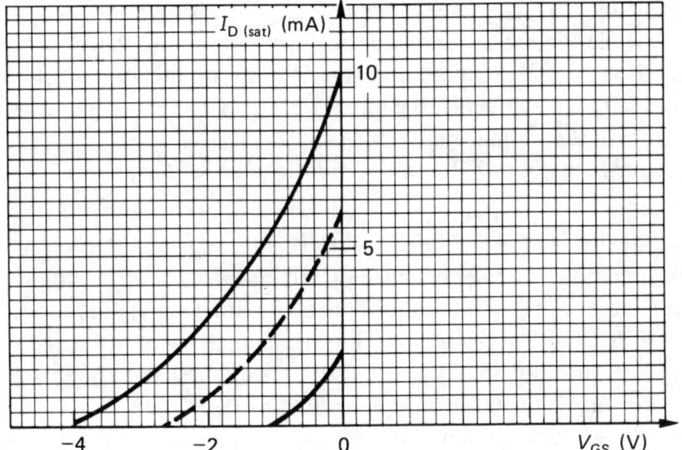

Figure 3.21

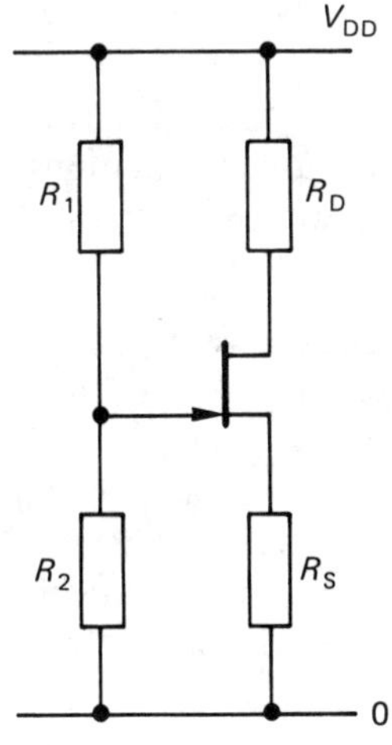

Figure 3.22

of approximately 1 mA, 5 V for $V_{DD} = 15$ V such that the spread of I_D over the max–min range of transfer characteristic does not exceed 400 μA. The input resistance of the circuit when used as an amplifier is not to be less than 1 MΩ.
[Specimen answers: 4.7 kΩ, 8.2 MΩ, 2.2 MΩ, 5.6 kΩ]

Selection of bypass and coupling capacitor values

3.9 It is required to add input coupling and emitter bypass capacitors to the circuit designed in question 3.3 to enable it to be used as a small-signal amplifier (figure 3.6b). If the input resistance h_{ie} of the BJT is 3.5 kΩ at $I_C = 2$ mA and the lowest signal frequency is 30 Hz, select suitable E6 capacitance values.
[Answers: $C_B = 470\ \mu$F, $C_C = 33\ \mu$F]

3.10 In the single-stage FET amplifier of figure 3.6c the resistance values are those selected in question 3.8 while the bypass and coupling capacitors have values of 100 μF and 22 nF respectively. If the FET has a common-source transconductance g_{fs} of 8 mS, estimate the lowest signal frequency at which the amplifier can be used without the circuit capacitors severely reducing the voltage gain.
[Answer: Approximately 42 Hz limited by the effect of C_C]

Small-signal performance of amplifiers at mid-frequencies

3.11 The common-emitter amplifier of figure 3.6b operates from a 10 V supply with a quiescent collector current of 2 mA. What is the value of the small-signal forward transconductance g_{fe} of the BJT? If the corresponding input resistance h_{ie} of the BJT is 3.5 kΩ, estimate the small-signal current gain of the transistor. Using these parameter values calculate the small-signal voltage, current and power gains of the circuit and the input and output resistances, all for mid-frequency operation, the circuit resistance values being those selected in question 3.3.
[Answers: $g_{fe} = 80$ mS, $h_{fe} = 280$, $A_{v(amp)} = -144$, $A_{i(amp)} = 189$, $A_{p(amp)} = 2.72 \times 10^4$, $R_{i(amp)} = 2.37$ kΩ, $R_{o(amp)} = 1.8$ kΩ]

3.12 If the amplifier of question 3.11 is driven from a 600 Ω signal source and the circuit drives a 5 kΩ external load, what would be the *overall* voltage gain obtained?
[Answer: −84.49]

3.13 Since the value of collector resistor R_C in a common-emitter amplifier (figure 3.6b) features in both the setting of the Q-point (equations 3.22 and 3.23) and in the small-signal voltage gain of the amplifier (equation 3.65), it follows that the gain and static conditions must be related.

(a) If 20 per cent of V_{CC} is dropped across R_E for stability purposes and the remainder of V_{CC} is divided equally between R_C and the output terminals of the BJT, derive an expression relating R_C to V_{CC} and I_C.

(b) By combining the result of part (a) above with the expression for the small-signal voltage gain of the circuit in terms of BJT transconductance g_{fe}, show that the mid-frequency voltage gain is proportional to the power supply voltage V_{CC}. Note that this is a significant observation because it means gain is ultimately limited by the power supply voltage.

[Answers: $R_C = 0.4V_{CC}/I_C$, $A_{v(amp)} \simeq -16V_{CC}$]

3.14 Show that the small-signal voltage gain of the circuit of figure 3.23 is approximately $-R_C/R_E$ at frequencies at which C_C provides an effective ac short circuit provided $g_{fe} \gg 1/h_{ie}$ (that is, $h_{fe} \gg 1$, equation 3.62) for the BJT and $g_{fe}R_E \gg 1$. Demonstrate that these approximations are valid in this case, taking h_{ie} as 2.5 kΩ and hence calculate the gain of the circuit. If the 470 Ω resistor was shunted by a large-value capacitor, to what value would the gain increase?
[Answers: −4.68, −158]

Note: The analysis techniques explained in this chapter in relation to circuits incorporating npn BJTs apply equally to pnp BJT circuits; the only difference is that *static* voltage polarities and *static* current directions are reversed.
Figure 3.23 has been drawn using the standard convention that the most positive power rail is shown at the top of the diagram.

3.15 By using the complete *h*-parameter model of figure 3.9d to represent the small-signal performance of the BJT, show that analysis of the common-emitter circuit of figure 3.6b

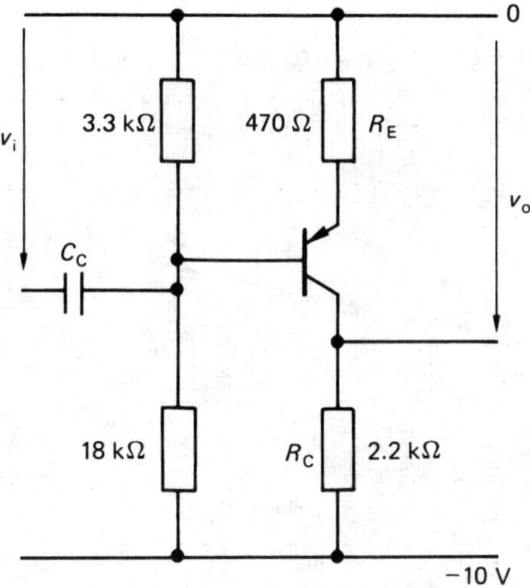

Figure 3.23

for mid-frequency operation results in the relationships

$$i_b = \frac{v_i - h_{re} v_o}{h_{ie}}, \qquad v_o = \frac{-h_{fe} i_b}{h_{oe} + G_C}$$

where $G_C = 1/R_C$.
Hence show that the small-signal voltage gain and input resistance of the amplifier are given by

$$A_{v(amp)} = \frac{-h_{fe}}{(h_{oe} + G_L)h_{ie} - h_{fe}h_{re}}$$

and

$$R_{i(amp)} = \left(h_{ie} - \frac{h_{fe}h_{re}}{h_{oe} + G_L}\right) \Big/\!\!\Big/ R_B$$

where R_B is the parallel combination of the bias resistances R_1 and R_2.
If the h-parameters of the BJT at the Q-point are $h_{ie} = 5\text{ k}\Omega$, $h_{re} = 10^{-4}$, $h_{fe} = 200$, $h_{oe} = 15\ \mu\text{S}$ and circuit resistance values are $R_1 = 120\text{ k}\Omega$, $R_2 = 27\text{ k}\Omega$, $R_C = 6.8\text{ k}\Omega$, determine the corresponding values of voltage gain and input resistance. By comparing the results with those obtained in example 3.9 using the simplified BJT model of figure 3.9e which ignores the effects represented by h_{re} and h_{oe}, calculate the percentage error incurred by use of the simplified model in determination of $A_{v(amp)}$ and $R_{i(amp)}$.
[Answers: −253, +7.5 per cent; 3.99 kΩ, +2 per cent]

3.16 Show that if the small-signal performance of the FET in the common-source amplifier of figure 3.6c is represented by the model of figure 3.10, the small-signal voltage gain, input resistance and output resistance of the amplifier are given by

$$A_{v(amp)} = \frac{-g_{fs}}{g_{os} + G_D}$$

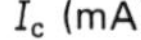

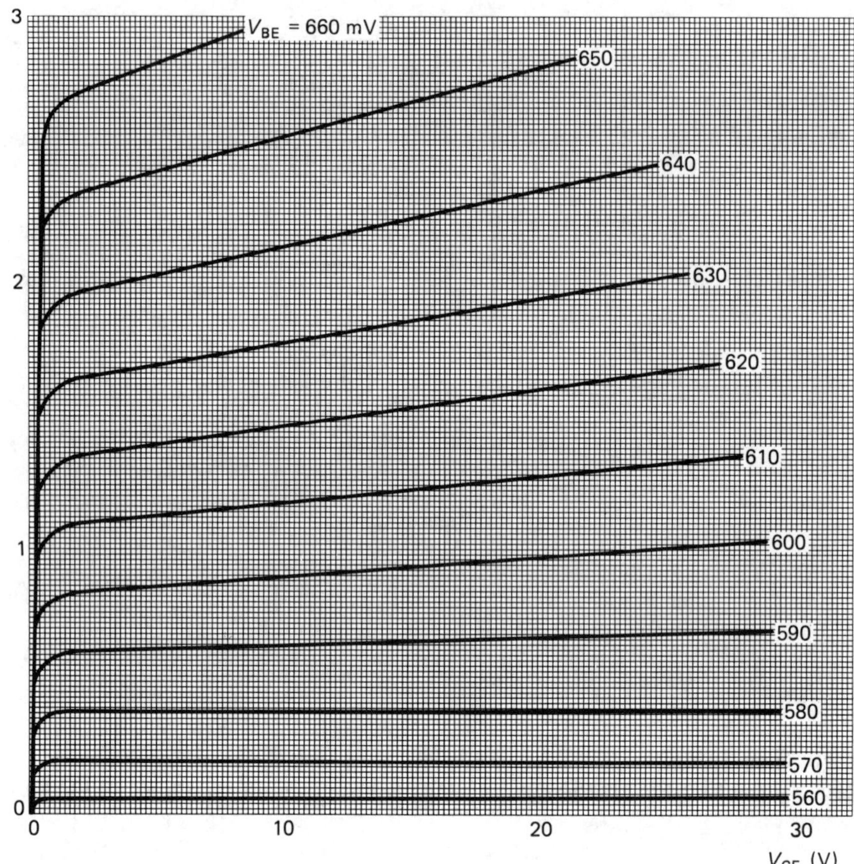

Figure 3.24

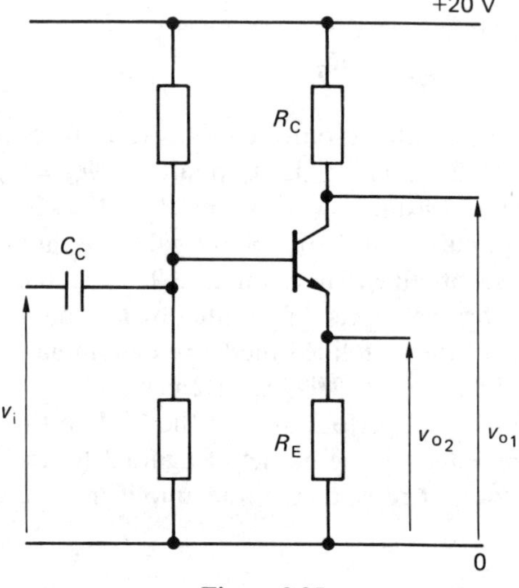

Figure 3.25

$$R_{\mathrm{i(amp)}} = \left(g_{\mathrm{is}} + G_{\mathrm{B}} - \frac{g_{\mathrm{fs}} g_{\mathrm{rs}}}{g_{\mathrm{os}} + G_{\mathrm{D}}} \right)^{-1}$$

$$R_{\mathrm{o(amp)}} = \left(g_{\mathrm{os}} - \frac{g_{\mathrm{fs}} g_{\mathrm{rs}}}{G_{\mathrm{os}} + G_{\mathrm{B}} + g_{\mathrm{is}}} \right)^{-1} \Big/\!\!\Big/ R_{\mathrm{D}}$$

at mid-frequencies where all capacitive effects are insignificant. Drain load resistance $R_D = 1/G_D$, external signal source resistance $R_{os} = 1/G_{os}$ and $R_B\,(=1/G_B)$ is the parallel combination of the bias resistances R_1 and R_2.

3.17 The small-signal conductance parameters of the transistor in question 3.16 are $g_{is} = 1$ nS, $g_{rs} = 100$ pS, $g_{fs} = 10$ mS, $g_{os} = 100\ \mu$S and the circuit resistance values are $R_1 = 12$ MΩ, $R_2 = 2.7$ MΩ + 270 kΩ, $R_D = 2.7$ kΩ. Calculate the voltage gain and input resistance of this circuit using the expressions derived in question 3.16. If the circuit is driven from a voltage-producing transducer having a source resistance of 100 kΩ, what is the output resistance of the amplifier? By comparing the values obtained for $A_{v(\mathrm{amp})}$, $R_{i(\mathrm{amp})}$ and $R_{o(\mathrm{amp})}$ with those using the simplified expressions listed in table 3.2 corresponding to representation of the transistor properties by the simplified model of figure 3.10c, calculate the errors incurred by use of the simpler model in this case.
[Answers: −21.26, 2.4 MΩ, 2.13 kΩ; errors +27 per cent, <1 per cent, +27 per cent respectively]

3.18 Figure 3.24 shows the output characteristics of the BJT in the circuit of figure 3.6b. If $V_{CC} = 20$ V, $R_1 = 82$ kΩ, $R_2 = 18$ kΩ, $R_C = 8.2$ kΩ and $R_E = 3.3$ kΩ, use load line construction to find the amplitudes of the collector signal current and the signal voltage across the collector load when a sinusoidal input signal of amplitude 20 mV is applied. What is the modulus of the small-signal voltage gain of the circuit? It may be assumed that the static base–emitter voltage of the transistor is 0.6 V and that its static current gain is sufficiently high for the base current to be neglected in bias calculations. It may also be assumed that the output resistance of the signal source is negligible and that the circuit capacitors provide effective ac short-circuit paths at the frequency of the input signal.
[Answers: 0.5 mA, 4.1 V, 205]

3.19 Figure 3.25 shows a phase-splitter circuit in which, at mid-frequencies, the outputs v_{o_1} and v_{o_2} are out-of-phase. Derive expressions for the small-signal mid-frequency voltage gains from the input to each output using the simplified BJT model of figure 3.9e. Hence show that for $R_C = R_E$, the modulus of the voltage gains are both approximately unity provided $h_{fe} \gg 1$ and $R_E \gg 1/g_{fe}$.
[Answers:

$$A_{v_1(\mathrm{amp})} = \frac{-h_{\mathrm{fe}} R_{\mathrm{C}}}{h_{\mathrm{ie}} + (h_{\mathrm{fe}} + 1) R_{\mathrm{E}}}$$

$$A_{v_2(\mathrm{amp})} = \frac{(h_{\mathrm{fe}} + 1) R_{\mathrm{E}}}{h_{\mathrm{ie}} + (h_{\mathrm{fe}} + 1) R_{\mathrm{E}}}$$
]

3.20 A source-follower circuit comprises a MOST having g_{fs} of 250 mS, a 100 Ω resistor in series with the transistor source terminal and bias resistors of 100 kΩ and 330 kΩ. Calculate the overall small-signal voltage gain obtained at mid-frequencies when this circuit is given by a circuit having an output resistance of 50 kΩ and it drives an 80 Ω external load.
[Answer: 0.26]

4 Frequency Response

Coverage

- The meaning and significance of frequency response: gain and phase, distortion.
- Causes of gain and phase variation with frequency.
- Gain and phase responses of basic *CR* networks.
- Approximate graphical constructions that simplify representation.
- Investigation of the sinusoidal response of amplifiers at low and high frequencies.
- Overall sinusoidal response of specific amplifier configurations.
- Requirements for low amplitude and phase distortion.
- Investigation of pulse response: rise time and sag.

Important small-signal performance properties of an amplifier are the variation of *gain* and *phase* with input signal frequency. These variations are termed the *gain response* and *phase response* respectively and are collectively described as the *frequency response* of the amplifier.

The dependence of amplifier performance on signal frequency is due to capacitance and inductance within the amplifier and the variation of the corresponding reactances with frequency (equations 2.26 and 2.38). In general, amplifier circuits contain coupling and bypass capacitors (section 3.3), transistors have internal capacitance (figures 3.9b and 3.10b) while additional *stray* capacitance is added by printed circuit boards and connection cables; at very high frequencies, transistor inductance and stray inductances also become important.

Figure 4.1 shows the typical gain response of an ac coupled amplifier. In the mid-frequency range, the values of the reactances are such that they have negligible effect on the amplifier response so that the gain is independent of signal frequency, termed a *flat* response. It is performance within this range that is investigated in section 3.3 under ac (small-signal) performance. Many applications require the amplification of a complex waveform, such as speech, which comprises many frequency components. If the various components are not amplified by the same amount, amplitude distortion (section 4.6) results and the output is then not a true amplified version of the input. To avoid such distortion all the frequency components of the input signal must be amplified by the same amount and therefore the mid-frequency band is the normal operating range of the amplifier. Such response is termed *broadband* because of the wide frequency range between the cut-off points (figure 4.1). By contrast some applications require *narrow-band* response which provides frequency selection; a tuned amplifier (section 6.9) is the extreme case of narrow-band performance.

The gain response gives the variation of the ratio of output-to-input signal *amplitudes* for

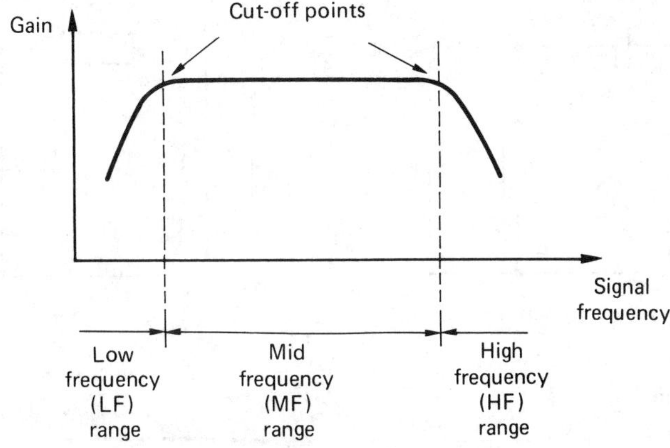

Figure 4.1 Typical gain response of a broadband ac coupled amplifier

change of frequency of the *sinusoidal* signal. Gain is given either as a dimensionless number, for example, a gain of 100 indicating that the amplitude of the output signal is 100 times that of the input signal, or more commonly on a logarithmic scale in *decibels* (note 4.1). Phase response gives the phase difference between the output and input signals in terms of degrees where the period of the signal corresponds to 360°.

Note 4.1: The decibel

The *bel* is fundamentally a logarithmic scale of power ratio. If a system has input and output powers p_i and p_o, the system is said to have a power gain of $\log(p_o/p_i)$ *bels* or $10\log(p_o/p_i)$ *decibels* (dB).

Although basically a unit of power ratio, the decibel is widely used in electronics to describe a voltage ratio. Since $p = vi$ and $v = Ri$ (equations 2.1 and 2.20), $p = v^2/R$, from which $p_o/p_i = (v_o/v_i)^2$ assuming equal value resistances at input and output.

The power ratio in decibels therefore becomes

$$10\log(v_o/v_i)^2 = 20\log(v_o/v_i)$$

This expression is also used to describe a *voltage ratio* irrespective of the resistance levels at the input and output, thus if the amplitudes of sinusoidal input and output voltages of an amplifier are 5 mV and 1.4 V respectively (as in the graphical example 3.10) the amplifier is said to have a voltage gain of $20\log(1.4\text{ V}/5\text{ mV}) = 20\log 280 \simeq 20 \times 2.45 = +49$ dB.

Note that 0 dB denotes a numerical gain of unity ($v_o = v_i$) while a negative gain in decibels indicates a voltage reduction, termed attenuation.

4.1 Sinusoidal response of *CR* networks

Subsequent consideration of the performance of amplifiers at low and high signal frequencies shows that there are two fundamental situations which can be represented by the *CR* networks of figures 4.2a, b and so it is useful to consider these networks initially.

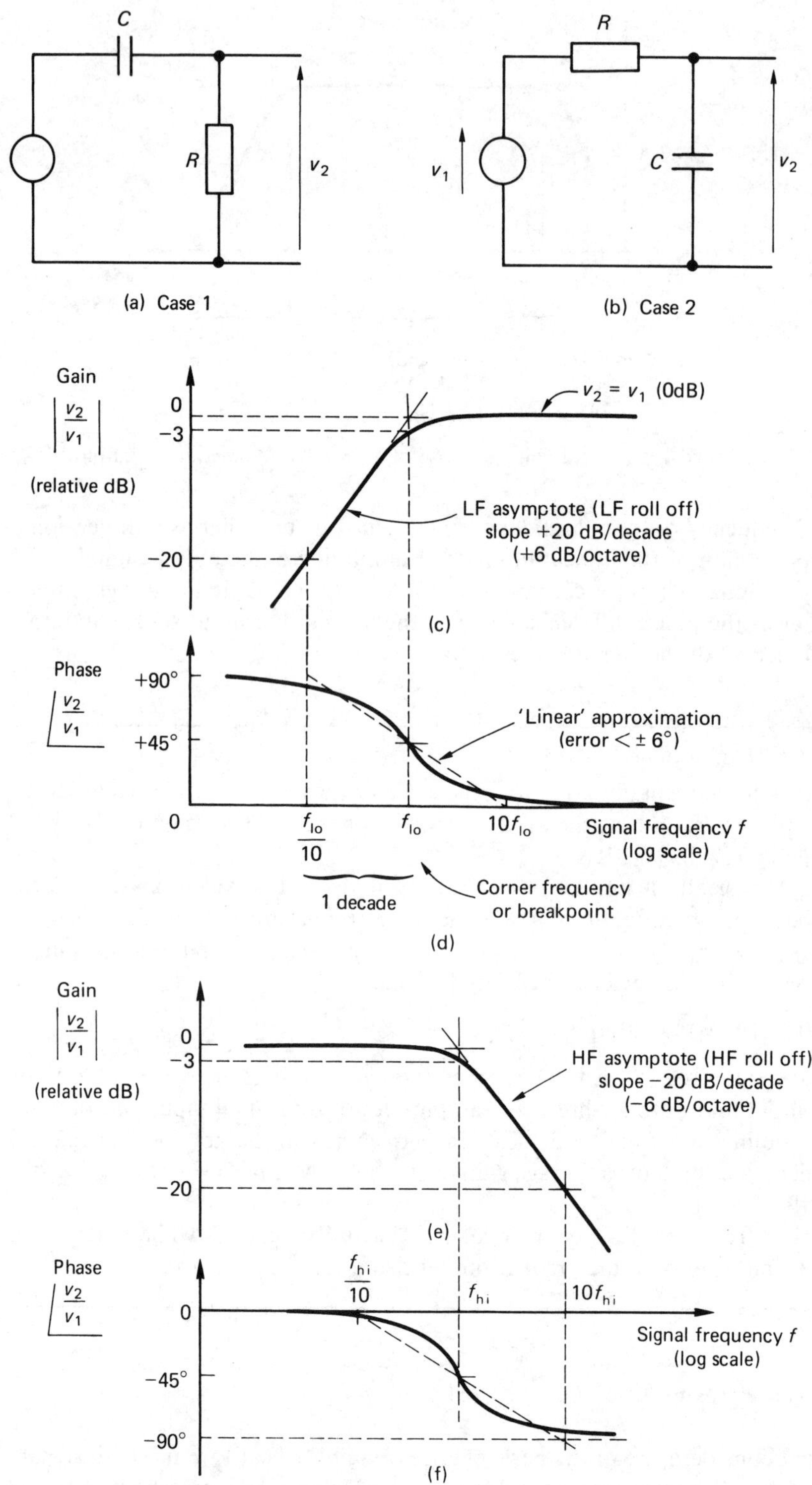

Figure 4.2 *CR* network frequency response

In the 'case l' circuit of figure 4.2a, C and R form a potential divider so that if v_1 is sinusoidal

$$\frac{v_2}{v_1} = \frac{R}{R - jX_C} = \frac{R}{R - j\left(\dfrac{1}{\omega C}\right)} \tag{4.1}$$

where $-jX_C$ is the operational reactance of the capacitor (equation 2.27) and $X_C = 1/\omega C$ from equation 2.26.

At relatively high frequencies $1/\omega C \ll R$ and the $-j\dfrac{1}{\omega C}$ term in equation 4.1 is negligible giving

$$\frac{v_2}{v_1} = 1 \angle 0^\circ \tag{4.2}$$

indicating a gain $|v_2/v_1|$ of unity and zero phase difference between v_2 and v_1. This corresponds to C being an effective ac short circuit, X_C being very low, whereby $v_2 = v_1$ (figure 4.2a).

As the signal frequency is reduced, the $1/\omega C$ term becomes more significant, $|v_2/v_1|$ reduces and a phase difference appears between v_2 and v_1.

A *cut-off, corner* or *breakpoint* frequency ω_{lo} is defined at which $1/\omega C = R$, that is,

$$\omega_{lo} = \frac{1}{CR} \text{ or } f_{lo} = \frac{1}{2\pi CR} \tag{4.3}$$

since ω (rad/s) $= 2\pi f$ (Hz).
From equations 4.1 and 4.3

$$\frac{v_2}{v_1} = \frac{1}{1 - j\left(\dfrac{1}{\omega CR}\right)} = \frac{1}{1 - j\left(\dfrac{\omega_{lo}}{\omega}\right)} = \frac{1}{1 - j\left(\dfrac{f_{lo}}{f}\right)} \tag{4.4}$$

so that at $f = f_{lo}$

$$\frac{v_2}{v_1} = \frac{1}{1 - j1} = \frac{1}{\sqrt{2}} \angle +45^\circ \tag{4.5}$$

showing that at this frequency (f_{lo}) the circuit gain is $1/\sqrt{2}$ or $20\log(1/\sqrt{2})$ dB $= 20\log(2)^{-\frac{1}{2}} = -10\log 2 = -10(0.301) \simeq -3$ dB and that v_2 *leads* v_1 by 45° (an eighth of a period).

At low frequencies $\ll f_{lo}$, $f_{lo}/f \gg 1$ and the unity in the denominator of equation 4.4 becomes negligible, whereby

$$\left.\frac{v_2}{v_1}\right|_{f \ll f_{lo}} \simeq \frac{1}{-j\left(\dfrac{f_{lo}}{f}\right)} = +j\left(\frac{f}{f_{lo}}\right) \tag{4.6}$$

from which the gain $|v_2/v_1| \propto f$ and $\angle v_2/v_1$ approaches $+90^\circ$. Notice that from $|v_2/v_1| \propto f$, an increase of frequency by a factor of 10, termed a *decade*, within this range ($\ll f_{lo}$) causes the gain to change by a factor of 10 which is a change of 20 dB (from 20 log 10). This corresponds to a change of 6 dB over an *octave* (a doubling of frequency), from 20 log 2.

The gain and phase responses of this network are therefore as shown in figures 4.2c, d. The gain response is 3 dB below the high frequency value of 0 dB at $f = f_{lo}$, and for $f \ll f_{lo}$ the response tends to a straight line when plotted on a logarithmic frequency scale (note that the gain scale in dB is also logarithmic) of slope +20 dB/decade which is equivalent to

+6 dB/octave. This straight line is termed the *LF asymptote* and shows the reduction or *roll-off* of voltage gain as the frequency falls owing to the increasing reactance of C. Notice that the asymptote intersects the 0 dB line at f_{lo} which provides a convenient way of plotting the response.

The phase response of figure 4.2d shows that as the frequency falls, the phase lead between v_2 and v_1 increases from zero at $f \gg f_{lo}$ (v_2 in phase with v_1) to 90° (quarter cycle) at $f \ll f_{lo}$. A convenient approximation that is accurate to within $\pm 6°$ can be constructed as a straight line between the points ($f_{lo}/10$, $+90°$) and ($10f_{lo}$, 0°).

A similar analysis of the 'case 2' network of figure 4.2b gives the gain and phase responses of figures 4.2e, f. At low frequency the capacitor approximates to an open circuit so that $v_2 = v_1$; the low frequency gain is 0 dB with v_2 in phase with v_1. As the frequency increases, the reactance of C falls, resulting in reduced gain and a phase lag between v_2 and v_1.

Considering the network as a potential divider

$$\frac{v_2}{v_1} = \frac{-j\left(\dfrac{1}{\omega C}\right)}{R - j\left(\dfrac{1}{\omega C}\right)} = \frac{1}{1 + j\omega CR} \tag{4.7}$$

for v_1 sinusoidal.

A breakpoint ω_{hi} is defined at which $\omega CR = 1$, that is:

$$\omega_{hi} = \frac{1}{CR} \text{ or } f_{hi} = \frac{1}{2\pi CR} \tag{4.8}$$

Combining equations 4.7 and 4.8

$$\frac{v_2}{v_1} = \frac{1}{1 + j\left(\dfrac{\omega}{\omega_{hi}}\right)} = \frac{1}{1 + j\left(\dfrac{f}{f_{hi}}\right)} \tag{4.9}$$

For frequencies $\ll f_{hi}$, $f/f_{hi} \ll 1$ giving

$$\frac{v_2}{v_1} = 1 \angle 0° \tag{4.10}$$

indicating a gain of unity (0 dB) and v_2 in phase with v_1.

At $f = f_{hi}$

$$\frac{v_2}{v_1} = \frac{1}{1 + j1} = \frac{1}{\sqrt{2}} \angle -45° \tag{4.11}$$

from equation 4.9, showing that the gain is -3 dB at this frequency and v_2 lags v_1 by 45°.

For $f \gg f_{hi}$, $f/f_{hi} \gg 1$ and equation 4.9 reduces to

$$\frac{v_2}{v_1} = \frac{1}{+j\left(\dfrac{f}{f_{hi}}\right)} = -j\left(\frac{f_{hi}}{f}\right) \tag{4.12}$$

resulting in a *HF asymptote* describing the gain roll-off as the frequency increases above f_{hi} The slope of this asymptote, from $|v_2/v_1| \propto 1/f$ is -20 dB/decade (-6 dB/octave) since a 10-fold increase in frequency above f_{hi} results in the gain falling by a factor of 10 and

$20 \log(0.1) = -20$ dB. Correspondingly the phase difference between v_2 and v_1 increases to $-90°$ at very high frequency. Approximations for constructing the gain and phase responses using the HF gain asymptote and a straight line phase response on a logarithmic frequency scale apply to this case in a similar way to that described for the network of figure 4.2a.

4.2 General small-signal amplifier model

Corresponding to the development of the small-signal performance model of an amplifier stage in chapter 3 (figures 3.7, 3.8 and 3.11) whereby the V_{CC} (V_{DD}) power supply provides an effective low impedance route for signal current and the transistor is represented by its small-signal model (figures 3.9 and 3.10), a general model representing the small-signal performance of common-emitter (CE) and common-source (CS) stages is presented in figure 4.3.

In the CE case, the BJT model is the hybrid-π model of figure 3.9b although the output capacitance of the BJT has been added for completeness. At low current levels, $r_{bb'}$ has little significance and has therefore been omitted. For representation of the CS amplifier, the FET model corresponds to that of figure 3.10b although in order to produce a general representation, the in-phase component of internal feedback within the FET is represented by a feedback resistance r_f instead of the current source $g_{rs}v_{ds}$ as in the model of figure 3.10b.

In figure 4.3 r_i, r_o and C_i, C_o represent the input and output resistances and capacitances of the transistor respectively, while r_f, C_f model internal feedback; the corresponding parameters for BJTs and FETs are given in table 4.1. References [1a] and [1b] give further details of the relevant small-signal parameters for BJTs and FETs. R_B is the effective resistance at the input given by the parallel combination of the R_1, R_2 bias resistors in the CE and CS circuits of figures 3.6b, c. $R_C(R_D)$ is the collector (drain) load and $R_E(R_S)$ provides dc negative

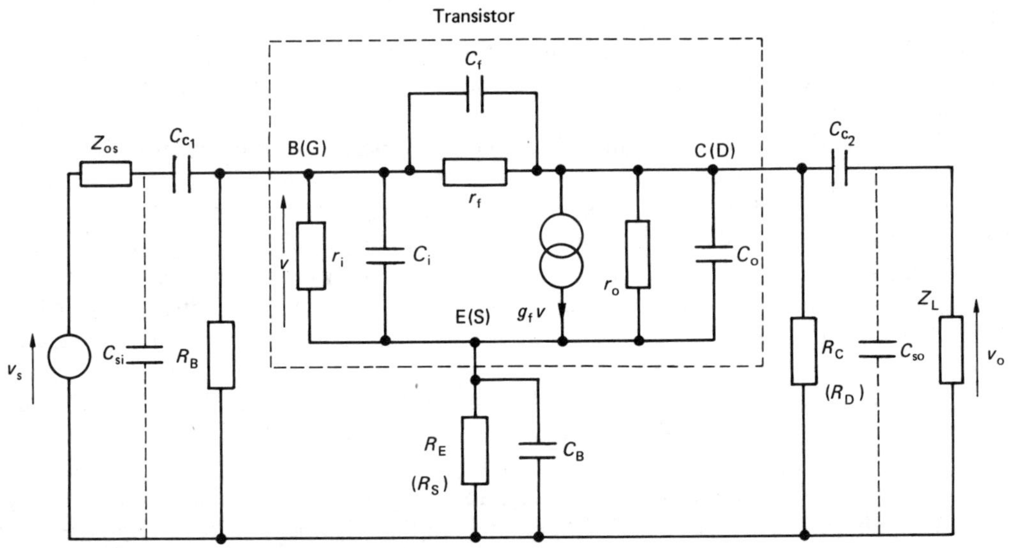

Figure 4.3 General model of the small-signal performance of a CE (CS) single-stage amplifier

Table 4.1 Small-signal parameters for BJTs and FETs with reference to the model of figure 4.3

	r_i	r_o	r_f	C_i	C_o	C_f
BJT*	$r_{b'e}$	r_{ce}	$r_{b'c}$	$C_{b'e}$	C_{ce}	$C_{b'c}$
	$\simeq h_{ie} = \dfrac{h_{fe}}{g_{fe}}$	$\simeq \dfrac{1}{h_{oe}}$	$\simeq \dfrac{h_{fe}}{h_{re}g_{fe}}$	$= \dfrac{g_{fe}}{2\pi f_T} - C_{T_c}$	usually negligible	$\simeq C_{T_c}$
FET†	r_{gs}	r_{ds}	r_{gd}	C_{gs}	C_{ds}	C_{gd}
	$\simeq \dfrac{1}{g_{is}}$	$\simeq \dfrac{1}{g_{os}}$	$\simeq \dfrac{1}{g_{rs}} - \dfrac{1}{g_{is}}$	$\simeq C_{iss} - C_{rss}$	usually negligible	$\simeq C_{rss}$

f_T = BJT transition frequency [1a].
* Reference [1a].
† Reference [1b].

feedback for stability purposes (sections 3.1 and 3.2); C_B provides ac bypass to remove ac negative feedback at normal operating frequencies so as to improve the small-signal gain. The amplifier is capacitively coupled (C_{C_1}) to the signal source which has output impedance Z_{os}; this source may be a signal producing transducer or the output stage of a driving circuit. The output of the stage is capacitively coupled (C_{C_2}) to an external load of impedance Z_L. In situations where this stage drives another circuit, Z_L would be the input impedance of that circuit. Capacitances C_{si} and C_{so} represent the stray capacitance at the input and output comprising inter-track capacitance on printed circuit boards, capacitance due to wiring and, in the case of circuits under test, the capacitance introduced by connected measurement equipment.

At *mid-frequencies* (MF) the capacitance values are such that C_{C_1}, C_{C_2} and C_B are effective ac short circuits while transistor and stray capacitances (C_i, C_o, C_f, C_{si}, C_{so}) are effective ac open circuits. In this range of signal frequencies the output impedance of the source Z_{os} and the external load impedance Z_L can usually be considered to be purely resistive, R_{os} and R_L respectively. These conditions enable the model to be simplified for MF analysis as considered in section 3.4.3.

At *low frequencies* (LF) the transistor and stray capacitances are effective ac open circuits because of their high reactance and it is likely that Z_{os} and Z_L can be considered as resistive; but the coupling and bypass capacitors can no longer be considered as effective ac short circuits because of their finite reactance. Thus the LF response of the circuit is dependent on C_{C_1}, C_{C_2} and C_B.

At *high frequencies* (HF) the coupling and bypass capacitors are effective ac short circuits because of their low reactance but the amplifier response will be affected by the low reactance of the transistor and stray capacitances. In addition, at HF, it *may* not be valid to treat Z_{os} and Z_L as being purely resistive; the reactive components may have a significant effect. Thus at HF, the circuit response is dependent on C_i, C_o, C_f, C_{si} and C_{so} and maybe the reactive components of Z_{os} and Z_L as well.

A similar consideration applies to the other amplifier configurations. The model of figure 4.3 would apply to emitter- and source-follower circuits (CC and CD amplifiers) if C_B was removed, R_C (R_D) made zero (short circuit) and the output circuit comprising C_{C_2}, C_{so} and Z_L connected across R_E (R_S); see also figure 3.15g. In the case of CB and CG circuits, the required modifications to the model of figure 4.3 are that R_B and R_E (R_S) are interchanged and the transistor model is reconfigured to make E(S) the input and B(G) the common terminal (see also figure 3.15f).

4.3 Amplifier response at LF

Section 4.2 identifies that the LF response is dominated by C_{C_1}, C_{C_2} and C_B, other capacitances (figure 4.3) being effectively open circuit at these frequencies. For clarity the effects due to the coupling and bypass capacitors will be considered separately.

Response due to the coupling capacitors C_{C_1} and C_{C_2}

It is assumed here that the value of C_B is sufficiently large that the LF response is dominated by the coupling capacitors.

Making the appropriate simplifications to the model of figure 4.3 and representing the basic amplifier stage by its performance parameters $A_{v(amp)}$, $R_{i(amp)}$ and $R_{o(amp)}$ (section 3.4), the amplifier may be represented as in figure 4.4a showing that it behaves as a cascade of two 'case 1' CR circuits of section 4.1.

From figure 4.4a:

$$v_o = (A_{v(amp)})\, v_i \left[\frac{R_L}{(R_L + R_{o(amp)}) - j\left(\dfrac{1}{\omega C_{C_2}}\right)} \right] \tag{4.13}$$

and

$$v_i = v_s \left[\frac{R_{i(amp)}}{(R_{i(amp)} + R_{os}) - j\left(\dfrac{1}{\omega C_{C_1}}\right)} \right] \tag{4.14}$$

giving the overall voltage gain $A_{v(sys)}$ as

$$A_{v(sys)} = \frac{v_o}{v_s} = A_{v(amp)} \left[\frac{R_{i(amp)}}{(R_{i(amp)} + R_{os}) - j\left(\dfrac{1}{\omega C_{C_1}}\right)} \right] \left[\frac{R_L}{(R_L + R_{o(amp)}) - j\left(\dfrac{1}{\omega C_{C_2}}\right)} \right]$$

$$= \frac{A_{v(amp)} R_{i(amp)} R_L}{(R_{i(amp)} + R_{os})(R_L + R_{o(amp)})} \left[\frac{1}{1 - j\left(\dfrac{1}{\omega C_{C_1}(R_{i(amp)} + R_{os})}\right)} \right] \left[\frac{1}{1 - j\left(\dfrac{1}{\omega C_{C_2}(R_L + R_{o(amp)})}\right)} \right]$$

$$= A_{v(sys)mid} \left[\frac{1}{1 - j\left(\dfrac{f_{lo_1}}{f}\right)} \right] \left[\frac{1}{1 - j\left(\dfrac{f_{lo_2}}{f}\right)} \right] \tag{4.15}$$

where, by comparison with equations 4.3 and 4.4, the two breakpoint frequencies are

$$f_{lo_1} = \frac{1}{2\pi C_{C_1}(R_{i(amp)} + R_{os})} \quad \text{and} \quad f_{lo_2} = \frac{1}{2\pi C_{C_2}(R_L + R_{o(amp)})} \tag{4.16}$$

Note that $A_{v(sys)mid}$ is the overall gain at mid-frequencies at which the effect of C_{C_1} and C_{C_2} is negligible; the link between $A_{v(sys)}$ and $A_{v(amp)}$ in equation 4.15 corresponds to equation 3.55.

The product of the [ ] terms in equation 4.15 results in a *sum* of gain responses in decibels, since the logarithm of a product is the sum of the logarithms of the individual terms, and a *sum* of phase responses resulting in the approximate 'linearised' LF responses of figure 4.4b.

Several points should be noted regarding these responses:

(1) Which of f_{lo_1} and f_{lo_2} is the higher depends entirely on the relative values of resistance and capacitance involved; figure 4.4b represents a purely arbitrary case.

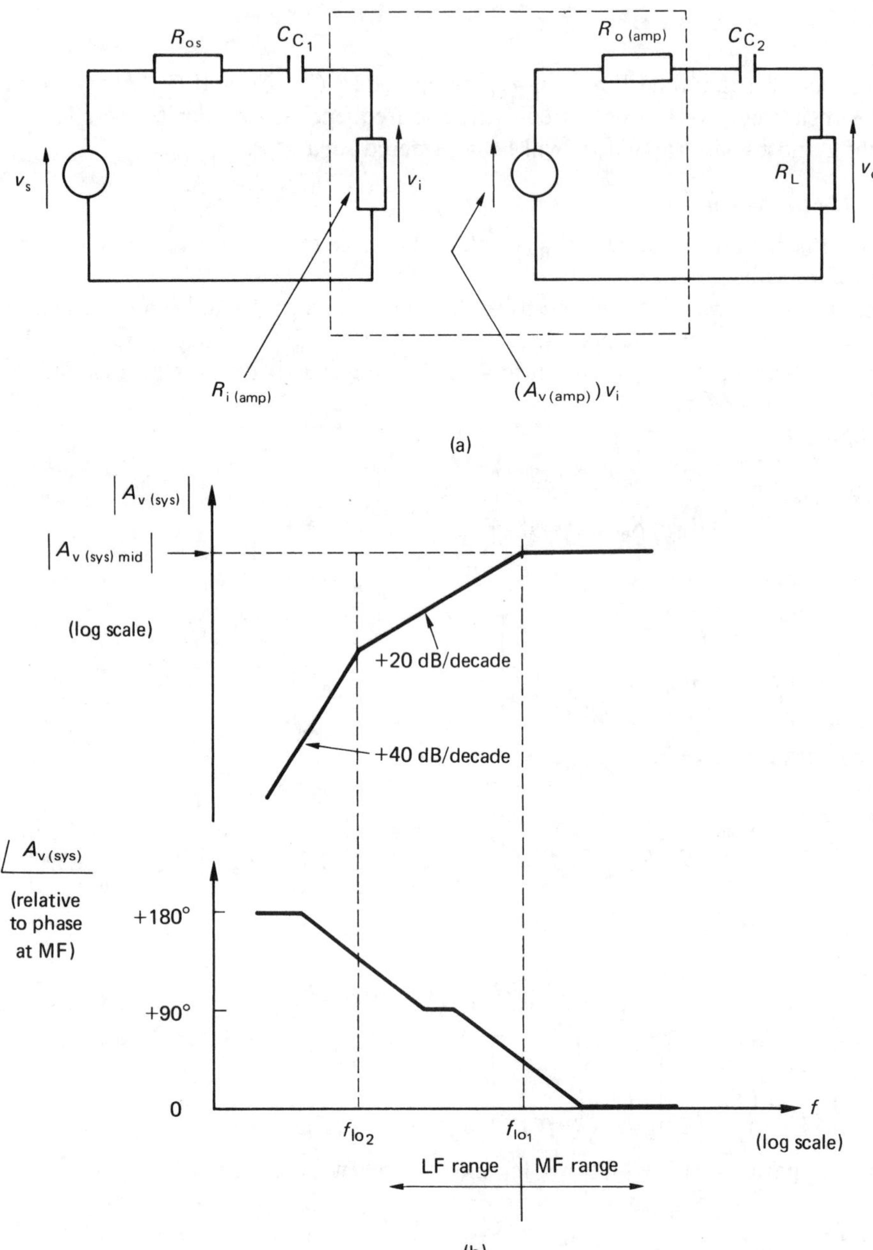

Figure 4.4 Gain and phase responses of a single-stage amplifier at low frequency due to coupling capacitors at input and output

(2) If f_{lo_1} and f_{lo_2} are of similar order, the individual responses merge near the breakpoints and the effects due to individual breakpoints are then not easily identifiable.

(3) The phase response $\angle A_{v(sys)}/f$ shown in figure 4.4b shows the phase difference introduced solely by the *CR* networks at the input and output of the amplifier and is therefore relative to the *phase relationship at mid-frequency.* CE and CS circuits provide inversion

(phase lag of 180°) at MF (section 3.4.3) and so the actual phase difference between v_o and v_s at very low frequency is $-180°$ (due to amplifier inversion) $+180°$ (due to the two *CR* networks) resulting in 0°, that is, v_o is *in phase* with v_s at frequencies very much lower than the breakpoints.

Response due to the bypass capacitor C_B

Here it is assumed that the values of the coupling capacitors are sufficiently large that the LF response is dominated by the bypass capacitor. As the signal frequency is reduced, eventually C_B no longer provides an effective ac short circuit, and the impedance of the R_E $(R_S)//C_B$ combination rises so increasing ac negative feedback and causing the gain to fall (section 5.1).

Using the CE circuit as an example, making the appropriate simplifications to the model of figure 4.3 and ignoring the effects of r_f and r_o due to their relatively large values, the performance of the amplifier as far as C_B is concerned can be represented as in figure 4.5a. Thévenin reduction (note 3.1) of the v_s, R_{os}, R_B combination to a voltage source $v_s R_B/(R_{os}+R_B)$ and series resistance $R_{os}//R_B$ leads to

$$\frac{v_s R_B}{R_{os}+R_B} = i_b[(R_{os}/\!/R_B)+h_{ie}+(h_{fe}+1)Z_E] \tag{4.17}$$

where Z_E is the impedance of the R_E, C_B combination.
The output voltage is given by

$$v_o = -h_{fe} i_b R_L' \tag{4.18}$$

and substitution of i_b from equation 4.17 into 4.18 leads to

$$A_{v(sys)} = \frac{v_o}{v_s} = \frac{-h_{fe} R_B R_L'}{R_{os}R_B + (R_{os}+R_B)[h_{ie}+(h_{fe}+1)Z_E]} \tag{4.19}$$

At mid-frequencies, C_B provides effective bypass of R_E so that $Z_E = 0$ and so

$$A_{v(sys)mid} = \frac{-h_{fe} R_B R_L'}{R_{os}R_B + (R_{os}+R_B)h_{ie}} \tag{4.20}$$

Notice that if R_{os} is neglected, this voltage relationship, which then corresponds to $A_{v(amp)mid}$ using the terminology of section 3.4.1, becomes $-h_{fe}R_L'/h_{ie}$ corresponding to equation 3.74 which applies to MF operation.

Combining equations 4.19 and 4.20:

$$A_{v(sys)} = A_{v(sys)mid}\left[\frac{1+j\omega C_B R_E}{(N+1)+j\omega C_B R_E}\right] \tag{4.21}$$

where N is the resistance ratio $\dfrac{(h_{fe}+1)R_E}{(R_{os}//R_B)+h_{ie}}$, noting that impedance Z_E is given by

$$Z_E = R_E//\frac{1}{j\omega C_B} = \frac{R_E/j\omega C_B}{R_E+(1/j\omega C_B)} = \frac{R_E}{1+j\omega C_B R_E} \tag{4.22}$$

The overall gain of the amplifier may therefore be expressed as

$$A_{v(sys)} = \frac{A_{v(sys)mid}}{N+1}\left[\frac{1+j\omega C_B R_E}{1+j\omega\left(\dfrac{C_B R_E}{N+1}\right)}\right] \tag{4.23}$$

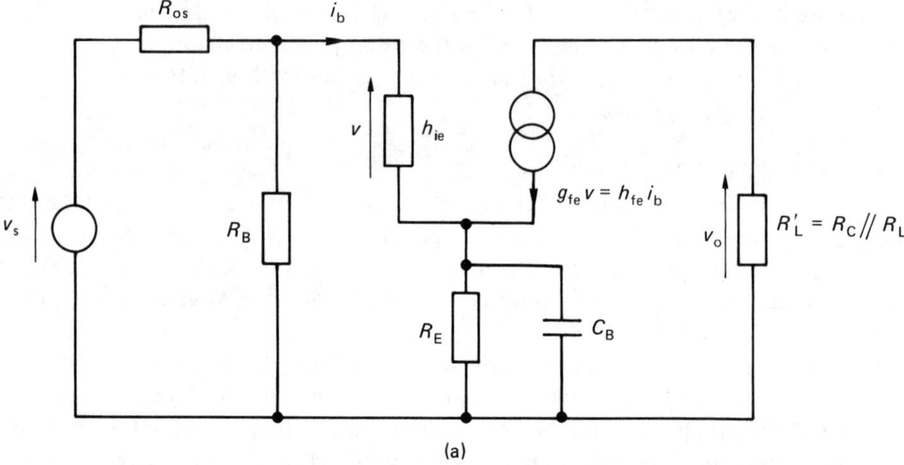

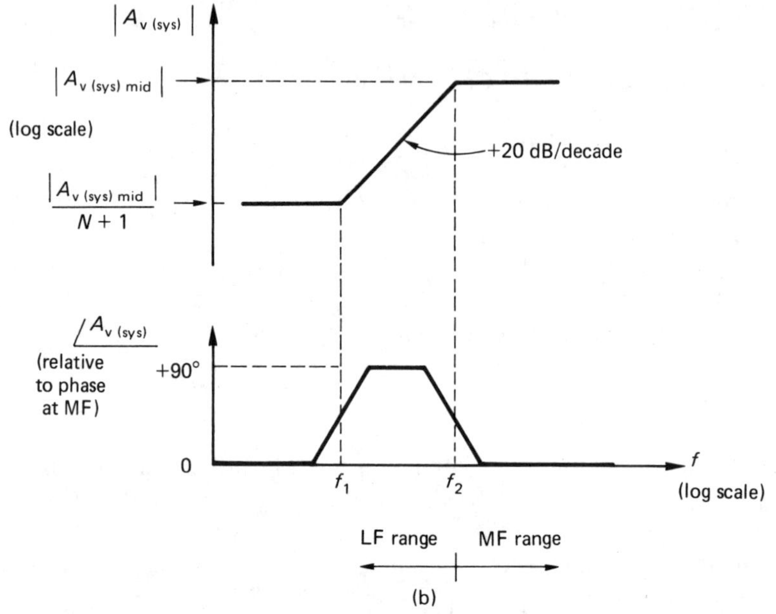

Figure 4.5 Gain and phase responses of a single-stage amplifier at low frequency due to the bypass capacitor

$$= \frac{A_{v(sys)mid}}{N+1}\left[\frac{1+j\left(\dfrac{f}{f_1}\right)}{1+j\left(\dfrac{f}{f_2}\right)}\right] \tag{4.24}$$

where $f_1 = \dfrac{1}{2\pi C_B R_E}$ and $f_2 = \dfrac{N+1}{2\pi C_B R_E}$.

Typical values of h_{fe}, R_E, R_{os}, R_B and h_{ie} usually ensure $N \gg 1$ for a CE stage, so that $f_2 \gg f_1$.

The linearised gain and phase responses corresponding to equation 4.24 are shown in figure 4.5b. At very low frequency ($\ll f_1$) the quadrature (j) components in equation 4.24 are negligible and the gain is independent of frequency, having a value $\dfrac{A_{v(sys)mid}}{N+1}$.

At such frequencies, C_B is effectively open circuit and the reduced gain is due to the ac negative feedback provided by R_E. With increase of signal frequency, the $1+j(f/f_1)$ term in equation 4.24 introduces a $+20$ dB/decade rise in gain above f_1 and a corresponding phase advancement due to C_B providing partial bypass of R_E, reducing the degree of negative feedback. With further frequency increase, the $1+j(f/f_2)$ term introduces a -20 dB/decade change of gain, cancelling the $+20$ dB/decade change previously introduced, together with a phase retard which cancels the previous advancement. At frequencies $> f_2$, C_B provides total bypass of R_E so removing the effect of ac negative feedback; operation has therefore entered the MF range.

The value of C_B is chosen so that the most significant breakpoint as far as low frequency cut off is concerned (f_2) is less than the minimum frequency (f_{min}) at which the amplifier is required to operate, that is

$$f_2 = \frac{N+1}{2\pi C_B R_E} \text{ must be } \leqslant f_{min}$$

Substituting for N from above gives

$$C_B \geqslant \frac{\dfrac{(h_{fe}+1)R_E}{(R_{os}//R_B)+h_{ie}}+1}{2\pi R_E f_{min}} \tag{4.25}$$

$$\simeq \frac{h_{fe}}{2\pi h_{ie} f_{min}} = \frac{g_{fe}}{2\pi f_{min}} \tag{4.26}$$

for high h_{fe} and low R_{os}. Notice that this simplified result is the same as that proposed in section 3.3 (equation 3.42) from a superficial treatment of bypassing.

The overall response of the amplifier at low frequency is given by the *product* of the responses corresponding to the individual time constants due to C_{C_1}, C_{C_2} and C_B. This product in terms of numerical gain corresponds to the *sum* of the gain responses in decibels and the *sum* of the phase responses. The LF cut-off frequency of the amplifier (f_{lo}, section 4.5) is fixed by the *dominant*, that is, highest, LF breakpoint.

4.4 Amplifier response at HF

HF response is dependent on the transistor and stray capacitances (section 4.2). The coupling and bypass capacitors are effective ac short circuits at high frequency and so the model representing HF performance, from the general model of figure 4.3, is as shown in figure 4.6a.

In practice, in-phase feedback within the transistor is negligible (r_f is very high) and can be ignored compared with the quadrature feedback component represented by C_f. Having dispensed with r_f, another useful simplification is to separate the input and output circuits of the amplifier by referring C_f to the input. The voltage across C_f causing a component of input current is $(v_i - v_o)$ which can be written $v_i\left(1-\dfrac{v_o}{v_i}\right)$.

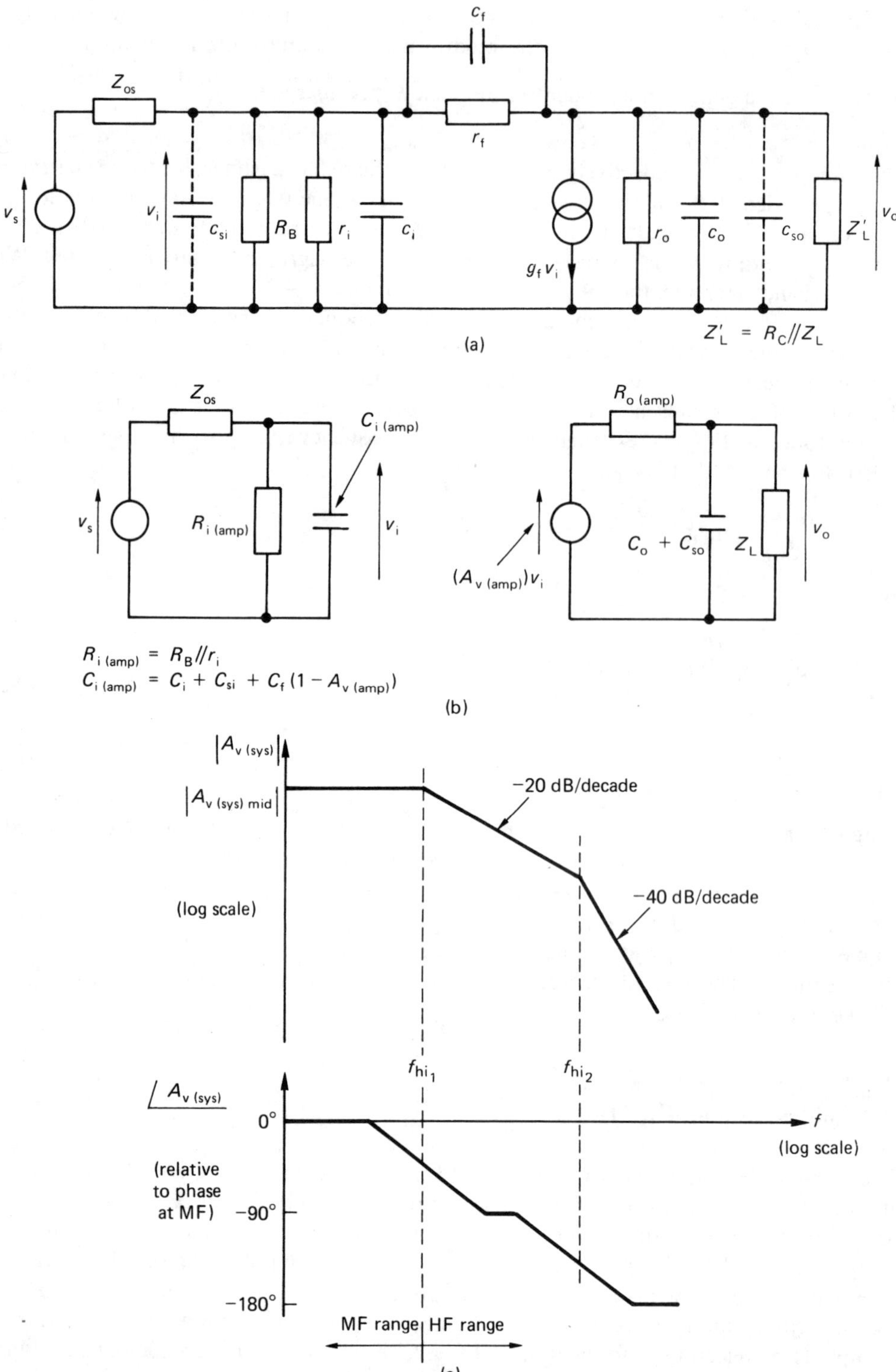

Figure 4.6 Gain and phase responses of a single-stage amplifier at high frequency due to transistor and stray capacitance

However v_o/v_i is the amplifier gain $A_{v(amp)}$ and so this voltage is equal to $v_i(1 - A_{v(amp)})$. Thus as far as the component of input signal current drawn by C_f is concerned, it is as if a capacitance $C_f(1 - A_{v(amp)})$ appeared across the input terminals of the transistor as this would draw the same current with v_i across it as C_f does in the model of figure 4.6a with voltage $(v_i - v_o)$ across it. This new value of capacitance is termed Miller capacitance and since, for CE and CS amplifiers, $A_{v(amp)}$ is numerically large and negative, its value is very much larger than C_f.

With C_f referred to the input as a new value $C_f(1 - A_{v(amp)})$, it is then in parallel with the transistor input capacitance C_i and the stray input capacitance C_{si} which can all be combined to form the *effective* input capacitance of the amplifier. The input circuit of the amplifier can then be represented as in figure 4.6b.

With the input and output circuits now separated, the output of the amplifier comprising $g_f v_i$, r_o and R_C can be represented by the Thévenin circuit $(A_{v(amp)})v_i$ and $R_{o(amp)}$, simplifying representation of the output circuit as shown in figure 4.6b.

This simplified model shows that as far as the HF response is concerned, the amplifier behaves as a cascade of two 'case 2' CR circuits (section 4.1). From potential division within the input and output models of figure 4.6b:

$$v_i = v_s\left\{\frac{R_{i(amp)} /\!/ \dfrac{1}{j\omega C_{i(amp)}}}{Z_{os} + \left[R_{i(amp)} /\!/ \dfrac{1}{j\omega C_{i(amp)}}\right]}\right\} \tag{4.27}$$

$$v_o = (A_{v(amp)})v_i\left\{\frac{Z_L /\!/ \dfrac{1}{j\omega(C_o + C_{so})}}{R_{o(amp)} + \left[Z_L /\!/ \dfrac{1}{j\omega(C_o + C_{so})}\right]}\right\} \tag{4.28}$$

If, for simplicity, it can be assumed that the reactive components of Z_{os} and Z_L are negligible at the signal frequencies of interest, combination of equations 4.27 and 4.28 gives the overall voltage gain as

$$A_{v(sys)} = A_{v(sys)mid}\left[\frac{1}{1 + j\left(\dfrac{f}{f_{hi_1}}\right)}\right]\left[\frac{1}{1 + j\left(\dfrac{f}{f_{hi_2}}\right)}\right] \tag{4.29}$$

where

$$f_{hi_1} = \frac{1}{2\pi C_{i(amp)}(R_{os}/\!/R_{i(amp)})} \tag{4.30}$$

and

$$f_{hi_2} = \frac{1}{2\pi(C_o + C_{so})(R_L /\!/ R_{o(amp)})} \tag{4.31}$$

noting that the impedance of the parallel combination of R and $1/j\omega C$ is $R/(1 + j\omega CR)$ corresponding to equation 4.22.

Each of the [ ] terms of equation 4.29 is of the form of equation 4.9 and therefore provides a gain and phase response of the form shown in figures 4.2e, f. The product in equation 4.29 corresponds to a *sum* of gain responses in decibels and a *sum* of phase responses resulting in the linearised HF responses of figure 4.6c.

Points to note about these responses:

(1) The relative values of f_{hi_1} and f_{hi_2} depend entirely on the resistances and capacitances involved in a particular case.

(2) If f_{hi_1} and f_{hi_2} are close, that is, within about three octaves of each other ($f_{hi_2} < 8f_{hi_1}$), the effects of the two breakpoints merge and cannot be identified individually in the overall response.

(3) The phase response shown in figure 4.6c is given *relative to the phase at MF*, that is, for a CE or CS amplifier for which v_o lags v_s by 180° at MF; the *actual* phase shift between v_o and v_s varies from $-180°$ at MF to $-360°$ (0°) at very high frequency.

(4) The HF cut-off frequency of the amplifier (f_{hi}, section 4.5), which is the upper limit of the amplifier bandwidth, is fixed by the *dominant*, that is, lowest, HF breakpoint.

4.5 **Overall response of specific amplifiers**

Combining the results of sections 4.3 and 4.4, the overall gain and phase responses of a single-stage CE or CS amplifier are as shown in figure 4.7 assuming that the breakpoint frequencies at LF, and HF, are sufficiently different that one breakpoint dominates in each case.

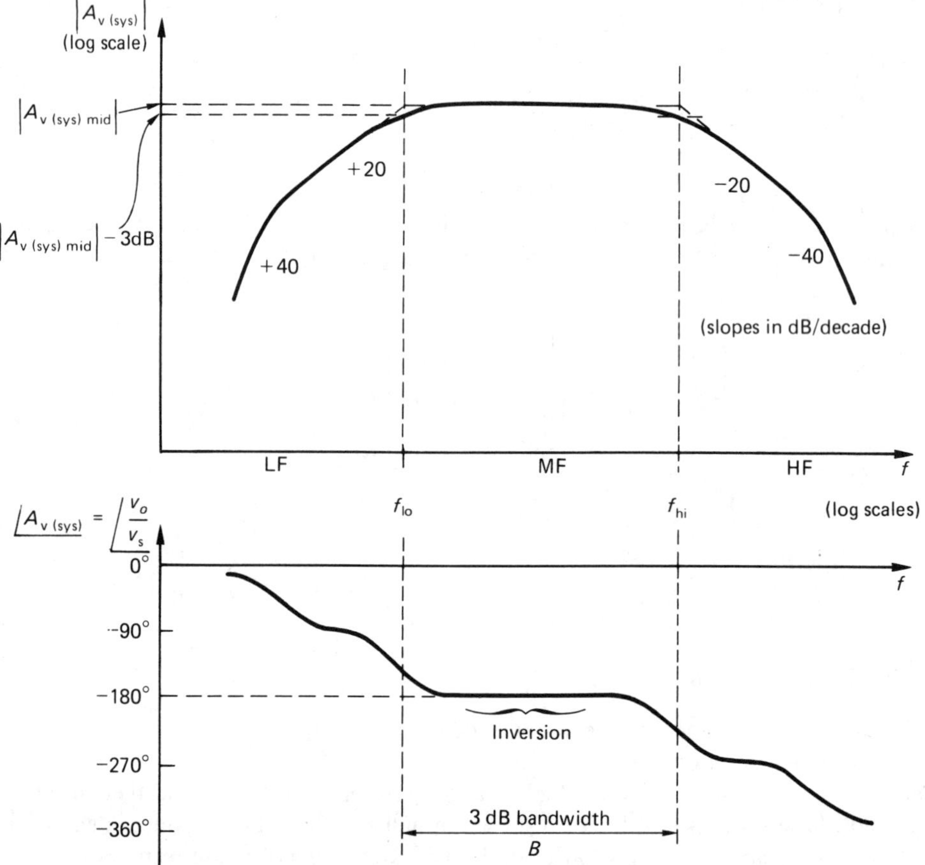

Figure 4.7 Frequency response of a single-stage CE or CS amplifier

The frequencies at which the gain has dropped to 3 dB below the mid-frequency value $|A_{v(sys)mid}|$ are termed the *lower* and *upper cut-off frequencies* f_{lo} and f_{hi} of the amplifier, and the 3 dB *bandwidth* is

$$B = f_{hi} - f_{lo} \tag{4.32}$$

If $f_{hi} \gg f_{lo}$ the amplifier performance is described as *wideband* or *broadband* in which case

$$B \simeq f_{hi} \tag{4.33}$$

The product $|A_{v(sys)mid}|\, B$, termed the *gain–bandwidth* or *GB product*, is often used as a performance index for an amplifier. The higher this product, the 'better' the amplifier as far as wideband amplification is concerned, that is, providing a high gain over a wide range of signal frequencies.

In wideband applications it is the HF response of the amplifier that is most significant (from equation 4.33) and the HF performance depends on transistor capacitances C_i, C_f, C_o and strays C_{si}, C_{so} (section 4.4). Assuming that strays can be reduced to negligible proportions by good design, such as printed circuit board layout, it is C_i, C_f, C_o that dictate the amplifier bandwidth. Because these values of capacitance of a transistor are not equal, different configurations (CE, CB, CC or CS, CG, CD) provide different bandwidths *for the same transistor*. Table 4.2 gives typical capacitance values for low-power transistors.

Common-emitter (CE) BJT and common-source (CS) FET stages

C_i ($= C_{b'e}$, C_{gs}) is the largest of the three values (table 4.2) but magnification of C_f ($= C_{b'c}$, C_{gd}) by the high negative voltage gain of these stages (Miller effect) causes this term to dominate $C_{i(amp)}$. At the output, C_o ($= C_{ce}$, C_{ds}) is sufficiently low that the f_{hi_2} breakpoint is very much larger than the f_{hi_1} breakpoint (equations 4.30 and 4.31). Thus the HF response, and hence the bandwidth, of CE and CS stages is dominated by the f_{hi_1} breakpoint due to high Miller capacitance.

Table 4.2 Typical values of capacitances for low-power transistors

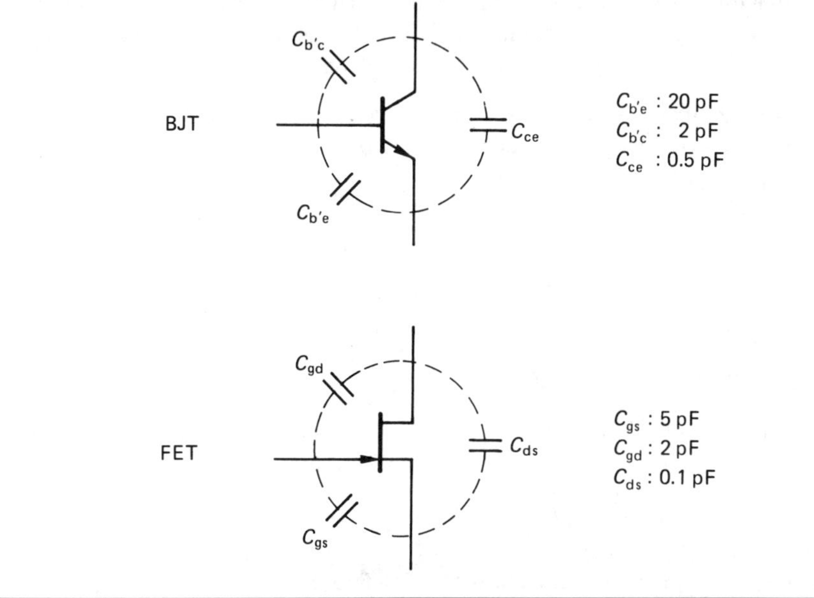

Common-base (CB) BJT and common-gate (CG) FET stages

C_i is the same as in the CE, CS case ($C_{b'e}$, C_{gs}) but C_f is C_{ce}, C_{ds} which is very small, and so although the voltage gain is high the Miller effect is of little significance. In addition, $R_{i(amp)}$ is low for CB and CG stages (tables 3.1 and 3.2) and so the f_{hi_1} breakpoint (equation 4.30) is at very high frequency. At the output C_o is $C_{b'c}$, C_{gd} which makes the f_{hi_2} breakpoint (equation 4.31) more significant than in the CE and CS cases; note that $R_{o(amp)}$ for CB and CG stages has a similar value to that of the corresponding CE and CS configurations (tables 3.1 and 3.2). The HF response of CB and CG stages is likely to be dominated by the f_{hi_2} breakpoint but the resulting bandwidth is much higher than for CE, CS stages and so CB, CG stages are popular as high frequency amplifiers required to operate well in excess of 1 MHz.

Common-collector (CC) BJT and common-drain (CD) FET stages (emitter and source followers)

C_i ($= C_{b'c}$, C_{gd}) has a moderate value but as these stages have a voltage gain of only unity (tables 3.1 and 3.2) there is no Miller magnification of C_f ($= C_{b'e}$, C_{gs}) and so $C_{i(amp)}$ is low and f_{hi_1} relatively high. C_o is C_{ce}, C_{ds} as in the CE, CS case but $R_{o(amp)}$ of CC, CD stages is low (tables 3.1 and 3.2) so that f_{hi_2} is also high. These stages therefore provide high bandwidth but with the limitation of only unity voltage gain.

Example 4.1: Amplifier frequency response

Determine the bandwidth of the single-stage CE amplifier designed in examples 3.3, 3.6a and 3.7a when it is driven from a 600 Ω (resistive) source and feeds a resistive 10 kΩ external load via a 10 μF coupling capacitor. The BJT has a small-signal CE current gain h_{fe} of 200 at the quiescent current of 1 mA and a transition frequency f_T of 300 MHz. Transistor capacitances C_{Tc} and C_{ce} are 2.5 pF and 0.5 pF respectively. Stray capacitance at the input may be considered negligible but the cabling between the output coupling capacitor and the external load introduces a stray capacitance of 10 pF.

The circuit arrangement is shown in figure 4.8a. Consideration of the mid-frequency performance of this arrangement in example 3.9 shows:

$$R_B = R_1 /\!/ R_2 \simeq 22\ \text{k}\Omega$$

$$h_{ie} \simeq 5\ \text{k}\Omega$$

$$R_{i(amp)} \simeq 4\ k\Omega$$

$$R_{o(amp)} = 6.8\ \text{k}\Omega$$

$$A_{v(sys)mid} \simeq -142\ (|A_{v(sys)mid}| \simeq 43\ \text{dB})$$

LF response: Breakpoints f_{lo_1} and f_{lo_2} (equations 4.16) due to the input and output coupling capacitors and f_2 (equation 4.24) due to the emitter bypass capacitor determine the LF response.

$$f_{lo_1} = \frac{1}{2\pi C_{C_1}(R_{i(amp)} + R_{os})} \simeq \frac{1}{2\pi(6.8\mu\text{F})(4\ \text{k}\Omega + 600\ \Omega)} \simeq 5\ \text{Hz}$$

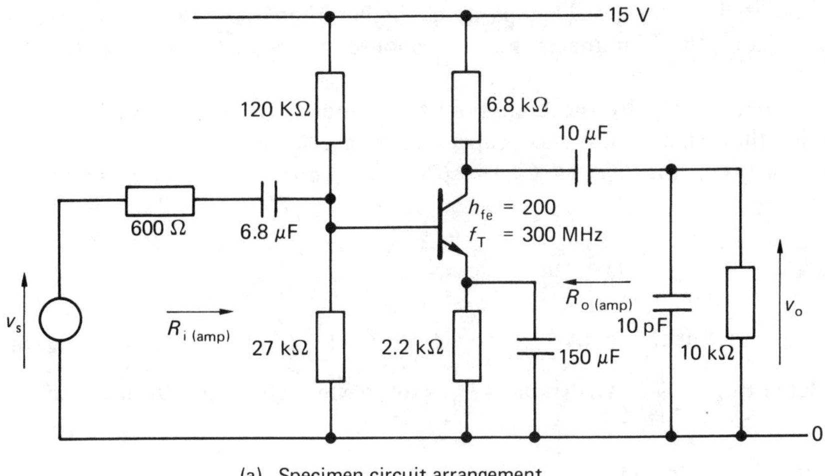

(a) Specimen circuit arrangement

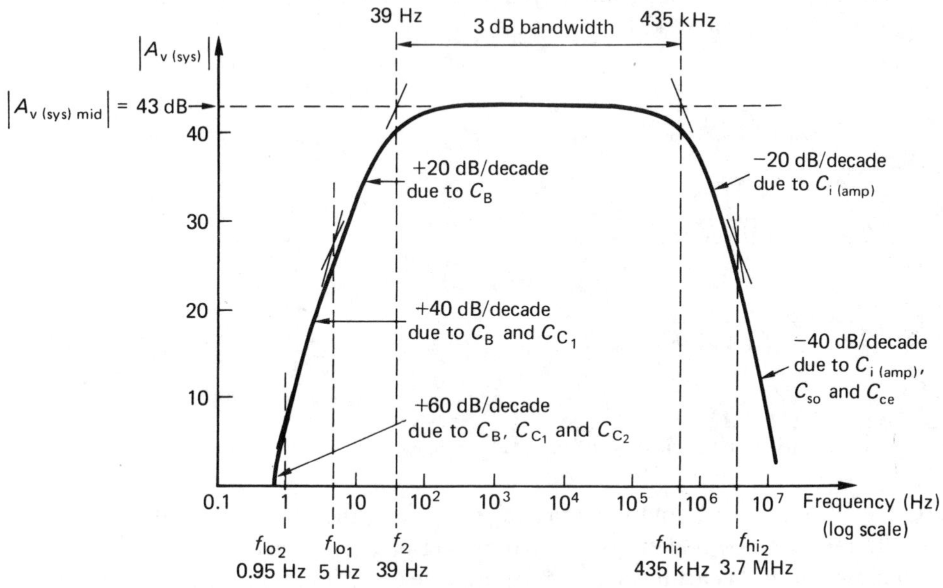

(b) Frequency response

Figure 4.8 Frequency response investigation (example 4.1)

$$f_{lo_2} = \frac{1}{2\pi C_{C_2}(R_L + R_{o(amp)})} = \frac{1}{2\pi(10\,\mu F)(10\,k\Omega + 6.8\,k\Omega)} \simeq 0.95\text{ Hz}$$

$$f_2 = \frac{N+1}{2\pi C_B R_E} \text{ where } N = \frac{(h_{fe}+1)R_E}{(R_{os}/\!/R_B) + h_{ie}} \simeq \frac{(200+1)2.2\,k\Omega}{(600\,\Omega/\!/22\,k\Omega) + 5\,k\Omega} \simeq 79.2$$

$$\therefore f_2 = \frac{79.2+1}{2\pi(150\,\mu F)(2.2\,k\Omega)} \simeq 39\text{ Hz}$$

As the breakpoint due to C_B (39 Hz) is much higher than those due to C_{C_1} (5 Hz) and C_{C_2} (0.95 Hz), it is C_B that dominates the LF response in this particular case (figure 4.8b).

HF response is determined by the breakpoints f_{hi_1} and f_{hi_2} (equations 4.30 and 4.31). In a CE amplifier the general transistor capacitances C_i, C_o and C_f (figures 4.3 and 4.6a, table 4.1) are $C_{b'e}$, C_{ce} and $C_{b'c}$ ($= C_{Tc}$) respectively. Thus $C_{i(amp)}$ in the simplified model of figure 4.6b is

$$C_{i(amp)} = C_{b'e} + C_{b'c}\,(1 - A_{v(amp)})$$

since stray capacitance at the input C_{si} is negligible. C_{T_c} ($= C_{b'c}$) is given as 2.5 pF while $C_{b'e}$ can be calculated from $\dfrac{g_{fe}}{2\pi f_T} - C_{Tc}$ (table 4.1) as approximately 19 pF, from which

$$C_{i(amp)} = 19\text{ pF} + 2.5\text{ pF}\,(1 - (-272)) \simeq 701.5\text{ pF}$$

noting that $A_{v(amp)}$ is taken, for simplicity, as the MF value -272 calculated in example 3.9.

Using equations 4.30 and 4.31:

$$f_{hi_1} = \frac{1}{2\pi C_{i(amp)}(R_{os} /\!/ R_{i(amp)})}$$

$$\simeq \frac{1}{2\pi(701.5\text{ pF})(600\,\Omega /\!/ 4\text{ k}\Omega)} \simeq 435\text{ kHz}$$

$$f_{hi_2} = \frac{1}{2\pi(C_{ce} + C_{so})(R_L /\!/ R_{o(amp)})}$$

$$\simeq \frac{1}{2\pi(0.5\text{ pF} + 10\text{ pF})(10\text{ k}\Omega /\!/ 6.8\text{ k}\Omega)} \simeq 3.7\text{ MHz}$$

since C_{ce} is given as 0.5 pF and the stray capacitance at the output is 10 pF.

Clearly the HF response is dominated by the effect of $C_{i(amp)}$ since f_{hi_1} is less than f_{hi_2}.

The bandwidth of this arrangement therefore extends from about 39 Hz to an upper limit of approximately 435 kHz, the complete gain response being as shown in figure 4.8b.

4.6 **Distortion**

The non-linear spacing of transistor output characteristics along the load line for equal changes of input variable causes an amplifier to have a non-linear transfer characteristic; v_o/v_i is not constant but is a function of signal amplitude. This results in distortion, as shown in figure 3.14a for the BJT case, which is termed *harmonic distortion* [2] because a single-frequency (pure sinusoidal) input results in a multiple-frequency output; the non-sinusoidal output signal comprises a number of harmonics as demonstrated by Fourier analysis (appendix A). If the input itself is multifrequency, this non-linearity results in *intermodulation distortion* whereby sum and difference frequency components are generated which are termed intermodulation or beat frequencies [2].

In the context of amplifier frequency response, other sources of distortion exist when the input signal is multifrequency, which is usually the case, *even if the transfer characteristic of the amplifier was perfectly linear.* Distortion-free amplification requires that the shape of the output waveform is the same as that of the input waveform, though maybe different in amplitude. For a multifrequency input, each component must be amplified by the same amount to maintain the waveshape, otherwise *amplitude distortion* results. Therefore, to avoid this form of distortion, the gain response of the amplifying arrangement $|A_{v(sys)}|/f$ must be perfectly flat over the entire frequency range of components of the input waveform.

Additionally, the passage of a voltage fluctuation through an amplifier is subject to a time delay and if the various frequency components of the input signal are not each subject to the same time delay, the corresponding components in the output signal will be shifted in time relative to one another resulting in *phase distortion.* If an input signal $v_i = V_{im}\sin(\omega t + \phi)$ is applied to an amplifier having gain $A_v = |A_v| \angle A_v$ at frequency ω, the output signal would be

$$
\begin{aligned}
v_o &= (V_{im}|A_v|)\sin(\omega t + \phi + \angle A_v) \\
&= V_{om}\sin\left[\omega\left(t + \frac{\angle A_v}{\omega}\right) + \phi\right]
\end{aligned}
$$

where $\angle A_v/\omega$ is the time delay t_d introduced by the amplifier. For t_d to be constant, that is independent of frequency as required to avoid phase distortion, *the phase response of the amplifier* $\angle A_v$ *must be linear with frequency* ($\angle A_v \propto f$).

Notice that the use of an amplifier over its entire 3 dB bandwidth introduces amplitude distortion because of the gain reduction as the lower and upper cut-off frequencies f_{lo} and f_{hi} are approached (figure 4.7), as well as phase distortion since the phase response is not proportional to signal frequency in the MF range (figure 4.7).

If, in a wideband application ($B \simeq f_{hi}$), it is specified that the tolerable limit to amplitude distortion is that no frequency component amplitude should be reduced by more than 10 per cent, for purposes of example, relative to mid-band components then, assuming one of the HF breakpoints f_{hi} dominates the HF response:

$$
\frac{|A_{v(sys)}|}{|A_{v(sys)mid}|} = \frac{1}{\sqrt{\left[1 + \left(\frac{f_{max}}{f_{hi}}\right)^2\right]}} = 0.9 \text{ (for 10 per cent limit)} \tag{4.34}
$$

from equation 4.29, where f_{max} is the highest frequency component of the input signal.

From equation 4.34, the bandwidth f_{hi} must be at least $2.1f_{max}$ while for a 1 per cent limit (equation 4.34, but equal to 0.99) the bandwidth must be $\geqslant 7.2$ times f_{max}. Notice the implication of the above comments regarding the monitoring of signals using an oscilloscope; if the signal frequency is near the upper limit of the instrument bandwidth, then considerable errors are introduced.

4.7 **Pulse response**

The response of an amplifier to a pulse input, termed the *pulse* or *step* response, is important

for two reasons:
(1) It links pulse-shape deterioration to the limited bandwidth of signal processing equipment.
(2) Pulse testing is a convenient method of determining the bandwidth of an amplifier.

Rise time

If a step input is applied to an amplifier the rate of rise of the output, described in terms of the *rise time* t_r (figure 4.9a), depends on the dominant upper cut-off frequency f_{hi} of the amplifier. The response of a single-stage amplifier at HF may be represented by the model of figure 4.6b, which may be simplified to the model of figure 4.2b by Thévenin reduction (note 3.1) by restricting consideration to the dominant, that is lowest, breakpoint. In this

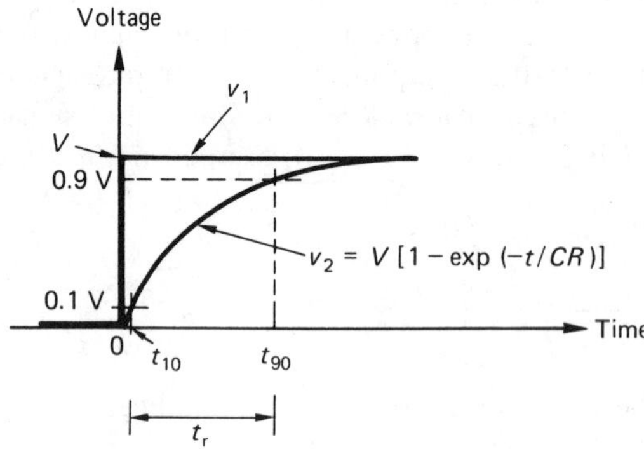

(a) Amplifier rise time for a step input

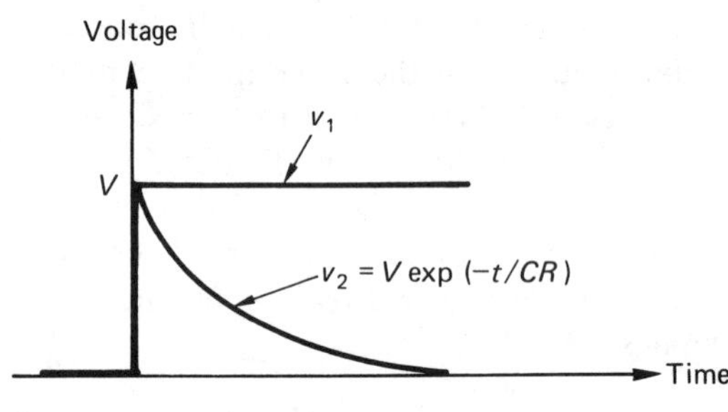

(b) Amplifier sag for a step input

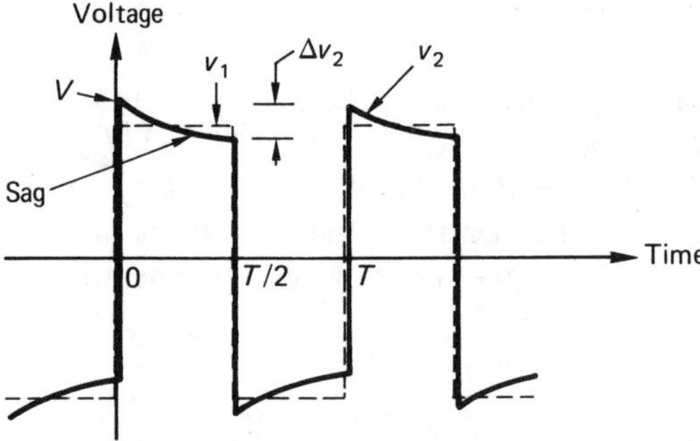

(c) Input and output waveforms for low-frequency square-wave excitation

Figure 4.9 Amplifier pulse response

representation, v_1 is proportional to the input signal to the amplifier v_s while v_2 is proportional to the amplifier output though any signal inversion provided by the amplifier, in the case of CE and CS stages, has not been represented.

If v_1 is a voltage step of amplitude V then v_2 rises exponentially to V with a time constant CR as shown in figure 4.9a assuming the capacitor is uncharged at $t=0$, given by

$$v_2 = V[1 - \exp(-t/CR)] \tag{4.35}$$

corresponding to the result of example 1.2a.
Rearranging equation 4.35, the time t' taken for v_2 to rise from zero to a specific value $v_2(t')$ is

$$t' = CR \ln\left[\frac{V}{V - v_2(t')}\right] \tag{4.36}$$

If t_{10} and t_{90} are the times taken for v_2 to reach 10 per cent and 90 per cent of the final value V, respectively, $t_{10} = CR \ln[V/(V-0.1V)] = -CR \ln 0.9$, and correspondingly $t_{90} = -CR \ln 0.1$ from which the 10–90 per cent rise time t_r is

$$\begin{aligned} t_r &= t_{90} - t_{10} \\ &= -CR \ln 0.1 - (-CR \ln 0.9) \\ &= CR \ln 9 \\ &\simeq 2.2CR \end{aligned} \tag{4.37}$$

Combining this result with equation 4.8 shows that the upper cut-off frequency and rise time of an amplifier are related by

$$f_{hi} \simeq \frac{2.2}{2\pi t_r} = \frac{0.35}{t_r} \tag{4.38}$$

For a wideband amplifier, the bandwidth $B \simeq f_{hi}$ (equation 4.33), giving

$$B \simeq \frac{0.35}{t_r} \tag{4.39}$$

so that measurement of rise time provides a simple method of determining the bandwidth of a wideband amplifier. Equation 4.39 is also useful in relating the rise time of a measurement instrument such as an oscilloscope to its bandwidth, which is important in accessing the contribution to the measured system response attributable to the instrument. For example, an oscilloscope with a quoted bandwidth of 25 MHz introduces a rise time of $0.35/(25 \times 10^6\ \text{Hz}) = 14$ ns, which may be significant when displaying HF pulse waveforms.

Sag

The LF response of a single-stage amplifier can be represented by the model of figure 4.4a which simplifies to the basic arrangement of figure 4.2a representing the dominant (highest) breakpoint, v_1 being $\propto v_s$ and $v_2 \propto v_o$. If v_1 is a step of magnitude V, the capacitor charges from zero to V exponentially and v_2 correspondingly falls from V to zero as shown in figure 4.9b. Note that the time scales in figures 4.9a, b are different so that the exponential rise of 4.9a is contained within the sharp rise at $t=0$ in 4.9b, the numerical values of the time constants being different.

If the single step excitation is replaced by a low-frequency square wave as in figure 4.9c, the capacitor will not have time to charge fully before the input voltage changes sign. Thus

v_2 will not decay to zero but each pulse top will show an exponential decay, termed *sag* or *droop*. Assume v_2 rises to V at $t=0$, then the variation of v_2 over the half cycle of the input square wave $t=0 \rightarrow T/2$ is given by $V\exp(-t/CR)$ from figure 4.9b. The drop in voltage over this time Δv_2 is

$$\Delta v_2 = v_2(0) - v_2(T/2)$$
$$= V - V\exp(-T/2CR) \qquad (4.40)$$

Sag S is defined as the ratio of Δv_2 to the starting value V, thus

$$S = 1 - \exp(-T/2CR) \qquad (4.41)$$

If the frequency of the input square wave ($f = 1/T$) is adjusted to make the sag relatively small, that is, no more than about 0.2 (20 per cent), the exponential term can be approximated, from the series

$$\exp x = 1 + x + \frac{x^2}{2!} + \frac{x^3}{3!} + \ldots,$$

to $1-(T/2CR)$, with an accuracy of better than 3 per cent. Substituting this approximation in equation 4.41 gives

$$S \simeq \frac{T}{2CR} = \frac{1}{2CRf} \qquad (4.42)$$

where f is the frequency of the square wave.

The link between sag and lower cut-off frequency is obtained by combining equations 4.3 and 4.42 from which

$$f_{lo} \simeq \frac{Sf}{\pi} \qquad (4.43)$$

Example 4.2: Amplifier pulse response

Estimate the rise time and sag of v_o in the arrangement of figure 4.8a when v_s is an ideal 1 kHz square wave.

From example 4.1 the dominant cut-off frequencies of the arrangement are $f_{lo} = 39$ Hz and $f_{hi} = 435$ kHz.

Using these results in conjunction with equations 4.38 and 4.43 gives

$$t_r \simeq \frac{0.35}{f_{hi}} = \frac{0.35}{435\text{ kHz}} \simeq 0.8\ \mu\text{s}$$

$$S \simeq \frac{\pi f_{lo}}{f} = \frac{\pi(39\text{ Hz})}{(1\text{ kHz})} = 0.123 \text{ or } 12.3 \text{ per cent}$$

References and further reading

1. M.E. Goodge, *Semiconductor Device Technology* (Macmillan, 1985)
   (a) section 2.2.26,
   (b) section 2.3.9

2. P.M. Chirlian, *Analysis and Design of Integrated Electronic Circuits*, 2nd edition, pp. 153–155 (Harper and Row/Wiley, 1987)
3. T.L. Floyd, *Electronic Devices*, 2nd edition, chapter 11 (Merrill, 1988)
4. C.J. Savant, M.S. Roden and G.L. Carpenter, *Electronic Circuit Design*, chapter 10 (Benjamin/Cummings, 1987)
5. T.F. Bogart, *Electronic Devices and Circuits*, chapter 10 (Merrill, 1986)
6. F.H. Mitchell, *Introduction to Electronics Design*, chapter 10 (Prentice-Hall, 1988)
7. G.M. Glasford, *Analog Electronic Circuits*, chapter 4 (Prentice-Hall, 1986)
8. M.S. Ghausi, *Electronic Devices and Circuits*, chapter 7 (Holt-Saunders, 1985)
9. W.H. Hayt and G.W. Neudeck, *Electronic Circuit Analysis and Design*, 2nd edition, chapter 7 (Houghton Mifflin, 1984)
10. A.S. Sedra and K.C. Smith, *Microelectronic Circuits*, 2nd edition, chapter 11 (Holt, Rinehart and Winston, 1987)
11. P.M. Chirlian, *Analysis and Design of Integrated Electronic Circuits*, 2nd edition, chapter 12 (Harper and Row/Wiley, 1987)
12. R.J. Maddock and D.M. Calcutt, *Electronics: A Course for Engineers*, chapter 5 (Longman, 1988)
13. J. Millman and A. Grabel, *Microelectronics*, 2nd edition, chapter 11 (McGraw-Hill, 1988)
14. R.A. Colclaser, D.A. Neamen and C.F. Hawkins, *Electronic Circuit Analysis*, chapter 12 (Wiley, 1984)
15. E.N. Lurch, *Fundamentals of Electronics*, 3rd edition, chapters 11 and 15 (Wiley, 1981)
16. M. Cirovic, *Basic Electronics*, 2nd edition, chapter 9 (Prentice-Hall, 1979)
17. C.A. Holt, *Electronic Circuits*, chapter 18 (Wiley, 1978)
18. S.A. Knight, *Electronics for Higher TEC*, chapter 6 (Granada, 1983)

Tutorial questions

Note: Answers correspond to rounding to 2 decimal places during calculation.

4.1 An amplifier has a mid-frequency voltage gain of -1000 with lower and upper cut-off frequencies of 100 Hz and 1 MHz respectively. Using asymptotic approximations of voltage gain roll-off at LF and HF, estimate the amplifier gain for sinusoidal input signals of 10 Hz, 50 Hz, 1 kHz, 4 MHz and 100 MHz. What would be the phase lag introduced by the amplifier at 10 Hz, 1 kHz, 10 MHz?

[Answers: 40 dB, 54 dB, 60 dB, 48 dB, 20 dB; 90°, 180°, 270°]

4.2 The single-stage CE amplifier of figure 3.6b has $R_1 = 82\,\text{k}\Omega$, $R_2 = 18\,\text{k}\Omega$, $R_C = 5.6\,\text{k}\Omega$, $R_E = 1.2\,\text{k}\Omega$, $C_C = 6.8\,\mu\text{F}$, $C_B = 220\,\mu\text{F}$ and is driven by a source having $R_{os} = 600\,\Omega$. Taking $V_{CC} = 10$ V, $V_{BE} = 0.6$ V and $h_{fe} = 300$, determine the cut-off frequencies due to C_C and C_B. If the circuit is directly coupled to a 10 kΩ external load via a cable having a capacitance of 100 pF, determine the upper cut-off frequency assuming the transition frequency of the BJT to be very high. What is the bandwidth of this arrangement? *Note*: It is first necessary to determine h_{ie} by calculation of I_C and g_{fe}.

[Answers: 4.2 Hz, 27.55 Hz, 443.36 kHz, 443.33 kHz)

4.3 If the connecting cable to the external load in question 4.2 is shortened so that the stray capacitance becomes negligible, what would be the bandwidth of the arrangement if the BJT has $C_{Tc} = 2$ pF and $f_T = 200$ MHz?

Note: In order to calculate the Miller capacitance it is first necessary to determine the mid-frequency voltage gain corresponding to the effective load $R_C /\!/ R_L$.

[Answer: 931.85 kHz]

4.4 An oscilloscope has a quoted bandwidth of 50 MHz. If a step change of voltage is applied to the input such that the voltage switches instantaneously from zero to 20 V, how long would it take for the spot on the screen to (a) move between the 2 V and 18 V levels, (b) reach the 10 V level from zero?

[Answers: 7 ns, 2.21 ns]

4.5 When a 1 kHz square wave is applied to an ac coupled amplifier, the sag of the output pulse top is 10 per cent. Assuming the low frequency response of the amplifier to be dominated by the input coupling capacitor, determine the value of this capacitor if the input resistance of the amplifier is 4 kΩ. Mention any assumptions made to enable a solution to be obtained.

[Answer: 1.25 μF, assuming $R_{os} \ll R_{i(amp)}$]

4.6 Show that the cut-off frequencies due to coupling, bypass and transistor capacitances for the CS JFET amplifier stage of figure 3.6c are given by

$$\frac{1}{2\pi C_C(R_B + R_{os})}, \quad \frac{1 + g_{fs}R_S}{2\pi C_B R_S} \quad \text{and} \quad \frac{1}{2\pi C_{i(amp)}(R_{os} /\!/ R_B)} \quad \text{respectively}$$

where $R_B = R_1 /\!/ R_2$ and $C_{i(amp)} = C_{gs} + C_{gd}(1 - A_v)$, assuming the effects represented by g_{is}, g_{rs}, g_{os} and C_{ds} are negligible.

5 Feedback

Coverage

- Terminology: forward path gain, loop gain and closed-loop gain, feedback fraction, negative and positive feedback.
- Effect of negative feedback on amplifier performance with respect to gain sensitivity, frequency response, distortion, noise, input resistance and output resistance.
- The various feedback configurations and their practical implementation.

The performance of the basic amplifiers of chapter 3 can be improved by the introduction of *feedback* whereby the amplifier output is *sampled* and the sample *mixed* with the original source signal to create a modified input signal to the amplifier. If the resultant input signal is less than the source signal the feedback is described as *negative* and the overall gain of the amplifier is reduced, while if the input signal amplitude is increased by the addition of the feedback signal the feedback is termed *positive*.

Negative feedback is applied to a linear amplifier

(1) to reduce the sensitivity of amplifier gain to device parameter variations and hence to improve stability,
(2) to increase bandwidth,
(3) to reduce non-linear distortion,
(4) to improve the signal-to-noise quality,
(5) to modify the input and output resistances of an amplifier to suit the application.

While negative feedback improves stability and linearity and is therefore widely used in *linear amplifiers*, positive feedback creates instability and is important in oscillators (section 9.1) and switching/pulse circuits (section 7.3.2 and chapter 10).

5.1 **Fundamentals**

Figure 5.1 represents a feedback amplifier in which the upper block is the basic amplifier of voltage gain A usually termed the *forward path amplifier*. The output is applied to a *feedback network* of gain β and the resulting *feedback signal* v_f is mixed with the source signal v_s to form the input to the forward amplifier v_i.

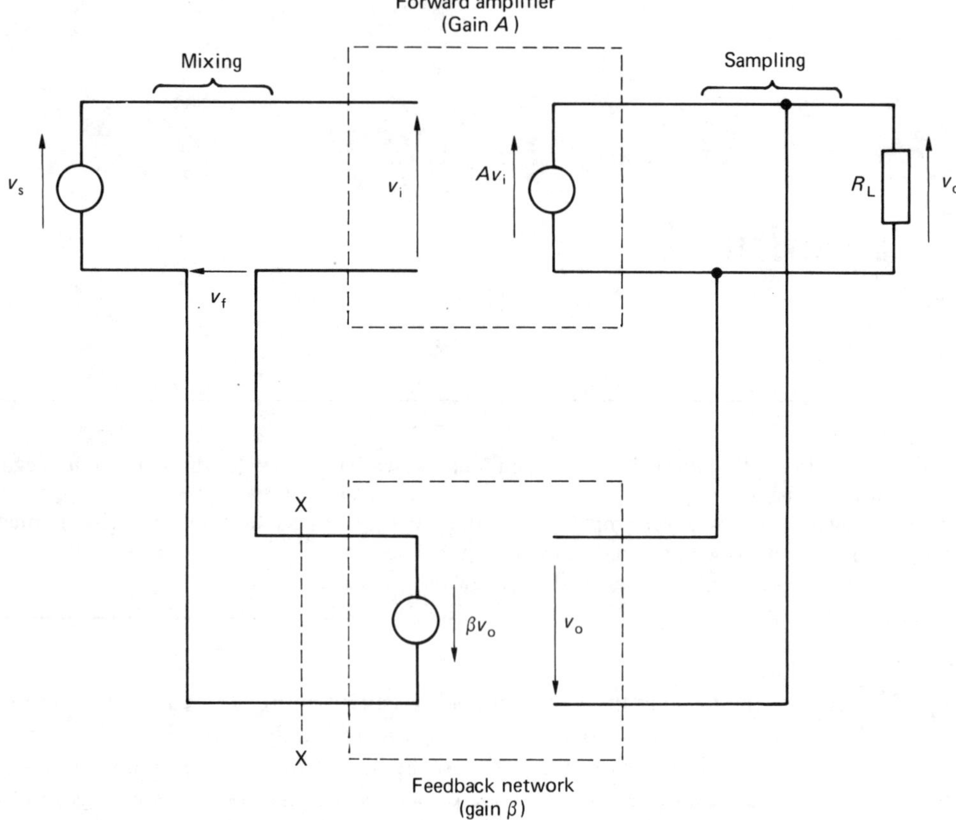

Figure 5.1 Representation of a feedback amplifier

Gain definitions:

Forward path gain (also called *open-loop gain* and *gain without feedback*),

$$A = \frac{v_o}{v_i} \tag{5.1}$$

Feedback fraction, $$\beta = \frac{v_f}{v_o} \tag{5.2}$$

Loop gain $$= \frac{v_f}{v_i} = \left(\frac{v_o}{v_i}\right)\left(\frac{v_f}{v_o}\right) = A\beta \tag{5.3}$$

Closed-loop gain, $$A_{cl} = \frac{v_o}{v_s} \tag{5.4}$$

If the loop is broken at XX (figure 5.1), the ratio of the signal at XX (βv_o) to that applied to the forward amplifier (v_i) is the 'gain around the loop' or *loop gain* $A\beta$. Note that although the loop is broken, the feedback network must be loaded appropriately in such an analysis/measurement to simulate conditions when the loop is closed.

From figure 5.1:

$$v_o = Av_i = A(v_s + v_f) = A(v_s + \beta v_o) \tag{5.5}$$

giving

$$v_o(1 - A\beta) = Av_s$$

from which the closed-loop gain is

$$A_{cl} = \frac{v_o}{v_s} = \frac{A}{1 - A\beta} \tag{5.6}$$

The term $(1 - A\beta)$ is called the *feedback factor* and $20\log(1 - A\beta)$, that is $20\log(A/A_{cl})$, is sometimes described as *the amount of feedback in decibels* (see also note 4.1 on the decibel).

In general, A and β are mathematically complex quantities and so the loop gain $A\beta$ is also complex, corresponding to the magnitude and phase relationship between v_f and v_i. If the modulus $|1 - A\beta|$ is >1, the modulus of the gain with feedback $|A_{cl}|$ is *less* than the gain without feedback $|A|$, feedback has *reduced* the overall gain; this is described as *negative feedback*. Note that if $|A\beta| \gg 1$ the unity in the denominator of equation 5.6 becomes insignificant and the closed-loop gain becomes

$$A_{cl} \simeq -\frac{1}{\beta} \tag{5.7}$$

showing that for high loop gain, the *overall gain is controlled by the feedback network*. If $|1 - A\beta| < 1$ the feedback is termed *positive* and the gain is increased by feedback, $|A_{cl}| > |A|$, leading to instability as discussed in section 9.1 in the context of linear oscillators.

Example 5.1: Reduction of gain by negative feedback

A single-stage CE amplifier has a mid-frequency voltage gain of 45 dB without feedback. What would be the corresponding gain if negative feedback were applied with $\beta = 0.1$?

With reference to note 4.1 on the decibel:

$$20\log|A_{mid}| = 45$$

$$|A_{mid}| = \text{antilog } 2.25 \text{ or } 10^{2.25} = 177.8$$

A single-stage CE amplifier provides inversion in the mid-frequency range (figure 4.7) and so the gain of the amplifier without feedback $A = -177.8$. From equation 5.6, the closed-loop gain for $\beta = 0.1$ is given by

$$A_{cl} = \frac{A}{1 - A\beta} = \frac{-177.8}{1 - (-177.8)(0.1)} = -9.47$$

and

$$20\log|A_{cl}| = 20\log(9.47) = 19.52 \text{ dB}$$

Note that the approximate relation (equation 5.7) gives A_{cl} as -10 or 20 dB for $\beta = 0.1$.

Capacitance within an amplifier causes the magnitude and phase of the gain to vary with signal frequency (figure 4.7) and correspondingly $|A\beta|$ and $\angle A\beta$ also depend on frequency.

An important consequence is that the feedback within an amplifier may change from negative to positive as the signal frequency changes, resulting in instability. Avoidance of this situation is considered in section 7.4.5 with particular regard to operational amplifiers.

5.2 Gain sensitivity

Without feedback the gain of an amplifier is sensitive to the values of transistor parameters and if these have a wide production spread, as is usually the case, the value of gain cannot be closely defined without the measurement of the parameters of individual transistors, which is not practical.

The application of negative feedback reduces the *sensitivity* of the (overall) gain to parameter variation. This is extremely important as amplifiers can then be produced to meet a close gain specification using *unselected* general-purpose components. Usually close-tolerance components are required only for the feedback network so as to define closely the feedback fraction β and hence the closed-loop gain (equation 5.7). Note that the same mechanism improves the stability of amplifier gain for temperature variation.

Gain sensitivity therefore refers to the change of closed-loop gain δA_{cl} due to a change in forward amplifier gain δA. From equation 5.6

$$\frac{d}{dA}(A_{cl}) = \frac{d}{dA}\left(\frac{A}{1-A\beta}\right) = \frac{1}{(1-A\beta)^2} \tag{5.8}$$

from which

$$\delta A_{cl} = \frac{\delta A}{(1-A\beta)^2} \tag{5.9}$$

thus

$$\frac{\delta A_{cl}}{A_{cl}} = \frac{\delta A}{A_{cl}(1-A\beta)^2} = \frac{\delta A}{A}\left(\frac{1}{1-A\beta}\right) \tag{5.10}$$

as $A_{cl}(1-A\beta) = A$ from equation 5.6.

Equation 5.10 shows that the fractional change of gain is considerably reduced by negative feedback as $\delta A_{cl}/A_{cl} \ll \delta A/A$ for $|1-A\beta| \gg 1$; $\delta A/A$ is the fractional change without feedback.

Example 5.2: Reduction of gain sensitivity due to negative feedback

Because of component tolerances and parameter spreads, the numerical mid-frequency gain of the amplifier of example 5.1, without feedback, has a spread of ± 40 per cent. Determine the corresponding percentage spread in the closed-loop gain when negative feedback is applied with $\beta = 0.1$.

Thus, from example 5.1, the gain without feedback is in the range 177.8 ± 40 per cent, that is, 106.68 to 248.92.

Using equation 5.6, this range of A corresponds to a range of closed-loop gain, for $\beta = 0.1$, of 9.14 to 9.61 which represents a spread of approximately $+3.4$ per cent, -1.5 per cent about the mean value of 9.47 (example 5.1).

Notice that these results can be obtained from equation 5.10 for $\delta A/A$ of 40 per cent or 0.4, giving $\delta A_{cl}/A_{cl}$ of 0.034 or 3.4 per cent corresponding to $A = 106.68$ and $\delta A_{cl}/A_{cl} = 1.5$ per cent for $A = 248.92$.

5.3 **Effect of feedback on frequency response and bandwidth**

As the bandwidth of a wideband amplifier is limited by the HF response (section 4.5) it is the effect of feedback on the HF response that is important here. From equation 4.29, the gain of an amplifier at high frequency, *without feedback*, can be expressed as

$$A_{hi} = A_{mid}\left[\frac{1}{1 + j\left(\dfrac{f}{f_{hi}}\right)}\right] \tag{5.11}$$

where A_{hi} is the gain at HF, A_{mid} is the gain at mid-frequencies (A representing $A_{v(sys)}$ for simplicity) and f_{hi} is the *dominant* upper cut-off frequency without feedback.

When feedback is applied, the resultant (closed-loop) gain is given by equation 5.6 which, for the high-frequency range, can be written

$$(A_{cl})_{hi} = \frac{A_{hi}}{1 - A_{hi}\beta} \tag{5.12}$$

where $(A_{cl})_{hi}$ is the closed-loop gain at high frequency.
Substituting for A_{hi} from equation 5.11:

$$(A_{cl})_{hi} = \frac{\dfrac{A_{mid}}{1 + j\left(\dfrac{f}{f_{hi}}\right)}}{1 - \left[\dfrac{A_{mid}\beta}{1 + j\left(\dfrac{f}{f_{hi}}\right)}\right]} = \frac{A_{mid}}{1 + j\left(\dfrac{f}{f_{hi}}\right) - A_{mid}\beta}$$

$$= \frac{A_{mid}}{(1 - A_{mid}\beta)\left[1 + j\left(\dfrac{f}{f_{hi}(1 - A_{mid}\beta)}\right)\right]} = \frac{(A_{cl})_{mid}}{1 + j\left(\dfrac{f}{(f_{cl})_{hi}}\right)} \tag{5.13}$$

where the closed-loop gain at mid-frequencies, corresponding to equation 5.6, is

$$(A_{cl})_{mid} = \frac{A_{mid}}{1 - A_{mid}\beta} \tag{5.14}$$

and the upper cut-off frequency *with feedback*, that is under closed-loop conditions, is

$$(f_{cl})_{hi} = f_{hi}(1 - A_{mid}\beta) \tag{5.15}$$

Comparison of equations 5.13 and 5.11 shows that the variation of gain with frequency when feedback is applied has the same *form* as without feedback. However the mid-frequency gain and the upper cut-off frequency are altered by application of feedback according to equations 5.14 and 5.15.

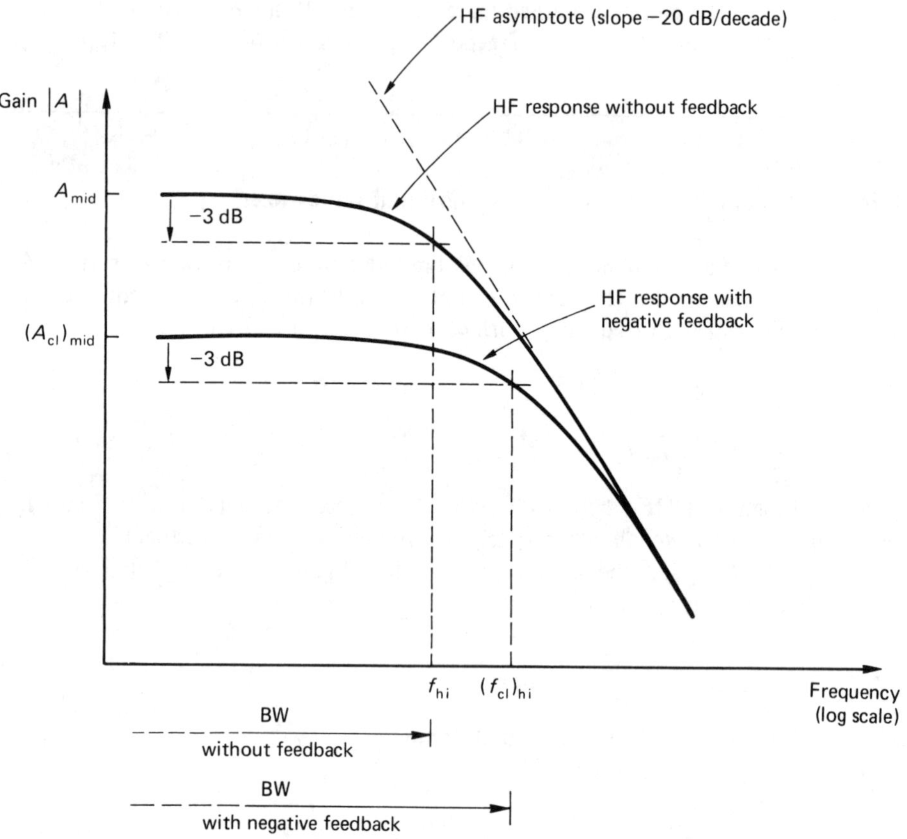

Figure 5.2 Effect of negative feedback on HF response and bandwidth

For *negative feedback* $|1 - A_{mid}\beta| > 1$, so that the mid-frequency gain is reduced and the upper cut-off frequency is increased, resulting in increased bandwidth. These changes are illustrated in figure 5.2 in which the response without feedback corresponds to that of figure 4.2e. Note that at very high frequency all responses tend to the same HF asymptote.

A corresponding analysis of the effect of feedback at low frequencies, taking the dominant breakpoint term in equation 4.15 as representation of the low-frequency response without feedback and obtaining the corresponding closed-loop response from

$$(A_{cl})_{lo} = \frac{A_{lo}}{1 - A_{lo}\beta} \tag{5.16}$$

shows that the lower cut-off frequency is reduced from f_{lo} to $(f_{cl})_{lo} = f_{lo}/(1 - A_{mid}\beta)$ for negative feedback, further increasing the bandwidth.

For a wideband amplifier, the bandwidth B is approximately equal to the upper cut-off frequency (equation 4.33) in which case the bandwidth with feedback B_{cl} is given, from equation 5.15, as

$$B_{cl} = B(1 - A_{mid}\beta) \tag{5.17}$$

where B is the bandwidth without feedback.

Combination of equations 5.14 and 5.17 shows that

$$(A_{cl})_{mid} B_{cl} = A_{mid} B \tag{5.18}$$

indicating that the product of the mid-frequency gain (numerical, not in dB) and bandwidth for a particular wideband amplifier is the same for closed-loop conditions as for the case of no feedback. This leads to the statement: *the gain–bandwidth product for a particular wideband amplifier is constant*, indicating that gain can be traded for bandwidth and vice versa. The (numerical mid-frequency) gain–bandwidth product is used as a performance index for wideband amplifiers (section 4.5).

5.4 Reduction of distortion using negative feedback

Non-linear transistor characteristics result in harmonic distortion (section 4.6). Consider the common case of second harmonic distortion where, for single-frequency sinusoidal excitation, the variation of output voltage is not symmetrical about the average value as shown in figure 3.14a. In figure 5.3a the non-linearity of the amplifier causes a second-harmonic distortion component v_{o2} at the output. Negative feedback is then applied in figure 5.3b and the source voltage increased to $v_{s(cl)}$ so that the output voltage v_o is the same as in the case without feedback. Making v_o the same in each case ensures that the forward amplifier is operating over the same voltage range in each case for comparison purposes. The distortion component at the output with feedback applied, $v_{o2(cl)}$, comprises the distortion component created by

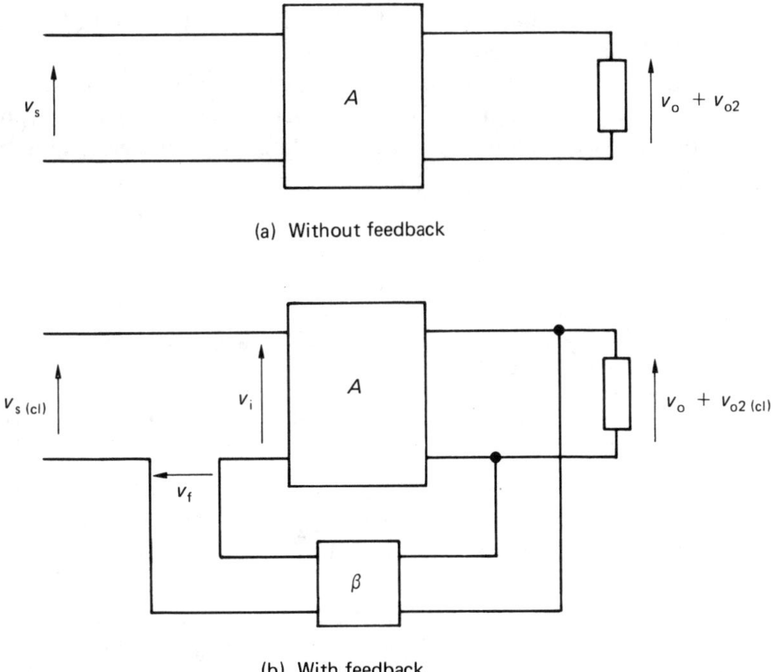

(a) Without feedback

(b) With feedback

Figure 5.3 Effect of feedback on distortion

the forward amplifier, v_{o2}, together with a component due to $v_{o2(cl)}$ being fed back around the loop, thus

$$v_{o2(cl)} = v_{o2} + A\beta v_{o2(cl)}$$

from which

$$v_{o2(cl)} = \frac{v_{o2}}{1 - A\beta} \tag{5.19}$$

For negative feedback $|1 - A\beta| > 1$ and so the distortion component at the output is less with negative feedback applied than in the case without feedback even though the forward amplifier is operating over the same voltage range. This is due to the cancelling effect of the fedback distortion component.

5.5 Noise reduction using negative feedback

In electronics, *noise* refers to unwanted voltage or current fluctuations superimposed on the true voltage or current signal. A widely used measure of quality in this context is the *signal-to-noise ratio* (S/N) which may be quoted as a dimensionless power, voltage or current ratio. More commonly however the S/N ratio is quoted in decibels (note 4.1) as $20 \log(S/N$ voltage or current ratio) or $10 \log(S/N$ power ratio). An improvement in quality as far as noise is concerned shows as an increase in the S/N ratio, that is, for the same magnitude signal, the magnitude of the noise is reduced.

Negative feedback cannot improve the S/N ratio with regard to noise introduced at the input of a feedback amplifier, as the reduction of gain created by negative feedback reduces the signal and noise components at the output by the same proportion so that the S/N ratio remains unchanged; there is no improvement in quality.

Consider however the multistage arrangement of figure 5.4 where the noise occurs after the first stage. The output voltage comprises two components: the input voltage v_i multiplied by gains A_1 and A_2 of the cascaded amplifier stages and the noise voltage v_n multiplied only by A_2, thus

$$v_o = A_1 A_2 v_i + A_2 v_n \tag{5.20}$$

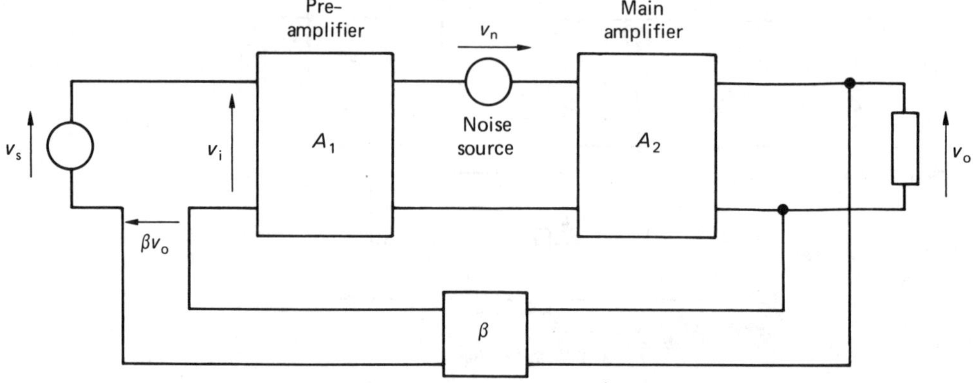

Figure 5.4 Use of a low-noise preamplifier to improve quality

But

$$v_i = v_s + \beta v_o$$

therefore

$$v_o = A_1 A_2 (v_s + \beta v_o) + A_2 v_n$$

Thus

$$v_o = \frac{A_1 A_2 v_s}{1 - A_1 A_2 \beta} + \frac{A_2 v_n}{1 - A_1 A_2 \beta} = \frac{A}{1 - A\beta}\left[v_s + \frac{v_n}{A_1}\right] \tag{5.21}$$

where $A = A_1 A_2$.

The relative magnitudes of signal and noise at the output are then v_s and v_n/A_1, and the S/N ratio is therefore $A_1 v_s/v_n$ which, provided $A_1 > 1$, is an improvement compared with the ratio v_s/v_n that would have been obtained had the first stage A_1 been omitted. Generally the noise performance of an amplifier stage is worse the higher its output power because of the higher current levels involved and associated unintended feedback within the amplifier due to induced voltages, together with poorer stabilisation of the dc power supply resulting in *mains hum*. The power stage of a complete amplifier is normally the output stage, as it is this stage that is required to deliver energy to the external load and therefore it is the output stage that is likely to have the worse noise performance of the various stages in the amplifier. This is the situation represented by the arrangement of figure 5.4 which demonstrates not only the improvement in noise performance that can be obtained by the application of negative feedback in such a situation but also the importance of low-noise performance for the input stage (or stages) in a multistage amplifier. An amplifier designed specifically as a low-noise amplifier to provide initial amplification, which itself may be a multistage amplifier, is often termed a *preamplifier*. A complete amplifier can therefore be represented as a preamplifier cascaded with a *main* amplifier (figure 5.4), the latter representing the output power stage. Design for low-noise performance is highly specialised and involves selection of the transistor type and its operating point for low-noise performance [1] as well as careful consideration of circuit resistances and the practical layout of components on the circuit board.

5.6 Basic feedback arrangements

The feedback arrangement of figure 5.1 shows the output voltage v_o being sampled and the fedback voltage v_f being added to the source voltage v_s to form the input voltage v_i to the forward amplifier. This is termed *series* (*input*)–*shunt* (*output*) feedback as the mixing of the fedback and source voltages at the input is provided by the *series* connection of v_f and v_s while the voltage sampling at the output involves the feedback block being in parallel with (*shunt*ing) the output of the forward amplifier. Although this arrangement has formed the basis for consideration of the effects of feedback above, it is only one of four possible arrangements (figure 5.5). The fedback signal can be a current and addition of the fedback and source *currents* can be provided by the shunt input arrangement as in figure 5.5b. Alternatively the output current of the amplifier may be sampled to provide the feedback signal by connecting the feedback block in *series* with the load as in figure 5.5c. A series connection at the output therefore provides *current sampling* and a shunt connection *voltage sampling* while a series input connection gives *voltage mixing* and a shunt input arrangement *current mixing*.

Previous analytical work involving $A\beta$ applies to all four cases *provided* the appropriate definition is used for A and β. In the series–shunt case used above as a general example, A is the voltage gain $A_v = v_o/v_i$ of the forward amplifier and β is the feedback voltage ratio $\beta_v = v_f/v_o$. In the shunt–shunt arrangement of figure 5.5b it is currents that are of interest at the input of the amplifier and so A is taken as the relationship between output *voltage* and input *current*, that is the transimpedance gain of the forward amplifier $A_z = v_o/i_i$, while the

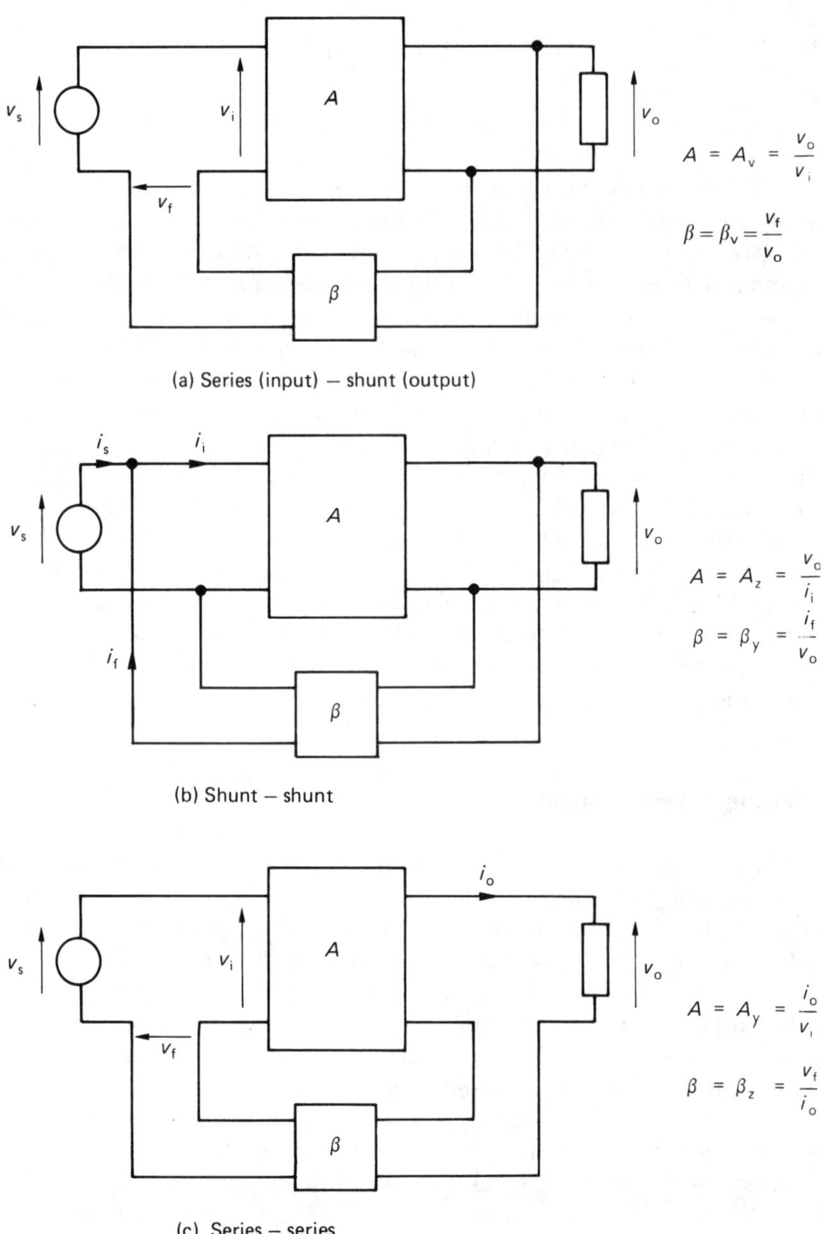

Figure 5.5 Basic feedback arrangements

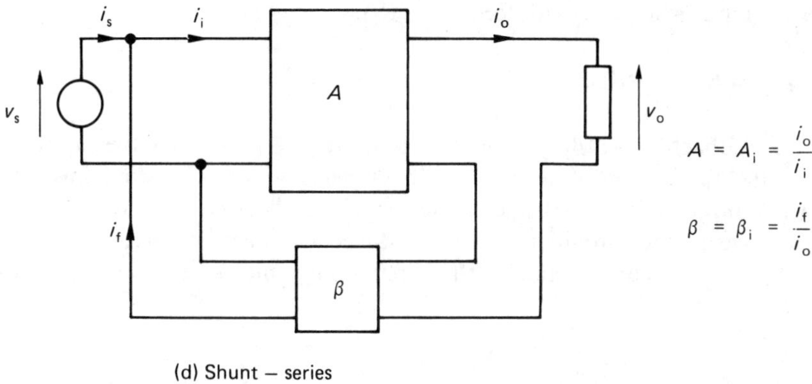

(d) Shunt – series

Figure 5.5 *continued*

feedback fraction β is the relationship between fedback *current* and output *voltage*, namely the feedback admittance $\beta_y = i_f/v_o$. The appropriate relationships for A and β in each of the four cases are given in figure 5.5. Note that in each case the product $A\beta$, the loop gain, is *dimensionless.*

5.7 **Effect of feedback on input and output resistances**

Input resistance for a series input connection

Figure 5.6a shows the input arrangement for a feedback amplifier with voltage mixing at the input, R_i being the input resistance of the amplifier *without feedback.*

With feedback applied:

$$i_s = \frac{v_i}{R_i} = \frac{v_s + v_f}{R_i} = \frac{v_s + A\beta v_i}{R_i} = \frac{v_s + A\beta i_s R_i}{R_i} \tag{5.22}$$

using equation 5.3, from which

$$i_s(1 - A\beta) = \frac{v_s}{R_i}$$

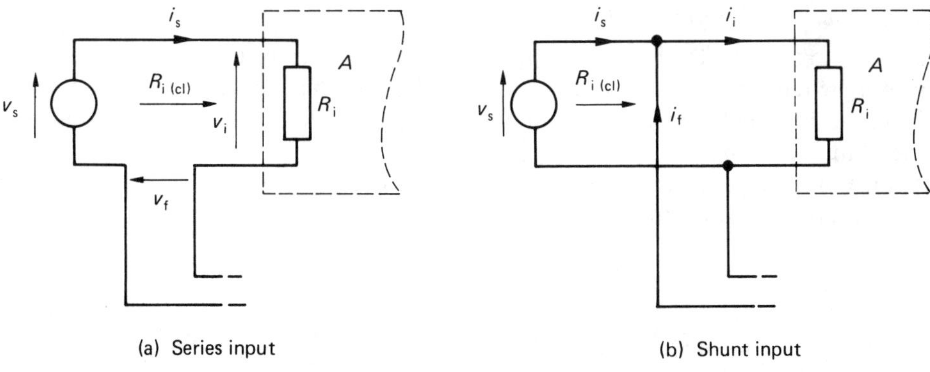

(a) Series input

(b) Shunt input

Figure 5.6 Input resistance with feedback

and hence the input resistance with feedback $(R_i)_{cl}$ is

$$(R_i)_{cl} = \frac{v_s}{i_s} = R_i(1 - A\beta) \tag{5.23}$$

For negative feedback $|1 - A\beta| > 1$ showing that $(R_i)_{cl} > R_i$ so that the input resistance is increased by the application of negative feedback using input voltage mixing. Qualitatively, this increase of input resistance is due to the cancelling effect between v_f and v_s, resulting in the input voltage to the amplifier v_i being reduced compared with the no-feedback case. Correspondingly i_s is reduced and, with v_s remaining unchanged, the input resistance is increased.

Input resistance for a shunt input connection

Current mixing at the input is shown in figure 5.6b. For this arrangement the loop gain is the ratio i_f/i_i, corresponding to v_f/v_i (equation 5.3) for voltage feedback, and so the fedback current

$$i_f = A\beta i_i = A\beta \frac{v_s}{R_i} \tag{5.24}$$

Now

$$v_s = R_i i_i = R_i(i_s + i_f)$$

and substituting for i_f from equation 5.24 gives

$$v_s = R_i i_s + A\beta v_s$$

from which the closed-loop input resistance is

$$(R_i)_{cl} = \frac{v_s}{i_s} = \frac{R_i}{1 - A\beta} \tag{5.25}$$

With $|1 - A\beta| > 1$ for negative feedback, $(R_i)_{cl} < R_i$ so that *current* mixing reduces input resistance. This reduction is due to the increase of i_s compared with the no-feedback case. The input current i_i remains unchanged at v_s/R_i but with negative feedback the cancelling action between i_f and i_i means that i_s must rise to maintain i_i at its no-feedback value.

Output resistance for a series output connection

Using the theoretical method of determination of output resistance as described in note 3.2, an appropriate representation is as shown in figure 5.7a. With a source v applied to the output, the output resistance of the feedback amplifier $(R_o)_{cl}$ is v/i; R_o is the output resistance of the amplifier without feedback.

Assuming that the feedback network does not load the output of the forward path amplifier, the voltage across R_o is v and so

$$i = \frac{v}{R_o} - A_i i_i \tag{5.26}$$

But with the source rendered passive

$$i_i = -i_f = -\beta_i i$$

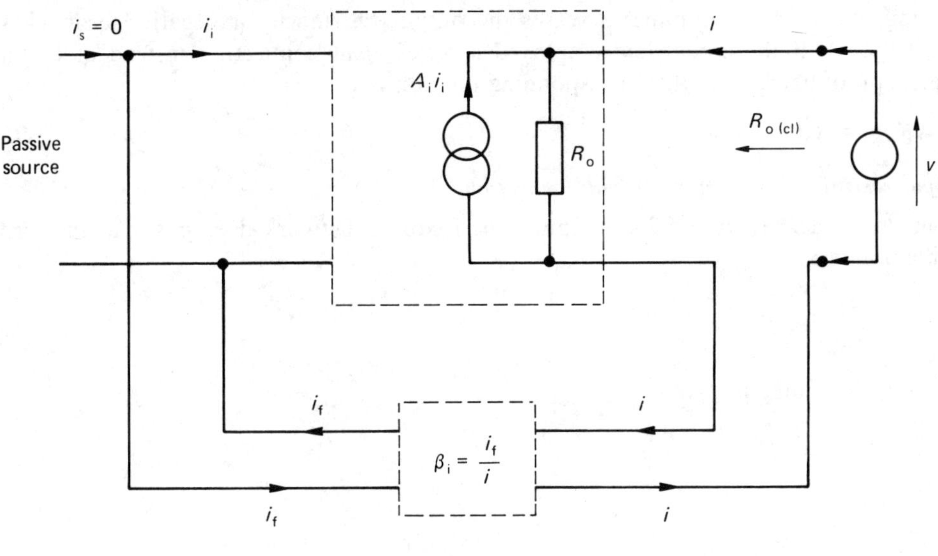

(a) Series output

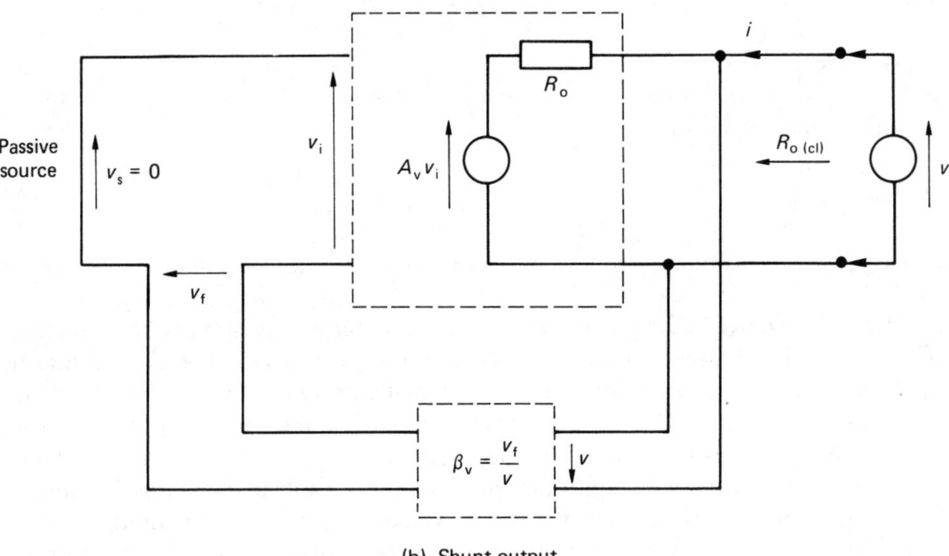

(b) Shunt output

Figure 5.7 Output resistance with feedback

thus

$$i = \frac{v}{R_o} + A_i \beta_i i$$

from which, the output resistance *with feedback* is

$$(R_o)_{cl} = \frac{v}{i} = R_o(1 - A_i \beta_i) \tag{5.27}$$

showing that *current* sampling increases the output resistance for negative feedback since $|1 - A_i\beta_i| > 1$. If the model had employed a series *input* connection instead of the shunt connection of figure 5.7a, the corresponding relation is

$$(R_o)_{cl} = R_o(1 - A_y\beta_z) \tag{5.28}$$

Output resistance for a shunt output connection

From the model of figure 5.7b, assuming the feedback network does not load the forward path amplifier:

$$i = \frac{v - A_v v_i}{R_o} \tag{5.29}$$

But with the source passive

$$v_i = v_f = \beta_v v$$

and so

$$i = \frac{v - A_v \beta_v v}{R_o}$$

showing that the closed-loop output resistance is

$$(R_o)_{cl} = \frac{v}{i} = \frac{R_o}{1 - A_v\beta_v} \tag{5.30}$$

or for a shunt *input* connection:

$$(R_o)_{cl} = \frac{R_o}{1 - A_z\beta_y} \tag{5.31}$$

In either case, *voltage* sampling reduces the output resistance for negative feedback because $|1 - A\beta| > 1$.

The effect of negative feedback on the input and output resistances of amplifiers is summarised in table 5.1: *series* connections *increase* resistance levels while *shunt* connections cause a *decrease*. The selection of input and output configuration in a particular case depends on the amplifier application. If the amplifier is to be driven from a voltage-producing source it requires a high input resistance to effect good voltage transfer, while current drive requires a low input resistance corresponding to the conclusions drawn from equations 3.55 and 3.56. Similarly, if the amplifier is required to *provide* voltage drive from its output, the output resistance should be low, while an output current drive requires a high output resistance, again corresponding to observations from equations 3.55 and 3.56.

Table 5.1 Effect of negative feedback on the input and output resistances of amplifiers

Configuration	*Input resistance*	*Output resistance*
Series (input)–shunt (output)	Increase	Decrease
Shunt–shunt	Decrease	Decrease
Series–series	Increase	Increase
Shunt–series	Decrease	Increase

5.8 Practical implementation of feedback

Table 5.2 gives examples of practical negative feedback amplifiers for each of the four basic arrangements of figure 5.5. Although the examples employ BJTs, the configurations apply equally to FET circuits. In each example, the left-hand diagram shows the practical circuit while the centre diagram is the corresponding ac model for mid-frequency operation. The right-hand diagram shows the model reconfigured in terms of a forward path amplifier A and a feedback network β to show how the arrangement corresponds to the foregoing theoretical work.

A particularly interesting case is that of the emitter-follower in example 1(ii) which is shown to employ series input, shunt output feedback via the unbypassed emitter resistor. With $\beta_v = -1$ for this circuit, the voltage gain is given, from equation 5.6, as $A/(1+A)$ which is approximately $+1$ for a high-gain transistor since $A \gg 1$. This confirms the result of equation 3.110 obtained from small-signal analysis of the circuit.

Example 5.3: Change of bandwidth, input resistance and output resistance of an amplifier due to negative feedback

A high-value potentiometer is connected across the output of the circuit of figure 4.8a to form a series–shunt feedback amplifier of the type shown in example 1(i), table 5.2. Determine the bandwidth and the input and output resistances of the amplifier when the potentiometer is set to feed back 10 per cent of the output voltage.

From example 3.9 the mid-frequency gain of the basic amplifier $A_{v(amp)}$ is -272, it has an input resistance of approximately 4 kΩ, the output resistance is 6.8 kΩ and, from example 4.1, the bandwidth is 435 kHz.

The loop gain under closed-loop conditions is effected by potential division between $R_{o(amp)}$ and R_L at the output, and so the effective value of A_v as far as calculation of loop gain $A_v\beta_v$ is concerned is

$$A_v = A_{v(amp)}\left(\frac{R_L}{R_L + R_{o(amp)}}\right) = -272\left(\frac{10\,\text{k}\Omega}{10\,\text{k}\Omega + 6.8\,\text{k}\Omega}\right) \simeq -162$$

R_L being 10 kΩ from example 4.1.

With the feedback potentiometer set to 10 per cent, $\beta_v = 0.1$ and so the loop gain at mid-frequency is $(-162)(0.1) = -16.2$.

From equation 5.17, the bandwidth of a wideband amplifier *with feedback* is

$$B_{cl} = B(1 - A_v\beta_v) = (435\,\text{kHz})[1-(-16.2)] = 7.48\,\text{MHz}$$

For a series-connected input, the input resistance under closed-loop conditions is given by equation 5.23, hence

$$(R_i)_{cl} \simeq (4\,\text{k}\Omega)[1-(-16.2)] = 68.8\,\text{k}\Omega$$

As far as output resistance is concerned, it is the output resistance of the circuit with the 10 kΩ external load disconnected that is of most interest. Under these conditions, A_v is the gain of the basic amplifier $A_{v(amp)}$ $(=-272)$ and so the loop gain is $(-272)(0.1) = -27.2$. The shunt connected output then modifies the output resistance (equation 5.30) to

$$(R_o)_{cl} = \frac{6.8\,\text{k}\Omega}{1-(-27.2)} \simeq 241\,\Omega$$

Table 5.2 Examples of the practical implementation of negative feedback in amplifiers

Practical circuit	AC model	AC model in general feedback form
(1) Series input–Shunt output (i) Common-emitter amplifier with potentiometer voltage feedback 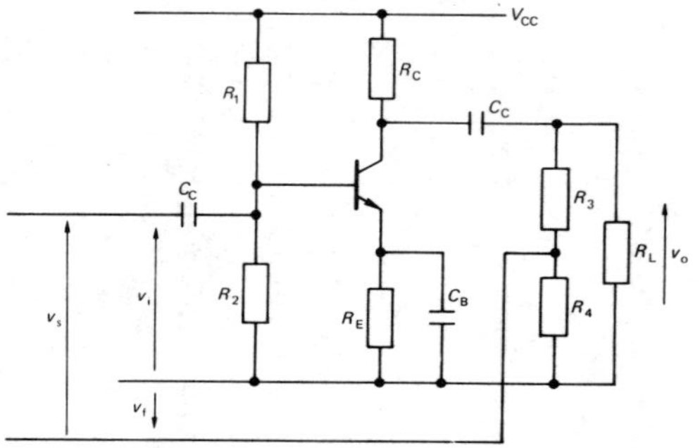	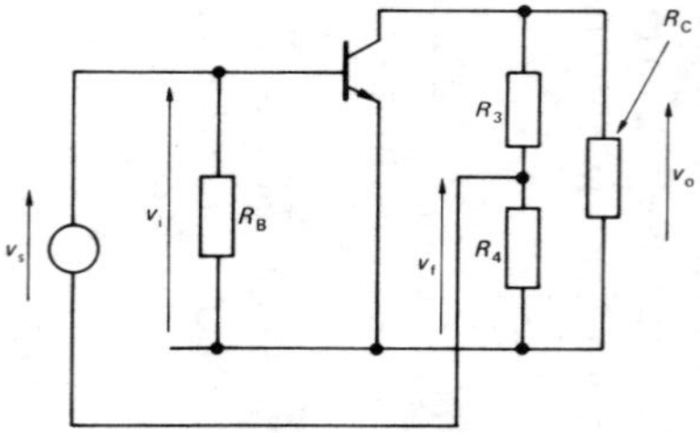 Voltage gain, $A_v = \frac{v_o}{v_i}$; Voltage feedback fraction, $\beta_v = \frac{v_f}{v_o} = \frac{R_4}{R_3 + R_4}$	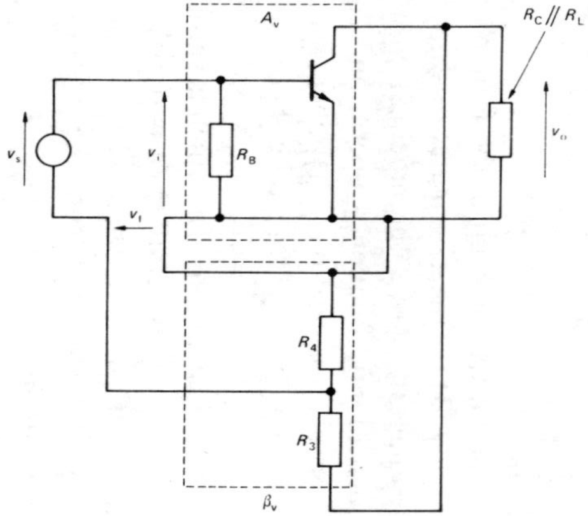
(ii) Emitter follower (common-collector amplifier) 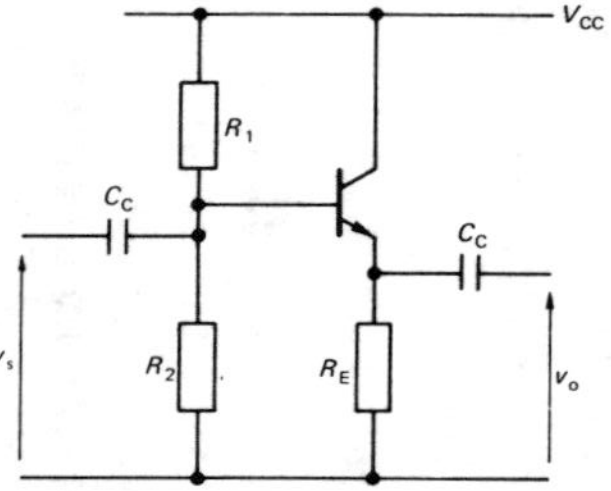	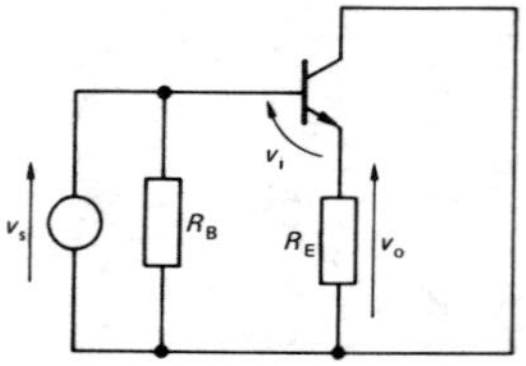 Voltage gain, $A_v = \frac{v_o}{v_i}$; Voltage feedback fraction, $\beta_v = \frac{v_f}{v_o} = -1$	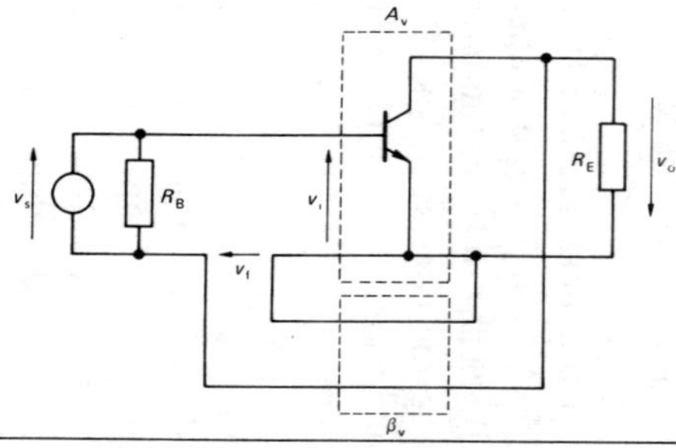
(2) Shunt input–Shunt output (Feedback resistor R_F connected between collector and base in a common-emitter 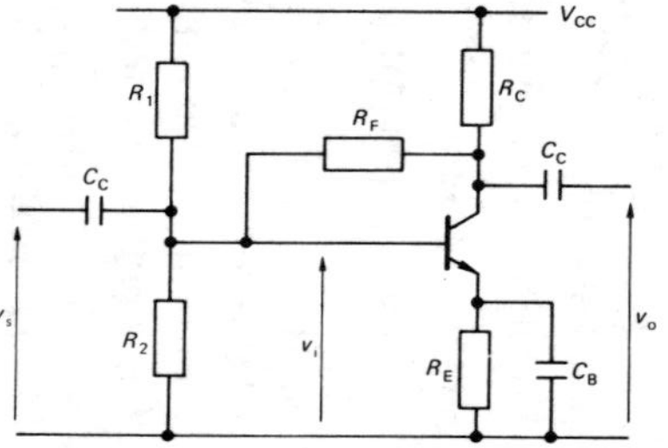	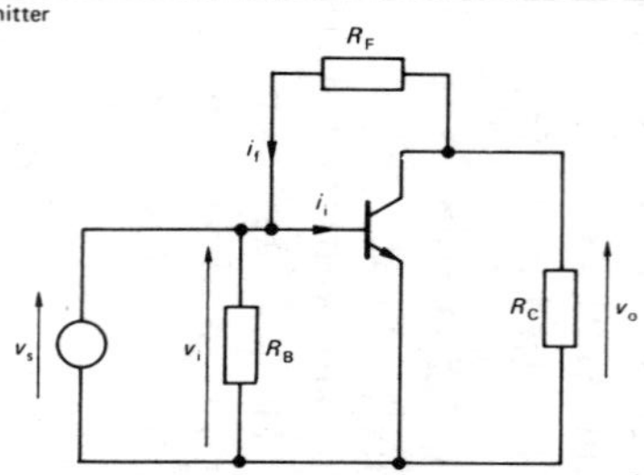 Transimpedance gain, $A_z = \frac{v_o}{i_i}$; Feedback admittance, $\beta_y = \frac{i_f}{v_o} \cong \frac{1}{R_F}$	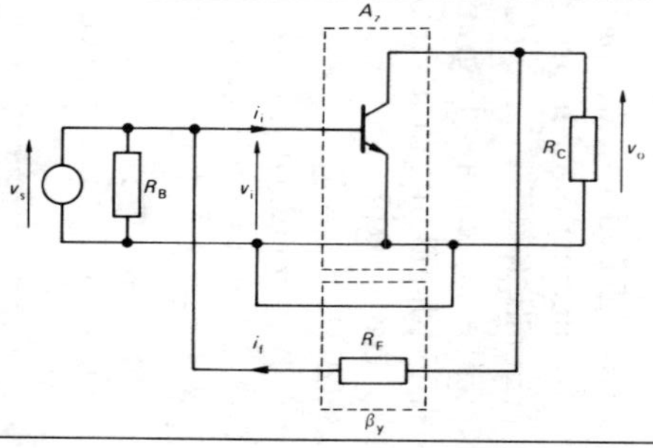

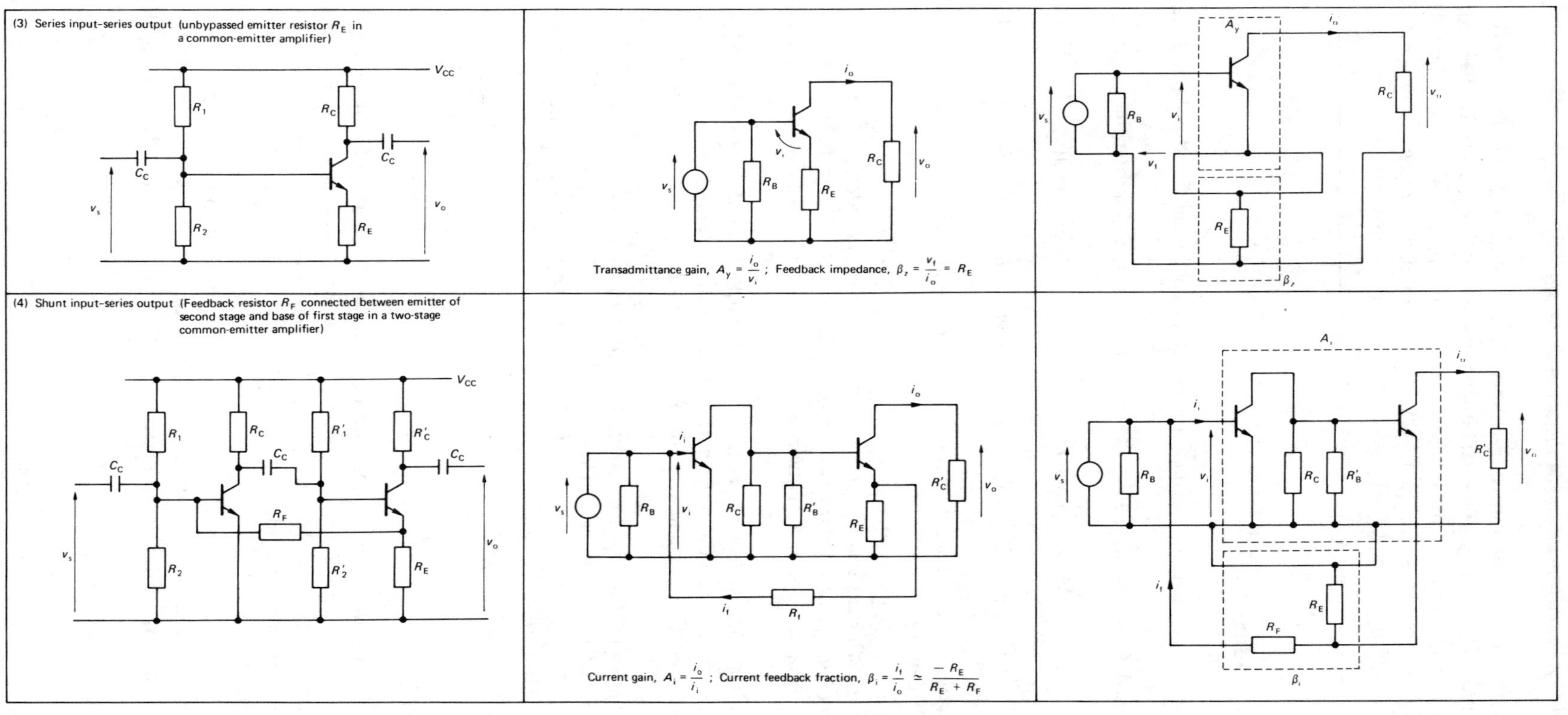
(3) Series input–series output (unbypassed emitter resistor R_E in a common-emitter amplifier)
V_{CC}
R_1
R_2
R_C
R_E
C_C
v_s
v_o
i_o
v_i
R_B
Transadmittance gain, $A_y = \frac{i_o}{v_i}$; Feedback impedance, $\beta_z = \frac{v_f}{i_o} = R_E$
A_y
v_f
β_z
(4) Shunt input–series output (Feedback resistor R_F connected between emitter of second stage and base of first stage in a two-stage common-emitter amplifier)
R'_1
R'_2
R'_C
R_F
R'_B
i_i
i_f
R_f
Current gain, $A_i = \frac{i_o}{i_i}$; Current feedback fraction, $\beta_i = \frac{i_f}{i_o} \simeq \frac{-R_E}{R_E + R_F}$
A_i
β_i

Note that, for simplicity, the effect of the source resistance R_{os} has been neglected in the above calculations, however, since $(R_i)_{cl}$ is high (68.8 kΩ) in comparison with R_{os} (600 Ω), the error introduced is small (<1 per cent). To include R_{os}, the input voltage must be taken as $(v_s + v_f - i_s R_{os})$ instead of simply $v_s + v_f$ (equation 5.5); this modifies the gain equation 5.6 by the inclusion of a multiplying factor $[1 - (R_{os}/(R_i)_{cl})]$ in the numerator.

References and further reading

1. M.E. Goodge, *Semiconductor Device Technology*, sections 2.2.25 and 2.3.8 (Macmillan, 1985)
2. R.J. Maddock and D.M. Calcutt, *Electronics: A Course for Engineers*, chapter 5 (Longman, 1988)
3. A.S. Sedra and K.C. Smith, *Microelectronic Circuits*, 2nd edition, chapter 12 (Holt, Rinehart and Winston, 1987)
4. C.J. Savant, M.S. Roden and G.L. Carpenter, *Electronic Circuit Design*, chapter 11 (Benjamin/Cummings, 1987)
5. P.M. Chirlian, *Analysis and Design of Integrated Electronic Circuits*, 2nd edition, chapter 16 (Harper and Row/Wiley, 1987)
6. G.M. Glasford, *Analog Electronic Circuits*, chapter 6 (Prentice-Hall, 1986)
7. M.S. Ghausi, *Electronic Devices and Circuits*, chapter 10 (Holt-Saunders, 1985)
8. E.N. Lurch, *Fundamentals of Electronics*, 3rd edition, chapter 16 (Wiley, 1981)
9. R.A. Colclaser, D.A. Neamen and C.F. Hawkins, *Electronic Circuit Analysis*, chapter 14 (Wiley, 1984)
10. J. Millman and A. Grabel, *Microelectronics*, 2nd edition, chapter 12 (McGraw-Hill, 1988)
11. M. Cirovic, *Basic Electronics*, 2nd edition, chapter 13 (Prentice-Hall, 1979)
12. D.H. Horrocks, *Feedback Circuits and Op. Amps.*, chapters 2, 4 and 5 (Van Nostrand Reinhold, 1983)
13. S.A. Knight, *Electronics for Higher TEC*, chapter 7 (Granada, 1983)
14. C.A. Holt, *Electronic Circuits*, chapter 20 (Wiley, 1978)
15. R. Boylestad and L. Nashelsky, *Electronic Devices and Circuit Theory*, 2nd edition, chapter 12 (Prentice-Hall, 1978)

Tutorial questions

5.1 The mid-frequency closed-loop voltage gain of a negative feedback amplifier is required to be −80. What value of mid-frequency forward path voltage gain is necessary if the feedback fraction is 0.01? Alternatively, if the forward path amplifier has a gain of −5000, what value of feedback fraction would be necessary?
[Answers: −400, 0.0123]

5.2 A feedback amplifier has a closed-loop gain of −50 and an increase in forward path gain to four times the original value causes the closed-loop gain to increase to −51. Is the feedback positive or negative? Find the feedback fraction and the original forward path gain.
[Answers: Negative, 0.01948, 1912.5]

5.3 A 1 mV, 1 kHz sinusoidal source signal is applied to a two-stage voltage amplifier having overall negative feedback with $\beta = 0.1$. The gain of the input stage is -100 and that of the output stage $+10$. A 1 mV, 100 Hz sinusoidal noise signal is induced at the input to the second stage. Calculate the 100 Hz and 1 kHz voltage components of the output signal and hence deduce the signal-to-noise ratio at the output.
[Answers: 99 μV, 9.9 mV, 100]

5.4 The negative feedback amplifier of example 1(i), table 5.2 has $R_3 = 10\ \text{k}\Omega$, $R_4 = 330\ \Omega$ and the load R_L is very high. If R_4 is short circuited, the voltage gain v_o/v_s is -1000. What is the voltage gain when the short circuit is removed? If the resistors in the feedback network have a tolerance of ± 5 per cent, calculate the maximum and minimum values of closed-loop gain.
[Answers: -30.35, -33.34, -27.63]

5.5 The single-stage CE amplifier of figure 3.6b has $V_{CC} = 10$ V, $R_1 = 82\ \text{k}\Omega$, $R_2 = 18\ \text{k}\Omega$, $R_C = 5.6\ \text{k}\Omega$, $R_E = 1.2\ \text{k}\Omega$, $C_C = 6.8\ \mu\text{F}$, $C_B = 220\ \mu\text{F}$ with BJT parameters $h_{fe} = 300$, $f_T = 200$ MHz and $C_{T_c} = 2$ pF. The circuit is driven from a 600 Ω source and is used to drive a 10 kΩ external load. Series–shunt feedback is introduced as in example 1(i), table 5.2 using a sampling potential divider at the output with $R_3 = 820\ \text{k}\Omega$ and $R_4 = 100\ \text{k}\Omega$. Determine the mid-frequency voltage gain, input resistance, output resistance (not including the external load) and bandwidth under closed-loop conditions.
Note: It is first necessary to determine g_{fe} by calculation of I_C so that the gain without feedback can be obtained (section 3.4), the external load being taken into account. Knowledge of g_{fe} and h_{fe} enables h_{ie} to be determined and hence $R_{i(amp)}$ (section 3.4). Determination of $R_{o(amp)}$ is also considered in section 3.4. Calculation of bandwidth without feedback is covered in section 4.4 and tutorial question 4.3.
[Answers: -8.65, 83.05 kΩ, 220.91 Ω, 15.48 MHz]

6 Small-signal Amplifiers: Advanced Topics

Coverage

- Examination of some advanced circuit techniques: *bootstrapping* to increase input resistance, efficient biasing using *current mirrors* and the use of an *active load* to obtain very high voltage gain.
- Consideration of the performance and advantages of *differential*, *Darlington* and *complementary* configurations.
- Treatment of *cascode* and *tuned* amplifiers.
- Effect of *cascading* amplifier stages.

The design and performance of basic common-emitter (CE) and common-source (CS) amplifier stages is covered in chapters 3 and 4, and the work is extended to the other basic configurations, CB, CG, CC and CD. This chapter concentrates on modifications to these basic circuits and more sophisticated configurations that provide improved performance.

6.1 Bootstrapping

The ac input resistance R_i of an emitter-follower, ignoring the input bias resistors, is very high which, in conjunction with its inherent low output resistance, appears to make the circuit an ideal voltage buffer. Equation 3.111 shows R_i to be approximately $h_{fe}R_E$ which for typical values $h_{fe} = 220$ and $R_E = 8.2\,\text{k}\Omega$ (example 3.12) gives $R_i \simeq 1.8\,\text{M}\Omega$. Unfortunately, this excellent high value is degraded by the input bias resistors so that the effective input resistance $R_{i(amp)}$ ($= R_i /\!/ R_B$, equation 3.112) is typically only a few tens of kilohms; $36.4\,\text{k}\Omega$ in example 3.12.

This degrading of the input resistance due to the bias resistors can be avoided by *bootstrapping* which involves the addition of R_3 and feedback capacitor C to the basic circuit of figure 3.15c, as shown in figure 6.1. The high-value resistor R_3, typically of the order of $100\,\text{k}\Omega$, effectively isolates the circuit input from the bias chain R_1, R_2 so that $R_{i(amp)}$ is increased from $R_i /\!/ R_B$ (where $R_B = R_1 /\!/ R_2$) to $R_i /\!/ (R_B + R_3)$ which provides considerable improvement if R_3 is chosen $\gg R_B$. Note however that the choice of R_1, R_2 must take account of the static drop $I_B R_3$ across R_3, the R_1, R_2 divider providing a voltage ($V_E + V_{BE} + I_B R_3$).

Further improvement is obtained by addition of C which provides a low impedance feedback path for the signal. Since the base–emitter voltage remains approximately constant (at about

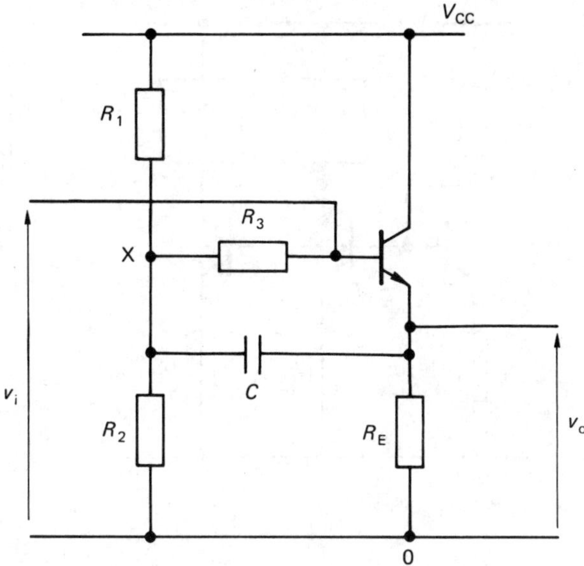

Figure 6.1 Bootstrapped emitter-follower

0.6 V), $v_o \simeq v_i$ and if C is an effective ac short circuit, both ends of R_3 have approximately the same *signal* potential so that the signal current drawn by the R_3, $R_1 /\!/ R_2$ combination is very small. As far as the ac input signal is concerned, the effect of R_3 is magnified thereby increasing $R_{i(amp)}$ appreciably. The same technique applied to a source follower can increase the ac input resistance to the order of 1000 MΩ.

The term 'bootstrapping' refers to the automatic change of the potential at node X (figure 6.1) in sympathy with v_i; the circuit 'pulls the potential of X up by its bootstraps (by itself)'.

6.2 Biasing by current mirror

The basic method of biasing using a resistive potential divider (R_1, R_2, figures 3.6b, c) is inefficient because of power dissipation; biasing by current mirror is more power efficient and in some cases the number of bias components is reduced.

The current mirror principle is shown in figure 6.2a. If the static $I - V$ characteristic of the diode is the same as the B–E characteristic of the BJT, then since the voltage across the two junctions is the same, the diode current $(I - I_B)$ must equal the BJT emitter current $(I_1 + I_B)$ and if h_{FE} of the BJT is high so that I_B is negligible, $I_1 \simeq I$. Thus the static current through the load *mirrors* (equals) the current established in R:

$$I_1 \simeq I = \frac{V_{CC} - V_{BE}}{R} \tag{6.1}$$

Note that the 'load' would be the circuit to be biased such as the active BJT and collector resistor in an amplifier. To improve matching of the $I - V$ characteristics the diode is usually replaced by a BJT with its C–B junction shorted, as T_1 in figure 6.2b; this is particularly

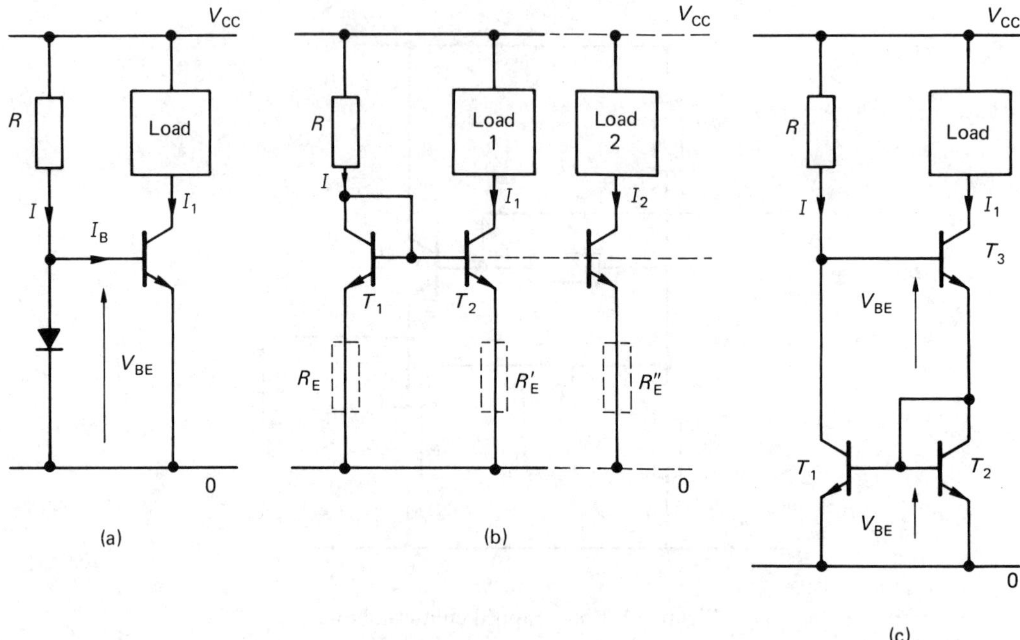

Figure 6.2 Biasing by current mirror

applicable to integrated circuit implementation where BJTs having the same geometry and fabricated simultaneously are closely matched.

The main advantage of biasing by current mirror is the reduction of the number of bias components when a single diode/resistor biasing branch is used to establish the quiescent current levels in several transistors by interconnecting the bases as represented in figure 6.2b. This technique is widely used in linear ICs such as op-amps as shown in figure 7.5. Inclusion of low-value emitter resistors R_E, R'_E enables the mirrored current I_1 to be different from the reference current I; if I_1 is required to be $<I$ then R'_E is made $>R_E$ so that $V_{BE(T_2)} < V_{BE(T_1)}$. The mirror arrangement with added emitter resistors is called a Widlar mirror.

Inclusion of emitter resistors also reduces the disadvantage whereby, because of $V_{CE(T_2)}$ fluctuating during ac operation of load 1, the bias current I_1 also varies corresponding to the slope of the output characteristic of T_2 in its active region. The Wilson mirror (figure 6.2c) lessens the dependence of I_1 on $V_{CE(T_2)}$ by the addition of T_3. With T_3 operating in its active region, its collector–emitter voltage can absorb changes of load voltage so allowing $V_{CE(T_2)}$ and hence I_1 to remain constant. Note that in the Wilson mirror $V_{CE(T_1)} = 2V_{BE}$ and so $R = (V_{CC} - 2V_{BE})/I_1$ corresponding to equation 6.1 for the basic mirror.

Biasing by current mirror is also used in integrated FET amplifiers [1]; matched FETs with gates commoned and sources commoned have identical values of V_{GS} and hence their static drain currents are the same, assuming matched FETs.

6.3 **Active loads**

Table 3.1 (3.2) shows that the voltage gains of BJT CE and CB (FET CS and CG) stages are proportional to the collector (drain) load; high voltage gain therefore implies high load

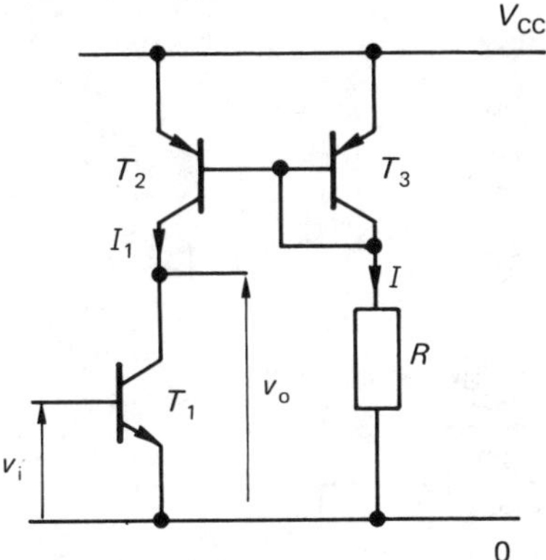

Figure 6.3 Active load

resistance. However, the load resistance also features in quiescent conditions (equations 3.23 and 3.36) and therefore the range of allowable values of load is restricted. In fact the conclusion drawn from tutorial question 3.13 is that voltage gain is ultimately limited by the power supply voltage.

High resistance corresponds to a large change in voltage for a small change of current, properties that correspond to the near-constant current properties of transistors; I_C varies only slightly with V_{CE} for active region operation of a BJT (figure 2.3c) and I_D varies only slightly with V_{DS} for saturation (pinch-off) operation of a FET (figures 2.4b, c).

Thus a technique to provide high ac resistance for the collector/drain load of an amplifier while maintaining practical dc conditions is to use the output port of a transistor as the load, termed an *active load*. In figure 6.3, T_1 is the amplifying transistor and the bias current I_1 is established by the T_2, T_3, R mirror (section 6.2). Note however that as the mirror is in the collector circuit and with V_{CC} positive, it is necessary to use pnp BJTs in this case in contrast to the use of npn mirror BJTs connected to 0 V in section 6.2.

With v_i applied, a fluctuation is superimposed on I_1 and $V_{CE(T_2)}$ and an output signal v_o is obtained. The output characteristic of T_2 provides the load line as far as T_1 is concerned and as the ac output resistance of T_2 is high ($=r_{ce}$ or $1/h_{oe}$, figures 3.9b, d), up to 1 MΩ or more, the corresponding ac voltage gain can be several thousand. Note that the input resistance of the circuit driven from the collector of T_1 shunts the load provided by T_2 and so this input resistance must be high if the high gain is to be maintained. A disadvantage of the high gain is the corresponding high Miller capacitance (section 4.4) which limits the bandwidth considerably. Active loads using FET current mirrors can be used correspondingly in FET amplifiers [2].

6.4 Differential stage

Figure 6.4a shows two CE amplifier stages sharing a single emitter resistor R_E, the two resistors R'_E being omitted initially. The two BJT bases provide two input terminals while the two collectors both provide outputs. The *modes* of operation can be identified: one in which the two input voltages v_{i_1} and v_{i_2} vary in unison, termed *common-mode operation* as the voltages at the two inputs are the same (common), and another in which v_{i_1} rises and v_{i_2} falls (or vice

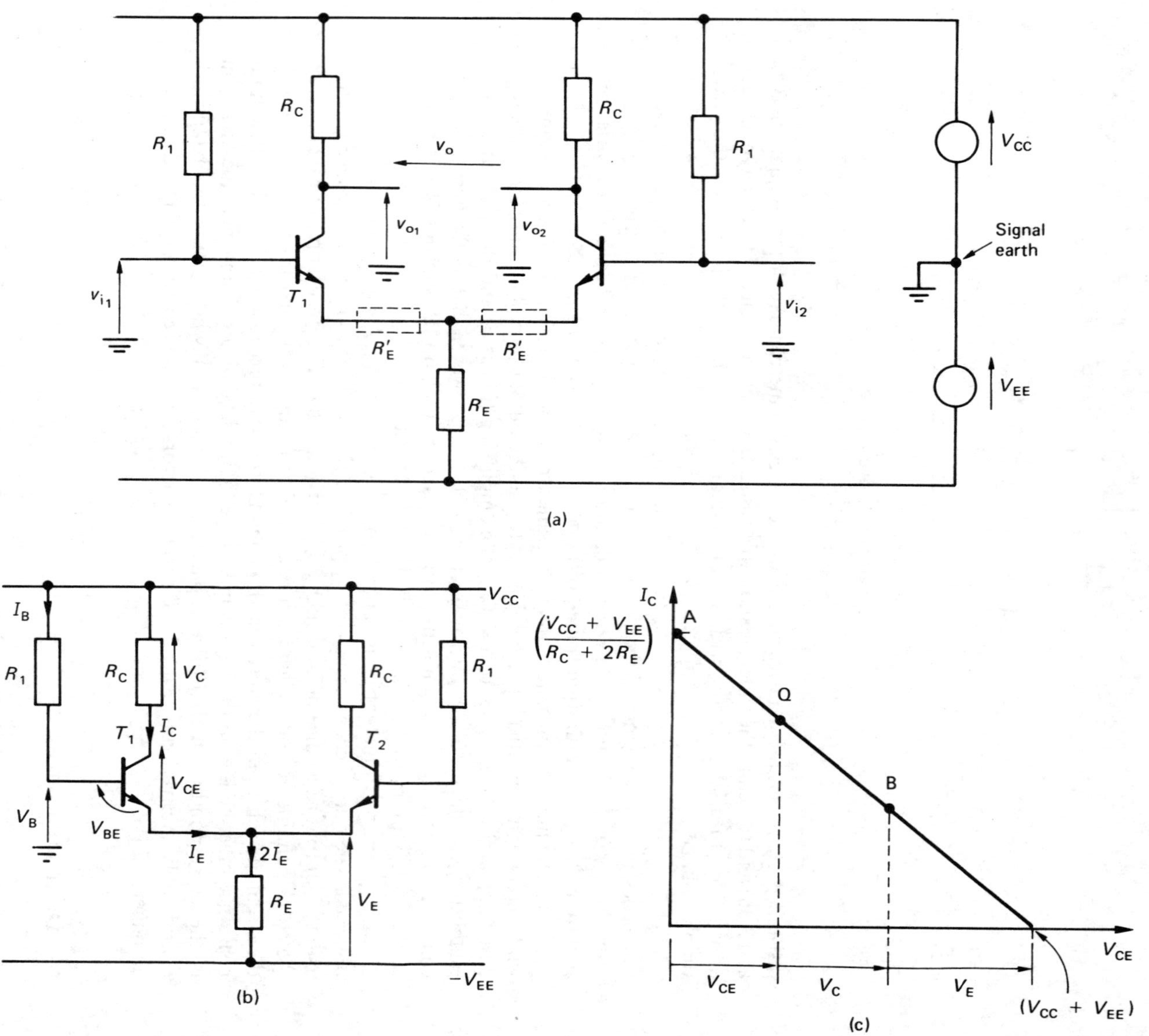

R_1
R_C
v_o
v_o1
v_o2
V_CC
Signal earth
v_i1
T_1
R'_E
v_i2
V_EE
R_E
(a)
I_B
R_1
R_C
V_C
T_1
I_C
V_CE
V_B
V_BE
I_E
2I_E
R_E
V_E
T_2
V_CC
−V_EE
(b)
I_C
(V_CC + V_EE)/(R_C + 2R_E)
A
Q
B
V_CE
V_CE
V_C
V_E
(V_CC + V_EE)
(c)

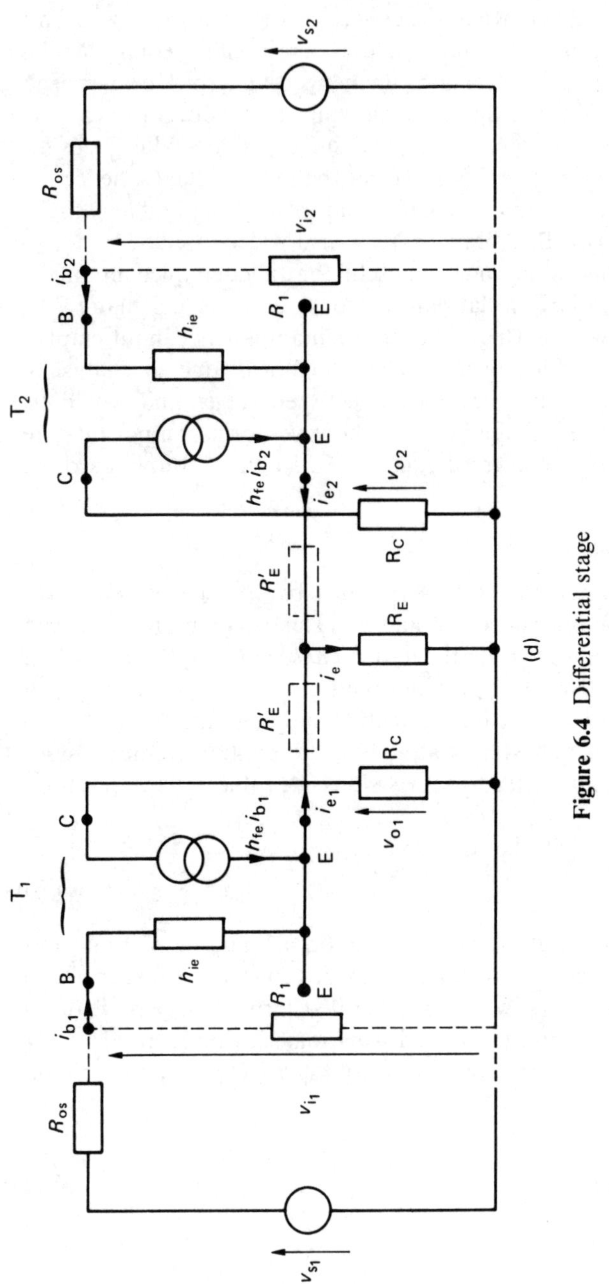

Figure 6.4 Differential stage

versa) in a 'see-saw' fashion, which is termed *differential-mode operation* as the effective input is the *difference* ($v_{i_1} - v_{i_2}$). If the circuit is perfectly symmetrical, that is, the BJTs are matched, their Q-points are the same and the collector loads are equal, common-mode operation results in zero output; the output is taken as the difference in the collector potentials ($v_{o_1} - v_{o_2}$). This is because, for perfect symmetry, equal changes of v_{i_1} and v_{i_2} cause corresponding equal changes in v_{o_1} and v_{o_2} so that the difference $v_{o_1} - v_{o_2} = v_o$ remains unchanged at zero. However if v_{i_1} rises and v_{i_2} falls, T_1 conducts more heavily causing v_{o_1} to fall while T_2 conducts less causing v_{o_2} to rise ('see-saw' action) whereby the difference ($v_{o_1} - v_{o_2}$) assumes a finite value. Thus for perfect symmetry, the circuit responds only to the *difference* of the input voltages, hence the name *differential amplifier*. Alternative descriptions as *emitter-coupled amplifier* and *long-tailed pair* (referring to R_E as the 'tail' of the two BJT branches) are also widely used.

The common-mode performance of this circuit makes it useful for direct-coupled amplifiers such as op-amps (chapter 7) required to have a flat gain response down to dc (figure 7.1), enabling amplification of static and slowly-varying voltages. Such amplifiers cannot employ ac (capacitive) coupling between stages which means that voltage *drift* due to change of transistor parameters with temperature cannot be blocked between stages and would be amplified with the true signal. In the ideal differential stage, however, drift components are common-mode signals as both transistors are affected equally and so direct coupling can be used without incurring the drift problem.

DC analysis

To ensure zero static common-mode input, the BJT bases must be biased to signal earth which is the reference potential of the input signals v_{i_1} and v_{i_2}. This is commonly achieved using a balanced dual supply as shown in figure 6.4a; the term *balanced* means that $V_{CC} = V_{EE}$. The common point of the two supplies (0 V) then provides the signal earth to which v_{i_1} and v_{i_2} are referred. Note that although the use of a balanced dual supply is the usual way to power this circuit, it can operate from a single supply although the resulting common-mode voltage degrades performance and is likely to lead to level-shifting problems in application (section 7.5).

From the symmetrical circuit of figure 6.4b the base voltage is

$$V_B = V_{BE} + 2I_E R_E - V_{EE} \tag{6.2}$$

Selection of I_E is a compromise between high gain values (static h_{FE} and ac h_{fe}) and low power dissipation. Typically I_E in the range 100 to 500 μA provides gains of the order of 200 using modern discrete low-power silicon BJTs, while in integrated form I_E may be reduced to 10 μA or even lower (section 7.2) to minimise power dissipation. Having selected I_E, R_E can be calculated using equation 6.2 for zero base bias ($V_B = 0$), $V_{BE} \simeq 0.6$ V for active region operation and the chosen supply voltage V_{EE}.

From the R_C, BJT, R_E branch:

$$I_C R_C + V_{CE} + 2I_E R_E = V_{CC} - (-V_{EE}) \tag{6.3}$$

For high h_{FE}, $I_E \simeq I_C$ giving

$$I_C = -\left(\frac{1}{R_C + 2R_E}\right)V_{CE} + \left(\frac{V_{CC} + V_{EE}}{R_C + 2R_E}\right) \tag{6.4}$$

Equation 6.4 is the load line that can be superimposed on the (identical) output characteristics of the BJT(s) (figure 6.4c) corresponding to the graphical analysis of a single BJT stage (sections 1.2.2 and 3.4). In the absence of a specific gain requirement, R_C can be selected to centralise the Q-point, corresponding to single BJT biasing in section 3.1. With $V_B = 0$, voltage $(V_{EE} - V_{BE})$ is dropped across R_E (equation 6.2) leaving $(V_{CC} + V_{BE})$ to be dropped across R_C and the C-E terminals of the BJT. Centralising the Q-point within the maximum range A–B (figure 6.4c) gives

$$V_C = \frac{V_{CC} + V_{BE}}{2} \text{ from which } R_C = \frac{V_C}{I_C} = \frac{V_{CC} + V_{BE}}{2I_C} \tag{6.5}$$

Resistor R_1 supplies the necessary static base current I_B $(= I_C/h_{FE})$, thus with $V_B = 0$:

$$R_1 = \frac{V_{CC}}{I_B} = \frac{h_{FE} V_{CC}}{I_C} \tag{6.6}$$

although often the low value of I_B required can be supplied by the direct-coupled driving stage, avoiding the need for bias resistors R_1.

Example 6.1: Component selection for a differential stage

Select values for R_E, R_C and R_1 in the differential stage of figure 6.4b. The power supplies are ± 15 V, the BJTs have $h_{FE} = 100$ and the static base bias is required to be zero.

Emitter current I_E ($\simeq I_C$ for high h_{FE}) is selected at a suitable value in the range 100–500 μA; 200 μA is chosen for purposes of this example. From equation 6.2, for $V_B = 0$, with $-V_{EE} = -15$ V, $I_E = 200\ \mu$A and $V_{BE} = 0.6$ V for active region operation:

$$R_E = \frac{V_{EE} - V_{BE}}{2I_E} = \frac{15\text{ V} - 0.6\text{ V}}{2(200\ \mu\text{A})} = 36\text{ k}\Omega$$

allowing $R_E = 36$ kΩ to be chosen from the E24 preferred range; alternatively 33 kΩ or 39 kΩ could be selected from the E12 range (appendix D). Equation 6.5 allows R_C to be calculated as

$$R_C = \frac{V_{CC} + V_{BE}}{2I_C} = \frac{15\text{ V} + 0.6\text{ V}}{2(200\ \mu\text{A})} = 39\text{ k}\Omega \text{ (E12 value)}$$

to split the available voltage $V_{CC} + V_{BE}$ $(= 15.6\text{ V})$ equally between V_C (across R_C) and V_{CE}, so allowing a maximum swing of $\pm 15.6\text{ V}/2$ $(= \pm 7.8\text{ V})$ about the static collector potential of $V_{CC} - V_C$ $(= 15\text{ V} - 7.8\text{ V} = +7.2\text{ V})$ relative to signal earth.
With $I_C = 200\ \mu$A and $h_{FE} = 100$, a static base current of $200\ \mu\text{A}/100 = 2\ \mu$A must be supplied via R_1.
From equation 6.6:

$$R_1 = \frac{V_{CC}}{I_B} = \frac{15\text{ V}}{2\ \mu\text{A}} = 7.5\text{ M}\Omega$$

allowing 7.5 MΩ (E24) or 6.8 MΩ (E12) to be selected.

AC analysis

Figure 6.4d gives an ac model of the circuit of figure 6.4a using simplified *h*-parameter representations of the identical BJTs (figure 3.9e).

The signal current through R_E, i_e, is the sum of i_b and $h_{fe}i_b$ for each BJT, thus

$$\begin{aligned} i_e &= h_{fe}i_{b_1} + h_{fe}i_{b_2} + i_{b_1} + i_{b_2} \\ &= (h_{fe}+1)(i_{b_1}+i_{b_2}) \end{aligned} \tag{6.7}$$

Considering the left half of the model, that associated with T_1, ignoring the dashed resistor R'_E initially:

$$\begin{aligned} v_{i_1} &= h_{ie}i_{b_1} + R_E i_e \\ &= h_{ie}i_{b_1} + R_E(h_{fe}+1)(i_{b_1}+i_{b_2}) \\ &= [h_{ie} + R_E(h_{fe}+1)]i_{b_1} + R_E(h_{fe}+1)i_{b_2} \\ &\simeq (h_{ie} + R_E h_{fe})i_{b_1} + R_E h_{fe} i_{b_2} \end{aligned} \tag{6.8}$$

substituting for i_e from equation 6.7 and taking $h_{fe} \gg 1$.
Similarly, for T_2:

$$v_{i_2} \simeq (h_{ie} + R_E h_{fe})i_{b_2} + R_E h_{fe} i_{b_1} \tag{6.9}$$

The two output voltages v_{o_1} and v_{o_2} are given by the $h_{fe}i_b$ currents flowing through the respective collector loads, and taking account of the polarities shown:

$$v_{o_1} = -h_{fe}i_{b_1}R_C \tag{6.10}$$

and

$$v_{o_2} = -h_{fe}i_{b_2}R_C \tag{6.11}$$

Elimination of i_{b_2} from equations 6.8 and 6.9 enables i_{b_1} to be written in terms of v_{i_1} and v_{i_2} as

$$i_{b_1} = \frac{h_{ie}v_{i_1} + R_E h_{fe}(v_{i_1} - v_{i_2})}{h_{ie}^2 + 2R_E h_{ie} h_{fe}} \tag{6.12}$$

Substitution into equation 6.10 then gives

$$v_{o_1} = -\frac{h_{fe}R_C}{h_{ie}^2 + 2R_E h_{ie} h_{fe}}[h_{ie}v_{i_1} + R_E h_{fe}(v_{i_1} - v_{i_2})] \tag{6.13}$$

Similarly, elimination of i_{b_1} from equations 6.8 and 6.9 gives

$$i_{b_2} = \frac{h_{ie}v_{i_2} + R_E h_{fe}(v_{i_2} - v_{i_1})}{h_{ie}^2 + 2R_E h_{ie} h_{fe}} \tag{6.14}$$

which, from equation 6.11 gives v_{o_2} as

$$v_{o_2} = -\frac{h_{fe}R_C}{h_{ie}^2 + 2R_E h_{ie} h_{fe}}[h_{ie}v_{i_2} + R_E h_{fe}(v_{i_2} - v_{i_1})] \tag{6.15}$$

If the *differential* output from the amplifier v_{od} is taken as the difference $(v_{o_1} - v_{o_2})$, then from equations 6.13 and 6.15

$$v_{od} = v_{o_1} - v_{o_2} = \frac{-h_{fe}R_C}{h_{ie}}(v_{i_1} - v_{i_2}) \tag{6.16}$$

where $(v_{i_1} - v_{i_2})$ is the *differential* input voltage v_{id}. The *differential voltage gain* for the symmetrical amplifier, $A_{vd(amp)}$, is then

$$A_{vd(amp)} = \frac{v_{o_1} - v_{o_2}}{v_{i_1} - v_{i_2}} = \frac{v_{od}}{v_{id}} = \frac{-h_{fe}R_C}{h_{ie}} \simeq -g_{fe}R_C \tag{6.17}$$

as $h_{fe}/h_{ie} \simeq g_{fe}$ (equation 3.62). Notice that this result for $A_{vd(amp)}$ is the same as that for $A_{v(amp)}$ of a basic CE amplifier (equations 3.65 and 3.74).

Both amplifiers provide inversion and the gain is proportional to the collector load although whereas the basic CE amplifier of section 3.4.3 amplifies the actual input signal, the gain of the differential stage refers to amplification of the differential input signal $v_{id}(=v_{i_1} - v_{i_2})$. Note that the output signal of the differential stage can be taken as $(v_{o_2} - v_{o_1})$ so that non-inverting amplification can be obtained; the circuit therefore provides flexibility in that, simply by selection of output connection, inverting or non-inverting performance can be obtained.

The above analysis is for the isolated amplifier, no account being taken of the effect of the resistance of the source(s) providing the input signal voltage(s) or of any external loading at the output. Using the same designation as in section 3.4.3 whereby suffix (sys) is used to indicate overall *system* performance from source to load, the overall differential voltage gain becomes

$$A_{vd(sys)} = \frac{v_{o_1} - v_{o_2}}{v_{s_1} - v_{s_2}} = \frac{v_{od}}{v_{sd}} = \frac{-h_{fe}R_C}{R_{os} + h_{ie}} \tag{6.18}$$

assuming R_1 very high and equal-value source resistances R_{os} at the two inputs; h_{ie} in equation 6.17 then becomes $(R_{os} + h_{ie})$.

Note that for *balanced differential operation of the symmetrical circuit*, the two emitter currents i_{e_1} and i_{e_2} are in antiphase and therefore cancel in R_E. Thus there is no *signal* voltage established across R_E and therefore no need for a bypass capacitor to be included to avoid gain reduction by ac negative feedback as there is for the basic CE circuit (section 3.3).

With no signal voltage across R_E and resistors R'_E omitted, the ac input resistance at each input of the symmetrical circuit for balanced operation is the parallel combination of R_1 and h_{ie}, thus

$$R_{i(amp)} = R_1 /\!/ h_{ie} \tag{6.19}$$

A modification which greatly increases the input resistance is to include equal-value resistors R'_E, then the input signal voltage at each input becomes $h_{ie}i_b + R'_E\,(h_{fe}+1)i_b$ whereby the input resistance becomes

$$R_{i(amp)} = R_1 /\!/ (h_{ie} + h_{fe}R'_E) \tag{6.20}$$

for $h_{fe} \gg 1$. With h_{fe} typically > 100, a small value of R'_E such as $100\,\Omega$ provides a usefully high value of $R_{i(amp)}$. Notice however that inclusion of resistors R'_E reduces the differential gain because of an additional term $h_{fe}R'_E$ in the denominator of equations 6.17 and 6.18. For differential operation where the amplifier input v_{id} is taken as the difference $v_{i_1} - v_{i_2}$, the two inputs are effectively in series and so the *differential ac input resistance* R_{id} is twice the single input value $R_{i(amp)}$.

For common-mode operation the two input voltages vary in unison, $v_{i_1} = v_{i_2}$ and so from equations 6.13 and 6.15

$$v_{o_1} = v_{o_2} = -\frac{h_{fe}R_C v_{ic}}{h_{ie} + 2R_E h_{fe}} \tag{6.21}$$

where the common-mode input $v_{ic} = v_{i_1} = v_{i_2}$. Although the differential output $(v_{o_1} - v_{o_2})$ is zero, the individual output voltages vary with v_{ic} and the *common-mode voltage gain* $A_{vc(amp)}$ for the symmetrical amplifier is

$$A_{vc(amp)} = \frac{v_{o_1}}{v_{ic}} = \frac{v_{o_2}}{v_{ic}} = -\frac{h_{fe}R_C}{h_{ie} + 2R_E h_{fe}} \tag{6.22}$$

Under common-mode conditions the two emitter signal currents through R_E are additive; they do not cancel as they do for differential operation, and therefore a signal voltage is established across R_E. The ac input resistance corresponding to common-mode operation is therefore different from that for differential operation. From equations 6.12 and 6.14, for $v_{i_1} = v_{i_2} = v_i$:

$$i_{b_1} = i_{b_2} = \frac{v_i}{h_{ie} + 2R_E h_{fe}} \tag{6.23}$$

and so the *common-mode ac input resistance* at each input, R_{ic}, is

$$R_{ic} = R_1 /\!/ (h_{ie} + 2R_E h_{fe}) \tag{6.24}$$

which is higher than the corresponding differential-mode value (equation 6.19)

From introductory comments in this section regarding direct-coupling and the problem of drift, it follows that the common-mode gain should be as low as possible, ideally zero. The ratio of differential gain to common-mode gain, termed the *common-mode rejection ratio* (CMRR) is used as a figure-of-merit for a differential amplifier:

$$\text{CMRR} = \frac{|\text{differential gain}|}{|\text{common-mode gain}|} = \frac{|A_{vd(amp)}|}{|A_{vc(amp)}|} = 1 + 2g_{fe}R_E \tag{6.25}$$

from equations 6.17, 6.22 and 3.62, indicating that for good rejection of common-mode signals, R_E should be high. Note that if the output is taken as the difference $(v_{o_1} \sim v_{o_2})$, the common-mode gain for the symmetrical circuit is zero as $v_{o_1} \sim v_{o_2} = 0$ (equation 6.21) resulting in CMRR $= \infty$.

Example 6.2: AC performance of a differential stage

Calculate the small-signal differential and common-mode voltage gains, and the corresponding CMRR, of the circuit designed in example 6.1 if the BJTs have $h_{fe} = 200$.

For $I_C \simeq I_E = 200\ \mu\text{A}$, g_{fe} for the BJTs (equation 3.63) is $40 \times (200 \times 10^{-6}) = 8$ mS.
With $h_{fe} = 200$, h_{ie} (equation 3.62) is approximately $h_{fe}/g_{fe} = 200/8\ mS = 25\ \text{k}\Omega$.
Selected resistance values in example 6.1 are $R_E = 36\ \text{k}\Omega$ and $R_C = 39\ \text{k}\Omega$.
From equations 6.17 and 6.22 the differential and common-mode gains are

$$A_{vd(amp)} = -g_{fe}R_C = -(8\ \text{mS})(39\ \text{k}\Omega) = -312$$

$$A_{vc(amp)} = \frac{-h_{fe}R_C}{h_{ie} + 2R_E h_{fe}} = -\frac{(200)(39\ \text{k}\Omega)}{(25\ \text{k}\Omega) + 2(36\ \text{k}\Omega)(200)} = -1.85$$

Hence, $\text{CMRR} = \dfrac{312}{1.85} = 168.65$ or 44.5 dB.

Improvements to the basic circuit

Figure 6.5 shows various modifications to the basic differential stage of figure 6.4a to improve performance. From equation 6.25, high common-mode rejection requires a high value of R_E but R_E also features in the quiescent conditions and so the maximum value of R_E is limited by biasing constraints. What is required is that the R_E branch should offer high resistance to change of current while allowing the static component to flow; that is, the branch should operate ideally as a constant-current source. Figure 6.5a shows R_E replaced by a fixed-bias BJT which approximates to a constant-current arrangement; V_2 is chosen as about 20 per cent of V_E to provide reasonable stability, resistance selection as in section 3.1. An alternative

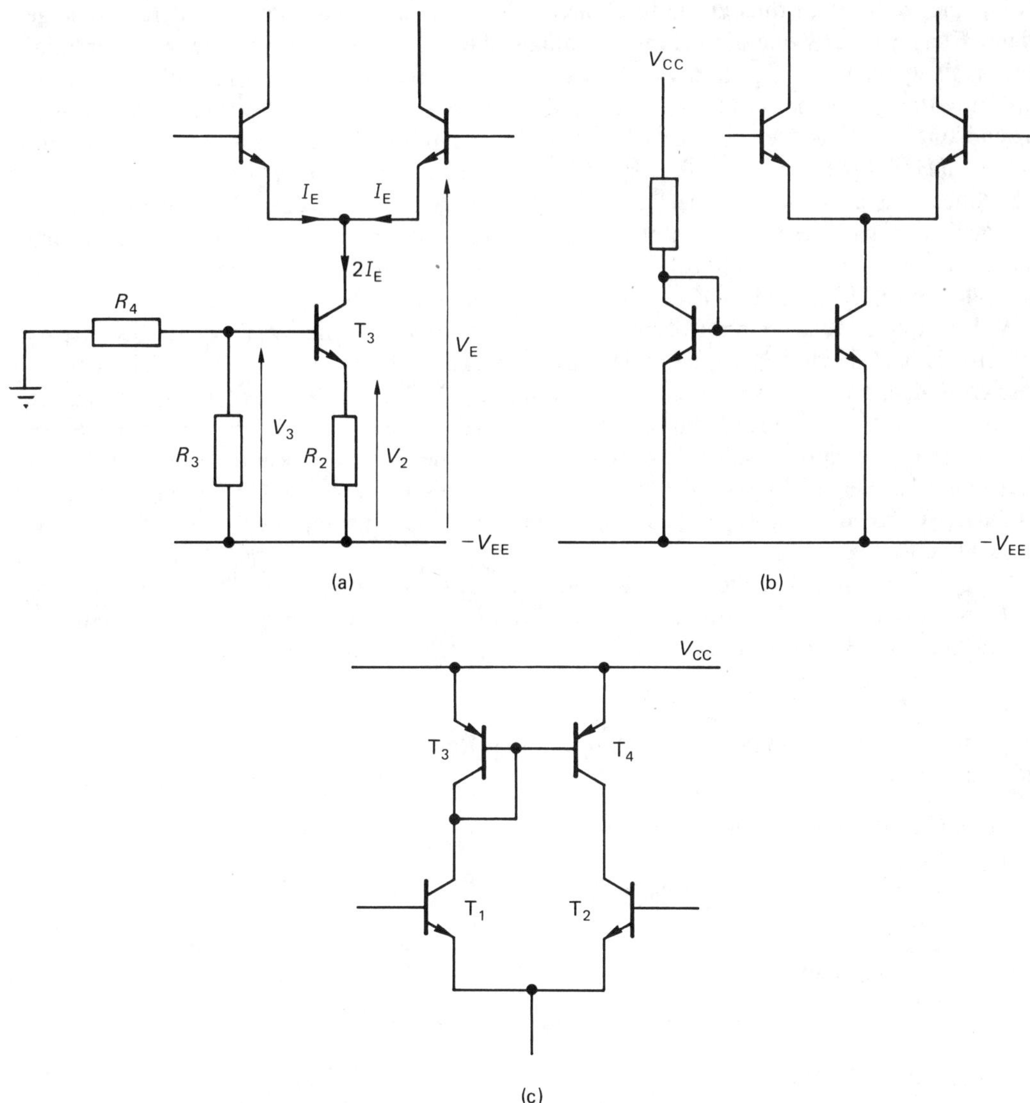

Figure 6.5 Improved differential amplifier performance by use of current-source biasing and an active load

technique is to use a current mirror arrangement (figure 6.5b), details of which are covered in section 6.2.

As with the basic CE stage, voltage gain depends on the value of collector load R_C (equation 6.17) and a considerable increase in gain can be achieved using an active load (section 6.3) as shown in figure 6.5c. Notice however that with T_3 connected as a diode the circuit loses its symmetry, although as discussed below this is not significant in many cases, as the circuit usually has to be used with a single-ended (unbalanced) output.

Unbalanced operation

The ideal balanced conditions at the input and output of a differential amplifier considered in the above analysis often cannot be implemented. The input signal is usually only available with reference to earth thus grounding one of the bases of the BJTs in the differential stage (figure 6.6a). Similarly one of the input terminals of the circuit to be driven by the differential stage is likely to be grounded, in which case direct connection from the two collectors of the differential stage to the input terminals of the driven stage is not allowable as this would ground one of the collectors. The solution is to use the differential stage with its output *single-ended* (figure 6.6a); one collector load is removed so that *as far as the signal is concerned* that collector is grounded via the V_{CC} supply and the output is taken as the potential at the other collector with respect to signal earth. The circuit of figure 6.6a provides non-inverting amplification; if the other collector is taken as the output, with R_C changed over to T_1 and the collector of T_2 shorted to V_{CC}, inverting amplification is obtained.

With v_i applied to the circuit of figure 6.6a, the emitter potential of T_1 varies because its collector is held fixed at V_{CC}. The variation at the emitter is the input to T_2 which, with its base grounded, operates as a common-base amplifier. With the emitter potential varying, the voltage across R_E does not remain constant as it does for balanced differential operation of the symmetrical circuit considered above and it may appear that the resulting feedback would cause considerable loss of gain. However the ac input resistance of the CB stage is low (table 3.1) thereby providing effective bypass of R_E and avoiding substantial gain reduction due to ac negative feedback.

A small-signal model of the circuit of figure 6.6a is shown in figure 6.6b, the performance of T_2 being represented by the simplified common-*base* h-parameter model. The current through the parallel combination of R_E and h_{ib} is $i_{b_1} + h_{fe}i_{b_1}$ thus

$$v_i = h_{ie}i_{b_1} + (R_E /\!/ h_{ib})(i_{b_1} + h_{fe}i_{b_1}) \tag{6.26}$$

from which the small-signal input resistance of the circuit R_i (figure 6.6b), which ignores any bias resistors, is

$$\begin{aligned} R_i = \frac{v_i}{i_{b_1}} &= h_{ie} + (R_E /\!/ h_{ib})(1 + h_{fe}) \\ &\simeq h_{ie} + h_{ib}(1 + h_{fe}) \text{ as } h_{ib} \ll R_E \\ &\simeq 2h_{ie} \end{aligned} \tag{6.27}$$

as $h_{ib}(1 + h_{fe}) \simeq h_{ie}$[3].

The output voltage is developed by current $h_{fb}i_{b_2}$ flowing through R_C thus

$$v_o = -h_{fb}i_{b_2}R_C \tag{6.28}$$

With $h_{ib} \ll R_E$, current $(i_{b_1} + h_{fe}i_{b_1})$ from T_1 almost all flows through h_{ib}, thus

$$i_{b_2} \simeq (1 + h_{fe})i_{b_1} \tag{6.29}$$

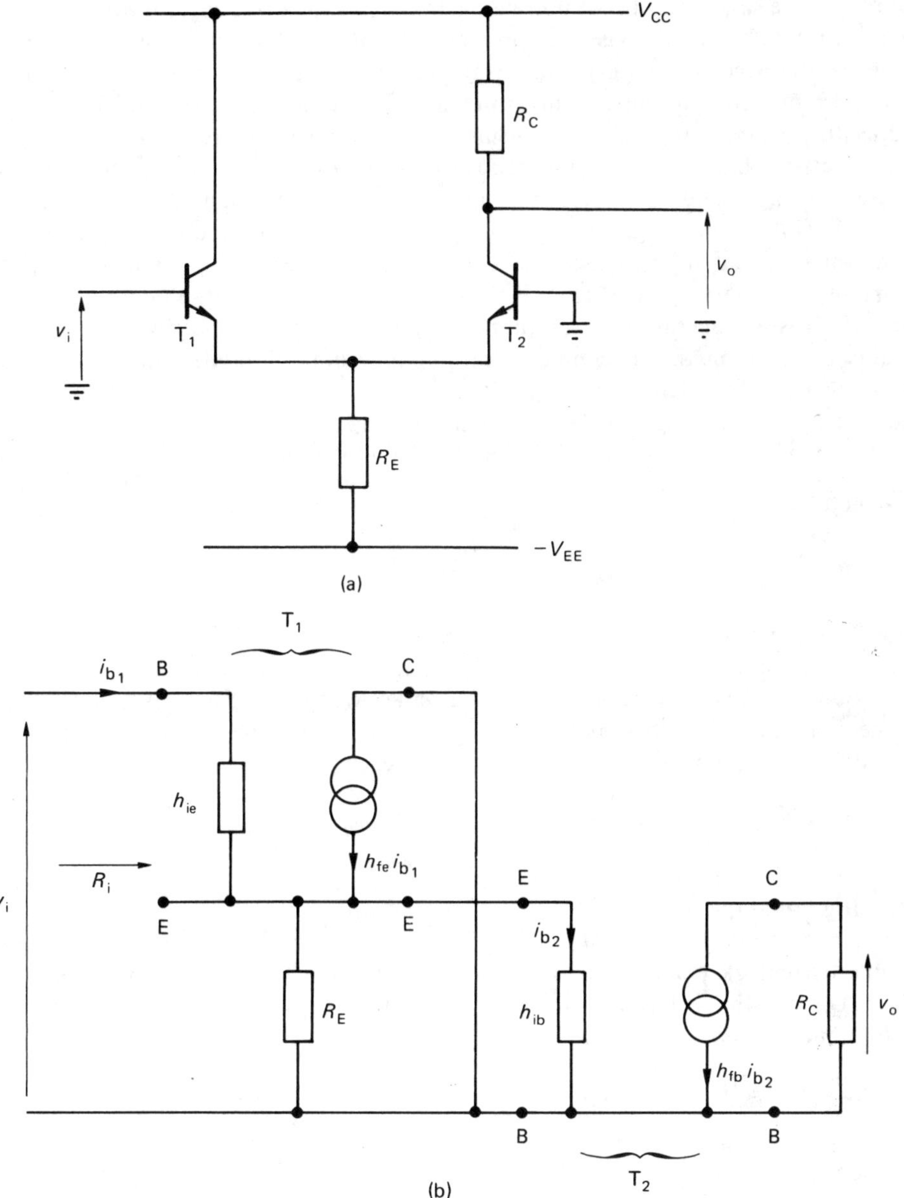

Figure 6.6 Basic differential amplifier with unbalanced input and output

From equation 6.27

$$i_{b_1} \simeq \frac{v_i}{2h_{ie}} \tag{6.30}$$

and by combining equations 6.28, 6.29 and 6.30 the voltage gain of this unbalanced stage is

$$A_{v(amp)} = \frac{v_o}{v_i} \simeq \frac{-h_{fb} R_C (1 + h_{fe})}{2h_{ie}} \simeq \frac{h_{fe} R_C}{2h_{ie}} = \frac{g_{fe} R_C}{2} \tag{6.31}$$

for $h_{fe} \gg 1$, as the small-signal common-base current gain of a BJT $h_{fb} \simeq -1$ [3]. Notice that the gain of the unbalanced stage is approximately half the differential gain of the balanced symmetrical stage (equation 6.17) and, configured as in figure 6.6a, the stage is non-inverting.

An important feature of this non-inverting amplifier is the absence of Miller magnification of the feedback capacitance $C_{b'c}$ of T_1 since, with its collector grounded (figure 6.6b) the voltage across the base–collector junction is simply v_i not $v_i(1 - A_{v(amp)})$ as for the basic CE stage (section 4.4). This lack of capacitance magnification means that the single-ended non-inverting differential stage has a high upper cut-off frequency and hence wide bandwidth. Common-mode signals do not cancel at the output in this circuit because the output is referred to constant potential (signal earth). However, as far as common-mode components are concerned, T_2 is not operating in common-base and so R_E is not effectively bypassed by the low value of h_{ib} as in the differential case and the common-mode gain is therefore low, maintaining a good CMRR.

The FET equivalent of figure 6.4a with identical FETs each having common-source forward transconductance g_{fs}, equal-value drain loads R_D and a common source resistance R_S has

$$\text{Differential gain, } A_{vd(amp)} = -g_{fs} R_D \tag{6.32}$$

$$\text{Common-mode gain, } A_{vc(amp)} = \frac{-g_{fs} R_D}{1 + 2g_{fs} R_S} \tag{6.33}$$

The low value of g_{fs} for low-power FETs ($\simeq 1$ mS for a J201 JFET, appendix E, section E.7) results in appreciable common-mode gain and hence poor CMRR. Even using current-source biasing to increase the effective value R_S, the CMRR is likely to be less than 10 per cent of that for the corresponding bipolar amplifier. Further work on the performance of FET differential amplifiers can be found in reference [2].

6.5 **Darlington stage**

Very high current gain can be obtained by using one BJT to directly drive another (figure 6.7a); the combination is termed a *Darlington pair*. If BJTs T_1 and T_2 have static CE current gains h_{FE_1} and h_{FE_2} both $\gg 1$ then

$$I_{E_1} \simeq I_{C_1} \simeq h_{FE_1} I_{B_1} \tag{6.34}$$

and

$$I_{E_2} \simeq I_{C_2} \simeq h_{FE_2} I_{B_2} \tag{6.35}$$

using equation 2.12 and ignoring C–E leakage.
But, in the basic circuit of figure 6.7a omitting R, $I_{E_1} = I_{B_2}$ and so

$$I_{E_2} \simeq h_{FE_1} h_{FE_2} I_{B_1} \tag{6.36}$$

With $I_{E_2} \gg I_{B_1}$, the combined collector current $I_C \simeq I_{E_2}$ from which the static current gain of the Darlington combination h_{FE_D} is

$$h_{FE_D} = \frac{I_C}{I_{B_1}} \simeq h_{FE_1} h_{FE_2} \tag{6.37}$$

Correspondingly, using the small-signal relations $i_{e_1} \simeq h_{fe_1} i_{b_1}$ and $i_c \simeq i_{e_2} \simeq h_{fe_2} i_{b_2} = h_{fe_2} i_{e_1}$

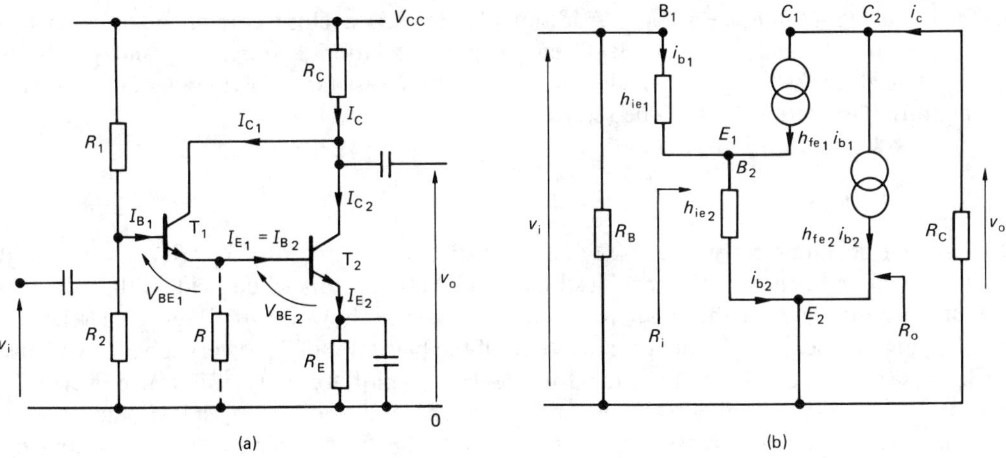

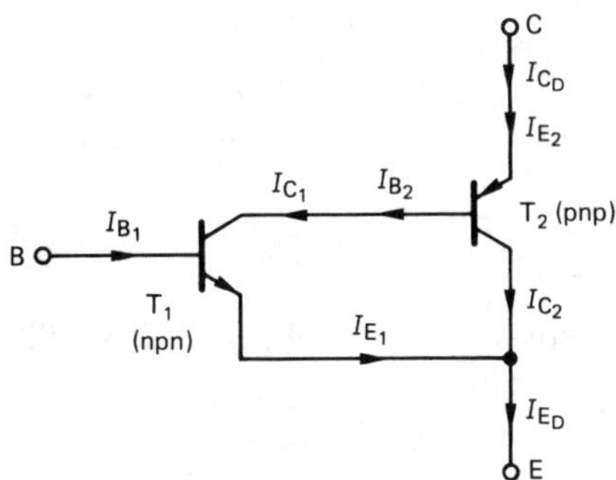

Figure 6.7 Darlington stage

for high small-signal gains h_{fe_1} and h_{fe_2}, the small-signal gain of the pair h_{fe_d} is

$$h_{fe_d} = \frac{i_C}{i_{b_1}} \simeq h_{fe_1} h_{fe_2} \tag{6.38}$$

The products in equations 6.37 and 6.38 show that the Darlington combination acts as a high-gain BJT. Figure 6.7a shows the combination incorporated in a standard CE amplifier stage with the corresponding ac model in figure 6.7b, from which

$$\begin{aligned} v_i &= h_{ie_1} i_{b_1} + h_{ie_2} i_{b_2} \\ &\simeq h_{ie_1} i_{b_1} + h_{ie_2}(h_{fe_1} i_{b_1}) \end{aligned}$$

thus

$$R_i = \frac{v_i}{i_{b_1}} \simeq h_{ie_1} + h_{fe_1} h_{ie_2} \tag{6.39}$$

The different bias levels of the two BJTs cause h_{ie_1} and h_{ie_2} to have very different values. From equation 6.35, $I_{C_2} \simeq h_{FE_2} I_{C_1}$ as $I_{B_2} = I_{E_1} \simeq I_{C_1}$, and since h_{ie} for a BJT is approximately inversely proportional to I_C (see appendix E, section E.5 for the $h_{ie} - I_C$ plot for a typical low-power

BJT), it follows that $h_{ie_1} \simeq h_{FE_2} h_{ie_2}$. Additionally there is a close correspondence between the values of h_{FE} and h_{fe} for a BJT, enabling the relation between h_{ie_1} and h_{ie_2} to be approximated to $h_{ie_1} \simeq h_{fe_2} h_{ie_2}$ which allows the input resistance of the basic Darlington configuration (equation 6.39) to be reduced to

$$R_i \simeq 2h_{fe}h_{ie_2} \tag{6.40}$$

for $h_{fe_1} \simeq h_{fe_2} = h_{fe} \gg 1$.

The overall ac input resistance $R_{i(amp)}$ is then $R_i /\!/ R_B$ where $R_B = R_1 /\!/ R_2$. Theoretically the high gain and hence low I_{B_1} enables high-value bias resistors to be used so that R_B does not significantly degrade the input resistance. In practice, however, the high gain relies on both h_{fe_1} and h_{fe_2} being high (equation 6.38) but if the bias level of T_1 is very low, h_{fe_1} will also be low (see appendix E, section E.5 for the h_{fe}–I_C plot for a typical low-power BJT) and so much of the gain advantage and the high input resistance is lost. Inclusion of resistor R (figure 6.7a) increases the bias level of T_1 but in so doing $i_{b_2} \neq i_{e_1}$, reducing the gain; in practice a compromise is necessary. The inclusion of R also ensures that I_{E_1} is much larger than leakage I_{CBO_2}; note that the basic equations 6.34 and 6.35 assume leakage to be insignificant.

From figure 6.7b

$$\begin{aligned} v_o &= -R_C i_c \\ &= -R_C(h_{fe_1} i_{b_1} + h_{fe_2} i_{b_2}) \\ &\simeq -R_C(h_{fe_1} i_{b_1} + h_{fe_1} h_{fe_2} i_{b_1}) \end{aligned} \tag{6.41}$$

since $i_{b_2} \simeq h_{fe_1} i_{b_1}$. Combination with equation 6.39 gives the small-signal voltage gain of the Darlington pair circuit as

$$A_{v(amp)} = \frac{v_o}{v_i} \simeq \frac{-R_C(h_{fe_1} + h_{fe_1} h_{fe_2})}{h_{ie_1} + h_{fe_1} h_{ie_2}} \tag{6.42}$$

$$\simeq \frac{-h_{fe} R_C}{2h_{ie_2}} = \frac{-g_{fe} R_C}{2} \tag{6.43}$$

where $h_{fe_1} \simeq h_{fe_2} = h_{fe} \gg 1$ and $h_{ie_1} \simeq h_{fe_2} h_{ie_2}$ because of the different bias levels of the two BJTs. Notice that the gain (equation 6.43) is *half* that of a CE stage using a single BJT (equation 3.65). Inclusion of resistor R to increase the bias level of T_1 reduces h_{ie_1} and then equation 6.42 approaches $-h_{fe_2} R_C / h_{ie_2}$ for $h_{fe} \gg 1$, corresponding to the gain of a single transistor CE stage.

Darlington combinations are produced as single packaged units, usually with the additional resistor R connected between B_2 and E_2. In contrast to the arrangement of figure 6.7a the additional current drain through R also flows through R_E, a factor which must be taken into account in selection of R_E. Notice also that there are two pn junctions between B_1 and E_2 so that active region operation requires $V_{B_1E_2} = 2 \times 0.6\text{ V} = 1.2\text{ V}$. This increased base–emitter voltage causes impaired bias stability for change of temperature (section 3.1) compared with a single BJT. This disadvantage is avoided with the *complementary* (npn–pnp) *Darlington pair* of figure 6.7c which has only one pn junction between B and E. Note that the effective *emitter* of this Darlington is the collector of T_2, and the emitter of T_2 forms the effective *collector* of the pair as far as equivalency with a single BJT is concerned. The complementary Darlington provides a direct replacement for the basic npn–npn Darlington although the additional resistor R to modify the bias level of T_1 is connected between C_1 and E_2 in the complementary version.

The Darlington combination can be used as an effective buffer. In the circuit of figure 6.7a, if R_C is replaced by a short circuit, the emitter bypass capacitor removed and the circuit output taken from the emitter, a high input resistance, low output resistance, unity gain Darlington emitter-follower is formed, termed a *common-collector cascade pair*. Analysis of the small-signal performance of this arrangement shows that

$$A_{v(amp)} \simeq 1 \text{ for high } h_{fe_1} \text{ and } h_{fe_2} \tag{6.44}$$

$$R_{i(amp)} \simeq R_B /\!/ (h_{fe_1} h_{fe_2} R_E) \text{ for } h_{fe_2} R_E \gg h_{ie_2} \tag{6.45}$$

$$R_{o(amp)} \simeq R_E /\!/ (h_{ie_2}/h_{fe_2}) \text{ for low source resistance} \tag{6.46}$$

6.6 Complementary stage

Basic analog circuits achieve approximately linear operation, output proportional to input, by biasing the transistors to establish quiescent operation at a mid-range level of conduction (sections 3.1 and 3.2). When the signal is then applied, the level of conduction can increase and decrease about this mid-range value. The power dissipation associated with the static bias currents is not only wasteful, which is a major disadvantage in battery-powered circuitry, but the associated rise in temperature has implications with regard to stability and component ratings which is particularly significant in high power circuits (chapter 8).

An alternative approach to mid-range biasing is to use two transistors as in figure 6.8a, each biased to cut-off, such that T_1 delivers power to the load when v_i is positive, T_2 remaining at cut-off (figure 6.8b), while T_2 conducts for v_i negative, T_1 then remaining off (figure 6.8); termed *push–pull* operation. The two transistors must have *complementary* conduction characteristics, one conducting for v_i positive, the other for v_i negative; hence the name of this arrangement. The circuit thus operates as an emitter-follower providing good power transfer to a low impedance load (sections 8.4 and 8.5).

The complementary circuit (figure 6.8a) uses equal-magnitude positive and negative power supplies, the common connection providing signal earth/ground as with the differential amplifier of figure 6.4a. With equal-value bias resistors R_1, R_2, node X (figure 6.8a) is biased to signal earth so that both BJTs are at cut-off. With v_i increasing positively, both v_{BE_1} and v_{BE_2} increase positively and when v_i exceeds the conduction threshold for T_1 ($V_{\gamma 1}$, figure 2.3c) the BJT starts to conduct. The unity gain of the emitter-follower results in the transfer characteristics AB in figure 6.8d, v_o being able to rise to a maximum value $V_{CC} - V_{CE_1(sat)}$ at the onset of saturation of T_1. During this time v_{BE_2} has been increasing positively but since T_2 is a pnp type BJT this transistor remains at cut-off. With v_i negative, complementary operation occurs with T_2 conducting for v_i more negative than the threshold $V_{\gamma 2}$ for T_2, resulting in the transfer characteristic CD. Superposition of a sinusoidal input signal and projection on to the v_o-axis shows *cross-over distortion* due to the 'dead zero' AC between the threshold values. This distortion can be reduced by including two series diodes between X and Y (figure 6.8a) to compensate for the turn-on thresholds (figure 8.4a).

6.7 Cascode amplifier

The basic CE stage provides moderate voltage gain and input resistance (table 3.1) but Miller effect causes bandwidth limitation (section 4.4). In contrast, the CB configuration offers wide bandwidth because of the absence of Miller magnification, but its low input resistance results

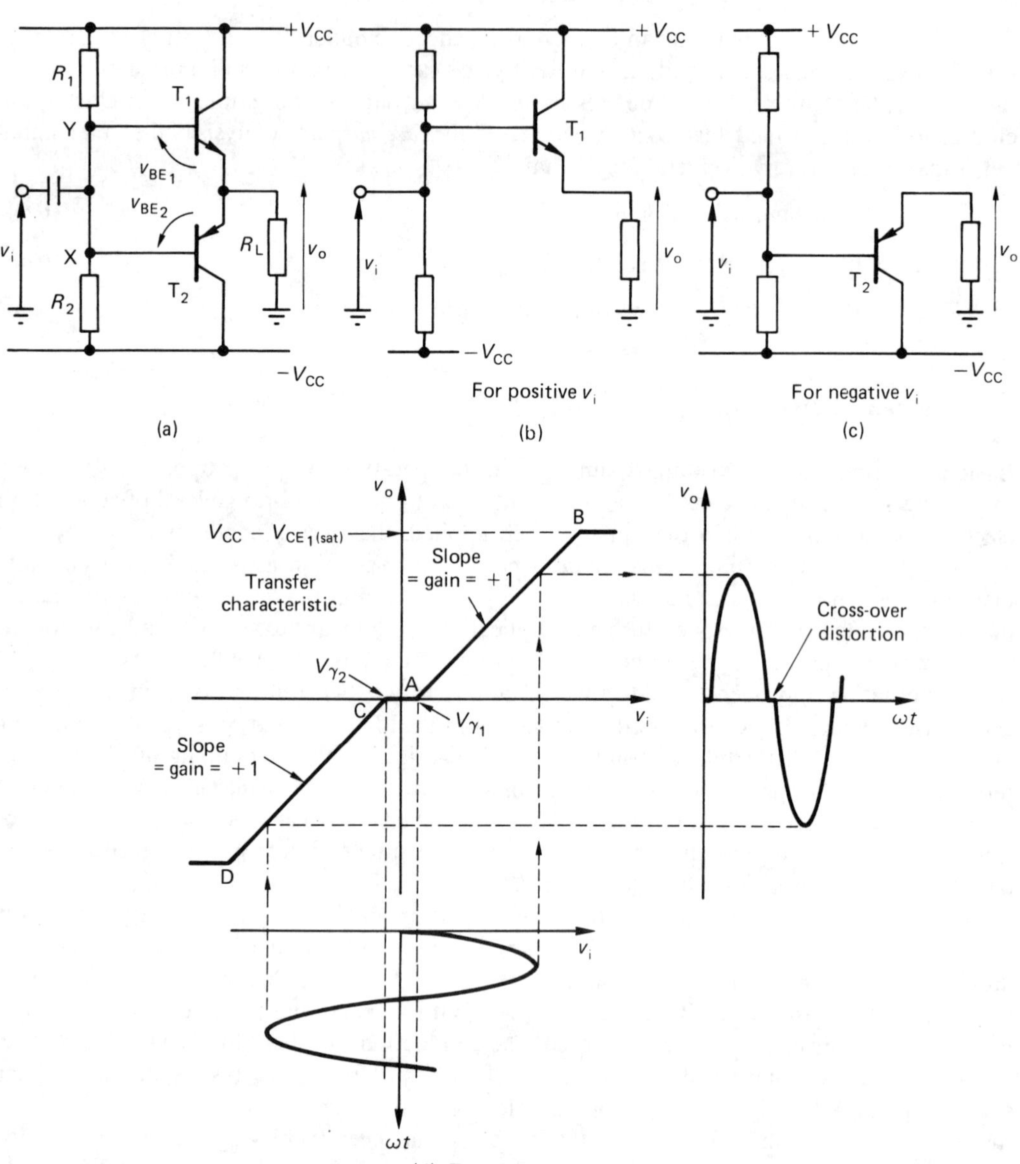

Figure 6.8 Complementary stage

in poor voltage transfer from the signal source and hence poor overall gain. However, excellent performance can be obtained by combining these two configurations to form what is termed a *cascode* amplifier (figure 6.9).

The low input resistance of the CB transistor (T_2) means the effective load on the CE transistor (T_1) is low, resulting in low voltage gain from the CE stage (equation 3.65). This low gain keeps Miller magnification low and ensures wide bandwidth from the CE configuration which has moderate input resistance, so providing good voltage transfer from a low-resistance signal source. The loss of gain of the CE stage is compensated by the high gain of the CB output stage, thus ensuring high gain *and* wide bandwidth.

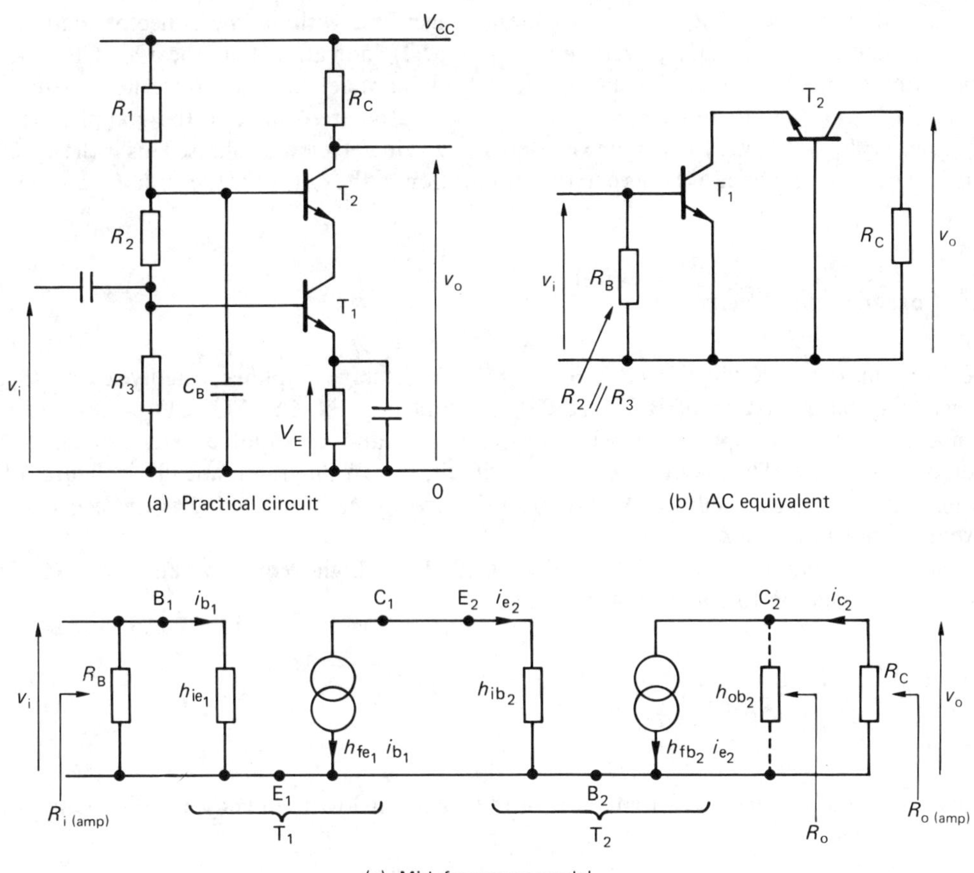

Figure 6.9 Cascode amplifier

Bias resistors R_1, R_2, R_3 are selected taking account of static base currents of the BJTs to provide V_{BE_1} and V_{BE_2} of the order of 0.6 V to ensure active region operation. C_B provides effective bypass of the $R_1 // (R_2 + R_3)$ combination so that T_2 operates in common-base as far as the signal is concerned.

From the corresponding mid-frequency model of figure 6.9c

$$R_{i(amp)} \simeq R_B // h_{ie_1} \tag{6.47}$$

where $R_B = R_2 // R_3$.

Since $1/h_{ob_2}$ is high compared with R_C, h_{ob_2} can be neglected and

$$v_o \simeq -h_{fb_2} i_{e_2} R_C \tag{6.48}$$

but $i_{e_2} = -h_{fe_1} i_{b_1}$ and $i_{b_1} = v_i / h_{ie_1}$ from which

$$A_{v(amp)} = \frac{v_o}{v_i} = \frac{h_{fb_2} h_{fe_1} R_C}{h_{ie_1}} \simeq \frac{-h_{fe_1} R_C}{h_{ie_1}} \tag{6.49}$$

as the CB current gain of a BJT, h_{fb}, is approximately -1 [3]. Equation 6.49 corresponds to that for a basic CE stage (equation 3.74).

The output resistance R_o of the cascode arrangement, without the collector load R_C, is approximately $1/h_{ob_2}$ which is very high ($\geqslant 10\,\mathrm{M\Omega}$) indicating that the CE–CB cascode approximates to an ideal BJT as far as the output characteristics are concerned, the output current i_{c_2} being almost independent of $v_{c_2e_1}$. The output resistance of the complete circuit $R_{o(amp)}$ is $(1/h_{ob_2})/\!/R_C$ which is approximately R_C, a value of a few kilohms. This is the effective value of output resistance as far as external connection to the output of the circuit is concerned.

6.8 Cascaded amplifiers

Few amplification specifications can be met by a single-stage amplifier; usually several stages, which may be a mixture of BJT CE, CB, CC and/or FET CS, CG, CD stages, must be connected output-to-input to provide adequate gain and/or suitable values of input and output impedance. The resulting *multistage* circuit, shown diagrammatically in figure 6.10a, is termed a *cascaded amplifier*. An important consequence of cascading is the effect on the overall bandwidth (figure 6.10b).

Each of the stages A_1, A_2, ... A_n in figure 6.10a has a high-frequency gain response of the form, corresponding to equation 4.29:

$$A_{hi} = A_{mid}\left[\frac{1}{1+j\left(\dfrac{f}{f_{hi}}\right)}\right] \qquad (6.50)$$

where f_{hi} is the upper cut-off frequency of the stage. At low frequency, from equation 4.15,

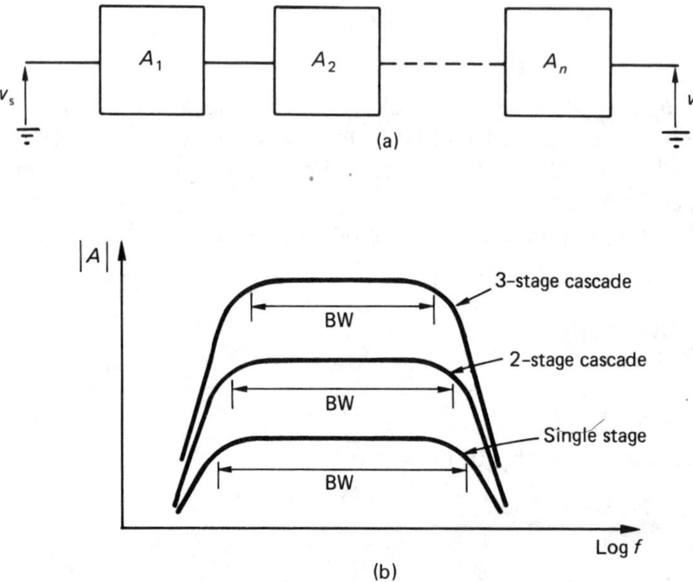

Figure 6.10 Cascading to form a multistage amplifier and associated bandwidth reduction

the response is of the form

$$A_{lo} = A_{mid}\left[\frac{1}{1 - j\left(\frac{f_{lo}}{f}\right)}\right] \tag{6.51}$$

where f_{lo} is the lower cut-off frequency.

Consider an amplifier comprising n identical stages, each having high and low-frequency responses as given by equations 6.50 and 6.51. It is assumed that signal voltage transfer at each interstage coupling is perfect, that is, there is no voltage loss due to potential division between $R_{i(amp)}$ of the driven stage and $R_{o(amp)}$ of the driver stage as considered in example 3.13. The response of the complete amplifier at high frequency $(A_{hi})_{overall}$ is given by the product of A_{hi_1}, A_{hi_2}, ... A_{hi_n}, thus

$$(A_{hi})_{overall} = A^n_{mid}\left[\frac{1}{1 + j\left(\frac{f}{f_{hi}}\right)}\right]^n \tag{6.52}$$

The gain $|v_o/v_s|$ is given by the modulus of equation 6.52, that is

$$|(A_{hi})_{overall}| = \frac{|A^n_{mid}|}{\sqrt{\left[1 + \left(\frac{f}{f_{hi}}\right)^2\right]^n}} \tag{6.53}$$

The upper cut-off frequency of the complete amplifier, $(f_{hi})_{overall}$, is given by

$$\frac{|(A_{hi})_{overall}|}{|A^n_{mid}|} = \frac{1}{\sqrt{2}} \tag{6.54}$$

corresponding to the modulus of equation 4.11.
Thus, from equations 6.53 and 6.54, at $f = (f_{hi})_{overall}$

$$\left[1 + \left(\frac{(f_{hi})_{overall}}{f_{hi}}\right)^2\right]^n = 2$$

from which

$$(f_{hi})_{overall} = f_{hi}\sqrt{(2^{1/n} - 1)} \tag{6.55}$$

For two stages ($n = 2$), $(f_{hi})_{overall} = 0.64 f_{hi}$; for three stages, $(f_{hi})_{overall}$ reduces to $0.51 f_{hi}$. A similar analysis for the low-frequency response of an ac amplifier based on equation 6.51 gives

$$(f_{lo})_{overall} = \frac{f_{lo}}{\sqrt{(2^{1/n} - 1)}} \tag{6.56}$$

Thus as the number of stages increases, the upper cut-off frequency of the multistage amplifier falls and the lower cut-off frequency rises restricting the bandwidth as shown in figure 6.10b. For a wideband amplifier, the bandwidth is dominated by the upper cut-off frequency (equation 4.33) and the bandwidth of the multistage amplifier, from equation 6.55, is given by

$$B_{overall} = B\sqrt{(2^{1/n} - 1)} \tag{6.57}$$

where B is the bandwidth of the (identical) individual stages.

6.9 Tuned amplifier

Equations 3.65 and 3.88 show that the voltage gain of basic CE and CS amplifiers (figures 3.6b, c) is approximately proportional to the load resistance (R_C, R_D) so that if the load is increased, the voltage gain increases correspondingly. However, the value of load resistance is limited by the biasing requirements (section 3.4.3) thus restricting the gain that may be obtained from a single stage with a resistive load (see also tutorial question 3.13). If the load is replaced by a tuned circuit as in the CS circuit of figure 6.11a, the effective load as far as the signal is concerned is very high at the resonant frequency f_o of the tuned circuit (appendix B, section B.1 and reference [4]) resulting in high small-signal voltage gain; the quiescent conditions are established via the dc path through the coil.

For C_C and C_B effective ac short circuits at the operating frequency, which is typically in the megahertz range for this type of amplifier, the corresponding ac model is as shown in figure 6.11b. The performance of the FET is represented by the model of figure 3.10c, g_{fs} being replaced by the forward trans*admittance* gain y_{fs} at this frequency. Shunt resistance R'' includes the effective coil resistance R' ($=Q_L^2 R$, equation B.19, appendix B), the output conductance g_{os} of the FET (figure 3.10b) and the input resistance of the circuit connected to the amplifier output. The output capacitance of the FET, C_{ds} (figure 3.10b), and stray capacitance at the amplifier output is included in C'.

From figure 6.11b:

$$v_o = -y_{fs} v_i Z'$$

$$= \frac{-y_{fs} v_i}{\dfrac{1}{R''} + \dfrac{1}{j\omega L'} + j\omega C'} \tag{6.58}$$

where $1/j\omega L'$ and $j\omega C'$ are the operational susceptances of L' and C' at frequency ω which are the reciprocals of the operational reactances of equations 2.39 and 2.27; note that parallel-connected conductances and susceptances simply add in complex form to give the operational admittance of the combination. The voltage gain of the circuit is therefore

$$A_{v(amp)} = \frac{v_o}{v_i} = \frac{-y_{fs}}{\dfrac{1}{R''} + \dfrac{1}{j\omega L'} + j\omega C'} = \frac{-y_{fs} R''}{1 + jR''\left(\omega C' - \dfrac{1}{\omega L'}\right)} \tag{6.59}$$

which is a maximum at a frequency ω_o such that $\omega_o C' = 1/\omega_o L'$, the resonance condition for the tuned circuit (appendix B, section B.1). The maximum gain is therefore

$$A_{v(amp)}\max = A_{v(amp)}(\omega_o) = -y_{fs} R'' \tag{6.60}$$

For input signal frequencies less than and greater than ω_o, the magnitude of the denominator of equation 6.59 is > 1 resulting in the peaked response of figure 6.11c.

Combining equations 6.59 and 6.60:

$$A_{v(amp)} = \frac{A_{v(amp)}\max}{1 + jR''\left(\omega C' - \dfrac{1}{\omega L'}\right)}$$

$$= \frac{A_{v(amp)}\max}{1 + j\dfrac{R''}{\omega_o L'}\left(\omega\, \omega_o L'C' - \dfrac{\omega_o}{\omega}\right)} \tag{6.61}$$

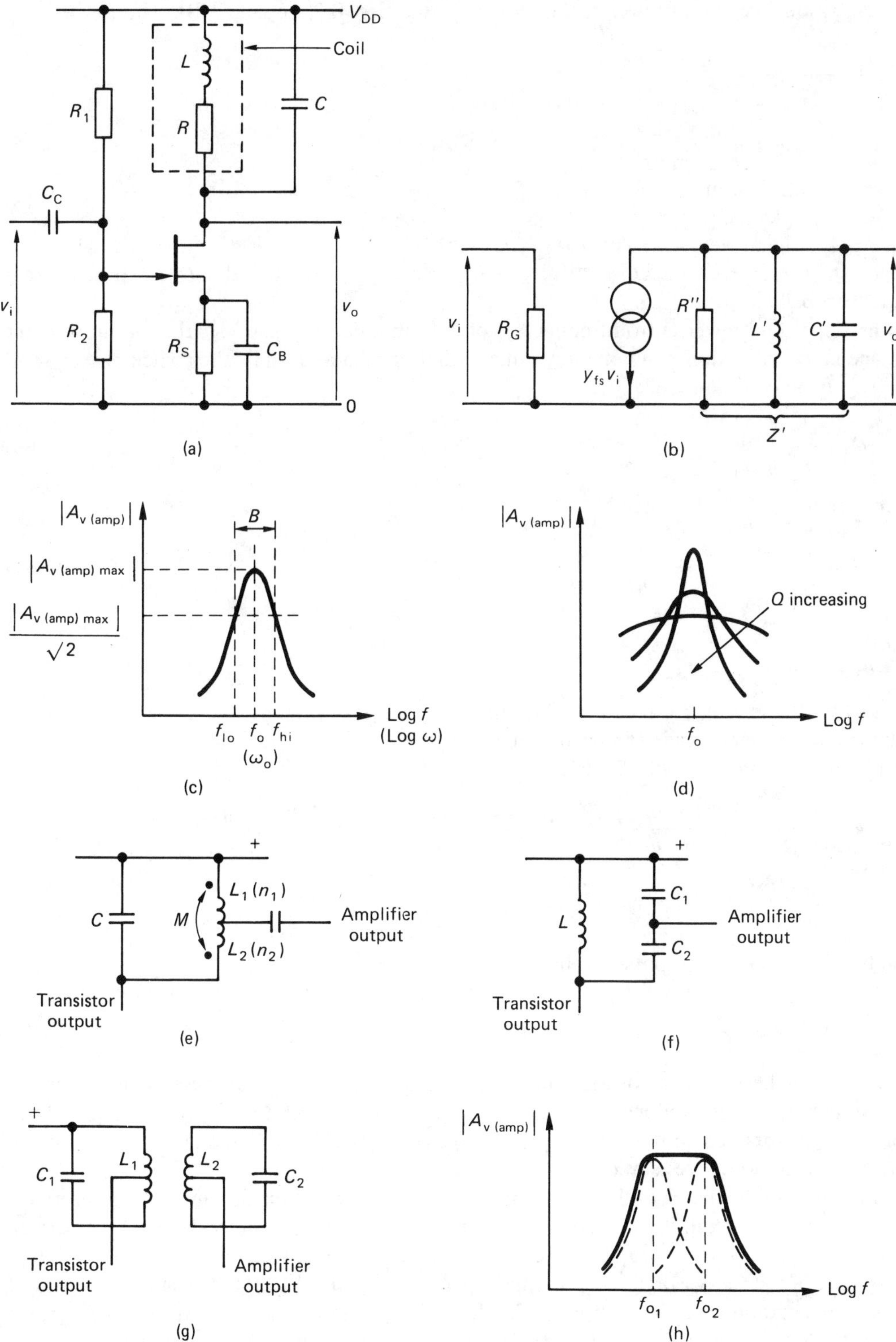

Figure 6.11 Tuned amplifier

But the resonance condition gives $L'C' = 1/\omega_o^2$ (equation B.2, appendix B), therefore

$$A_{v(amp)} = \frac{A_{v(amp)}\max}{1 + j\dfrac{R''}{\omega_o L'}\left(\dfrac{\omega}{\omega_o} - \dfrac{\omega_o}{\omega}\right)}$$

$$= \frac{A_{v(amp)}\max}{1 + jQ\left(\dfrac{\omega}{\omega_o} - \dfrac{\omega_o}{\omega}\right)} \tag{6.62}$$

where Q $(= R''/\omega_o L')$ is the *quality* $(Q-)$ *factor* of the parallel R'', L', C' tuned circut (equation B.28, appendix B).

At the upper and lower cut-off frequencies of the amplifier, ω_{hi} and ω_{lo}, the modulus of the voltage gain is $1/\sqrt{2}$ of its maximum value (equations 4.5 and 4.11), thus when $\omega = \omega_{hi}$ and $\omega = \omega_{lo}$, from equation 6.62:

$$\left| Q\left(\frac{\omega}{\omega_o} - \frac{\omega_o}{\omega}\right)\right| = 1 \tag{6.63}$$

from which

$$\frac{\omega_{hi}}{\omega_o} - \frac{\omega_o}{\omega_{hi}} = -\left(\frac{\omega_{lo}}{\omega_o} - \frac{\omega_o}{\omega_{lo}}\right) = \frac{1}{Q} \tag{6.64}$$

giving

$$\omega_o = \sqrt{\omega_{lo}\omega_{hi}} \tag{6.65}$$

Thus ω_o is the 'geometric mean' of ω_{lo} and ω_{hi}, giving a symmetrical peak about ω_o on a logarithmic frequency scale (figure 6.11c).

Combining equations 6.64 and 6.65:

$$\frac{1}{Q} = \frac{\omega_{hi}^2 - \omega_o^2}{\omega_o \omega_{hi}} = \frac{\omega_{hi}^2 - \omega_{lo}\omega_{hi}}{\omega_o \omega_{hi}} = \frac{\omega_{hi} - \omega_{lo}}{\omega_o}$$

$$= \frac{f_{hi} - f_{lo}}{f_o} \tag{6.66}$$

The bandwidth of the amplifier is therefore

$$B = f_{hi} - f_{lo} = \frac{f_o}{Q} \tag{6.67}$$

showing that the *selectivity* of the amplifier, as indicated by the sharpness of the response, improves (bandwidth is reduced) as the Q-factor of the tuned circuit is increased (figure 6.11d). For other factors remaining unchanged, the peak gain falls as Q reduces because of the reduction of the shunt resistance R''.

As the input impedance of the circuit driven from the output of the tuned stage effectively shunts the tuned circuit, it can have a significant effect on the overall response. If the driven circuit has a FET input, careful choice of biasing components (section 3.2) usually enables the output of the tuned stage to be simply capacitively coupled to the driven circuit without significant degrading of the response. For lower input impedance driven circuits, various techniques can be used to maintain the Q of the tuned circuit. One method is to use an inter-stage transformer having primary turns $\gg$ secondary turns so that the reflected load

(R', equation 2.46) is very high; although successful in practice, transformer cost is a disadvantage. Alternatively a tapped-inductor or tapped-capacitor form of tuned circuit (figures 6.11e, f) can be used with similar effect. In the former arrangement the total inductance as far as the tuned stage is concerned is $(L_1 + L_2 + 2M)$ where M is the mutual inductance [4] between the two sections of the inductor; the dots in figure 6.11e indicate the phase relationship of the signal voltages across the two sections and hence their relative winding directions, the variation of potentials at the 'dotted nodes' relative to the tap being in the same sense. It the turns ratio of L_2:L_1 is such that $n_2 \ll n_1$, the input impedance of the driven stage is effectively stepped-up as far as the tuned circuit is concerned, reducing the loading effect. The tapped-capacitor arrangement has a similar effect although here the capacitors also provide capacitive coupling to the driven circuit, avoiding the need for an additional coupling capacitor. The effective capacitance of the tuned circuit is C_1 and C_2 in series $(= C_1C_2/(C_1 + C_2))$, and if $C_2 \gg C_1$ the loading effect of the driven stage is considerably reduced.

In many applications, the selectivity of a single-tuned amplifier stage is inadequate and *double tuning* is used either in the form of a two-stage amplifier each with its tuned load, or as a single-stage circuit with a double-tuned circuit as its load (figure 6.11g). In either case, if the two tuned circuits have the same resonant frequency (*synchronous tuning*) the bandwidth is lower than for the corresponding single-tuned arrangement, corresponding to the bandwidth reduction for cascaded untuned amplifiers considered in section 6.8. The double-tuned principle can also be used to advantage in another way; not all applications of tuned amplifiers require high selectivity, some require high gain, as provided by the resonance condition of the tuned circuit, but over a wider bandwidth. A double-tuned circuit can be *stagger tuned* so that one tuned circuit resonates at f_{o_1} and the other at f_{o_2} (figure 6.11h), whereby the combined response provides high gain over a *relatively* wide bandwidth. Reasonable flatness in the mid-frequency range requires careful choice of Q-factors and the staggered resonant frequencies f_{o_1} and f_{o_2}.

The reactance chart (appendix B, section B.4) linking inductive and capacitive reactance to frequency for a wide range of inductances and capacitances can be extremely useful for work involving tuned circuits. Relative values of L and C to provide a particular resonant frequency can be read directly from the chart, albeit with limited accuracy.

Example 6.3: Tuned amplifier design

Select suitable component values for the single-tuned stage of figure 6.11a to provide a peak voltage gain of at least 15 at 1 MHz with a bandwidth not exceeding 50 kHz when driving a circuit of input resistance 10 kΩ. A type 2N5457 JFET is to be used for which the relevant parameters, as 1 MHz, are $g_{fs} = 5$ mS, $g_{os} = 30\ \mu$S; b_{fs}, b_{os} and the input capacitance of the driven circuit may be assumed negligible.

Components R_1, R_2, R_S are selected to provide suitable bias conditions as considered in section 3.2. C_C and C_B are selected to provide adequate coupling and bypass (section 3.3), taking account of the operating frequency of approximately 1 MHz. The practical tuned circuit of figure 6.11a may be represented as the parallel R'', L', C' circuit of 6.11b where $C' = C$, $L' = L$ (appendix B, section B.2) while R'' is the parallel combination of the transformed resistance R' $(= Q_L^2 R$, appendix B, section B.2), the output conductance of the JFET (g_{os})

and the input resistance R_i of the driven stage, thus

$$R'' = R' /\!/ \left(\frac{1}{g_{os}}\right) /\!/ R_i$$

$$= Q_L^2 R /\!/ \left(\frac{1}{g_{os}}\right) /\!/ R_i$$

where Q_L is the Q-factor of the coil at the operating frequency (1 MHz). From equation 6.60 the peak value of gain

$$|A_{v(amp)} \max| = y_{fs} R'' = g_{fs} R''$$

since b_{fs} is negligible in this case. For a peak gain $\geqslant 15$ with $g_{fs} = 5$ mS,

$$R'' = \frac{|A_{v(amp)} \max|}{g_{fs}} \geqslant \frac{15}{5\text{ mS}} = 3\text{ k}\Omega$$

With $R_i = 10\text{ k}\Omega$ and $1/g_{os} = 1/(30\ \mu\text{S}) = 33.3\text{ k}\Omega$, $R_i /\!/ (1/g_{os}) \simeq 7.7\text{ k}\Omega$ and so to ensure $R'' \geqslant 3\text{ k}\Omega$, R' must not be less than 4.9 kΩ from $7.7R'/(7.7 + R') \geqslant 3\text{ k}\Omega$. For $f_o = 1$ MHz and $B \leqslant 50$ kHz, the Q of the tuned circuit (equation 6.67) is

$$Q = \frac{f_o}{B} \geqslant \frac{1\text{ MHz}}{50\text{ kHz}} = 20$$

thus from equation B.28 (appendix B):

$$\frac{R''}{2\pi f_o L} \geqslant 20$$

Using the minimum value of R'' of 3 kΩ for calculation purposes, the inductance is

$$L \leqslant \frac{3\text{ k}\Omega}{40\pi(1\text{ MHz})} = 23.9\ \mu\text{H}$$

from which a value of 20 μH can be chosen to keep the bandwidth well within specification.

Provided the coil has adequate Q_L (> 10, appendix B, section B.1) the resonant frequency is given to within 0.5 per cent by

$$f_o = \frac{1}{2\pi\sqrt{LC}} \tag{6.68}$$

from which, for $f_o = 1$ MHz, using $L = 20\ \mu\text{H}$

$$C = \frac{1}{4\pi^2 f_o^2 L} = \frac{1}{4\pi^2(1\text{ MHz})^2(20\ \mu\text{H})} = 1267\text{ pF}$$

There still remains the matter of the coil resistance R. The Q-factor of the coil, Q_L $(= 2\pi f L/R)$ must be high enough for equation 6.68 to hold (appendix B, section B.1). Also $Q_L^2 R$ must be sufficiently high to provide the required gain, that is, $R'' \geqslant 3\text{ k}\Omega$ which requires $R'(\simeq Q_L^2 R) \geqslant 4.9\text{ k}\Omega$ from the above calculation. At 1 MHz, the reactance of the 20 μH coil is $\omega L = 2\pi f L \simeq 126\ \Omega$ and therefore from equation B.19 (appendix B):

$$R' \simeq Q_L^2 R = \frac{(\omega L)^2}{R}$$

giving

$$R \simeq \frac{(\omega L)^2}{R'} \leqslant \frac{(126\,\Omega)^2}{4.9\,\text{k}\Omega} = 3.2\,\Omega$$

With a coil resistance of 3.2 Ω, $Q_L = 2\pi f L/R = 126\,\Omega/3.2\,\Omega = 39$ at 1 MHz, indicating that equation 6.68 gives a sufficiently accurate relationship for f_o in this case ($Q_L > 10$).

A suitable design for the tuned circuit to meet the specification is therefore a 20 μH coil shunted by a capacitance of 1267 pF. Such a value of capacitance would require the parallel combination of a number of capacitors and for this application close-tolerance high-stability types such as polystyrene, low-loss ceramic or silvered-mica (section 2.4,2) would be required. The resistance of the coil must not exceed 3.2 Ω.

References and further reading

1. G.M. Glasford, *Analog Electronic Circuits*, section 5.15 (Prentice-Hall, 1986)
2. R.A. Colclaser, D.A. Neamen and C.F. Hawkins, *Electronic Circuit Analysis*, chapter 13 (Wiley, 1984)
3. M.E. Goodge, *Semiconductor Device Technology*, section 2.2.26 (Macmillan, 1985)
4. R.J. Smith, *Circuits, Devices and Systems*, 4th edition, chapters 7 and 8 (Wiley, 1984)
5. C.J. Savant, M.S. Roden and G.L. Carpenter, *Electronic Circuit Design*, chapter 7 (Benjamin/Cummings, 1987)
6. A.S. Sedra and K.C. Smith, *Microelectronic Circuits*, 2nd edition, chapters 9 and 14 (Holt, Rinehart and Winston, 1987)
7. P.M. Chirlian, *Analysis and Design of Integrated Electronic Circuits*, 2nd edition, chapters 12, 14 and 17 (Harper and Row/Wiley, 1987)
8. G.J. Ritchie, *Transistor Circuit Techniques*, 2nd edition, chapters 4 and 5 (Van Nostrand Reinhold, 1987)
9. T.F. Bogart, *Electronic Devices and Circuits*, chapters 11 and 12 (Merrill, 1986)
10. C.L. Alley and K.W. Atwood, *Microelectronics*, chapters 7, 10, 11 and 17 (Prentice-Hall, 1986)
11. M.S. Ghausi, *Electronic Devices and Circuits*, chapters 5 and 11 (Holt-Saunders, 1985)
12. R.J. Maddock and D.M. Calcutt, *Electronics: A Course for Engineers*, chapter 5 (Longman, 1988)
13. J. Millman and A. Grabel, *Microelectronics*, 2nd edition, chapters 10 and 14 (McGraw-Hill, 1988)
14. R.A. Colclaser, D.A. Neamen and C.F. Hawkins, *Electronic Circuit Analysis*, chapters 13 and 15 (Wiley, 1984)
15. W.H. Hayt and G.W. Neudeck, *Electronic Circuit Analysis and Design*, 2nd edition, chapter 8 (Houghton Mifflin, 1984)
16. S.A. Knight, *Electronics for Higher TEC*, chapter 8 (Granada, 1983)
17. E.N. Lurch, *Fundamentals of Electronics*, 3rd edition, chapter 12 (Wiley, 1981)
18. M. Cirovic, *Basic Electronics*, 2nd edition, chapters 11 and 14 (Prentice-Hall, 1979)
19. C.A. Holt, *Electronic Circuits*, chapters 14, 15, 19 and 22 (Wiley, 1978)

Tutorial questions

Note: Where applicable, answers correspond to rounding to 2 decimal places during calculation.

Biasing

6.1 If the circuit of figure 6.2a operates from a 10 V power supply, is it possible to select a value of resistance R from the E12 series (appendix D) to establish a bias current within the range 5 mA $\pm$ 5 per cent in the load? If so, what is the value? Assume the static current gain of the BJT is high and V_{BE} is 0.6 V for active operation.

[Answer: Yes, 1.8 kΩ]

Differential amplifiers

6.2 Select component values from the E12 series (appendix D) for the basic symmetrical differential stage of figure 6.4b. The static collector current of each BJT is to be of the order of 400 μA, at which h_{FE} is approximately 180, and the circuit is to operate from $\pm$ 12 V supplies. Subsequently the circuit is required to provide balanced ac operation.

[Answers: $R_E = 15$ kΩ, $R_C = 15$ kΩ, $R_1 = 5.6$ MΩ]

6.3 If the values of h_{ie} and h_{fe} for the BJTs in the differential stage of question 6.2 are 12 kΩ and 200 respectively, calculate the differential and common-mode small-signal voltage gains for the circuit corresponding to the component values selected in question 6.2. What is the common-mode rejection ratio for the circuit?

[Answers: -250, -0.5, 53.98 dB]

6.4 The emitter resistor in the differential stage of question 6.2 is to be replaced by an active current-source biasing arrangement as given in figure 6.5a. Select E12 resistor values (appendix D) for such a circuit making any realistic assumptions that may be necessary.

[Specimen answers: $R_2 = 2.7$ kΩ, $R_3 = 15$ kΩ, $R_4 = 47$ kΩ allowing approximately 20 per cent of V_E to be dropped across R_2 to provide adequate stability and a bias chain current of 200 μA assuming $h_{FE} \geqslant 100$ for T_3].

Darlington stage

6.5 Select resistance values from the E12 series (appendix D) for the basic Darlington stage of figure 6.7a. To ensure that $h_{FE} \geqslant 100$ for each BJT, the collector currents must not be less than 500 μA although static power dissipation is to be kept as low as possible. The circuit is to operate from a 15 V supply and approximately 20 per cent of the supply voltage should be dropped across the emitter resistor for adequate stability against the variation of V_{BE} with temperature.

[Specimen answers: $R_E = 5.6$ kΩ, $R_C = 5.6$ kΩ, $R = 6.8$ kΩ, $R_1 = 82$ kΩ, $R_2 = 33$ kΩ for $I_{C_1} = I_{C_2} = 500$ μA giving $h_{FE} = 100$ with a bias chain current of 125 μA, that is, 25 times the static base current of T_1]

Cascode amplifier

6.6 The cascode amplifier of figure 6.9a is to operate from an 18 V supply. Making realistic assumptions, select E12 values for the circuit resistors and an E6 value for the bypass capacitor C_B (appendix D) for the circuit based on a quiescent collector current of 1 mA, assuming the bandwidth must extend down to 50 Hz.

[Specimen answers: $R_1 = 33\ \text{k}\Omega$, $R_2 = 18\ \text{k}\Omega$, $R_3 = 15\ \text{k}\Omega$, $R_E = 3.3\ \text{k}\Omega$, $R_C = 4.7\ \text{k}\Omega$ and $C_B = 2.2\ \mu\text{F}$; allowing 20 per cent of the supply voltage to be dropped across R_E for stability purposes, dividing the remaining 80 per cent of the supply voltage approximately equally between the 2 BJTs and R_C, and allowing a bias chain current of 250 μA which is 25 times the maximum base currents assuming $h_{FE} \geqslant 100$]

Cascaded amplifiers

6.7 A single-stage amplifier has a mid-frequency voltage gain of 45 dB with 3 dB frequencies of 40 Hz and 200 kHz. Assuming the input and output impedances of the stage are such that inter-stage loading effects can be neglected, what would be the overall voltage gain at mid-frequencies and the available bandwidth when three of these stages are cascaded? What would be the lower cut-off frequency of this arrangement?

[Answers: 135 dB, 101.97 kHz, 78.46 Hz]

Tuned amplifiers

6.8 The coil in the tuned amplifier of figure 6.11a has an inductance of 2 mH and a resistance of 50 Ω. What value of tuning capacitance is required if the circuit is to have a centre frequency of 400 kHz? What is the Q-factor of the coil at this frequency? If the relevant parameters of the JFET are $g_{fs} = 2$ mS and $g_{os} = 10\ \mu$S, what is the peak voltage gain of the circuit? Calculate the Q-factor of effective parallel *RLC* circuit at the output and hence determine the bandwidth of the amplifier.

[Answers: 79.16 pF, 100.53, −166.96, 16.61, 24.09 kHz]

6.9 A tuned-collector amplifier has a tuned circuit comprising a 2 μF capacitor in parallel with a coil of inductance 10 mH and Q-factor 14.15 at the resonant frequency. The amplifier has a small-signal input resistance of 700 Ω and a current gain of 152. Assuming that the shunting effect of the BJT is negligible, calculate (a) the frequency at which the voltage gain peaks, (b) the voltage gain at this frequency and (c) the amplifier bandwidth. What would be the effect on the bandwidth if the output of this tuned stage was to be cascaded with a wideband amplifier stage having an input resistance of 700 Ω? Mention any approximations made in the analysis.

[Answers: 1.13 kHz, −217.19, 79.51 Hz; increased to 193.10 Hz although the reduction of the Q-factor of the output circuit to a relatively low value (< 6) causes the resonant frequency to alter slightly, see appendix B, equation B.13]

7 Operational Amplifiers

Coverage

- Consideration of the structure, types, performance and modes of operation of op-amps.
- Examples of static and small-signal analysis of a general-purpose op-amp; the 741.
- Circumstances under which a practical op-amp may be considered as ideal.
- Some linear and switching applications treating the op-amp as ideal.
- Investigation of the various non-ideal aspects of op-amp performance and how they affect circuit performance.
- Consideration of some practical aspects that influence the use of op-amps.

An operational amplifier (op-amp) is a high-gain, direct-coupled voltage amplifier that in integrated form has become the basic building block of linear electronic systems.

The significance of direct coupling between stages is that the amplifier has a 'flat' gain-frequency response down to zero frequency (figure 7.1) enabling it to amplify very-low-frequency and constant-voltage signals that would be blocked by the inter-stage coupling capacitors in an ac coupled amplifier.

The need to amplify constant and slowly-varying voltages first arose with the development of electronic simulators in which circuitry was required to perform mathematical *operations* such as addition and integration (section 7.3.1), hence the name *op-amp*. Other applications developed, particularly in connection with transducers and instrumentation, and the appearance of *integrated* op-amps offering high performance at low cost heralded the use of this type of amplifier in linear applications covering the entire signal-processing frequency spectrum from dc to RF as well as in pulse circuits; see also sections 9.1 and 10.2.

7.1 **Basics**

Structure

Figure 7.2 shows a block diagram representation of a typical op-amp. The input stage is differential, incorporating active loads to give high differential gain and biasing via current mirrors (sections 6.2, 6.3 and 6.4). The stage provides high differential input impedance and good common-mode rejection, avoiding the drift problems that are associated with direct coupling even though it is usually single ended. Notice that the symbols used to represent the input and output voltages of the amplifier have upper case suffixes indicating that the circuit is capable of amplifying dc and ac components; thus the 'total' input voltage v_I

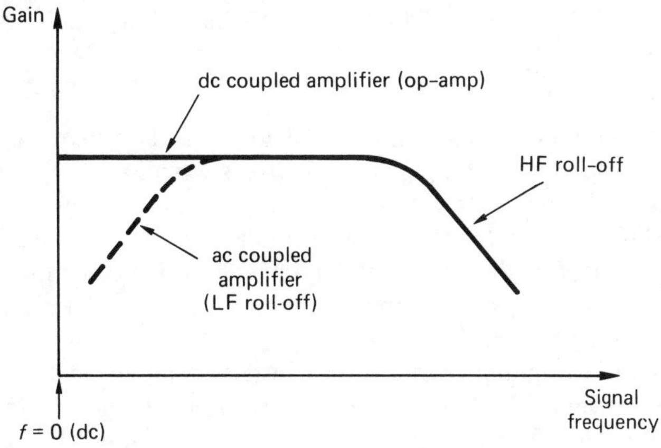

Figure 7.1 Voltage gain–frequency response for an op-amp

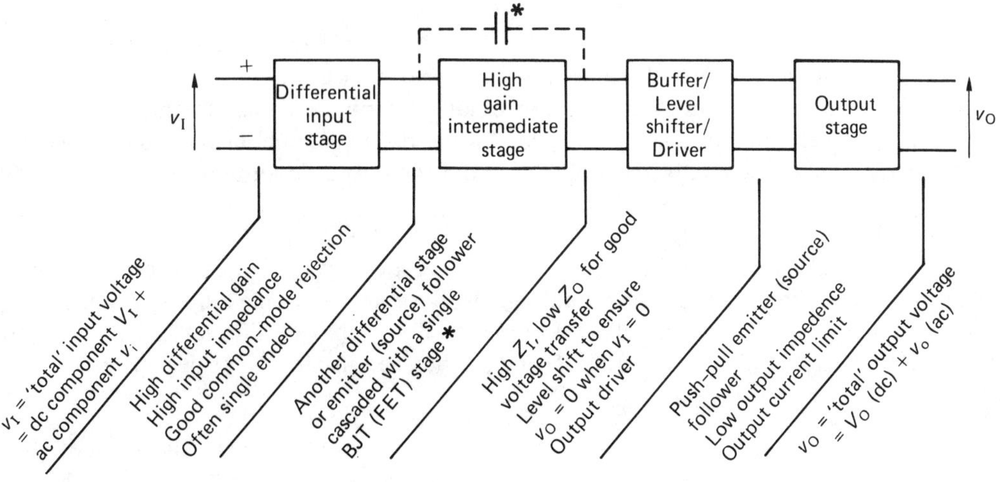

Figure 7.2 Typical op-amp structure

comprises, in general, a steady component V_I and a time-varying component v_i while correspondingly at the output $v_O = V_O + v_o$.

The main contribution to voltage gain is usually provided by the second (intermediate) stage which is typically a cascade of emitter (source) follower and a high-gain basic BJT (FET) stage. The follower acts as a buffer between the input and main gain stages to avoid gain loss by potential division, the situation highlighted in example 3.13. To avoid stability problems, the intermediate stage may incorporate a compensating network to modify the gain and phase responses. Such an amplifier is said to be *internally compensated* and is stable, that is, it will not oscillate, in negative feedback applications although this stability is achieved at the expense of bandwidth (section 7.4.5).

The third stage normally incorporates buffering to maintain high gain; it may include a level-shifting network to ensure v_O is zero when v_I is zero and a driver for the push–pull output stage. The latter is usually a complementary stage operating in class AB (section 8.5) and incorporates current-limiting protection.

Representation and terminology

The general symbol for an op-amp is shown in figure 7.3a. To provide good common-mode rejection it is usual to power the amplifier using dual supplies with the common node of the supplies being the signal reference (earth, ground) as shown in figure 6.4a for an isolated differential stage. The link between dual power supplies and good common-mode rejection is explained in section 6.4. Note that in circuit diagrams involving op-amps it is usual to assume connection to the $+V_{CC}$, $-V_{EE}$ power supplies without them being shown explicitly. Normally the supplies are *balanced* whereby $V_{CC} = V_{EE}$.

The two inputs to the op-amp correspond to the two inputs to the differential stage of figure 6.4a and are designated $-$ and $+$ to indicate *inversion* and *non-inversion* respectively between input and output. For comparison, v^- and v^+ in figure 7.3a correspond to v_{i_1} and v_{i_2} respectively in figure 6.4a as far as phase relationships with the output signal are concerned.

The convention is adopted that the *differential input voltage* to the amplifier, v_I, is the potential applied to the non-inverting (+) input *relative to* the inverting (−) input, thus

$$v_I = v^+ - v^- \tag{7.1}$$

Figure 7.3b gives a basic model representing the performance of an op-amp. The differential input and output impedances Z_I and Z_O can usually be considered as resistances R_I and R_O since, except at very high frequency, the effect of the reactive components is negligible. A_{VD} is the *differential voltage gain* of the amplifier and if the output loading is negligible ($i_O \simeq 0$):

$$v_O = A_{VD} v_I \tag{7.2}$$

In section 6.4 it is shown that the input impedance of a differential stage for common-mode signals is different from that for differential signals; the common-mode input impedances Z_{CM}^+ and Z_{CM}^- in figure 7.3b model this effect. In practice, however, the values of Z_{CM}^+ and Z_{CM}^- are at least 100 times the differential value Z_I and so they can usually be neglected.

Op-amp types and performance

Table 7.1 surveys the various types of op-amp currently available, listing typical values of the main performance parameters and the most significant features.

All-bipolar op-amps generally offer low noise performance, fast response in terms of slew

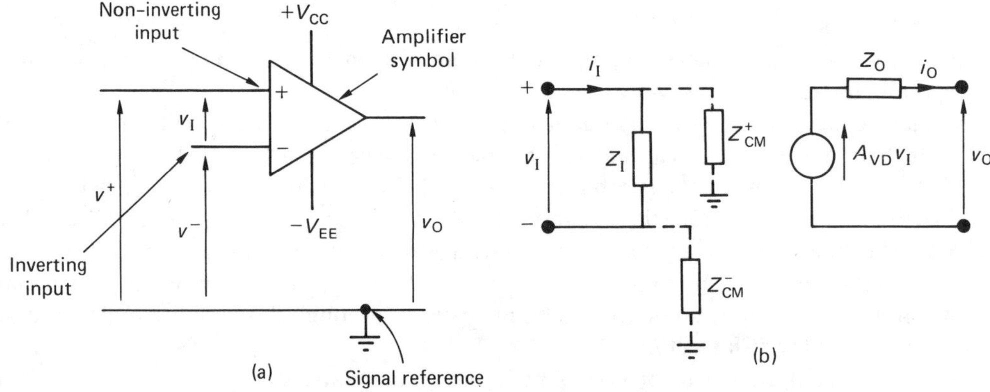

Figure 7.3 Op-amp symbol and model

Table 7.1 Op-amp performance comparison

	All-bipolar	*Bifet*†	*All-MOS*†	*Theoretical ideal*
Open-loop differential voltage gain at dc: $A_{VD(dc)}$ (dB)	80–130	75–110	100–105	∞
CMRR (dB)	70–130	75–100	90–100	∞
Typical differential input resistance: R_I (Ω)	10^6	10^{12}	10^{12}	∞
Typical output resistance: R_O (Ω)	75	75	10^3	0
Open-loop bandwidth	←	1 Hz–10 kHz‡	→	∞
Most significant features	Lowest noise Fastest Highest power	High R_I	High R_I Lowest supply voltage Lowest supply current	—
Typical commercial types	OP07, 301 531, 709, 741, 748	351, 3130 3140, 13741	251, 271 7611 7650	—

* Mostly JFET or MOST input stage with remainder of amplifier bipolar.
† CMOS and NMOS types; CMOS types have lowest power dissipation.
‡ Depending on degree of frequency compensation employed for stability (section 7.4.5).

rate (section 7.4.4) and highest output power capability. Hybrid bipolar-FET, *bifet*, designs provide very high input resistance while retaining the low output resistance, and hence good output current capability, associated with bipolar circuitry.

All-MOS types have very high input resistance but are noted for their low quiescent current requirement and their ability to operate from very low supply voltages, both factors being important for battery-powered equipment.

Op-amps have:

(1) High open-loop differential voltage gain A_{VD}.
(2) Good rejection of common-mode signals.
(3) High differential input resistance R_I.
(4) Low output resistance R_O, though MOS types tend to be rather poor in this respect.

Although the basic op-amp can have a bandwidth under open-loop conditions, that is without external feedback applied, of up to 1 MHz or more, subsequent use with negative feedback (section 7.4.5) can be unstable. To avoid such instability, general-purpose op-amps such as the 741 employ internal compensation (section 7.4.5) to modify the open-loop response but the open-loop bandwidth is then severely restricted; for the 741 the open-loop bandwidth is only 7 Hz (figure 7.4 and appendix E, section E.9). Although such a limited bandwidth may appear a major disadvantage, it should be noted that in linear applications the amplifier is never used without negative feedback which reduces the overall gain. Since the gain–bandwidth product $|A_{VD(dc)}|B$ of the amplifier is constant, gain can be traded for bandwidth. $|A_{VD(dc)}|B$ is $(2 \times 10^5)(7\text{ Hz}) = 1.4$ MHz for a 741 and so, from figure 7.4, if negative feedback is used to reduce the gain to 100, the bandwidth is increased to 14 kHz while a gain of 10 corresponds to a closed-loop bandwidth of 140 kHz. A unity-gain buffer using a 741 has a bandwidth of 1.4 MHz.

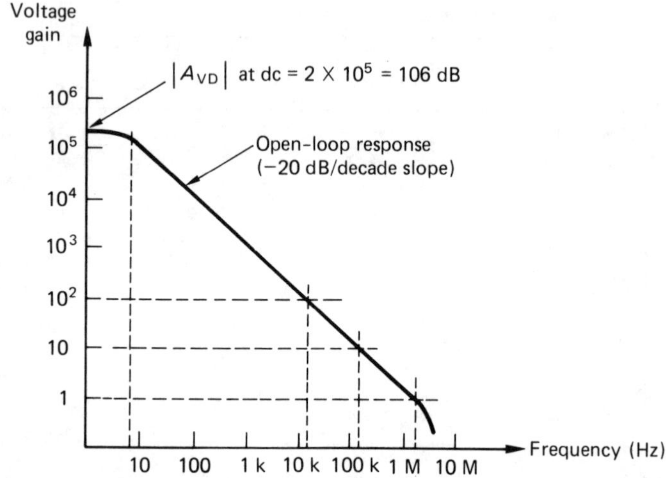

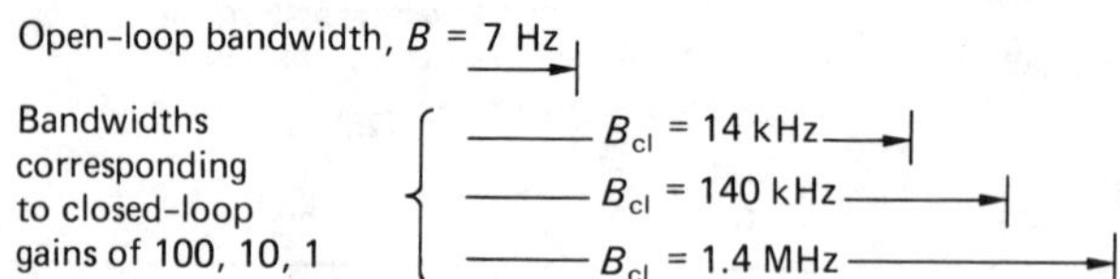

Figure 7.4 Gain–bandwidth relation for a 741 op-amp

Modes of operation

Op-amps are used in linear and switching applications. In either case the output voltage v_O cannot exceed the power supply voltage. If the input voltage v_I is increased from zero, v_O increases from zero until it (almost) reaches $+V_{CC}$ (or $-V_{EE}$) at which point the op-amp is said to be at *saturation.* Further increase in v_I has no effect on v_O.

In *linear* applications, saturation must be avoided as this would introduce severe distortion, thus v_I must be sufficiently small that v_O does not reach the power supply voltage. For the 741 op-amp, A_{VD} at dc and VLF is 2×10^5 and so, when operating from ± 15 V supplies, the maximum value of $|v_I|$ for linear operation at VLF is $15\text{ V}/(2 \times 10^5) = 75\ \mu\text{V}$ *which is very small.* In analysis of linear op-amp circuits (section 7.3.1) it is usual to take

$$v_I \simeq 0 \tag{7.3}$$

as the external circuit voltages are $\gg v_I$.

With v_I very low and the input resistance R_I very high (typically 2 MΩ for a 741, appendix E, section E.9), the input *signal* current i_I is minute, $75\ \mu\text{V}/2\text{ M}\Omega \simeq 38$ pA* for the example quoted. For analysis purposes it is usual to take

$$i_I \simeq 0 \tag{7.4}$$

as external circuit component values are chosen to ensure that the op-amp input current is negligible compared with the external circuit currents.

Where the op-amp is used as a *switch*, values of v_I are intentionally applied to drive the amplifier to saturation, although for safe operation v_I *must not exceed the power supply voltage.*

* Note that this value of *signal* current is swamped by the input *bias* current (section 7.4.2).

In switching applications, therefore, equation 7.3 is not valid. However, since v_I must remain less than the power supply voltage, the high value of R_I means that the input current approximation (equation 7.4) remains valid, $i_I$max being only $15\,V/2\,M\Omega = 7.5\,\mu A$ for 15 V supplies.

7.2 **Amplifier circuit analysis**

As an illustrative example, this section analyses the circuit of a popular general-purpose op-amp, the 741. The complete circuit is shown in figure 7.5 with the signal amplifying stages corresponding to the block diagram of figure 7.2 shown shaded; other components are involved in biasing and output current limiting.

T_{16}, R_{12} is the emitter-follower input buffer of the second stage which presents high resistance to the output of stage 1 and low resistance to the T_{13}, T_{17}, R_{11} amplifying stage to facilitate
$T_{16}R_{12}$ is the emitter-follower input buffer of the second stage which presents high resistance to the output of stage 1 and low resistance to the T_{13}, T_{17}, R_{11} amplifying stage to facilitate
efficient voltage transfer and high voltage gain.

T_{21} acts as an output stage driver, the T_{18}, T_{19}, R_8 network providing a level shift of $2V_{BE}$ to ensure class AB operation of the T_{14}, T_{20} complementary output stage thus reducing crossover distortion (section 8.5).

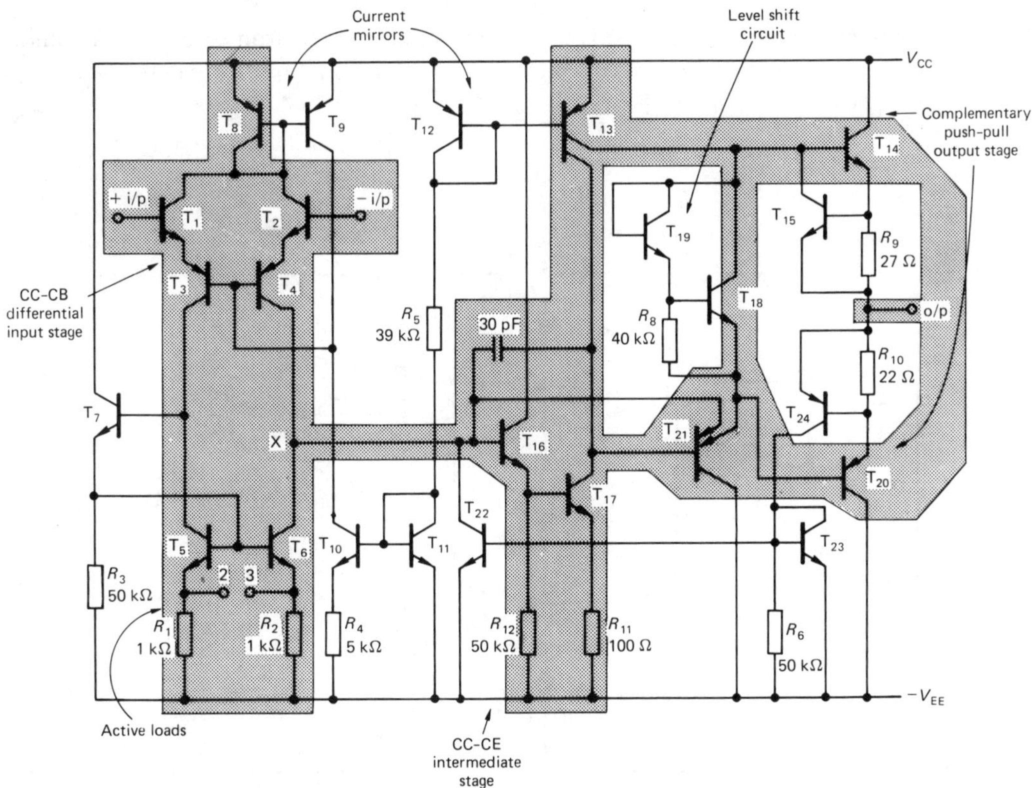

Figure 7.5 741 op-amp circuit

The ·R_5, T_{11}, T_{12} (diodes) branch provides the reference bias current. T_{12}, T_{13} mirrors (section 6.2) this current to provide the quiescent current for the T_{17} amplifier and T_{21} driver. The twin collector of T_{13} enables the mirrored current to be split in the desired proportions for T_{17} and T_{21}, the relative length of the collector diffusions of T_{13} determining the proportions of the current split. The T_{10}, T_{11} Widlar mirror (section 6.2) produces a reduced reference current in T_9, T_{10} which is mirrored via T_8, T_9 to provide the bias current for the differential input stage. T_7, R_3 provides the base current for the T_5, T_6 active loads.

T_{15}, R_9 provides current limiting protection of the T_{14} output transistor. When the output current i_O flowing through R_9 is sufficient to turn T_{15} ON, which corresponds to $V_{BE_{15}} \simeq 0.55$ V, base current is diverted from T_{14}, limiting its conduction. Thus with $R_9 = 27\ \Omega$, the limiting current $i_O$max is $0.55\ \text{V}/27\ \Omega \simeq 20$ mA and since this current is very much larger than the currents drawn by the other stages, this limits the power dissipation to about (20 mA)(15 V) = 600 mA for 15 V supplies. The R_{10}, T_{24}, R_6, T_{23}, T_{22} circuit provides similar protection for T_{20} by diverting base current from T_{16}, hence limiting the conduction of T_{16}, T_{17}, T_{21} and finally T_{20}.

Static analysis

Figure 7.6 shows the bias components for the 741. For ± 15 V supplies and assuming $V_{BE} = 0.6$ V, the reference current I_1 is

$$\frac{V_{CC} - (-V_{EE}) - (V_{BE_{11}} + V_{BE_{12}})}{R_5} = \frac{15\ \text{V} - (-15\ \text{V}) - 2(0.6\ \text{V})}{39\ \text{k}\Omega} \simeq 738\ \mu\text{A} \tag{7.5}$$

Mirrored current I_2 is $< I_1$ as $B_{BE_{10}} < V_{BE_{11}}$ because of the voltage drop across R_4. Assuming $h_{FE_{10}}$ is high so that the emitter and collector currents of T_{10} are approximately equal:

$$I_2 R_4 = V_{BE_{11}} - V_{BE_{10}} \tag{7.6}$$

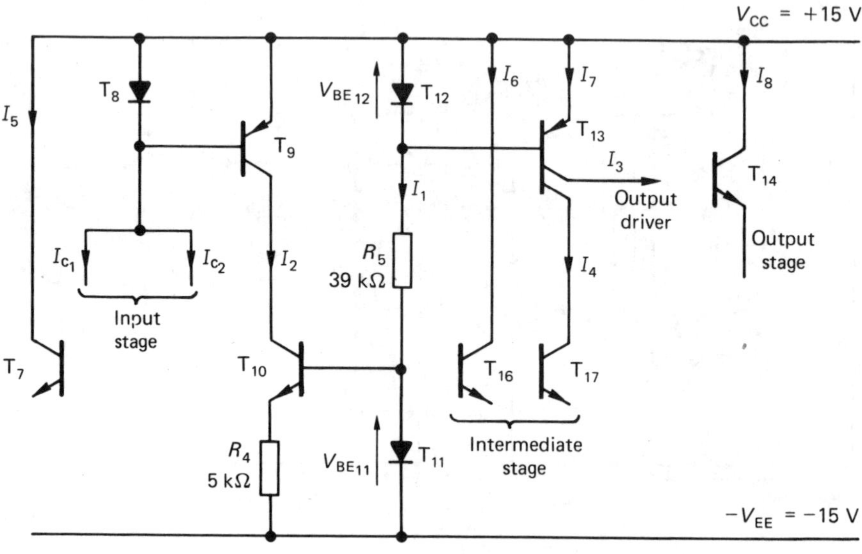

Figure 7.6 Bias current components for the 741 op-amp

If the forward $I-V$ relationship for the B–E junctions of the BJTs in the circuit is represented by the theoretical ideal for a pn junction (equation 2.8), which is valid at low current levels:

$$V_{BE} = \frac{kT}{e} \ln\left(\frac{I}{I_0}\right)$$

where I_0 is the theoretical reverse saturation current. Then from equation 7.6

$$I_2 = \frac{kT}{eR_4}\left[\ln\left(\frac{I_1}{I_0}\right) - \ln\left(\frac{I_2}{I_0}\right)\right]$$

$$= \frac{kT}{eR_4} \ln\left(\frac{I_1}{I_2}\right) \quad (7.8)$$

since, if the BJTs are matched, I_0 has the same value for both BJTs. The quantity kT/e has a value of approximately 26 mV at 25°C, R_4 is 5 kΩ and I_1 has been calculated (equation 7.5) as approximately 738 μA. Trial-and-error solution of equation 7.8 shows that I_2 is approximately 19 μA.

Input stage currents I_{C_1}, I_{C_2}

For a symmetrical input stage with high h_{FE} BJTs, I_2 mirrored over to T_8 would divide equally between I_{C_1} and I_{C_2} making each $I_2/2$, that is, 9.5 μA. However T_3 and T_4 are lateral pnp BJTs having h_{FE} of only about 5 [1a] and so their base currents cannot be neglected. Figure 7.7a shows the relevant section of the circuit; by mirror action

$$I_{C_1} + I_{C_2} = I_2 - (I_{B_3} + I_{B_4})$$

From symmetry $I_{C_1} = I_{C_2}$ and $I_{B_3} = I_{B_4}$ and so

$$I_{C_1} = I_{C_2} = \frac{I_2}{2} - I_{B_3} \quad (7.9)$$

Combining equations 2.11 and 2.12 for a BJT gives $I_B = I_E/(h_{FE} + 1)$ ignoring leakage. But for T_3, $I_{E_3} = I_{E_1}$ and $I_{E_1} \simeq I_{C_1}$ as T_1 has high gain, thus

$$I_{B_3} = \frac{I_{E_3}}{h_{FE_3} + 1} \simeq \frac{I_{C_1}}{h_{FE_3} + 1} \simeq \frac{I_{C_1}}{6} \quad (7.10)$$

as h_{FE_3} is typically about 5.
Substituting for I_{B_3} from equation 7.10 into 7.9 gives

$$I_{C_1} = I_{C_2} = \frac{3}{7} I_2 \simeq \frac{3}{7}(19\ \mu A) \simeq 8\ \mu\text{A} \quad (7.11)$$

Note that I_{C_3}, which is the current through the T_5, R_1 active load is $I_{E_3} - I_{B_3} \simeq I_{C_1} - I_{B_3} = I_{C_1} - (I_{C_1}/6) = \frac{5}{6}(I_{C_1}) \simeq 7$ μA. This current determines the effective ac load provided by T_5, R_1 (and T_6, R_2 by symmetry). The current I_5 drawn by T_7 depends on the voltage V_{R_3} (figure 7.7b) established by the T_6, R_3 active load. The loading on the collectors of T_5 and T_6 (figure 7.5) is low because of the high gains of T_7 and T_{16}, and so the emitter currents of T_5 and T_6 are approximately equal to the collector currents of T_3 and T_4 which are equal

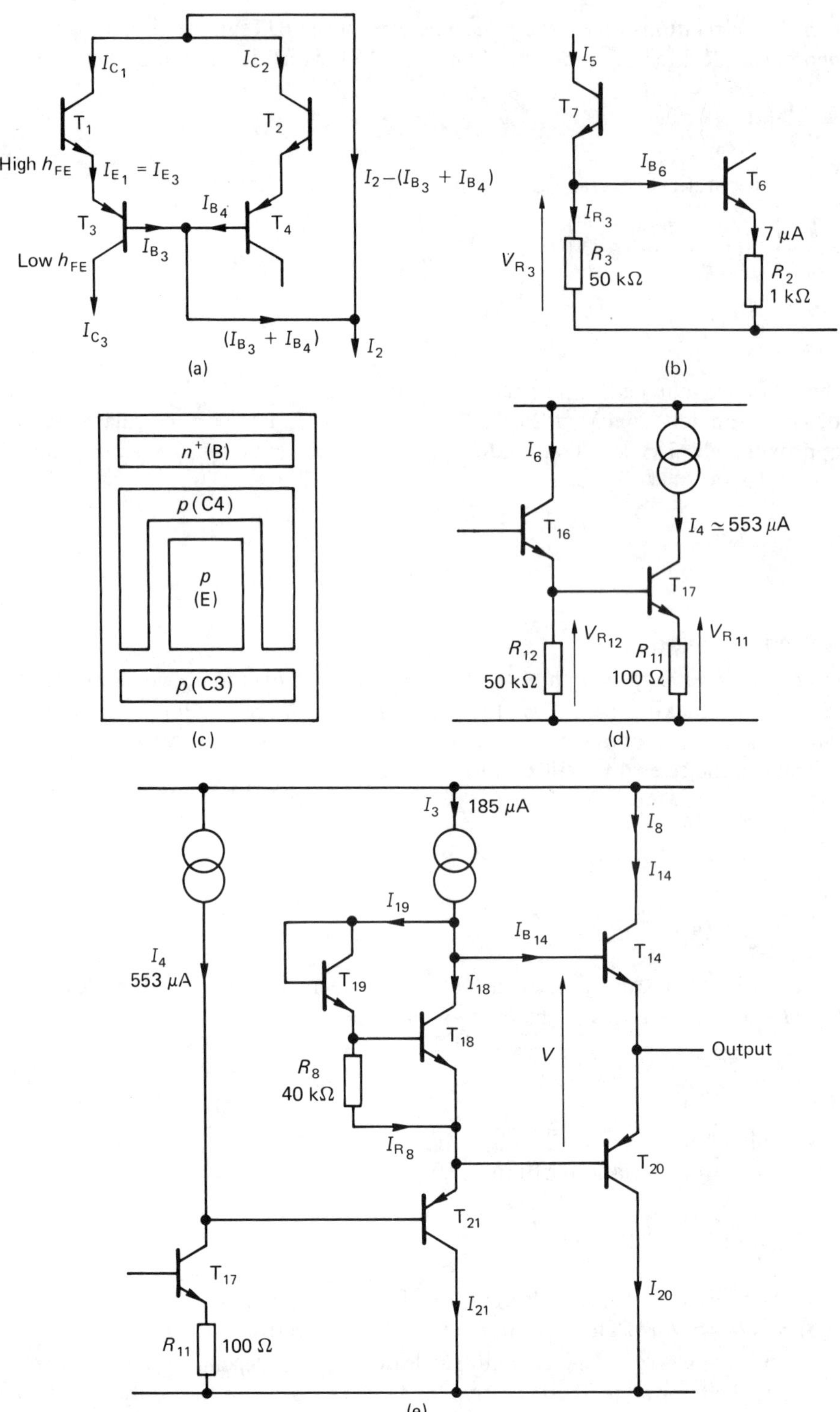

Figure 7.7 Bias current components for the 741 op-amp

by symmetry and calculated above (I_{C_3}) to be approximately 7 μA. Then, from figure 7.7b:

$$V_{R_3} \simeq V_{BE_6} + (7\ \mu A)(1\ k\Omega)$$
$$\simeq (0.6\ V) + (7\ mV) \simeq 0.6\ V \tag{7.12}$$

showing that V_{R_3} is dominated by V_{BE_6}.
Since T_6 and T_7 have high gain, $I_{B_6} \ll I_{R_3}$ and then $I_5 \simeq I_{R_3}$ from which

$$I_5 \simeq \frac{V_{R_3}}{R_3} \simeq \frac{0.6\ V}{50\ k\Omega} = 12\ \mu A \tag{7.13}$$

Intermediate stage currents I_3, I_4 and I_6

The reference current I_1 ($\simeq 738\ \mu$A, equation 7.5) is mirrored over to I_7 via T_{12}, T_{13} and so $I_7 \simeq 738\ \mu$A. Division of I_7 into I_3 and I_4 by the twin-collector BJT T_{13} depends on its geometry. Figure 7.7c is a plan view of this planar pnp device [1a] indicating that the length of collector C4 is of the order of 3 times that of C3. The ratio I_4/I_3 is approximately equal to the ratio of the lengths of the respective collectors because of the proportion of diffusing carriers collected by each region, and so $I_4/I_3 \simeq 3$ giving

$$I_3 \simeq \frac{I_7}{4} \simeq \frac{738\ \mu A}{4} \simeq 185\ \mu A \tag{7.14}$$

and

$$I_4 \simeq \frac{3I_7}{4} \simeq 553\ \mu A \tag{7.15}$$

The current I_6 drawn by T_{16} depends on the voltage established across R_{12} by T_{17}, R_{11}. The collector current I_4 of T_{17} (figure 7.7d) is approximately 553 μA (equation 7.15) and since T_{17} has a high gain:

$$V_{R_{11}} \simeq I_4 R_{11}$$

the collector and emitter currents of T_{17} being approximately equal. Then

$$V_{R_{12}} = V_{R_{11}} + V_{BE_{17}}$$

and for T_{16} having high gain

$$I_6 \simeq \frac{V_{R_{12}}}{R_{12}} \simeq \frac{I_4 R_{11} + V_{BE_{17}}}{R_{12}}$$
$$\simeq \frac{(553\ \mu A)(100\ \Omega) + 0.6\ V}{50\ k\Omega} \simeq 13\ \mu A \tag{7.16}$$

Output stage current I_8

Figure 7.7e shows the output stage and the essential features of the intermediate stage ignoring the protection circuitry.

$$I_{R_8} = \frac{V_{BE_{18}}}{R_8} \simeq \frac{0.6\ V}{40\ k\Omega} = 15\ \mu A$$

and with T_{18} having high gain, hence low base current:

$$I_{19} \simeq I_{R_8} = 15\ \mu A \tag{7.17}$$

Under quiescent conditions, I_8 is low (see class AB operation, section 8.5) and with T_{14} having high gain, base current $I_{B_{14}}$ is low so that

$$I_{18} \simeq I_3 - I_{19} = 185\,\mu A - 15\,\mu A = 170\,\mu A \tag{7.18}$$

The bias voltage V between the bases of the two output BJTs is $V_{BE_{14}} + |V_{BE_{20}}|$, noting that T_{20} is a pnp BJT and so $V_{BE_{20}}$ is negative. V is also equal to $V_{BE_{18}} + V_{BE_{19}}$ because of the level shifting network and so

$$V_{BE_{18}} + V_{BE_{19}} = V_{BE_{14}} + |V_{BE_{20}}| \tag{7.19}$$

Using the theoretical equation 7.7 for V_{BE}, equation 7.19 can be written

$$\ln\left(\frac{I_{18}}{I_{0_{18}}}\right) + \ln\left(\frac{I_{19}}{I_{0_{19}}}\right) = \ln\left(\frac{I_{14}}{I_{0_{14}}}\right) + \ln\left(\frac{I_{20}}{I_{0_{20}}}\right)$$

from which

$$\frac{I_{18}I_{19}}{I_{0_{18}}I_{0_{19}}} = \frac{I_{14}I_{20}}{I_{0_{14}}I_{0_{20}}}$$

giving

$$I_8 = I_{14} = I_{20} = \sqrt{\left(I_{18}I_{19}\frac{I_{0_{14}}I_{0_{20}}}{I_{0_{18}}I_{0_{19}}}\right)} \tag{7.20}$$

The theoretical saturation current of a pn junction is proportional to the junction area [1b] and since the output BJTs T_{14} and T_{20} are typically 3 times the area of the lower power BJTs in the circuit, $I_{0_{14}} \simeq 3I_{0_{18}}$ and $I_{0_{20}} \simeq 3I_{0_{19}}$. Further, from symmetry, $I_{0_{14}} \simeq I_{0_{20}}$ and $I_{0_{18}} \simeq I_{0_{19}}$, giving $\dfrac{I_{0_{14}}I_{0_{20}}}{I_{0_{18}}I_{0_{19}}} \simeq 9$ which from equation 7.20 leads to

$$\begin{aligned} I_8 &\simeq 3\sqrt{(I_{18}I_{19})} \\ &= 3\sqrt{(170\,\mu A)(15\,\mu A)} \simeq 151\,\mu A \end{aligned} \tag{7.21}$$

using the values established in equations 7.18 and 7.17 for I_{18} and I_{19}.

From figure 7.6, the total static current drain from the supplies is the sum of reference currents I_1 and I_2 (738 μA and 19 μA), input stage currents I_{C_1}, I_{C_2} (each approximately 8 μA) and I_5 (12 μA), intermediate stage currents I_3, I_4 and I_6 (185 μA, 553 μA and 13 μA) together with the output stage bias current I_8 (151 μA) making a total drain of approximately 1.69 mA. With $\pm$ 15 V supplies, the total static power dissipation is therefore (1.69 mA)(30 V) $\simeq$ 51 mW.

Small-signal analysis of the 741 op-amp

This section determines the input and output resistances of the 741 op-amp and the small-signal voltage gain of the circuit at low frequency. Numerical sub-suffixes indicate to which transistor a symbol refers, for example, h_{ie_2} is the value of h_{ie} for BJT T_2 while R_{i_4} is the input resistance of the stage incorporating T_4.

Input resistance

The differential ac input resistance R_{id} of the amplifier is the effective resistance presented to signals applied between the + and − inputs of the CC–CB differential stage. Figure 7.8a shows the essential features of the input stage; as far as the signal is concerned, the power supplies provide low impedance paths to signal earth (section 3.4.2) resulting in the model of

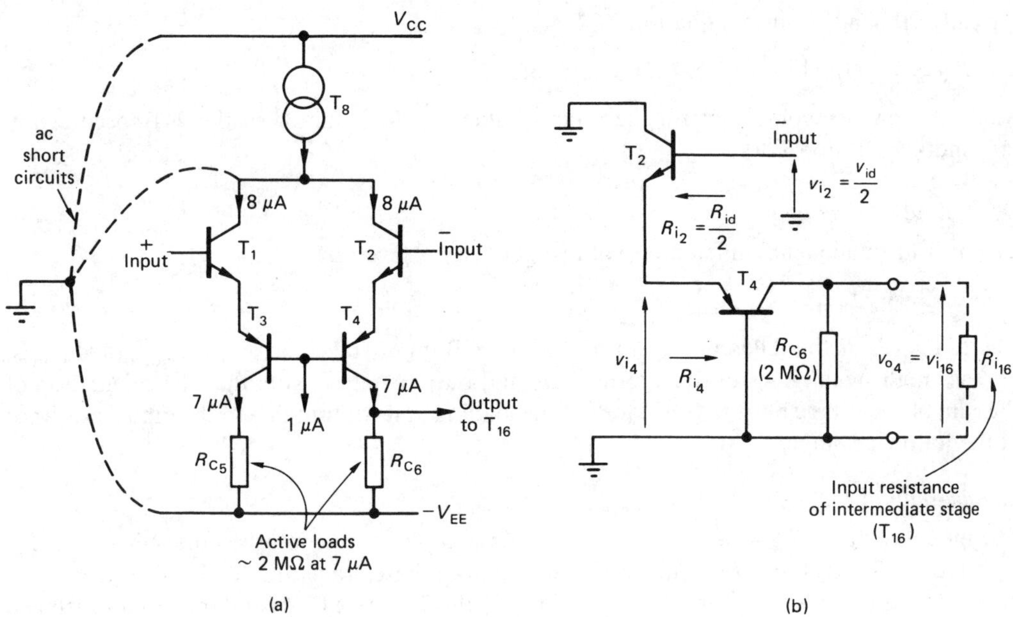

Figure 7.8 Small-signal operation of the input stage of a 741 op-amp

figure 7.8b for the output half of the stage. As this is a half stage, the input signal v_{i_2} and input resistance R_{i_2} to signal earth are each half the differential input values v_{id} and R_{id}.

T_2 is connected as an emitter-follower; there are no base bias resistors and the effective emitter resistance is the input resistance R_{i_4} of the common-base BJT T_4. Comparison with equation 3.111 for the input resistance of a basic emitter-follower ignoring its bias resistance gives

$$\begin{aligned} R_{i_2} &= h_{ie_2} + (1 + g_{fe_2} h_{ie_2}) R_{i_4} \\ &\simeq \frac{h_{fe_2}}{g_{fe_2}} + h_{fe_2} R_{i_4} \\ &= h_{fe_2}[(1/g_{fe_2}) + R_{i_4}] \end{aligned} \qquad (7.22)$$

using $h_{ie} \simeq h_{fe}/g_{fe}$ from equation 3.62 and noting that h_{fe_2} is $\gg 1$. Because the collector current of T_2 is very low (8 μA), the single h_{ie} term in the original expression for R_{i_2} above is not negligible and so the simplification made in equation 3.111 for the basic emitter-follower is not valid in this case.

The input resistance of the common-base BJT T_4 is given by equation 3.101 as

$$R_{i_4} \simeq 1/g_{fe_4} \qquad (7.23)$$

and therefore the differential ac input resistance of the amplifier is

$$R_{id} = 2R_{i_2} \simeq 2h_{fe_2}[(1/g_{fe_2}) + (1/g_{fe_4})] \qquad (7.24)$$

The static collector currents of T_2 and T_4 from previous analysis are 8 μA and 7 μA respectively (figure 7.8a) and therefore, using equation 3.63, $1/g_{fe_2}$ is $1/(40 \times 8 \times 10^{-6}) = 3125\ \Omega$ and $1/g_{fe_4}$ is $1/(40 \times 7 \times 10^{-6}) \simeq 3571\ \Omega$. The small-signal current gain of these low-power IC BJTs is typically 200 and so, from equation 7.24:

$$R_{id} \simeq 2(200)(3125\,\Omega + 3571\,\Omega) \simeq 2.68\,\text{M}\Omega \tag{7.25}$$

which compares favourably with the typical value of 2 MΩ quoted in the 741 specification (appendix E, section E.9).

Differential voltage gain

The overall small-signal differential voltage gain A_{vd} is given by

$$A_{vd} = A_{vd(input)} \times A_{v(intermed)} \times A_{v(output)} \tag{7.26}$$

where $A_{vd(input)}$ is the differential gain of the CC–CB input stage and $A_{v(intermed)}$ and $A_{v(output)}$ are the small-signal gains of the intermediate and output stages. Note that the calculation of the gain of each stage must take account of the loading at its output due to the input resistance of the following stage.

Voltage gain of the input stage, $A_{vd(input)}$

The model of figure 7.8b shows that the gain of the input stage comprises the gain of the T_1, T_2 emitter-followers and the gain of the T_4 common-base stage, the load on the CB stage being the parallel combination of R_{c_6} (provided by the T_6 active load) and the input resistance $R_{i_{16}}$ of the intermediate stage. Considering the half stage (figure 7.8b), the T_2 emitter-follower has a gain of approximately unity (table 3.1), thus $v_{i_4} \simeq v_{i_2}$ while the gain of the CB stage (v_{o_4}/v_{i_4}) is given by $g_{fe_4}(R_{c_6}/\!/R_{i_{16}})$ by comparison with equation 3.97, $R_{c_6}/\!/R_{i_{16}}$ providing the effective collector load on T_4. Thus

$$A_{vd(input)} = \frac{v_{o_4}}{v_{id}} = \frac{v_{o_4}}{2v_{i_2}} \simeq \frac{v_{o_4}}{2v_{i_4}} \simeq \frac{1}{2}\, g_{fe_4}(R_{c_6}/\!/R_{i_{16}}) \tag{7.27}$$

The effective resistance R_{c_6} of the T_6 active load is given by the reciprocal of the slope of the output characteristic of T_6 $(=1/h_{oe_6}$, section 6.3) which, at the static current of 7 μA (as calculated after equation 7.11) has a value of the order of 2 MΩ.

From figure 7.9a the input resistance $R_{i_{16}}$ of the intermediate stage is the input resistance of the T_{16} emitter-follower for which the effective emitter resistance is R_{12} in parallel with $R_{i_{17}}$, the input resistance of the T_{17} common-emitter stage which has an unbypassed emitter resistor (R_{11}). Thus, corresponding to equation 7.22 for the T_2 emitter-follower:

$$R_{i_{16}} = h_{fe_{16}}[(1/g_{fe_{16}}) + (R_{12}/\!/R_{i_{17}})] \tag{7.28}$$

where, correspondingly, for the T_{17} stage:

$$R_{i_{17}} = h_{fe_{17}}[(1/g_{fe_{17}}) + R_{11}] \tag{7.29}$$

The static collector currents of T_{16} and T_{17} have previously been determined as 13 μA (I_6, equation 7.16) and 553 μA (I_4, equation 7.15) from which, using equation 3.63, $1/g_{fe_{16}}$ is $1/(40 \times 13 \times 10^{-6}) \simeq 1923\,\Omega$ and $1/g_{fe_{17}}$ is $1/(40 \times 553 \times 10^{-6}) \simeq 45\,\Omega$.

With $R_{11} = 100\,\Omega$, $R_{12} = 50\,\text{k}\Omega$ and the values of h_{fe} of typically 200,

$$R_{i_{17}} = 200(45\,\Omega + 100\,\Omega) = 29\,\text{k}\Omega \tag{7.30}$$

and hence

$$R_{i_{16}} = 200[1923\,\Omega + (50\,\text{k}\Omega/\!/29\,\text{k}\Omega)] \simeq 4\,\text{M}\Omega \tag{7.31}$$

from equations 7.29 and 7.28.

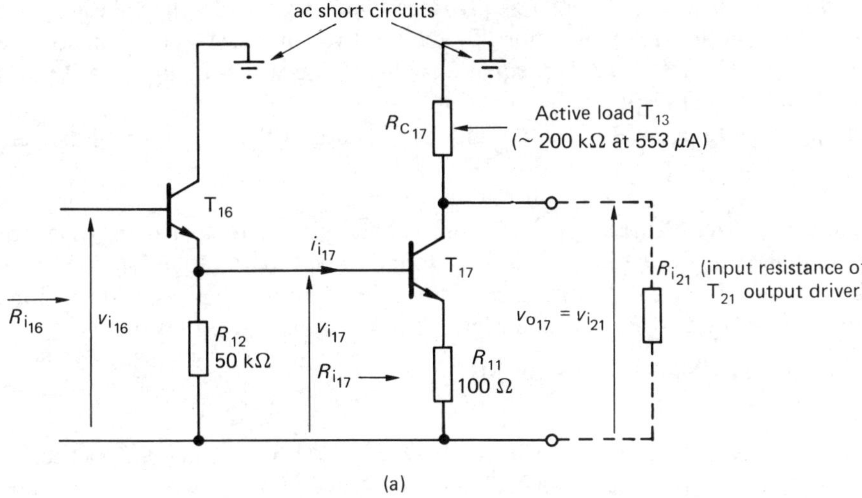

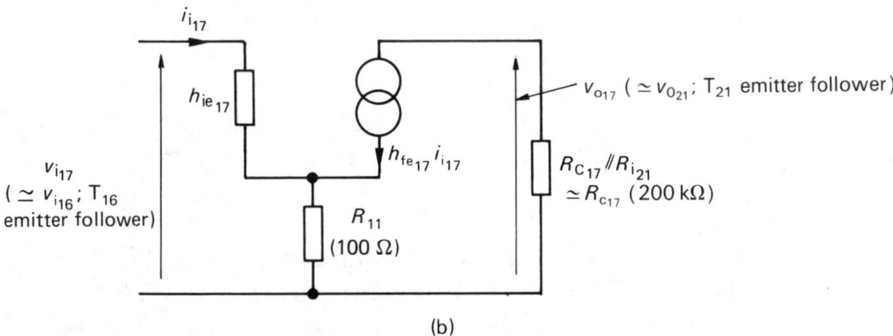

Figure 7.9 Small-signal operation of the intermediate stage of a 741 op-amp

Having determined $R_{i_{16}}$, the value of $A_{vd(input)}$ can be found from equation 7.27 using $g_{fe_4} \simeq 1/3571\ \Omega$ (calculated prior to equation 7.25) and the estimated value of 2 MΩ for the T_6 active load (following equation 7.27):

$$A_{vd(input)} \simeq \frac{1}{2}\left(\frac{1}{3571\ \Omega}\right)(2\ \mathrm{M\Omega} /\!/ 4\ \mathrm{M\Omega}) \simeq 187 \tag{7.32}$$

Using the definition of differential input voltage as $v^+ - v^-$ (equation 7.1 and figure 7.3a) instead of the potential on the − input relative to the + input, which is effectively the case in figure 7.8b, $A_{vd(input)}$ is − 187.

Voltage gain of the intermediate stage, $A_{v(intermed)}$

The intermediate stage is a cascade of T_{16} emitter-follower, T_{17} common-emitter amplifier with unbypassed emitter resistor R_{11} and T_{21} emitter-follower which acts as the output stage driver. The two emitter-followers each have a voltage gain of approximately unity (table 3.1) and so $A_{v(intermed)}$ is provided by the T_{17} stage for which the effective collector load is the parallel combination of $R_{c_{17}}$ (provided by the T_{13} active load) and the input resistance $R_{i_{21}}$ of the T_{21} emitter-follower.

Twin-collector BJT T_{13} (figure 7.5) provides two active loads, the collector load $R_{c_{17}}$ for T_{17} and the emitter load $R_{e_{21}}$ for T_{21}. The two quiescent components are 553 μA (I_4, equation 7.15) and 185 μA (I_3, equation 7.14) giving values of $R_{c_{17}}$ and $R_{e_{21}}$ of the order of 200 kΩ and 500 kΩ respectively.

Corresponding to equation 7.29, the input resistance of the T_{21} emitter-follower is

$$R_{i_{21}} = h_{fe_{21}}[(1/g_{fe_{21}}) + R_{e_{21}}] \qquad (7.33)$$

The quiescent collector current of T_{21} is approximately equal to I_{18} (figure 7.7) since the base current of high-gain T_{20} is low; I_{18} has been found to be 170 μA (equation 7.18) and so $1/g_{fe_{21}}$ is $1/(40 \times 170 \times 10^{-6}) \simeq 147\ \Omega$ using equation 3.63. With $h_{fe_{21}}$ typically 200, as for the other low-power IC BJTs, and $R_{e_{21}}$ of the order of 500 kΩ from above:

$$R_{i_{21}} \simeq 200(147\ \Omega + 500\ \text{k}\Omega) \simeq 100\ \text{M}\Omega \qquad (7.34)$$

using equation 7.33.

With $R_{i_{21}}$ so large in comparison with $R_{c_{17}}$ ($\simeq 200$ kΩ from above), the effective load on T_{17} is simply $R_{c_{17}}$ as represented in the model of figure 7.9b, from which

$$v_{i_{17}} = h_{ie_{17}} i_{i_{17}} + R_{11}\ (h_{fe_{17}} + 1) i_{i_{17}} \qquad (7.35)$$

and

$$v_{o_{17}} \simeq -h_{fe_{17}} i_{i_{17}} R_{c_{17}} \qquad (7.36)$$

giving

$$A_{v(\text{intermed})} = \frac{v_{o_{21}}}{v_{i_{16}}} \simeq \frac{v_{o_{17}}}{v_{i_{17}}} \simeq \frac{-h_{fe_{17}} R_{c_{17}}}{h_{ie_{17}} + h_{fe_{17}} R_{11}} = \frac{-R_{c_{17}}}{(1/g_{fe_{17}}) + R_{11}} \qquad (7.37)$$

for $h_{fe_{17}} \gg 1$, as $g_{fe_{17}} = h_{fe_{17}}/h_{ie_{17}}$ (equation 3.62). Substituting $R_{c_{17}} \simeq 200$ kΩ, $1/g_{fe_{17}} \simeq 45\ \Omega$ (calculated prior to equation 7.30) and $R_{11} = 100\ \Omega$ gives $A_{v(\text{intermed})} \simeq -1379$.

Voltage gain of the output stage, $A_{v(\text{output})}$

Each half of the complementary output stage forms an emitter-follower with the external load (section 6.6) and so $A_{v(\text{output})}$ is approximately unity.

Combining the above results $A_{vd(\text{input})} \simeq -187$, $A_{v(\text{intermed})} \simeq -1379$ and $A_{v(\text{output})} \simeq 1$ in equation 7.26 shows that the small-signal differential voltage gain of the 741 op-amp, *at frequencies at which the 30 pF compensating capacitor has negligible effect* (*section 7.4.5*), is

$$A_{vd} \simeq (-187)(-1379)(1) \simeq 2.58 \times 10^5 \text{ or } 108\ \text{dB} \qquad (7.38)$$

which corresponds closely with the typical value given in the specification (appendix E, section E.9).

Output resistance

With each half of the complementary output stage operating as an emitter-follower, the external load providing the emitter resistor (section 6.6), the output resistance, as far as the unloaded amplifier is concerned, is approximately $1/g_{fe}$ (equation 3.117).

The quiescent collector current of the T_{14} and T_{20} output BJTs is 151 μA (I_8, equation 7.21) and so $1/g_{fe_{14}}$ and $1/g_{fe_{20}}$ are each approximately $1/(40 \times 151 \times 10^{-6}) \simeq 166\ \Omega$ from equation 3.63.

Including the R_9 and R_{10} protection resistors, the output resistances of the two halves of the output stage are $166\ \Omega + 27\ \Omega$ and $166\ \Omega + 22\ \Omega$.

For a low amplitude output signal, both halves of the output stage conduct simultaneously (class A operation, section 8.3) and the output resistances of the two halves are effectively in parallel so that

$$R_o \simeq (166\,\Omega + 27\,\Omega)/\!/(166\,\Omega + 22\,\Omega) = 193\,\Omega/\!/188\,\Omega \simeq 95\,\Omega \tag{7.39}$$

At higher signal amplitudes, only one half of the output stage is operating at any instant (class B operation, section 8.4) and R_o then increases to about 190 Ω. The 741 op-amp specification quotes a typical value of R_o as 75 Ω (appendix E, section E.9) although it is known to vary considerably with operating conditions.

7.3 Op-amp applications

Ideally an op-amp has *infinite voltage gain, infinite input resistance* and *zero output resistance.* Infinite A_{VD} would mean that for linear applications the differential input voltage v_I would be zero while for switching applications no hysteresis (section 7.3.2) would occur, the switch from negative to positive saturation being at the same threshold as the switch in the opposite direction. Infinite input resistance would mean that the amplifier would draw no current from the circuitry connected to it while zero output resistance would mean that the output current capability of the op-amp was not limited.

Table 7.1 shows that the properties of many commercial op-amps approach these ideals and provided circuits are designed with care, particularly with regard to signal levels and component values, commercial op-amps can be treated as ideal in many applications.

In linear applications, if circuit voltages are very much greater than the differential input voltage v_I, the approximation $v_I \simeq 0$ (equation 7.3) is valid and if component values are chosen so that circuit currents are very much greater than the amplifier input current i_I, the approximation $i_I \simeq 0$ (equation 7.4) is valid.

In switching applications, provided the output voltage levels are very much greater than the value of v_I required to drive the amplifier to saturation, switching can be assumed to occur at $v_I \simeq 0$ and, as in linear applications, the $i_I \simeq 0$ approximation is valid provided circuit current levels are $\gg i_I$.

With v_I typically less than 200 μV for linear operation at low frequency, corresponding to $A_{VD(dc)} = 100$ dB with ± 20 V supplies, circuit voltages in excess of 10 mV provide near-ideal performance in this respect. Amplifier input current i_I is dominated by the bias current (section 7.4.2) which is usually < 1 μA even at high temperature and is as low as 10 pA for some types so that circuit current levels in excess of 10 μA normally ensure approximately ideal operation.

The following consideration of op-amp applications assumes an ideal amplifier, namely

$$v_I = 0 \tag{7.40}$$

$$i_I = 0 \tag{7.41}$$

but it must be remembered that if the 'ideal' performance is to be realised, selection of circuit component values (section 7.5) and operating signal levels must not violate the 10 mV and 10 μA lower limits for circuit voltages and currents.

7.3.1 *Linear applications*

Op-amp circuits required to provide linear amplification *always* employ negative feedback via an external circuit connected between the amplifier output and the *inverting* (−) input.

The feedback for linear applications is *never* to the non-inverting (+) input as this would introduce positive feedback and instability; positive feedback is employed in the *switching* circuits of sections 7.3.2 and 10.2 and in linear oscillators (section 9.1).

Voltage follower

Figure 7.10a shows the most basic, though very useful, linear amplifier utilising an op-amp: the unity-gain voltage follower, so named because $v_O = v_1$ where v_1 is the input voltage to the circuit. Note that care must be taken in this work to distinguish between the input voltage to the *circuit* v_1 and the input voltage to the *op-amp* v_I; for *linear* operation ideally $v_I = 0$ and $v_1 \gg v_I$.

Unity (100 per cent) negative feedback is provided by the direct connection between the output and the inverting input, from which

$$v^- = v_O \tag{7.42}$$

The circuit input v_1 is applied to the non-inverting terminal thus

$$v^+ = v_1 \tag{7.43}$$

and the amplifier input is then

$$\begin{aligned} v_I &= v^+ - v^- \\ &= v_1 - v_O \end{aligned} \tag{7.44}$$

Provided the op-amp is operating in its linear range, that is, v_O is within the range set by the

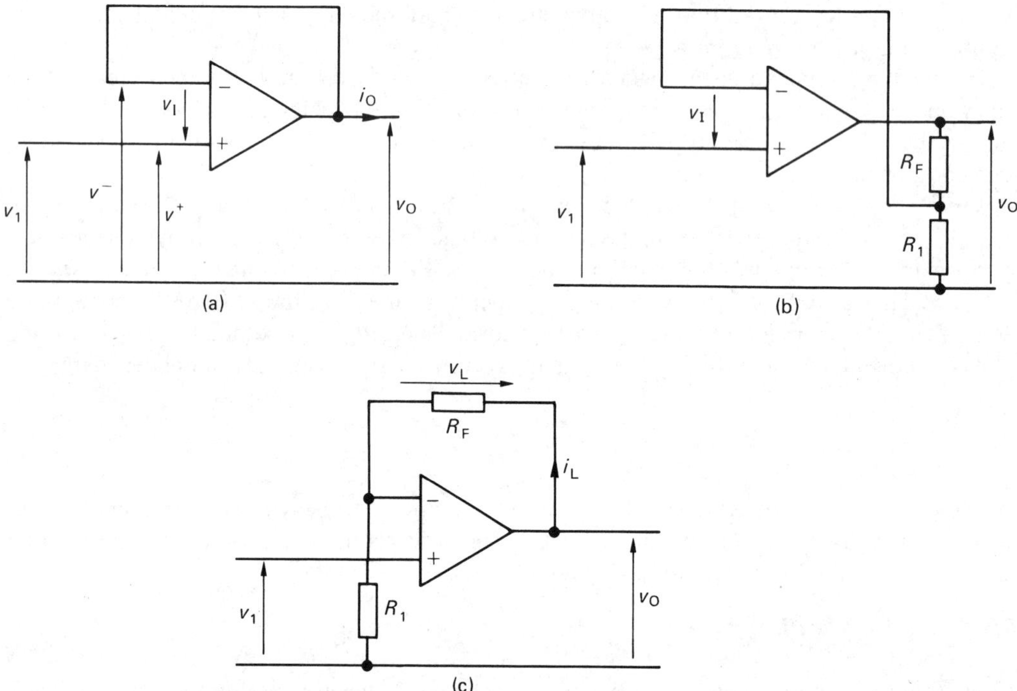

Figure 7.10 The op-amp as a non-inverting amplifier

dc power supplies ($-V_{EE} < v_O < V_{CC}$), $v_I = 0$ (equation 7.40), which means

$$v_O = v_1 \tag{7.45}$$

from equation 7.44.

In normal (linear) operation, when input v_1 changes, *instantaneously* the op-amp input voltage v_I acquires a finite value which, together with the high gain of the op-amp, causes v_O to change very rapidly to restore the $v_I = 0$ condition; thus as v_1 varies, v_O *follows.*

The input of the voltage follower is applied directly to the input of the op-amp and so, for the case of an ideal op-amp, the input resistance of the circuit

$$R_{I(CCT)} = \infty \tag{7.46}$$

corresponding to the closed-loop value of equation 5.23 with $A_V = \infty$ and $\beta_V = -1$ (minus because v_I is the *difference* of the input and fedback voltages in contrast to the *sum* in the analysis of section 5.7).

With the shunt output connection of the feedback loop, the output resistance of the voltage follower circuit is

$$R_{O(CCT)} = 0 \tag{7.47}$$

corresponding to equation 5.30 for the ideal case of $A_V = \infty$ and $\beta_V = -1$.

The unity gain, high input resistance and low output resistance make this basic circuit useful as a buffer in a similar way to the emitter-follower considered in example 3.13.

Non-inverting voltage amplifier

The voltage follower of figure 7.10a may be modified to provide a voltage gain greater than unity as shown in figure 7.10b. Using the potential divider across the output, a fraction of v_O is fed back to the inverting input. Thus, with circuit input v_1 applied, v_O must rise to a value $> v_1$ before the $v_I = 0$ condition is satisfied, resulting in a gain greater than unity. The arrangement is more usually drawn as in figure 7.10c and R_F is termed the feedback resistor.

From the R_F, R_1 potential divider, the fedback voltage is

$$v^- = \left(\frac{R_1}{R_1 + R_F}\right) v_O \tag{7.48}$$

With v^+ equal to the circuit input voltage v_1, the op-amp input voltage is

$$v_I = v_1 - \left(\frac{R_1}{R_1 + R_F}\right) v_O \tag{7.49}$$

For ideal linear operation ($-V_{EE} < v_O < V_{CC}$), $v_I = 0$ (equation 7.40), giving

$$v_O = \left(\frac{R_1 + R_F}{R_1}\right) v_1 \tag{7.50}$$

and the circuit (closed-loop) voltage gain A_{CL} is then

$$A_{CL} = \frac{v_O}{v_1} = 1 + \frac{R_F}{R_1} \tag{7.51}$$

Note that the gain of the *circuit* is fixed by the ratio of the external resistors R_1 and R_F.

If the feedback resistor R_F is regarded as the load (figure 7.10c), this circuit provides voltage-to-current conversion; note that R_F may not be a simple resistor, it could be replaced, for example, by a moving-coil meter as in tutorial question 7.5, in which case the circuit can be used as a high-resistance voltmeter. The current through R_F is

$$i_L = \frac{v_L}{R_F} = \frac{v_O - v^-}{R_F} = \frac{v_O - v_1}{R_F} \tag{7.52}$$

as $v_1 = v^+ = v^-$ for linear operation ($v_I = 0$).

Substituting for v_O from equation 7.50:

$$i_L = \left(\frac{R_1 + R_F}{R_1 R_F}\right) v_1 - \frac{v_1}{R_F}$$

$$= \frac{v_1}{R_1} \tag{7.53}$$

showing that, for R_1 constant, $i_L \propto v_1$. (7.54)

As for the voltage follower, the input and output resistances of this circuit are ideally:

$$R_{I(CCT)} = \infty \tag{7.55}$$

and

$$R_{O(CCT)} = 0 \tag{7.56}$$

since although $|\beta_V| < 1$, the op-amp gain A_V is ∞.

Inverting voltage amplifier

The circuit of figure 7.11a employs negative feedback as with the circuits of figure 7.10, but here it is the inverting terminal that is used as the circuit input, the non-inverting terminal being grounded. If a current i_1 is driven into the circuit from an external source, application of Kirchhoff's current law at node X gives

$$i_1 - i_F - i_I = 0 \tag{7.57}$$

from which

$$i_1 = i_F \tag{7.58}$$

as $i_I = 0$ (equation 7.41).

Also, applying Kirchhoff's voltage law to the loop formed by R_F and the input and output of the op-amp gives

$$v_O + v_F + v_I = 0 \tag{7.59}$$

which leads to

$$v_O = -v_F \tag{7.60}$$

as $v_I = 0$ for ideal linear operation (equation 7.40).
But $v_F = i_F R_F$ which, combined with equations 7.58 and 7.60, shows

$$v_O = -i_F R_F \tag{7.61}$$

$$= -i_1 R_F \tag{7.61}$$

so that

$$v_O \propto |-i_1| \tag{7.62}$$

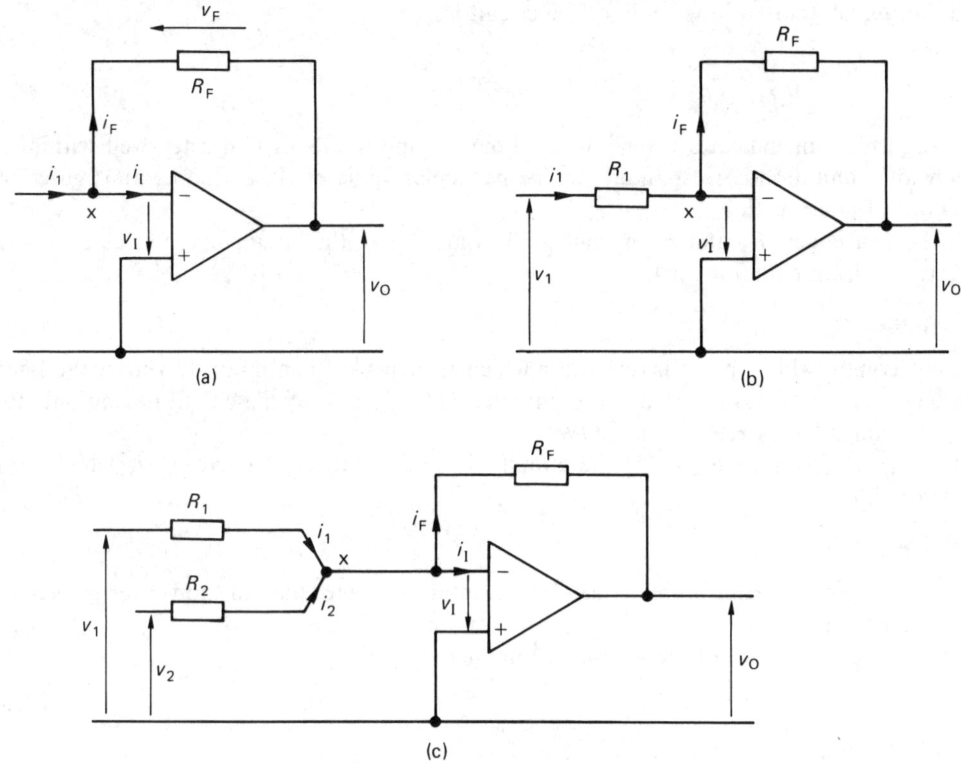

Figure 7.11 The op-amp as an inverting and summing/mixing amplifier

for R_F constant, indicating that this circuit arrangement (figure 7.11a) provides linear current-to-voltage conversion.

Note that care must be taken to distinguish between the input current to the *circuit* i_1 and the input current to the *op-amp* i_I; ideally $i_I = 0$ and $i_1 \gg i_I$ by careful component selection (section 7.5).

With the non-inverting input grounded (figure 7.11a) $v^+ = 0$ and since $v_I = 0$ for linear operation, it follows that $v^- = 0$. Thus the high gain of the amplifier has forced node X to be approximately at signal earth/ground; node X is termed a *virtual* earth.

By arranging the input current to the circuit i_1 to be proportional to the signal voltage v_1 causing it, the circuit can be converted into an inverting voltage amplifier. This is achieved by including a resistor (R_1) in series with the input as in figure 7.11b. With node X a virtual earth due to $v_I = 0$, v_1 is dropped across R_1 so that

$$i_1 = \frac{v_1}{R_1} \tag{7.63}$$

Combining equations 7.61 and 7.63 gives

$$v_O = -\left(\frac{R_F}{R_1}\right)v_1 \tag{7.64}$$

and the overall (closed-loop) gain of the circuit is

$$A_{CL} = \frac{v_O}{v_1} = -\frac{R_F}{R_1} \tag{7.65}$$

The negative sign indicates inversion; for time-varying inputs of frequency well within the bandwidth limitation corresponding to the particular value of closed-loop gain (figure 7.4), v_O is out-of-phase with v_1.

If the resistances R_1 and R_F in figure 7.11b are equal, the circuit operates as an *analog* inverter as, from equation 7.64:

$$v_O = -v_1 \tag{7.66}$$

Do not confuse this type of inverter, for which v_O can vary continuously within the linear range $(-V_{EE} < v_O < V_{CC})$, with a *digital* inverter which is a switching circuit having only two output voltage levels, HIGH and LOW.

The input resistance $R_{I(CCT)}$ of the circuit of figure 7.11b is given by v_1/i_1 which, from equation 7.63 is

$$R_{I(CCT)} = R_1 \tag{7.67}$$

showing that the inverting amplifier has a lower input resistance than the non-inverting version (figure 7.10c, equation 7.55).

The output resistance of the inverting amplifier is ideally

$$R_{O(CCT)} = 0 \tag{7.68}$$

as with the non-inverting circuit, because of A_V being infinite.

Example 7.5 (section 7.5) considers the selection of component values for a specific application.

Summing (mixing) amplifier

The inverting amplifier of figure 7.11b can be modified to form an analog summer or mixer by the addition of further inputs so that current i_F following through R_F (which generates v_O) is the sum of the input currents. For the 2-input circuit of figure 7.11c:

$$i_F = i_1 + i_2 \tag{7.69}$$

and with

$$v_I = 0:$$

$$i_1 = \frac{v_1}{R_1},\ i_2 = \frac{v_2}{R_2} \text{ and } i_F = -\frac{v_O}{R_F} \tag{7.70}$$

Combination of equations 7.69 and 7.70 gives

$$v_O = -\left[\left(\frac{R_F}{R_1}\right)v_1 + \left(\frac{R_F}{R_2}\right)v_2\right] \tag{7.71}$$

so that the weighted sum of signals v_1 and v_2 is obtained depending on the relative values of R_1, R_2 and R_F.

If the resistances are equal

$$v_O = -(v_1 + v_2) \tag{7.72}$$

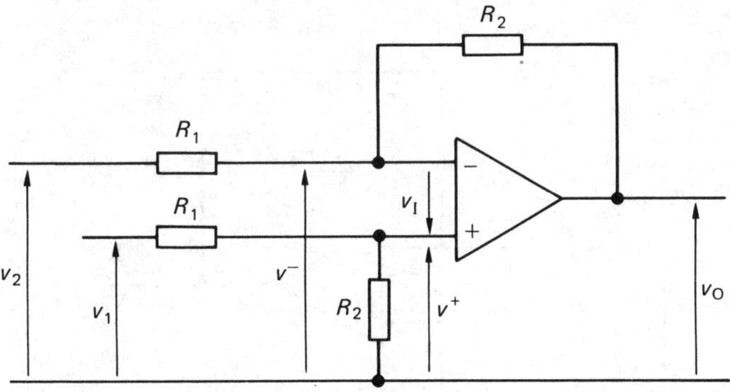

Figure 7.12 Active subtraction circuit

More than two signals can be mixed by adding further inputs v_3, R_3; v_4, R_4 etc. to point X.

Notice that the role of the op-amp in these circuits is, by virtue of its high differential gain, to force node X to be a virtual earth whereby $i_1 \propto v_1$, $i_2 \propto v_2$ and $v_O \propto |i_F|$ resulting in linear amplification and accurate summation via relation 7.69.

Subtraction amplifier

The difference of two signals v_1 and v_2 can be obtained by inverting v_2 using the circuit of figure 7.11b with $R_1 = R_F$ and then adding v_1 and $-v_2$ using the summer of figure 7.11c with $R_1 = R_2 = R_F$. However a more efficient method in terms of component count is provided by the circuit of figure 7.12.

Assuming an ideal op-amp such that no current is drawn by either amplifier input:

$$v^+ = v_1\left(\frac{R_2}{R_1 + R_2}\right) \tag{7.73}$$

by potential division between R_1 and R_2 connected to the + input, and

$$v^- = v_2\left(\frac{R_2}{R_1 + R_2}\right) + v_O\left(\frac{R_1}{R_1 + R_2}\right) \tag{7.74}$$

corresponding to the result of tutorial question 1.2 where v_1, v and v_2 (figure 1.10) correspond to v_2, v^- and v_O respectively in this case.

For operation in the linear range $(-V_{EE} < v_O < V_{CC})$, $v_I = v^+ - v^- = 0$ (equations 7.1 and 7.40), thus

$$v_1\left(\frac{R_2}{R_1 + R_2}\right) - v_2\left(\frac{R_2}{R_1 + R_2}\right) - v_O\left(\frac{R_1}{R_1 + R_2}\right) = 0 \tag{7.75}$$

using equations 7.73 and 7.74, from which

$$v_O = \frac{R_2}{R_1}(v_1 - v_2) \tag{7.76}$$

or

$$v_O = v_1 - v_2$$

for equal-value resistors.

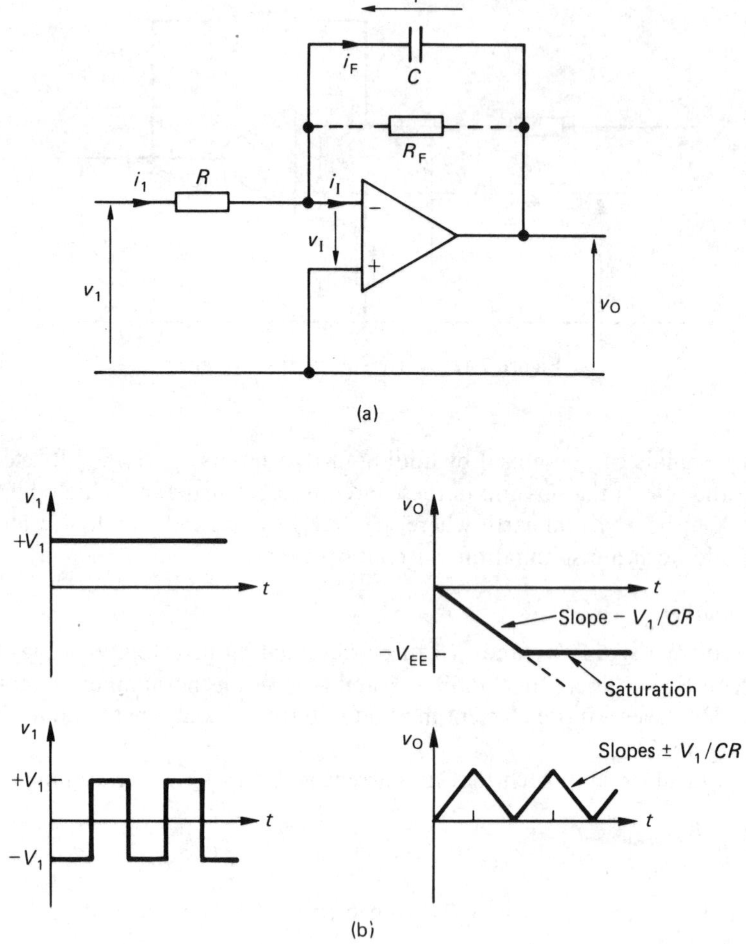

Figure 7.13 Op-amp integrator

Integrator

The use of capacitive feedback (figure 7.13a) produces an electronic integrator, the op-amp output being the (inverted) time integral of the input voltage v_1.

Considering the circuit initially without the resistor R_F:

$$i_F = i_1 \tag{7.77}$$

since ideally the amplifier input current i_I is zero (equation 7.41).

For operation within the linear range $-V_{EE} < v_O < V_{CC}$, $v_I = 0$ (equation 7.40) and so

$$i_1 = \frac{v_1}{R} \tag{7.78}$$

The current–voltage relationship for the capacitor corresponding to equation 2.24 is

$$i_F = C\,\frac{dv_F}{dt} \tag{7.79}$$

Combining these three equations, noting that $v_O = -v_F$ as $v_I = 0$:

$$i_F = \frac{v_1}{R} = C\frac{dv_F}{dt} = -C\frac{dv_O}{dt} \tag{7.80}$$

from which

$$v_O = -\frac{1}{CR}\int v_1 dt \tag{7.81}$$

where $1/CR$ is the *gain* or *integration rate* of the circuit.

If the input is a constant positive value V_1, v_O increases negatively with time at a rate of $\frac{dv_O}{dt} = -\frac{V_1}{CR}$ (from equation 7.81) as shown in the upper set of diagrams in figure 7.13b, assuming $v_O = 0$ at $t = 0$. As the output progressively ramps up or down for a constant input, eventually saturation is reached and the circuit is then no longer operating in the linear range; equation 7.81 does not then apply. In application, the slope of the ramp must be selected by choice of time constant CR, input voltage and linear range, as set by the power supply voltages V_{CC} and $-V_{EE}$, so that integration can be performed over the required time interval without saturation being reached. The second example in figure 7.13b shows a sawtooth response obtained for a symmetrical pulse input, common applications being for a pulse-width modulator as used in a class D power stage (figure 8.7) and as the drive waveform for a PWL shaper (section 9.2.3).

The input resistance of the integrator circuit $R_{I(CCT)}$ is

$$R_{I(CCT)} = \frac{v_1}{i_1} = R \tag{7.82}$$

from equation 7.78.

It is usual first to select a nominal value for R based on the required input resistance for the circuit, noting that i_1 must be large compared with the op-amp input current i_1 if near-ideal integration is to be obtained. Having selected R, the corresponding value of C can be calculated to provide the required integration rate ($1/CR$, equation 7.81). Because the range of preferred values of capacitance is usually more restricted than for resistance, it is usually necessary to select the nearest preferred value of capacitance to that calculated and then recalculate the corresponding value of resistance to provide the required integration rate. Care must be taken in selection of the type of capacitor used; a capacitor with poor leakage properties such as a wet aluminium electrolytic type behaves electronically as a parallel CR network resulting in non-ideal integration. Low-leakage plastic film types (section 2.4.2) are popular for such applications. Example 7.6 (section 7.5) shows the selection of component values for a typical application.

In some signal processing applications where v_1 is not constant, one way of avoiding saturation that may occur for low frequency inputs due to the corresponding high reactance of the feedback capacitor and hence high closed-loop gain, is to limit the gain at low frequency (and dc) by the addition of R_F (figure 7.13a) to $-R_F/R$. The circuit with R_F acts as a low-pass filter having a cut-off frequency $1/2\pi CR_F$, enabling it to be used to remove high frequency components such as noise from a signal. This arrangement is sometimes termed an *ac integrator* because it provides true integration only for input frequencies above the cut-off frequency.

As with the inverting amplifiers of figures 7.11b, c, additional inputs can be connected to the integrator forming a *summing integrator*, the output being proportional to the (inverted) time integral of the sum of the input signals.

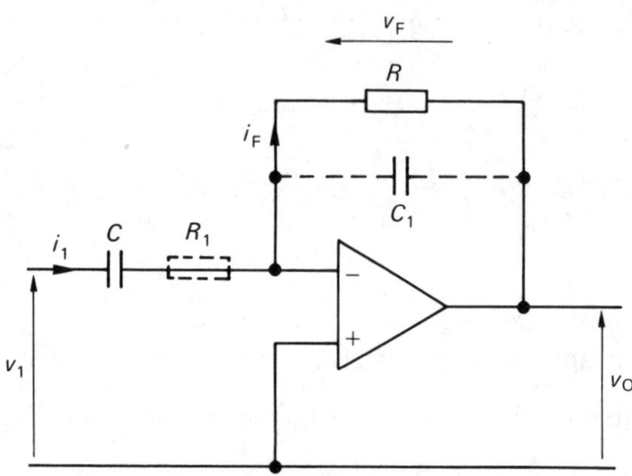

Figure 7.14 Op-amp differentiator

Note the important role of the op-amp in the basic integrator. By virtue of its high gain it forces the − input to be a virtual earth thereby making the circuit input current i_1, and hence the capacitor charging current, directly proportional to the input voltage v_1, thus providing true integration.

Differentiator

With C and R of the basic integrator (figure 7.13a) interchanged, as in figure 7.14 (without C_1 and R_1), v_O is proportional to the first-order *time* differential of v_1. For the ideal case of zero op-amp input current and input voltage (equations 7.40 and 7.41), $i_1 = i_F$ and $v_O = -v_F$ from which

$$i_1 = C\frac{dv_1}{dt} = i_F = \frac{v_F}{R} = -\frac{v_O}{R}$$

giving

$$v_O = -CR\frac{dv_1}{dt} \tag{7.83}$$

In practice, this basic differentiator is prone to saturation. If the input is sinusoidal of the form $V_1 \sin \omega t$, the corresponding output, from equation 7.83, is $-\omega CRV_1 \cos \omega t$ showing that the circuit gain (ratio of output-to-input signal amplitudes) is ωCR. The *gain thus increases with input signal frequency* so that if the input comprises any high frequency components such as induced noise, the circuit greatly amplifies these components, leading to saturation. A solution to this problem is to add R_1 to limit the gain at high frequency to $-R/R_1$ and/or to include C_1 so that the feedback impedance $(R /\!/ C_1)$ reduces as the frequency increases, thereby restricting the rise in gain with frequency.

Although not as widely used as the integrator, the differentiator is useful in detection of transients or discontinuities in signal processing. More detailed consideration of active differentiator performance can be found in references [2a] and [3].

7.3.2 *Switching applications*

An op-amp can be used in the switching mode by applying a differential input voltage v_I of sufficient magnitude to drive the amplifier output to saturation. Thus in the open-loop

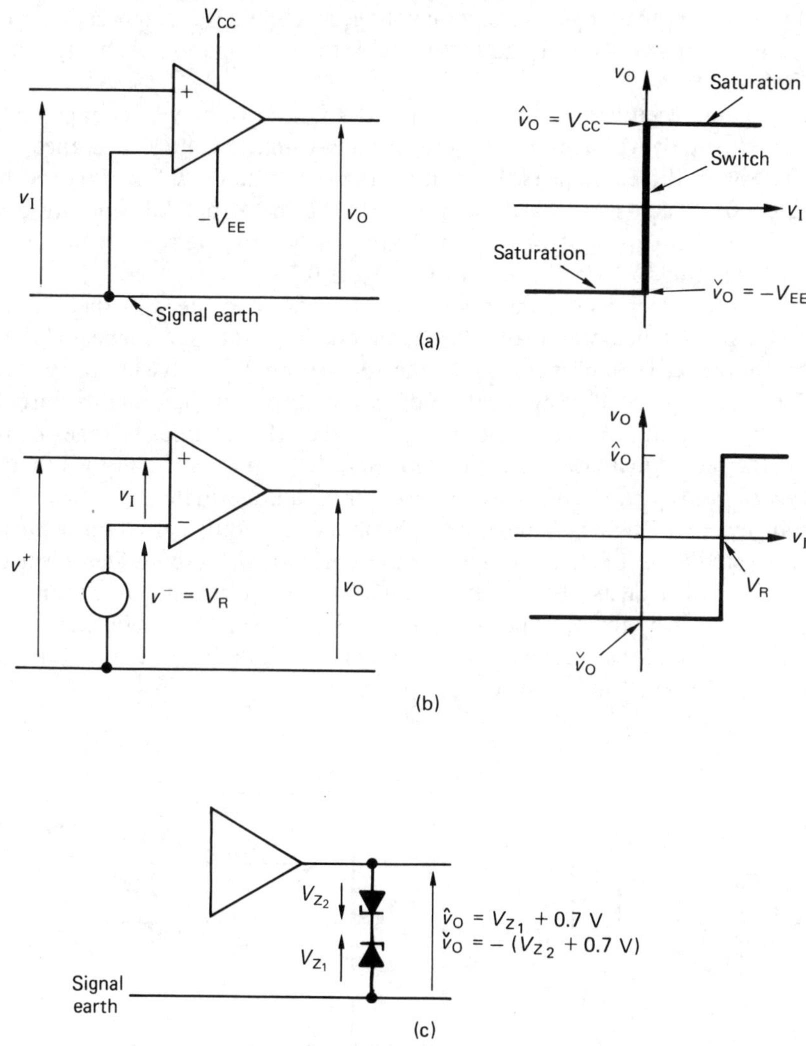

Figure 7.15 Open-loop op-amp as a comparator

arrangement of figure 7.15a, if the power supplies are ± 20 V and the differential gain of the op-amp is 100 dB (10^5), when $|v_I|$ is greater than $20\text{ V}/10^5 = 200\ \mu\text{V}$ the op-amp output will be driven to approximately $+20$ V ($\hat{v}_O$) or -20 V ($\check{v}_O$) depending on the polarity of v_I. The transfer characteristic is therefore as shown in figure 7.15a with the switch between the saturation levels being over the 400 μV (linear) range of v_I. In practice, the output saturation levels are slightly less than the power supply voltages because of the voltage drop across the output transistor(s) of the op-amp.

In this mode of operation the op-amp acts as a comparator, effectively comparing the potential at the + input with that at the − input which is signal earth in the configuration of figure 7.15a. It provides a positive output for $v_I > 0$ (strictly $> 200\ \mu$V for the example quoted above) and a negative output for $v_I < 0$ (more negative than $-200\ \mu$V); this arrangement therefore acts as a polarity detector.

Often it is necessary to compare two finite voltage levels and this can be achieved by making v^- equal to the reference value V_R as shown, with the corresponding transfer characteristic, in figure 7.15b.

The positive and negative output switching levels $\hat{v}_O$ and $\check{v}_O$ may be clamped at values less than the power supply voltages by the use of back-to-back voltage reference diodes as in figure 7.15c. For v_O driven sufficiently positive, the upper diode will be forward biased with approximately 0.7 V across it and the lower diode will be at breakdown with a voltage V_{Z_1} across it which will clamp $\hat{v}_O$ at $V_{Z_1} + 0.7$ V. With v_O negative, the roles of the two diodes are interchanged resulting in $\check{v}_O$ being equal to $-(V_{Z_2} + 0.7\text{ V})$.

In the above *open-loop* use of the op-amp as a switch, the speed of the switching action depends on the gain of the op-amp and the characteristics of the load connected to the op-amp output. Switching speed can be increased by the application of positive feedback as represented in figure 7.16a. If, as a result of application of v_I, the output of the op-amp starts to rise, the feedback to the + input causes this rise to augment the original input voltage change, thereby accelerating the rate of increase of v_O and hence speeding up the switch to $\hat{v}_O$; this mechanism is termed *regenerative action* and is widely used in op-amp switching circuits.

The arrangement of figure 7.16b is the simplest regenerative op-amp switching circuit commonly referred to as a Schmitt trigger. The circuit has two stable states, termed a *bistable* circuit, v_O being either at its positive maximum $\hat{v}_O$ or at its negative maximum $\check{v}_O$, the two levels being set either by the V_{CC} and $-V_{EE}$ power supply voltages or by clamping diodes as in figure 7.15c. The output state depends on the sign of the differential input voltage v_I; $v_O = \hat{v}_O$ for v_I positive and $v_O = \check{v}_O$ for v_I negative.

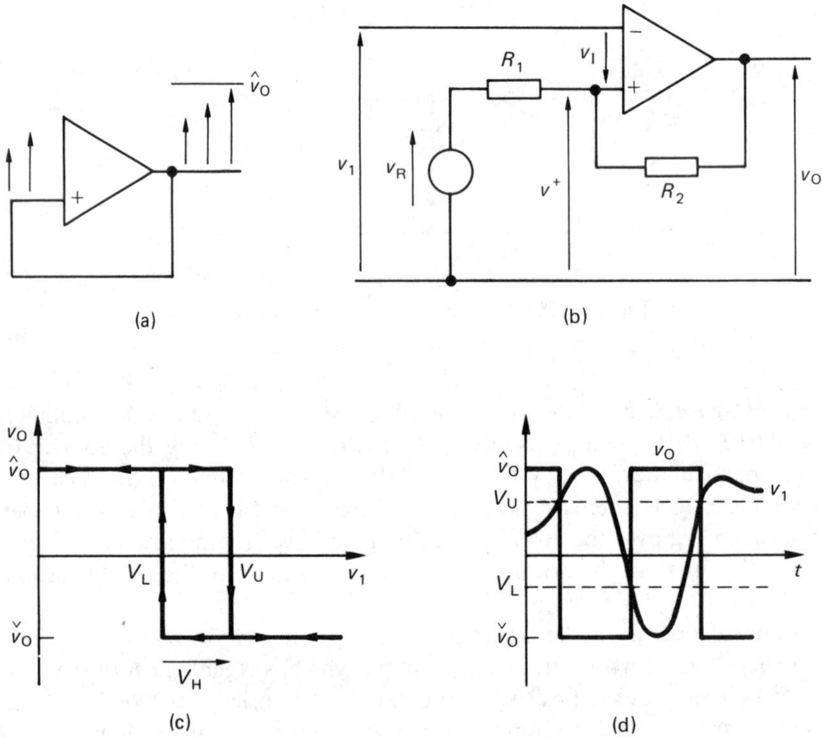

Figure 7.16 Regenerative switching

As a starting point for the analysis, assume the reference voltage v_R to be positive and the *circuit* input voltage v_1 to be zero. Under these conditions v_O will be at $\hat{v}_O$ because of v_R, and hence v_I, being positive. Under these conditions the potential at the + input relative to signal earth, v^+, is

$$v^+ = \frac{\hat{v}_O R_1 + v_R R_2}{R_1 + R_2} \tag{7.84}$$

corresponding to the result of tutorial question 1.2, v_R, v^+ and $\hat{v}_O$ corresponding to v_1, v and v_2 in figure 1.10.

If the input voltage v_1 is now increased from zero, the differential input voltage to the op-amp $v_I(= v^+ - v_1)$ decreases and when v_I becomes just slightly negative, the circuit output switches to $\check{v}_O$, regenerative action ensuring a rapid switch. The value of v_1 at switchover is termed the *upper trigger* or *trip* voltage V_U and is given by

$$V_U = v_1 \simeq v^+ = \frac{\hat{v}_O R_1 + v_R R_2}{R_1 + R_2} \tag{7.85}$$

from equation 7.84, noting that $v_I(= v^+ - v_1) \simeq 0$ at the switching point. For v_1 increasing further ($> V_U$), v_O remains fixed at $\check{v}_O$ as shown in the transfer characteristic of figure 7.16c.

With $v_O = \check{v}_O$:

$$v^+ = \frac{\check{v}_O R_1 + v_R R_2}{R_1 + R_2} \tag{7.86}$$

corresponding to equation 7.84 but with v_O now at its negative maximum. If v_1 is then reduced, v_I reduces from its negative value towards zero ($v_I = v^+ - v_1$ and v^+ is negative). Eventually v_1 becomes slightly more negative than the v^+ value, v_I then is slightly positive and regenerative action ensures a rapid switch back to the $\hat{v}_O$ state. The value of v_1 at switch back is termed the *lower trigger* (*trip*) *voltage* V_L where

$$V_L = v_1 \simeq v^+ = \frac{\check{v}_O R_1 + v_R R_2}{R_1 + R_2} \tag{7.87}$$

from equation 7.86 noting that $v_I(= v^+ - v_1) \simeq 0$ at switch back. The op-amp output remains at $\hat{v}_O$ for v_1 more negative than V_L.

Figure 7.16c shows that the switching point for v_1 increasing ($v_1 = V_U$) is higher than for v_1 decreasing ($v_1 = V_L$), a phenomenon termed *hysteresis*. The difference $V_U - V_L$ is termed the hysteresis voltage V_H and depends on the feedback fraction $\beta\ (= R_1/R_1 + R_2)$, see chapter 5). V_H can be decreased by reduction of β but if V_H is too small, indecision occurs at switching, causing high frequency oscillation.

The Schmitt trigger circuit is widely used as a voltage level detector, as shown in figure 7.16d for an arbitrary input voltage variation, and for 'squaring up' (reducing the rise and fall times) of a pulse waveform. This circuit forms the basis of astable and monostable pulse circuits considered in section 10.2.

7.4 Non-ideal op-amp performance

Section 7.3 considers the performance of some linear and switching op-amp circuits assuming the op-amp to be ideal, that is, having infinite voltage gain, infinite input impedance and zero output impedance. This approximation greatly simplifies the design of practical circuits and provides reliable results for a limited range of signal levels and operating speed.

Outside this 'ideal' range, the non-ideal nature of op-amp operation must be considered if circuit performance is to be reliably predicted. The most significant limitations are

(1) finite parameters A_{VD}, R_I, R_O and CMRR,
(2) dc offsets,
(3) finite open-loop bandwidth,
(4) limited speed of response,
(5) restricted output loading.

7.4.1 *Finite parameters*

Finite open-loop gain A_{VD} means that in linear circuits the differential input voltage to the op-amp v_I is not precisely zero, while in switching circuits the change of circuit state does not occur exactly at $v_I = 0$.

Finite input resistance causes the op-amp to draw a finite input *signal* current whereby the input and feedback currents in the linear circuits of section 7.3 are not identical; in figure 7.11a, for example, $i_F \neq i_1$ in practice as i_I is finite. It should be noted however that such input *signal* currents are usually swamped by the input *bias* currents (section 7.4.2) and are therefore insignificant in most cases.

Non-zero output resistance causes a drop in load voltage as the current drawn from the output increases and a finite CMRR results in a departure from true differential operation.

To demonstrate the significance of finite parameters, consider the effect of finite A_{VD}, R_I and R_O on the closed-loop gain ($A_{CL} = v_O/v_1$) of the inverting voltage amplifier of figure 7.11b. Using the op-amp model of figure 7.3b but neglecting common-mode impedances at the input and restricting the consideration to operating frequencies at which the input and output impedances may be considered to be purely resistive, the performance of the voltage amplifier may be modelled as in figure 7.17a where R_L is the external load.

The model may be rearranged as in figure 7.17b and application of Kirchhoff's current law at nodes A and B yields

$$\frac{v_1 - (-v_I)}{R_1} + \frac{v_O - (-v_I)}{R_F} + \frac{v_I}{R_I} = 0 \tag{7.88}$$

and

$$\frac{A_{VD}v_I - v_O}{R_O} + \frac{(-v_I) - v_O}{R_F} + \frac{(-v_O)}{R_L} = 0 \tag{7.89}$$

which give

$$\frac{v_1}{R_1} + \frac{v_I}{R'} + \frac{v_O}{R_F} = 0 \tag{7.90}$$

and

$$v_I\left(\frac{A_{VD}}{R_O} - \frac{1}{R_F}\right) - \frac{v_O}{R''} = 0 \tag{7.91}$$

respectively, where $R' = R_1 /\!/ R_F /\!/ R_I$ and $R'' = R_O /\!/ R_F /\!/ R_L$.
Note that R' and R'' are the parallel combinations of resistances connected to the − input and output of the op-amp respectively.

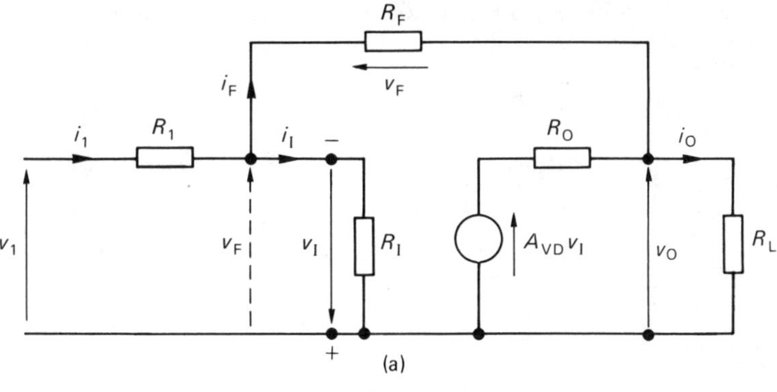

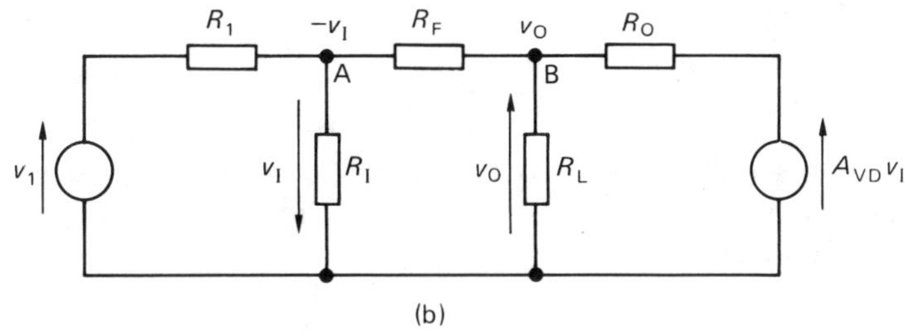

Figure 7.17 Effect of finite parameters on linear op-amp circuit performance

Elimination of v_I from equations 7.90 and 7.91 gives

$$A_{CL} = \frac{v_O}{v_1} = \frac{-R_F/R_1}{1 + \left[\dfrac{R_F}{R'R''\left(\dfrac{A_{VD}}{R_O} - \dfrac{1}{R_F}\right)}\right]} \tag{7.92}$$

The numerator in equation 7.92 is the value of closed-loop gain A_{CL} of the circuit if the op-amp is ideal (equation 7.65) and so the effect of finite A_{VD}, R_I and R_O is described by the [ ] term in the denominator. If this term is $\ll 1$, the op-amp performance is effectively ideal as far as A_{VD}, R_I and R_O are concerned. For the case where A_{VD} and R_I are finite but R_O is sufficiently small to be neglected, $v_O = A_{VD}v_I$ (figure 7.17) and combination with equation 7.90 then gives

$$A_{CL} = \frac{v_O}{v_1} = \frac{-R_F/R_1}{1 + \left(\dfrac{R_F}{A_{VD}R'}\right)} \tag{7.93}$$

If v_1 in figure 7.17a is made passive, the fedback voltage v_F is $v_O\left[\dfrac{R_1 /\!/ R_I}{(R_1 /\!/ R_I) + R_F}\right]$ by potential division between the R_1, R_I parallel combination (note $v_1 = 0$) and R_F. With A_{VD} defined in terms of v_I, the feedback fraction β must be defined in terms of v_I and as $v_I = -v_F$

$$\beta = \frac{v_I}{v_O} = -\frac{v_F}{v_O} = -\frac{R_1 /\!/ R_I}{(R_1 /\!/ R_I) + R_F}$$

$$= -\frac{R_1 R_I}{R_1 R_I + R_1 R_F + R_F R_I}$$

$$= -\frac{R'}{R_F} \qquad (7.94)$$

where $R' = R_1 /\!/ R_F /\!/ R_I$.

Substituting for R'/R_F from equation 7.94 into 7.93 gives

$$A_{CL} = \frac{v_O}{v_1} = \frac{-R_F/R_1}{1 - \dfrac{1}{A_{VD}\beta}} \qquad (7.95)$$

$A_{VD}\beta$ being the loop gain (equation 5.3). Notice that for very high loop gain $A_{VD}\beta \to \infty$, the closed-loop gain of the circuit approaches that for the ideal case $-R_F/R_1$.

The reduction in gain due to finite loop gain is

$$A_{CL}(\text{ideal}) - A_{CL}(\text{finite loop gain})$$

$$= -(R_F/R_1) - \left(\frac{-R_F/R_1}{1 - \dfrac{1}{A_{VD}\beta}} \right)$$

$$= \frac{-R_F/R_1}{1 - A_{VD}\beta} \qquad (7.96)$$

giving a *fractional* reduction, sometimes termed the *fractional error* ε, of

$$\varepsilon = \frac{1}{1 - A_{VD}\beta} \qquad (7.97)$$

Note that this result corresponds to that obtained in consideration of the gain sensitivity of a general feedback arrangement in section 5.2 although in the present case, because the op-amp input voltage v_I has been defined as in figure 7.17a, numerically A_{VD} is positive and β negative.

Example 7.1: Closed-loop gain reduction due to finite open-loop gain

A practical analog inverter (figure 7.11b) has $R_1 = R_F = 10\ \text{k}\Omega$ and employs an op-amp having an input resistance R_I of 2 MΩ. What is the lowest permissible value of op-amp open-loop gain A_{VD} if the circuit gain must be within 0.1 per cent of the ideal value?

$$R' = 10\ \text{k}\Omega /\!/ 10\ \text{k}\Omega /\!/ 2\ \text{M}\Omega \simeq 5\ \text{k}\Omega$$

$$\text{Feedback fraction } \beta = -\frac{R'}{R_F} \simeq \frac{-5\ \text{k}\Omega}{10\ \text{k}\Omega} = -0.5$$

A maximum gain reduction of 0.1 per cent corresponds to a fractional error of 0.001 for which, from equation 7.97:

$$(A_{VD}\beta)_{min} = -999$$

hence

$$(A_{VD})_{min} = \frac{-999}{\beta} = \frac{-999}{-0.5} \simeq 2000$$

In most practical cases, finite values of A_{VD}, R_I and R_O do not have a significant effect on the input and output resistances of the circuit incorporating the op-amp, $R_{I(CCT)}$ and $R_{O(CCT)}$. Take, for example, the case of the voltage follower for which ideally $R_{I(CCT)} = \infty$ and $R_{O(CCT)} = 0$ (equations 7.46 and 7.47). Applying equations 5.23 and 5.30 gives $R_{I(CCT)} = R_I(1 - A_{VD}\beta_V)$ and $R_{O(CCT)} = R_O/(1 - A_{VD}\beta_V)$ where $\beta_V = -1$ for this case of unity negative feedback. For a 741 op-amp, A_{VD} is typically 2×10^5 at dc, falling to 20 at 100 kHz (appendix E, section E.9) so that $(1 - A_{VD}\beta_V)$ is approximately 2×10^5 at dc and 21 at 100 kHz. With typical values of R_I and R_O for a 741 being 2 MΩ and 75 Ω respectively, it can be seen that $R_{I(CCT)}$ is very large and $R_{O(CCT)}$ very small at dc with values of 2 MΩ × 21 = 42 MΩ and 75 Ω/21 ≃ 3.6 Ω at 100 kHz, values which approximate to the ideal for most practical situations.

7.4.2 *DC offsets*

If the + and − inputs of an open-loop op-amp are shorted together* to make $v_I = 0$, the output voltage v_O should be zero, but in practice this is not so: v_O is finite and the op-amp is said to have a dc *offset* (voltage). Because of the high open-loop gain A_{VD}, the output stage of the amplifier is usually saturated under these conditions (figure 7.15a) and therefore quantitative description of offset is referred to the input:

Input offset voltage V_{IO} = Differential input voltage that must be applied to make $v_O = 0$ with no other inputs applied

Figure 7.18a gives an input offset model; the op-amp is ideal in this respect and the effect of the offset is represented by the V_{IO} source. V_{IO} can be of either polarity and $|V_{IO}|$ is typically in the range 0.5–10 mV. Consider the case of an op-amp with $|V_{IO}| = 1$ mV, $A_{VD(dc)} = 10^5$ operating open loop with ± 15 V power supplies; the amplifier output will be saturated because 1 mV × 10^5 > 15 V.

The importance of this effect depends on the application. If the applied differential input signal voltage v_I is $\gg V_{IO}$ as in a circuit with substantial negative feedback such as a voltage follower operating with an output voltage of several volts, the offset is insignificant but for low level inputs V_{IO} may dominate.

This effect is due to dc imbalance between the two halves of the input differential stage of the op-amp which is not perfectly symmetrical. Most op-amps have an *offset null* facility whereby an external offset may be applied to balance out the internal offset. In the 741 circuit of figure 7.5, nodes 2 and 3 (the emitters of T_5 and T_6) enable the offset to be nulled using an external potentiometer (10 kΩ is recommended, appendix E, section E.9) as in figure 7.18b.

---

* Using a *short* link to minimise noise pick up.

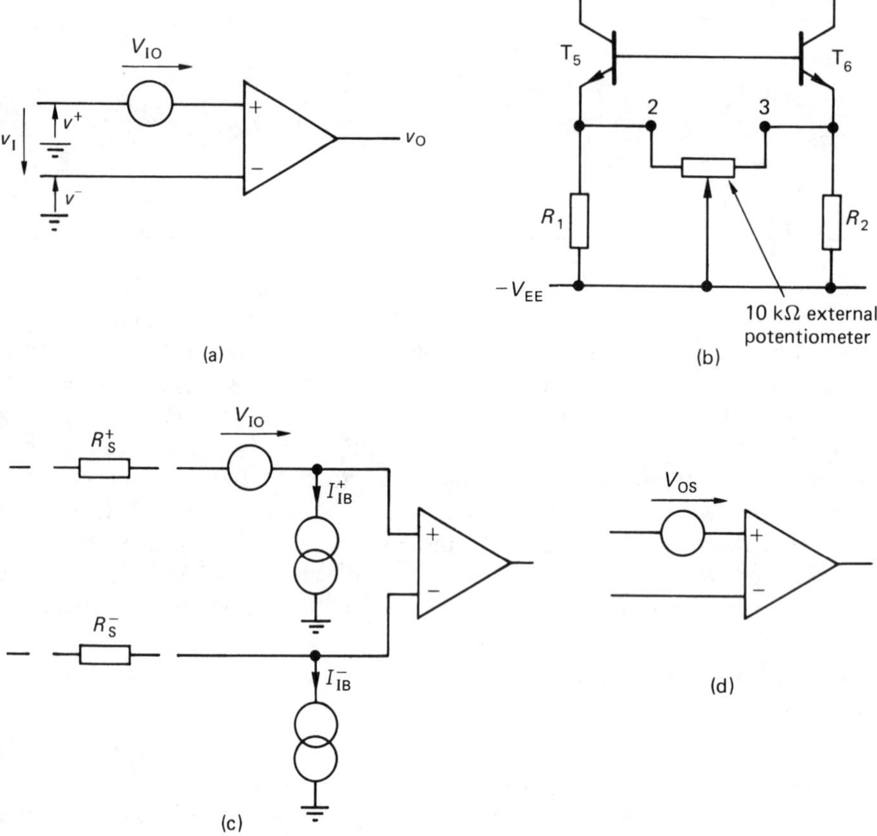

Figure 7.18 Op-amp offsets

With $v_I = 0$ by shorting the amplifier inputs, the potentiometer is adjusted until $v_O = 0$. Other offset correction arrangements are given in reference [4].

Another cause of imbalance is due to unequal bias currents I_{IB}^+ and I_{IB}^- drawn by the + and − op-amp inputs respectively. These *input bias currents* are the quiescent currents drawn by the two inputs for $v_O = 0$ *with no input offset voltage.* Lack of symmetry causes $I_{IB}^+ \neq I_{IB}^-$, and the difference results in a finite voltage offset at the op-amp output. The difference $I_{IB}^+ \sim I_{IB}^-$ is termed the *input offset current* I_{IO} which is typically up to 200 nA for a BJT input and up to 100 pA for a FET input at 25°C. An op-amp data sheet usually quotes a single *input bias current* I_{IB} which is the average of I_{IB}^+ and I_{IB}^-; this is typically up to 500 nA in the BJT case, 200 pA for a FET input, both at 25°C.

Figure 7.18c combines input offsets in a single model, the op-amp being ideal as far as offsets are concerned. R_S^+ and R_S^- are the effective (source) resistances in series with each input which are the parallel combinations of all resistive paths from each input to ground including any feedback resistance and the amplifier output resistance. By defining

$$V_{OS} = V_{IO} - I_{IB}^+ R_S^+ + I_{IB}^- R_S^- \tag{7.98}$$

where V_{OS} is the *total equivalent input offset voltage*, the offset model may be simplified to that of figure 7.18d. It should be noted that offsets are a function of temperature and power supply voltage, and so nulling for one set of operating conditions cannot be expected to maintain the null if conditions change. The slow change of v_O with change of temperature for constant applied input is termed *drift* and is quoted as offset (V_{IO}, I_{IO} or V_{OS}) variation in μV/°C, nA/°C.

Example 7.2: Op-amp offset error

An op-amp inverter has input and feedback resistors of 10 kΩ. If the op-amp has input offsets of 1 mV and 30 nA, an input bias current of 100 nA and an output resistance of 75 Ω, estimate the offset error at the output.

What is the minimum operating static input voltage if the error at the output must not be > 1 per cent?

Corresponding to the inverter circuit of figure 7.11b but incorporating the offset model of figure 7.18d and the output resistance of the amplifier, the arrangement may be represented as in figure 7.19. V_{OS} is given by equation 7.98.
There is no resistance in series with the + input and so $R_S^+ = 0$. R_S^- is the 10 kΩ input resistor in parallel with the series combination of the feedback resistor and R_O, thus

$$R_S^- = 10\,\text{k}\Omega /\!/ (10\,k\Omega + 75\,\Omega) \simeq 5\,k\Omega$$

From $I_{IO} = I_{IB}^+ \sim I_{IB}^- = 30$ nA and $I_{IB} = \dfrac{I_{IB}^+ + I_{IB}^-}{2} = 100$ nA, the values of the two bias currents are 85 and 115 nA although it is not known which is which. Since $R_S^+ = 0$, the value of I_{IB}^+ is not required (equation 7.98). I_{IB}^- will be taken as the mean value 100 nA for calculation purposes, thus

$$V_{OS} \simeq 1\,\text{mV} + (100\,\text{nA})(5\,\text{k}\Omega) = 1.5\,\text{mV}$$

The gain from the + input to the output corresponding to that of the non-inverting amplifier of figure 7.10c is $1 + (R_F/R_1)$ from equation 7.51 which is $1 + (10\,\text{k}\Omega/10\,\text{k}\Omega) = 2$ in this case, and so the offset error at the output is $1.5\,\text{mV} \times 2 = 3\,\text{mV}$.
For an offset error of no more than 1 per cent at the output, v_O must not be less than $3\,\text{mV} \times 100 = 300\,\text{mV}$. The gain v_O/v_1 for the inverter is unity and so the corresponding minimum value of v_1 is also 300 mV.

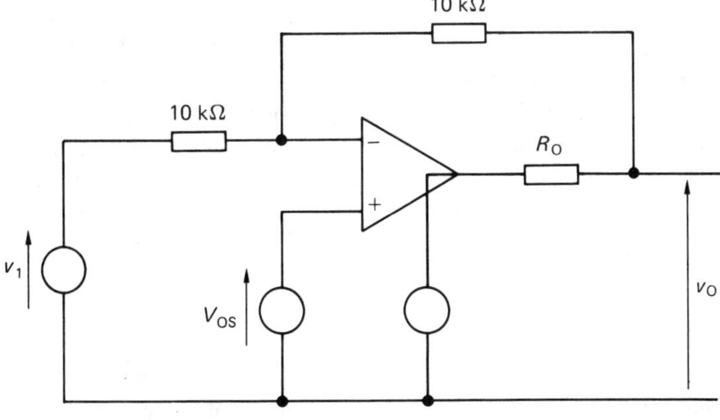

Figure 7.19 Offset error example

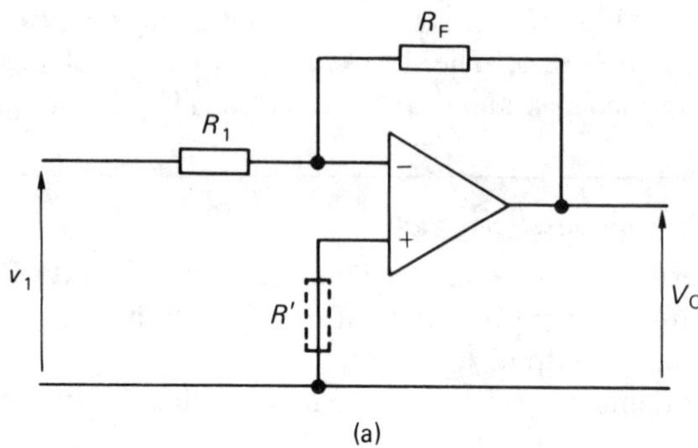

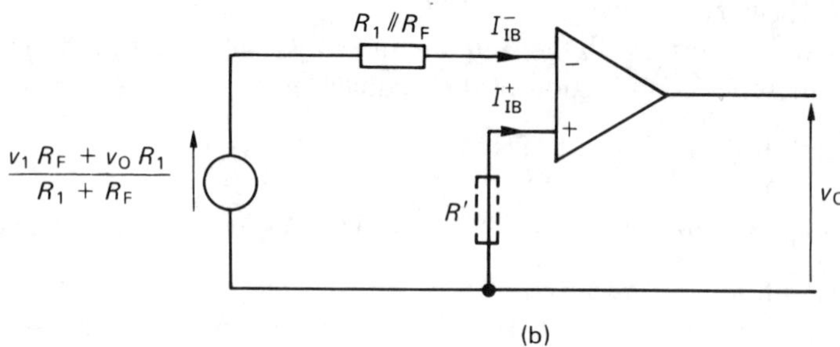

Figure 7.20 Reduction of bias current offset by equalisation of source resistances

Bias current offset may be reduced by equalisation of the source resistances connected to the − and + inputs of the op-amp. Consider the basic inverting amplifier in figure 7.20a. The potential at the − input comprises a component due to v_1 via R_1 and another due to v_O via R_F. Application of Thévenin reduction (note 3.1) enables the network to be represented as in figure 7.20b (the result of tutorial question 1.2 is useful here) showing that the effective resistance in series with the − input is the parallel combination of R_1 and R_F. If the bias currents drawn by the two inputs are the same, a resistor $R' = R_1 // R_F$ connected in series with the + input will result in the same offset voltages being established at the two inputs. The *differential* input voltage v_I would therefore be unaffected and the output offset due to the input bias currents would then be zero. In practice, $I_{IB}^+ \neq I_{IB}^-$ but they are not greatly different and so the simple addition of R' equal to the parallel combination of *all* resistances from the other input to ground provides effective offset reduction. For the non-inverting arrangement of figure 7.10c, offset reduction can similarly be achieved by inserting $R' = R_1 // R_F$ in series with the + input.

7.4.3 *Output loading*

The output current that an op-amp can supply is limited ultimately by the short-circuit protection normally included to protect the output transistors when the output is shorted to signal earth; for a 741 op-amp, this limit is 25 mA (appendix E, section E.9). Well below this limit, however, the voltage drop caused by the output current i_O flowing through the output resistance R_O of the amplifier (figure 7.17a) results in the maximum output voltage swing being progressively restricted as the load resistance is reduced (appendix E, section E.9). Provided the output voltage corresponding to true linear operation is within the restricted range, this effect is insignificant as the negative feedback, together with the high gain of the amplifier, causes v_O to attain a value such that v_I is maintained approximately at zero (equation 7.3); the drop across R_O simply causes $|A_{VD}v_I|$ (in figure 7.17a, for example) to rise to a higher value to compensate. This assumes that $|A_{VD}v_I|$ is able to rise to the required higher value *without reaching saturation*, that is, v_O remains within the restricted range; if this is not the case, the op-amp is no longer operating in its linear mode and the performance equations for the various arrangements considered in section 7.3.1 would not then be valid. Also the choice of value of feedback component is important in this context. In section 7.5 it is explained that the feedback resistance must be $\gg R_O$ so as not to load the output of the amplifier. As far as the present discussion is concerned, this means that the current flowing through the feedback resistor must be low, relative to the output current capability of the op-amp, otherwise the current that can be supplied to the external load R_L will be restricted unnecessarily.

7.4.4 *Slew rate*

The rate of change of the output voltage of an op-amp is limited by the maximum rate that capacitance, both internal and external, can be charged and discharged. The limiting value $|dv_O/dt|_{max}$ is termed the *slew rate SR* of the amplifier and is normally quoted in V/μs. Values range from less than 0.1 V/μs for some low-power CMOS op-amps to over 30 V/μs for high-speed bipolar types; the popular internally-compensated 741 has a slew rate of 0.5 V/μs (appendix E, section E.9).

Figure 7.21 shows the distortion produced by slew rate limitation at the output of a unity-gain inverter such as that of figure 7.11b with $R_1 = R_F$. In figure 7.21a the amplitude and frequency of the input signal v_1 are such that the corresponding maximum slope of v_O, which occurs at the zero-crossing points, is less than the slew rate of the amplifier and an undistorted output signal is produced. As the frequency is increased, with the amplitude remaining unchanged, the maximum slope increases and eventually the slew rate limit is reached, as in diagram b, the central portion of the waveform being distorted to a linear slope. Further increase in frequency causes increased distortion and eventually the output becomes a sawtooth as in diagram c. Similarly, distortion due to slew rate limiting occurs at constant signal frequency when the signal amplitude is progressively increased.

Consider the case of a linear op-amp circuit such as an inverter operating within the slew rate limit having a sinusoidal output

$$v_o = V_{om} \sin \omega t \tag{7.99}$$

By differentiating equation 7.99 with respect to time, the rate of change of v_O is

$$\frac{dv_o}{dt} = \omega V_{om} \cos \omega t \tag{7.100}$$

which has a maximum value

$$\left|\frac{dv_o}{dt}\right|_{max} = \omega V_{om} = 2\pi f V_{om} \tag{7.101}$$

occurring at the zero crossing points.

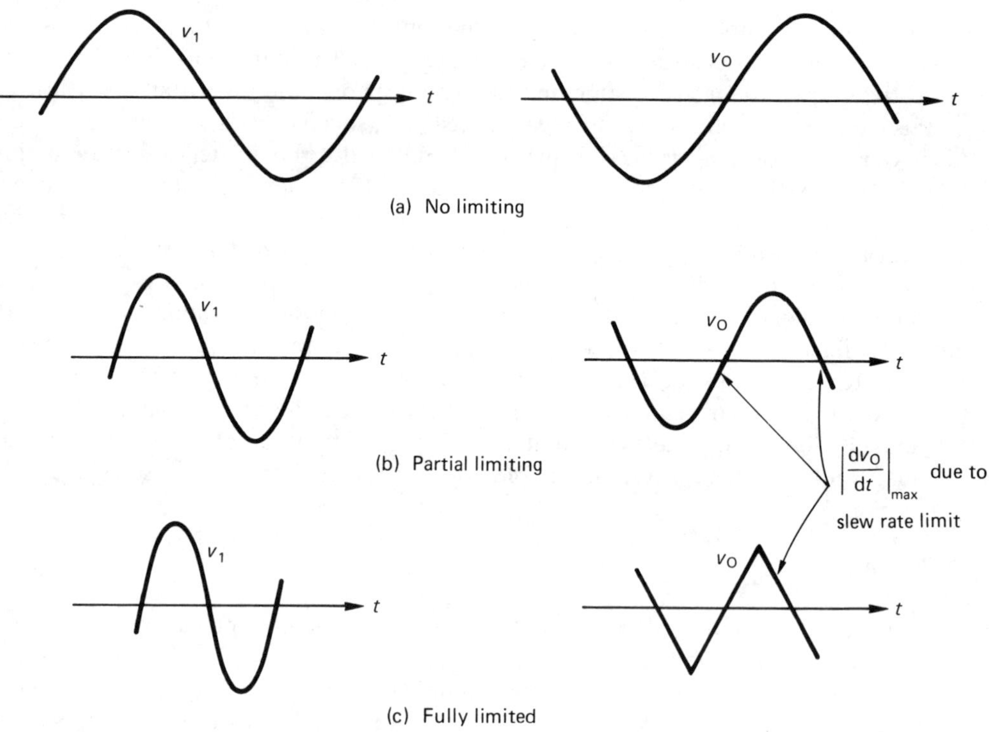

Figure 7.21 Slew rate limiting

If slew rate limiting is not to occur, the slew rate of the amplifier must be equal to or greater than this value, giving

$$SR \geqslant 2\pi f V_{om} \tag{7.102}$$

It should be noted that the addition of a compensating capacitor to an op-amp for stability purposes (section 7.4.5) increases the capacitance associated with the amplifier and therefore reduces the slew rate; in fact, it is usually the compensating capacitor that sets the slew rate of the op-amp.

For an op-amp with particular compensating components the value of SR is fixed, in which case the onset of distortion due to slew rate limitation depends on f and V_{om} (equation 7.102). Some op-amp data sheets give a plot of undistorted (sinusoidal) output voltage swing against signal frequency, and the term *full-power bandwidth* is sometimes used to describe the frequency range up to $SR/2\pi V_{om}$max, from equation 7.102, where V_{om}max is the maximum (sinusoidal) output signal amplitude corresponding to the power supply voltages.

Example 7.3: Slew rate limiting

An op-amp having a slew rate of 0.5 V/μs is used in a gain-of-10 circuit.

(a) What is the maximum amplitude of sinusoidal input signal if slew rate limiting is to be avoided at 10 kHz?

(b) If the sinusoidal input is 100 mV, at what frequency would slew rate limiting occur?

(a) From equation 7.102:

$$V_{om}\max = \frac{SR}{2\pi f} = \frac{0.5\ \text{V}/\mu\text{s}}{2\pi(10\ \text{kHz})} = 7.96\ \text{V}$$

With a circuit voltage gain of 10, the maximum input amplitude

$$V_{1m}\max = 7.96\ \text{V}/10 = 796\ \text{mV}$$

(b) The 100 mV refers to the rms value of the input signal to the gain-of-10 circuit and so the rms output signal $V_{o(rms)} = 100\ \text{mV} \times 10 = 1\ \text{V}$. Assuming no distortion is introduced by the circuit, the output waveform will be sinusoidal having an amplitude $V_{om} = 1\ \text{V} \times \sqrt{2} = 1.41\ \text{V}$ (note 11.1). From equation 7.102:

$$f_{max} = \frac{SR}{2\pi V_{om}} = \frac{0.5\ \text{V}/\mu\text{s}}{2\pi(1.41\ \text{V})} = 56.4\ \text{kHz}$$

7.4.5 ***Stability***

Analog (linear) op-amp circuits (section 7.3.1) employ negative feedback via an external connection from the output to the inverting input. In the amplifiers of figures 7.10c and 7.11b for example, the phase shift through the op-amp from − input to output is − 180° (inversion) at low frequency, and the phase shift through the feedback resistor R_F is zero so that the total phase shift around the loop $\angle A\beta$ (chapter 5) is − 180°, providing negative feedback and stable operation.

As the input signal frequency increases, the time constants within the op-amp cause the phase lag between v_O and v^- to increase progressively until, when the lag becomes a complete cycle (− 360°), the fedback signal is in-phase with the input ($\angle A\beta = -360°$ or 0°) which is likely to cause instability.

To maintain stability, additional time constants are introduced to modify the op-amp response so that at the frequency where instability would occur, the amplitude of the fedback signal is not sufficient to cause instability. Note from the general expression for the closed-loop gain of a feedback system, $A_{cl} = A/(1 - A\beta)$, equation 5.6, instability does not occur for positive feedback, positive $A\beta$, unless $|A\beta| \geqslant 1$. Modification of the basic op-amp response to avoid instability is termed *frequency compensation.*

Lag compensation

The most basic technique uses an additional capacitor to introduce a breakpoint in the |gain|–frequency Bode plot at a suitably low frequency, so that the resulting − 20 dB/decade roll off (section 4.1, figure 4.2e) causes the |gain| to fall to a sufficiently low value at the frequency that would correspond to instability. If the loop gain $|A\beta|$ has dropped to unity (0 dB) or less at the frequency corresponding to $\angle A\beta = -360°$, overall stability is assured.

Figure 7.22a, b shows typical |gain| and phase responses for an op-amp based on the approximations described in section 4.1. Frequencies f_1, f_2 and f_3 are the breakpoints of the uncompensated op-amp due to transistor and stray capacitances associated with the three stages of the amplifier; typical breakpoints are 100 kHz, 1 MHz and 10 MHz. In its uncompensated form the op-amp provides true inversion between the voltage v^- at the inverting input and the output v_O for signal frequencies from dc up to about one decade below the first breakpoint ($0.1f_1$), above which the phase lag progressively increases. At a frequency

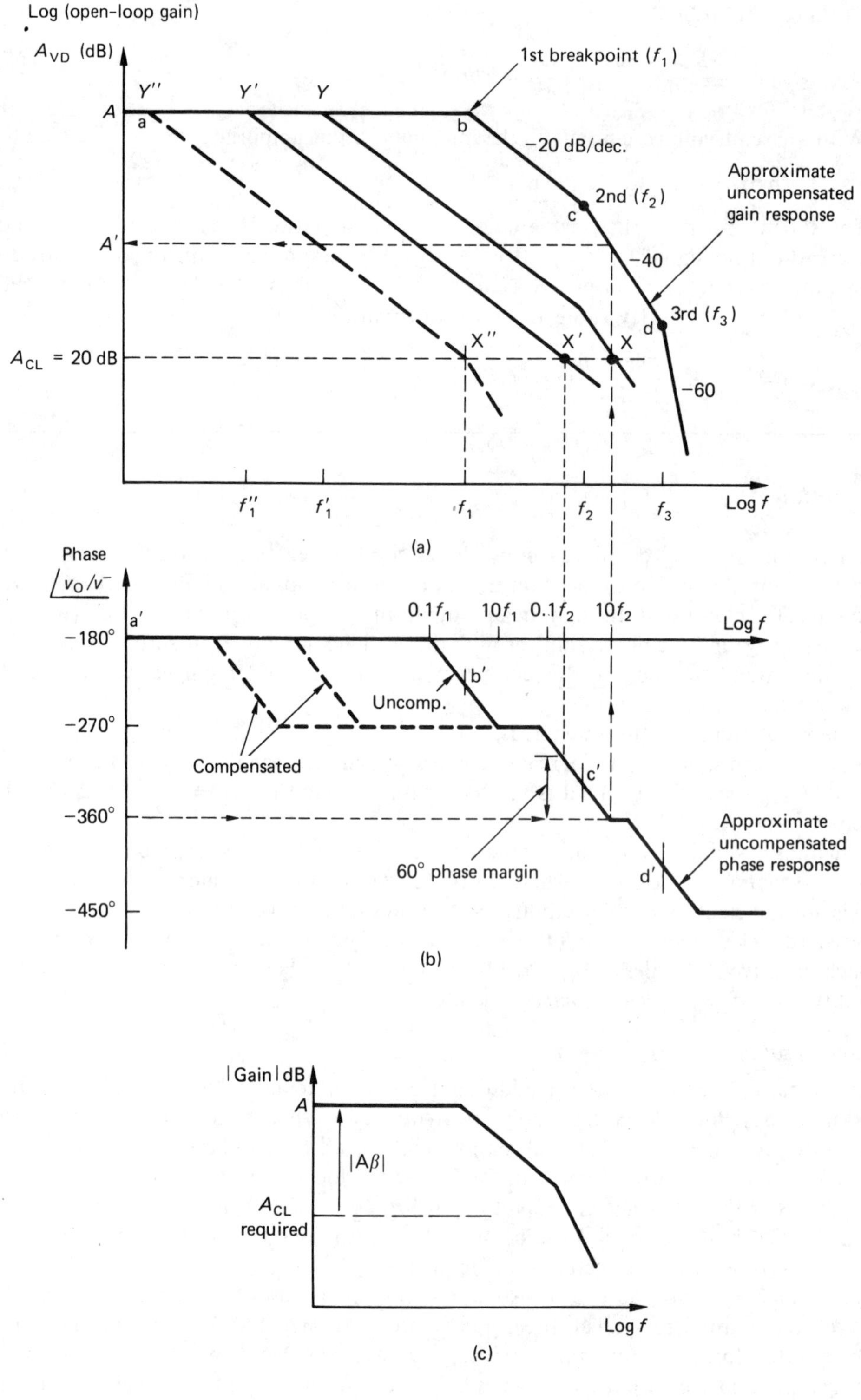

(a)

(b)

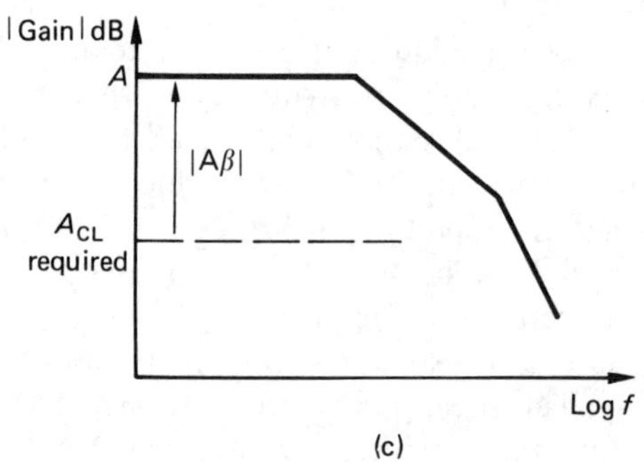

(c)

Figure 7.22 Op-amp gain and phase response

of $10f_2$ (one decade above the second breakpoint) $\angle v_O/v^-$ is approximately $-360°$, that is, v_O is in-phase with v^- and if the open-loop gain A' at this frequency is >1 (>0 dB) the closed-loop arrangement may be unstable. Whether it would be unstable or not depends on the fraction of v_O that is fed back, that is, it depends on the feedback fraction β (equation 5.2) and hence on the loop gain.

From the general expression for closed-loop gain (equation 5.6):

$$A_{CL}(\text{dB}) = A(\text{dB}) - (1 - A\beta)(\text{dB})$$

where A is the open-loop gain of the op-amp; upper case suffix CL is used here because the gain of an op-amp applies to static as well as time-varying signals. For the practical case of appreciable negative feedback, $|A\beta| \gg 1$ and therefore

$$A_{CL}(\text{dB}) \simeq A(\text{dB}) - |A\beta|(\text{dB})$$

from which, the modulus of the loop gain is

$$|A\beta|(\text{dB}) \simeq A(\text{dB}) - A_{CL}(\text{dB}) \tag{7.103}$$

The significance of this relationship is shown on the |gain| Bode plot of figure 7.22c. For a certain required closed-loop gain A_{CL} at low frequency using an op-amp having open-loop gain A at low frequency, the difference $A(\text{dB}) - A_{CL}(\text{dB})$ is the corresponding loop gain in decibels and this must fall to zero (dB) at the frequency corresponding to $\angle A\beta = -360°$ for the circuit to be just stable.

Consider the case where the op-amp having uncompensated gain and phase responses abcd and a′b′c′d′ (figures 7.22a, b) is to be used in a circuit providing a (closed-loop) voltage gain of 10, that is, 20 log 10 = 20 dB, at low frequency. If additional capacitance is introduced into the op-amp to lower the first breakpoint to f_1' (point Y), the open-loop gain of the op-amp will fall to the A_{CL} value of 20 dB ($|A\beta|$ will fall to 0 dB) at point X which corresponds to $\angle A\beta = -360°$ thereby rendering the 20 dB closed-loop circuit just stable. In practice, a *phase margin* of about 60° is introduced to allow a degree of tolerance and also to provide a satisfactory transient response [2b] whereby the loop gain is required to fall to 0 dB at the frequency corresponding to $-360° + 60° = -300°$ which is provided by construction Y′X′ in figure 7.22a. The design procedure using this technique is

(1) Ascertain the breakpoint frequencies of the uncompensated op-amp and hence determine the frequency corresponding to phase $\angle v_O/v^-$ of $-300°$ (for a phase margin of 60°).

(2) Construct a -20 dB/decade roll off Y′X′ where X′ is the point corresponding to the required closed-loop gain and the '$-300°$' frequency.

(3) Introduce additional capacitance *within* the op-amp to move the first breakpoint from f_1 to f_1'' (point Y′).

This stabilisation technique is termed *lag compensation* because the additional capacitance introduces additional phase lag at low frequency. The method is used by op-amp manufacturers to produce *internally-compensated* op-amps for general-purpose use, in which case the compensation is based on unity closed-loop gain which ensures stability for all levels of resistive feedback. The capacitor usually provides feedback in the intermediate stage of the amplifier where it effectively increases the Miller capacitance (section 4.4). In the 741 op-amp, lag compensation is provided by the 30 pF capacitor between the collector of T_{17} and the base of T_{16} (figure 7.5) which provides a first breakpoint at about 7 Hz, the second breakpoint being at about 1.5 MHz (figure 7.4).

Although lag compensation for unity gain provides stability for all situations involving resistive feedback, it causes severe bandwidth limitation and the slew rate (section 7.4.4) is drastically reduced resulting in poor transient response [2b]. Also, if the actual application requires $A_{CL} > 1$ (0 dB), compensation with respect to unity gain is an unnecessary degradation of performance. *Partially-internally-compensated* and *uncompensated* op-amps are available, enabling the user to add external compensating components to suit the particular application. In this way the user can provide sufficient compensation to provide stability for the particular A_{CL} required without causing unnecessary bandwidth limitation. Such op-amps have either a single compensation terminal or two terminals available externally, and the external compensating capacitor or network is connected either between the single terminal and ground, or the op-amp output, or between the two available terminals.

Basic lag compensation is not normally applicable to externally-compensated op-amps because the accessible nodes within the op-amp circuit do not normally allow an external capacitor to be connected *directly* in parallel with the internal capacitance to allow the first breakpoint to be shifted to a lower frequency. The resistance R in series with the compensation terminal means that connection of an external compensating capacitor C_x, from the compensating terminal to ground, for example, would introduce an *additional* breakpoint so that the compensated response would roll off at -40 dB/decade above f_1 with corresponding increased phase lag. To provide adequate compensation the -20 dB/decade roll off from frequency $1/2\pi C_x R$ (corresponding to equation 4.8) must cause the gain to fall to the particular closed-loop gain A_{CL} required for the application at or before the first natural break frequency f_1. Such a response is shown as Y″X″ in figure 7.22a. Often such severe reduction of gain–bandwidth product cannot be tolerated and more sophisticated techniques such as *lead-lag* (pole-zero) compensation or *lead* compensation are preferred.

Lead-lag compensation

The lead-lag method employs an added series CR network which, in conjunction with the internal resistance of the op-amp at the compensation terminal (figure 7.23a) introduces a -20 dB/decade roll-off (*pole* response) at a low frequency and a $+20$ dB/decade rise (*zero* response) at a higher frequency. By arranging the break frequency of the rise to coincide with the first break frequency f_1 of the uncompensated response of the op-amp, the rising response of the compensating network *cancels* the effect of the first natural breakpoint so that the -20 dB/decade roll off continues to the second break frequency f_2 of the original response of the op-amp. In this way the loop gain is reduced with increasing frequency without incurring excessive phase lag so that the frequency at which $\angle A\beta = -300°$ (allowing a phase margin of 60°) occurs is not too low. As a consequence, the break frequency introduced by the compensating network does not need to be too low, thereby retaining bandwidth and slew rate performance.

Consider the arrangement of figure 7.23a where C_x, R_x are the externally-connected compensating components and R is the internal resistance of the op-amp in series with the compensating terminal. The transfer function v_2/v_1 is

$$\frac{v_2}{v_1} = \frac{R_x + (1/j\omega C_x)}{(R + R_x) + (1/j\omega C_x)} = \frac{1 + j\omega C_x R_x}{1 + j\omega C_x(R + R_x)}$$

$$= \frac{1 + j(\omega/\omega_z)}{1 + j(\omega/\omega_p)} = \frac{1 + j(f/f_z)}{1 + j(f/f_p)} \tag{7.104}$$

where $f_z\,(= 1/2\pi C_x R_x)$ is the *zero* frequency and $f_p\,[= 1/2\pi C_x(R + R_x)]$ is the *pole* frequency. The terms pole and zero originate from the general consideration of system frequency response in terms of complex frequency $s\,(= \sigma + j\omega)$ which enables all excitation waveshapes, not only

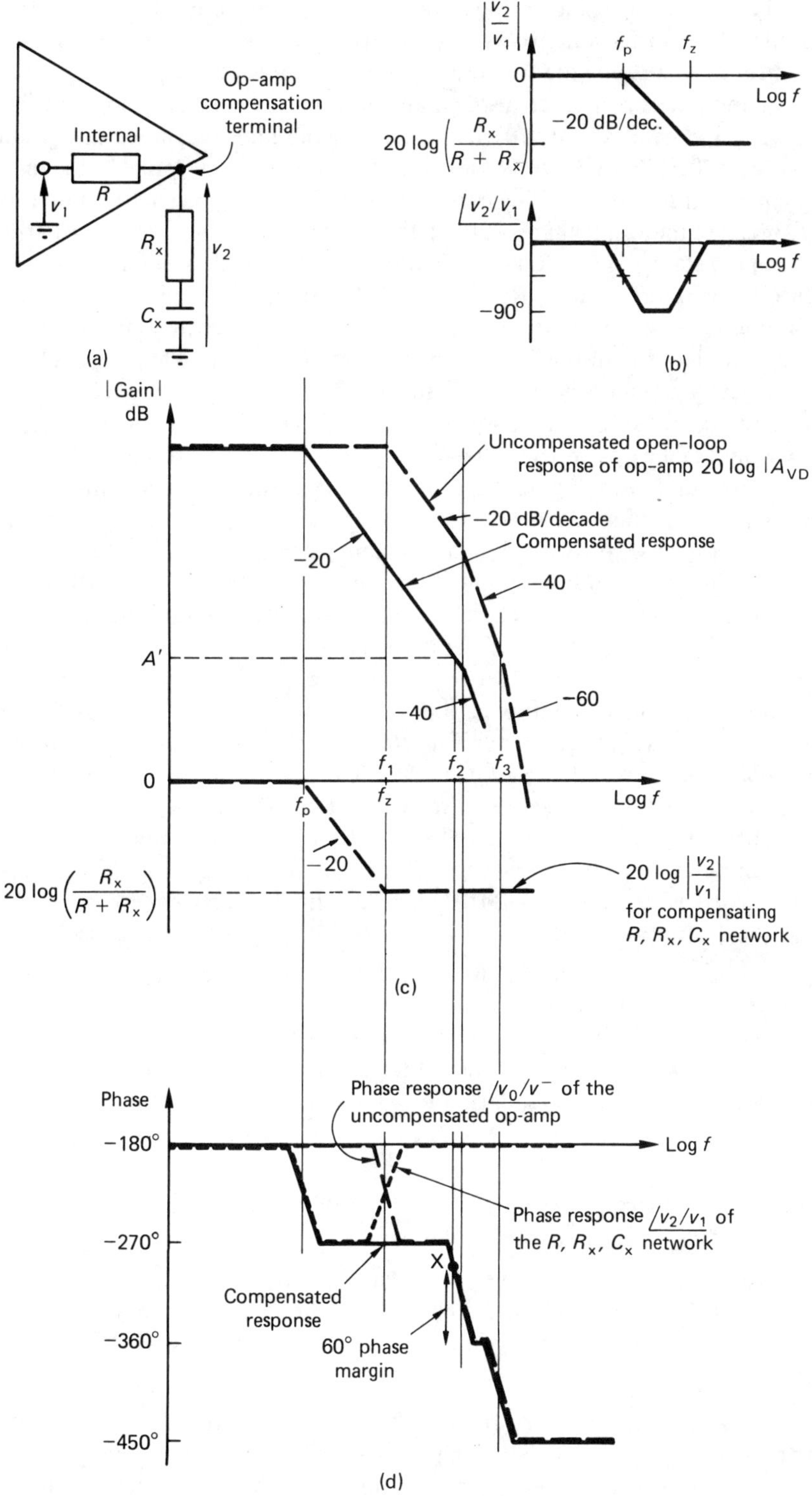

Figure 7.23 Lead-lag compensation

sinusoids, to be considered using a single unified technique [5, 6]. From equation 7.104 it can be seen that the transfer function is zero at a complex frequency $j\omega_z = -1/C_xR_x$, hence a zero is said to exist at ω_z, while it is infinite, termed a pole, at $j\omega_p = -1/C_x(R+R_x)$. The linearised gain and phase responses of the compensating network are shown in figure 7.23b. At low frequency the gain is unity (0 dB) because of the high reactance of C_x, and v_2 is in phase with v_1. A -20 dB/decade roll-off is introduced at frequency f_p due to the time constant C_xR_x and a corresponding phase change from 0° to $-90°$ occurs over the approximate range $0.1f_p \rightarrow 10f_p$ corresponding to figure 4.2f. At the zero frequency f_z the $+20$ dB/decade rise due to the time constant $C_x(R+R_x)$ cancels the -20 dB/decade slope due to C_xR_x and the gain response levels off at $20 \log [R_x/(R+R_x)]$, C_x being an effective short circuit at high frequency. The zero causes the phase response to return to 0° over the range of approximately $0.1f_z$–$10f_z$. Notice that this response corresponds to that of figure 4.5b, although in that case the pole frequency is greater than the zero frequency.

Combining the response of the compensating network with that of the uncompensated open-loop response of the op-amp, which has breakpoints f_1, f_2, f_3, results in the compensated response shown by full lines in figure 7.23c, a new first breakpoint being introduced at f_p. By selecting the zero frequency of the compensating network f_z to be the same as f_1, the 20 dB/decade rise for $f > f_z$ provided by the compensator cancels the -20 dB/decade roll-off introduced by the first natural breakpoint of the op-amp so that the -20 dB/decade roll-off introduced at f_p continues until f_2. Therefore the resultant phase does not fall to the critical $-360°$ value until approximately $10f_2$ and so a 'just stable' system results, for resistive feedback, if f_p is chosen so that the overall compensated response falls to the required closed-loop gain for the particular application (that is, the loop gain falls to 0 dB) at frequency $10f_2$. In practice, a phase margin of typically 60° is required corresponding to point X on the phase response of figure 7.23d, and f_p is thus selected so that the compensated response falls to the required working closed-loop value A' at the frequency corresponding to point X. Thus if the particular application required a closed-loop gain of 15 dB over the flat 'working' range, then A' in figure 7.23c would be chosen as 15 dB and the op-amp compensated so that the roll-off to 15 dB is entirely at -20 dB/decade. This ensures that for signal frequencies approaching the region of instability, $\angle v_O/v^- \rightarrow -360°$, the loop gain is less than unity (< 0 dB), providing overall stability as the amplitude of the fedback voltage is then sufficiently low at such frequencies that sustained oscillation does not occur. The advantage of lead-lag compensation compared with basic lag compensation is that the first breakpoint f_p, which is sometimes called the *dominant pole*, in the lead-lag case does not need to be as low as in the basic lag case, resulting in less degradation of bandwidth and slew rate.

Example 7.4: Lead-lag compensation of an op-amp

An uncompensated op-amp has a gain of 100 dB at low frequency and the open-loop response has breakpoints at 20 kHz, 1 MHz and 10 MHz. If the series resistance at the compensating terminal is 5 kΩ, select suitable compensating components C_x and R_x (figure 7.23a) if the required closed-loop gain at low frequency is 30 dB.

Figure 7.24 shows the necessary construction. Reference to figure 7.23d shows that the phase of v_O relative to v^- falls to $-300°$, allowing a phase margin of 60°, at a frequency just below the second breakpoint which is 1 MHz in this example. It is proposed therefore to compensate the op-amp so that the open-loop response falls to the required closed-loop value of 30 dB

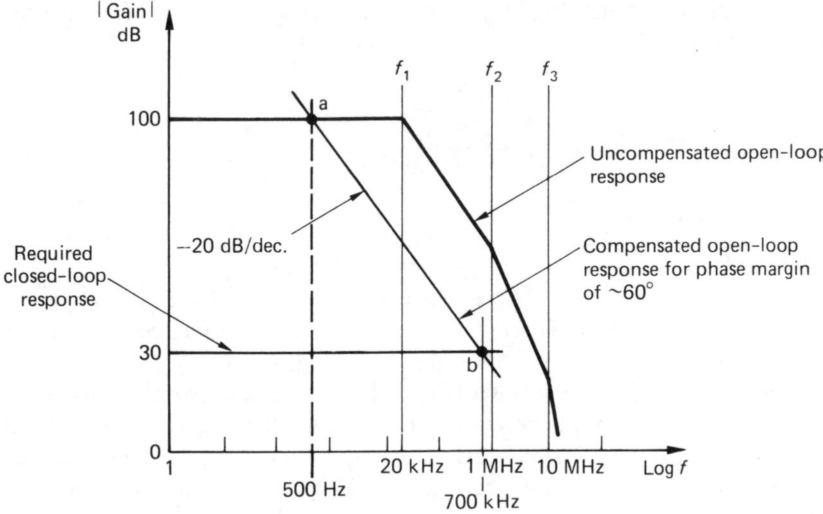

Figure 7.24 Construction for compensation example 7.5

at a frequency just below 1 MHz; 700 kHz is chosen for purposes of example, point b in figure 7.24.

Construction of the $-20\,\text{dB/decade}$ roll-off ab shows that the pole frequency to be introduced by the compensating network ($f_p = 1/2\pi C_x(R + R_x)$ from equation 7.104) is given by point a as 500 Hz. The zero must coincide with the first natural break frequency of the amplifier, f_1, of 20 kHz so as to cancel its effect and so, from equation 7.104, $f_z = 1/2\pi C_x R_x = 20\,\text{kHz}$. Therefore, from $\dfrac{f_z}{f_p} = \dfrac{R + R_x}{R_x} = \dfrac{20\,\text{kHz}}{500\,\text{Hz}} = 40$:

$$R_x = \frac{R}{39} \simeq 128\,\Omega$$

as $R = 5\,\text{k}\Omega$.

Having chosen $R_x = 128\,\Omega$, the value of C_x is calculated from the frequency of the zero as

$$C_x = \frac{1}{2\pi f_z R_x} = \frac{1}{2\pi(20\,\text{kHz})(128)} \simeq 0.06\,\mu\text{F}$$

Preferred values of $120\,\Omega$ and $0.068\,\mu\text{F}$ would give $f_p = 457\,\text{Hz}$ and $f_z = 19.5\,\text{kHz}$. Note that in choice of preferred component values, slightly larger time constants have been chosen compared with the calculated values. This is deliberate so that the breakpoints tend to be lowered compared with the design values, thereby increasing the phase margin rather than the converse. Note also that component tolerances must be considered as they inevitably cause a tolerance in the values of f_p and f_z obtained in practice.

Lead compensation

An alternative compensating method introduces a phase lead into the open-loop response of the op-amp at a suitable frequency so that the critical -360° phase shift point is not reached until higher frequency at which the loop gain is suitably low. The transfer function v_2/v_1 for the network of figure 7.25a is

$$\frac{v_2}{v_1}=\frac{R}{R+(R_x)/\!/\left(\dfrac{1}{j\omega C_x}\right)}=\frac{R}{R+\left[\dfrac{R_x(1/j\omega C_x)}{R_x+(1/j\omega C_x)}\right]}$$

$$=\left(\frac{R}{R+R_x}\right)\left[\frac{1+j(f/f_x)}{1+j(f/f_y)}\right] \qquad (7.105)$$

where $f_x=1/2\pi C_x R_x$ and $f_y=1/2\pi C_x R_y$; $R_y=R/\!/R_x=RR_x/(R+R_x)$. The gain and phase responses of the network are shown in figures 7.25b and c. At frequencies very much less than f_x, C_x is an effective open circuit giving a gain of $20\log[R/(R+R_x)]$ and zero phase shift. Between f_x and f_y, the gain rises at 20 dB/decade to 0 dB and a phase lead is introduced. Combination of responses for this network with those for the uncompensated op-amp which has breakpoints at f_1, f_2 and f_3, as in previous examples, results in the compensated responses as shown by full lines in figures 7.25b and c. The -20 dB/decade roll-off of the gain response then extends to f_3 as the 20 dB/decade rise provided by the compensating network after f_2, assuming f_x is chosen to be coincident with f_2, cancels the increased negative slope after f_2 due to the second time constant of the basic op-amp. As a consequence, the phase lag between v_O and v^- does not approach the critical $-360°$ value, or $-300°$ for a phase margin of 60° (point X in figure 7.25c), until a higher frequency than in the uncompensated case, providing a higher working (stable) bandwidth. In practice, lead compensation can be applied by adding the compensating capacitor C_x across the feedback resistor R_F. In the case of the non-inverting amplifier of figure 7.10c, for example, comparison with figure 7.25a shows that $R_F\equiv R_x$, v_O being the 'input' to the feedback network (v_1 in figure 7.25a) and $R_1\equiv R$, the output of the feedback network (v_2) being the voltage v^- applied to the inverting input of the op-amp. Some op-amps specifically designed for high-bandwidth applications have a lead compensation terminal (node 1, figure 7.25a) while node 2 is the amplifier output and R is the external load.

In all cases, the criterion for closed-loop stability can be seen to require that, to provide a $\angle v_O/v^-$ phase shift of less than $-360°$, the intersection of the required 'flat' closed-loop response (as A′ in figure 7.23c) with the compensated open-loop response of the op-amp must be at a point where the slope of the latter is no steeper than -20 dB/decade.

Phase margin and *gain margin* are used as quantitative indicators of the stability of a closed-loop arrangement:

Phase margin ϕ_m = Phase shift around the feedback loop $\angle A\beta$ when the loop gain $|A\beta|$ is unity (0 dB) (see figure 7.26a)

Thus ϕ_m is the additional phase shift that could theoretically be introduced in the feedback loop before the feedback system would be just on the verge of instability.

Gain margin A_m = Loop gain $|A\beta|$ in decibels at the frequency at which the total phase shift around the loop $\angle A\beta$ is $-360°$, that is, when the fedback and input signals are in phase (see figure 7.26a)

A_m is therefore the theoretical amount by which the loop gain may be increased before the onset of instability.

If the phase margin is too low, *peaking* of the closed-loop gain response is likely (figure 7.26b) particularly for low values of closed-loop gain. Reference [2c] considers in detail the

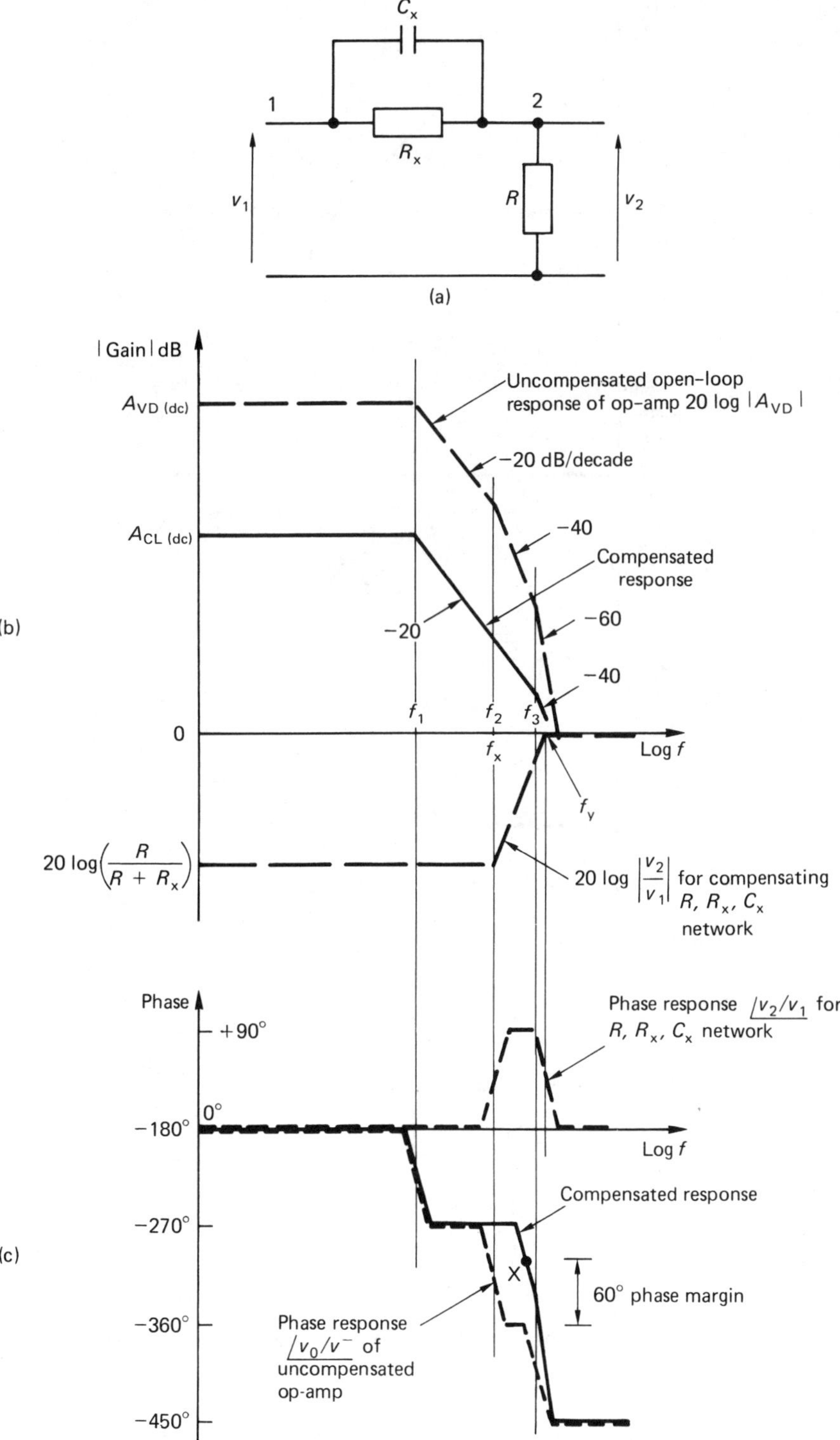

Figure 7.25 Lead compensation

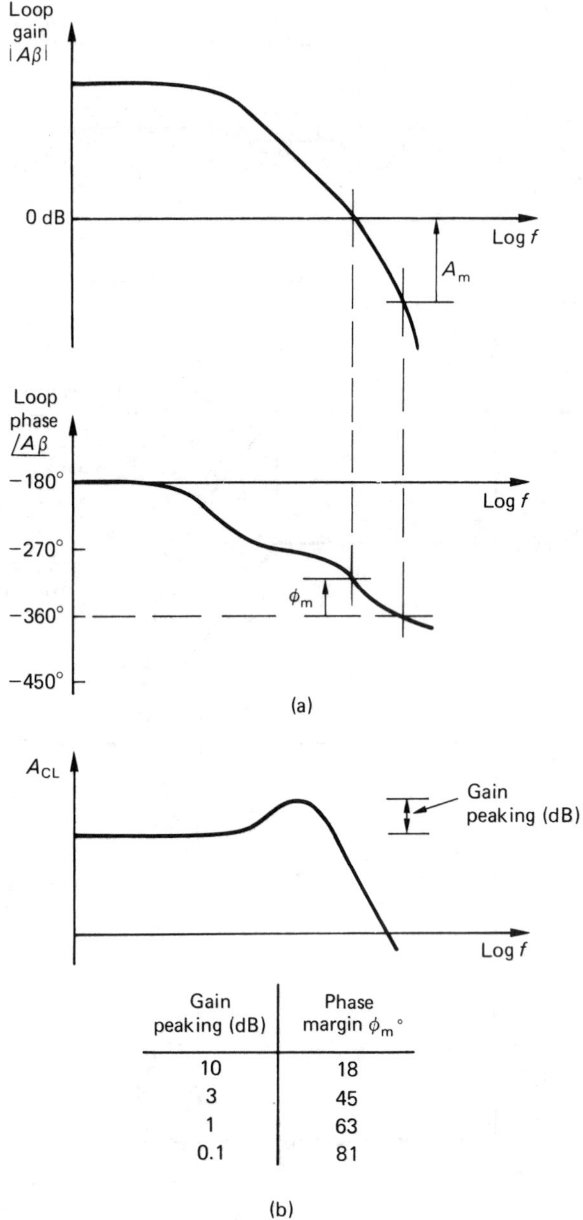

Gain peaking (dB)	Phase margin ϕ_m°
10	18
3	45
1	63
0.1	81

Figure 7.26 Margins and peaking

link between gain peaking, damping factor and phase margin. The work concludes that

$$\text{Gain peaking (dB)} = 20 \log \frac{x}{\sqrt{(2x-1)}} \tag{7.106}$$

$$\text{where } x = \frac{2 \cos \phi_m}{\sin^2 \phi_m}$$

This expression gives the relative peaking *versus* phase margin values tabulated in figure 7.26b, indicating that to keep the peaking to an acceptably low level of about 1 dB for most applications to avoid excessive output distortion, ϕ_m should be about 60°.

7.5 Some practicalities

Selection of component values

Most practical applications require the addition of external components to the basic op-amp. In many cases the overall circuit performance such as the voltage gain of linear amplifiers (figures 7.10c, 7.11b), the rate of integration of an integrator (figure 7.13a) or the output frequency of an astable oscillator (figure 10.5a) depends on the *ratio* or *product* of external component values (equations 7.51, 7.65, 7.81 and 10.41 respectively). Although the ratio (or product) of the component values is known for a particular application from the required performance, determination of suitable values for the individual components requires additional information related to the performance of the op-amp. In order that the latter may be treated as 'ideal' (see the introduction to section 7.3) the choice of values of external components is limited.

Consider as an example the choice of values for R_F and R_1 in the linear amplifier arrangement of figure 7.11b. R_F is effectively across the amplifier output as node X is the virtual earth point (section 7.1) which is almost at signal earth potential. So that this external (feedback) resistor does not load the output of the amplifier, its value should be very much greater than the output resistance R_O of the op-amp. The resistance of the external input resistor R_1 should be high if the input resistance of the overall *circuit* is not to be severely degraded compared with the excellent value afforded by the op-amp. However these input component values should not be so high that the input current to the *circuit* (i_1, figure 7.11b) becomes comparable with the input current of the *amplifier* (i_I, figure 7.11a) otherwise the 'ideal' equations describing the circuit performance are no longer valid and the simplicity of these design equations is a major attraction of the use of op-amps.

As the values of R_I and R_O for an op-amp are so widely different, typically 2 MΩ and 75 Ω for a 741, it is usual to take the geometric mean $\sqrt{(R_I R_O)}$ to obtain a mean working value rather than the arithmetic mean which may have been suitable had the values been of similar order. Input and feedback resistances are then chosen within the range of about 0.1 times to 10 times the geometric mean value to provide the required ratio. In some cases it is necessary to use values outside this 'ideal' range such as when the voltage gain is required to be greater than 100. Although such arrangements will function satisfactorily it must be appreciated that the further the resistance values from the ideal range, the less ideal the performance. It is wise to check the actual operating conditions of the circuit namely, that the minimum input signal current i_1 min is greater than the input bias current I_{IB} of the op-amp and that the output loading due to the feedback resistor is not excessive thereby restricting the signal current to the external load.

Example 7.5: Selection of component values for an op-amp voltage amplifier

An op-amp having input resistance R_I of 2 MΩ and output resistance R_O of 50 Ω is to be used as a linear inverting voltage amplifier having a gain of 10. Select suitable input and feedback resistance values from the E12 range (appendix D) noting that the input resistance of the *circuit* must not be less than 8 kΩ.

Figure 7.11b gives the required circuit arrangement and for $A_{CL} = -10$ the ratio R_F/R_1 must be 10 (equation 7.65).
The geometric mean of R_I and R_O is $\sqrt{(2\ \text{M}\Omega)(50\ \Omega)} = 10\ \text{k}\Omega$ and so suitable resistance values are in the range $(0.1 \times 10\ \text{k}\Omega)$ to $(10 \times 10\ \text{k}\Omega)$, that is, 1 kΩ to 100 kΩ.
Equation 7.67 shows that the input resistance of the *circuit* $R_{I(CCT)}$ is given by R_1 and from the specification this must be $\geqslant 8\ \text{k}\Omega$.
Suitable values for R_1, R_F are therefore 8.2 kΩ, 82 kΩ or 10 kΩ, 100 kΩ; the latter are chosen to provide the higher input resistance.

In cases where the design requires the provision of a certain time constant CR as for an integrator (figure 7.13a) or a phase-shift oscillator (figure 9.3a), it is usual to first select R according to the above procedure, preliminarily selecting the mid-range value $\sqrt{(R_I R_O)}$, and then to calculate the corresponding value of capacitance to give the required time constant. Because the range of preferred capacitance values is usually more restricted than the resistance range (appendix D), it is usually necessary to select the nearest preferred value of capacitance and then to recalculate the resistance value to provide the time constant required.

Example 7.6: Selection of component values for a basic integrator

Select values of R and C for the basic integrator of figure 7.13a to enable a 1 kHz symmetrical square wave of voltage range ± 10 V to be converted to a sawtooth waveform of amplitude 15 V; the waveforms are shown in figure 7.13b. The resistance and capacitance values are to be selected from the E12 and E6 ranges (appendix D) respectively; the input resistance of the circuit must not be less than 20 kΩ.

Period of input square wave $= 1/(1\ \text{kHz}) = 1$ ms.
Integration interval corresponding to each pulse of the input square wave $= 1\ \text{ms}/2 = 500\ \mu\text{s}$.
During the integration interval, the output is required to change by 15 V: a slope modulus of $15\ \text{V}/500\ \mu\text{s} = 3 \times 10^4\ \text{V/s}$.

From equation 7.81, the slope modulus of the output voltage $\dfrac{dv_O}{dt}$ depends on the input amplitude (10 V) and the time constant (CR) giving

$$\frac{10\ \text{V}}{CR} = 3 \times 10^4\ \text{V/s}$$

from which $CR = 33.3$ ms.

Selection of R and C

From equation 7.82, the input resistance of the integrator is equal to R which must be $\geqslant 20\ \text{k}\Omega$ to meet the specification. Consideration of circuit current levels at the beginning of this chapter proposed 10 μA as a minimum value to ensure near-ideal performance using commercial op-amps. For $i_1 \geqslant 10\ \mu\text{A}$ with $v_1 = 10$ V, R must be $\leqslant 1\ \text{M}\Omega$ from equation 7.78.
R can therefore be selected in the range 20 kΩ–1 MΩ; E12 values (appendix D) of 100, 120, 150, 180 kΩ are near the geometric mean of this range, and the corresponding values of C to provide $CR = 33.3$ ms are 333, 277.5, 222, 185 nF.
Both 330 nF and 220 nF values are available in the E6 range (appendix D) and so R, C combinations of either 100 kΩ, 330 nF or 150 kΩ, 220 nF could be chosen.

Single-supply operation

Consideration of op-amp performance and applications so far in this section has assumed 'dual-rail' dc power supplies $+V_{CC}$ and $-V_{EE}$ with the common terminal of the supplies providing the signal earth/reference, and indeed for most applications symmetrical supplies ($V_{CC} = |-V_{EE}|$) are used. The use of a dual-rail system allows the output v_O to swing positively and negatively with respect to signal earth, although the need to provide dual supplies is clearly a disadvantage particularly if other electronic circuitry in the overall system requires only a single supply.

Op-amps can be operated from a single supply although it is important to appreciate the limitations. Figure 7.27a shows a non-inverting arrangement corresponding to that of figure 7.10c but powered from a single supply V_{DC}. With V_{DC} positive it is evident that the circuit will function only for v_1 positive. Additionally, care must be taken to ensure that the potential at the input terminals relative to $V_{DC}/2$, the signal reference if V_{DC} is treated as a symmetrical

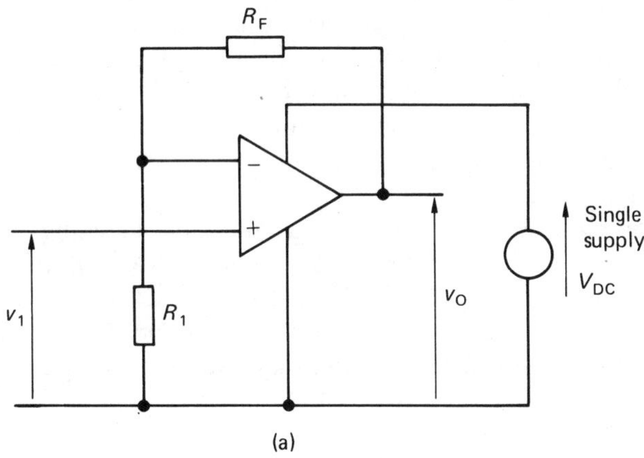

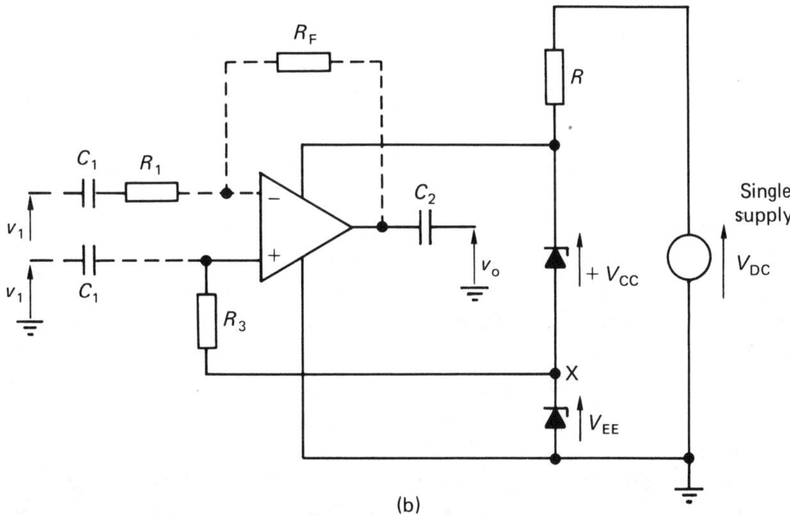

Figure 7.27 Single-supply operation of an op-amp

dual supply, is within the allowable common-mode input voltage range (section 6.4) of the op-amp as specified by the manufacturer. Some op-amps, specifically designed to permit single supply operation, have a common-mode range that includes the maximum specified supply voltage and can therefore be used safely in this way. If V_{DC} is negative in figure 7.27a, the positive terminal being grounded, the circuit can operate only for v_1 negative. An inverting dc arrangement corresponding to that of figure 7.11b but using a single supply is clearly not feasible because of the limited signal polarity. It should be noted that op-amps designed for single supply operation can equally be used with a conventional dual supply.

Not all linear op-amp applications require operation for static inputs or at very low frequency, in which case blocking capacitors can be used to remove bias levels. Figure 7.27b shows a single supply arrangement which uses two voltage-reference diodes to establish a reference point (X), thereby forming a pseudo-dual-supply. Note that the reference point is not at signal earth potential and it is therefore necessary to bias the + input to the reference voltage using R_3. For operation as an ac amplifier, a blocking capacitor C_1 can be included at the input to avoid the bias voltage interfering with the signal source. Similarly a blocking capacitor C_2 can be added at the output to remove the bias level. The use of blocking capacitors means that offsets and drift are not a major problem although the voltage offset at the output reduces the allowable output voltage swing because of clipping.

In addition to the basic supply connections, figure 7.27a shows dashed connections corresponding to particular applications. As an ac voltage follower or non-inverting ac amplifier, the input signal v_1 is applied to the + input via C_1 with negative feedback applied as in figures 7.10a and c. In the latter case an additional blocking capacitor is included in series with the lower branch of the feedback potential divider so that the quiescent output remains at the signal reference level, the feedback fraction being applied only to the ac component of v_O. Operation as an inverting ac amplifier involves connection of R_1 and R_F as in figure 7.11b, with the addition of blocking capacitors C_1 and C_2.

References and further reading

1. M.E. Goodge, *Semiconductor Device Technology* (Macmillan, 1985)
   (a) section 4.2.1
   (b) section 1.6.2
2. G.B. Clayton, *Operational Amplifiers*, 2nd edition (Butterworths, 1979)
   (a) chapter 6
   (b) chapter 2
   (c) appendix A2
3. W.D. Stanley, *Operational Amplifiers with Linear Integrated Circuits*, chapter 4 (Merrill, 1984)
4. J.V. Wait, L.P. Huelsman and G.A. Korn, *Introduction to Operational Amplifier Theory and Applications*, section 2.5 (McGraw-Hill, 1975)
5. R.J. Smith, *Circuits, Devices and Systems*, 4th edition, chapter 4 (Wiley, 1984)
6. W.H. Hayt and J.E. Kemmerly, *Engineering Circuit Analysis*, 4th edition, chapter 13 (Wiley, 1987)
7. F.H. Mitchell, *Introduction to Electronics Design*, chapters 12 and 13 (Prentice-Hall, 1988)
8. C.J. Savant, M.S. Roden and G.L. Carpenter, *Electronic Circuit Design*, chapters 7–9 (Benjamin/Cummings, 1987)
9. T.L. Floyd, *Electronic Devices*, 2nd edition, chapters 12–14 (Merrill, 1988)
10. P.M. Chirlian, *Analysis and Design of Integrated Electronic Circuits*, 2nd edition, chapters 13 and 14 (Harper and Row/Wiley, 1987)

11. T.F. Bogart, *Electronic Devices and Circuits*, chapters 12–14 (Merrill, 1986)
12. G.M. Glasford, *Analog Electronic Circuits*, chapter 7 (Prentice-Hall, 1986)
13. M.S. Ghausi, *Electronic Devices and Circuits*, chapters 5, 9 and 10 (Holt-Saunders, 1985)
14. A.S. Sedra and K.C. Smith, *Microelectronic Circuits*, 2nd edition, chapter 3 (Holt, Rinehart and Winston, 1987)
15. R.J. Maddock and D.M. Calcutt, *Electronics: A course for Engineers*, chapter 5 (Longman, 1988)
16. J. Millman and A. Grabel, *Microelectronics*, 2nd edition, chapters 10 and 14 (McGraw-Hill, 1988)
17. C.L. Alley and K.W. Atwood, *Microelectronics*, chapter 13 (Prentice-Hall, 1986)
18. W.H. Hayt and G.W. Neudeck, *Electronic Circuit Analysis and Design*, 2nd edition, chapters 9 and 10 (Houghton Mifflin, 1984)
19. R.A. Colclaser, D.A. Neaman and C.F. Hawkins, *Electronic Circuit Analysis*, chapters 13, 16 and 17 (Wiley, 1984)
20. P. Horowitz and W. Hill, *The Art of Electronics*, chapter 3 (Cambridge, 1982)
21. D.H. Horrocks, *Feedback Circuits and Op. Amps.*, chapter 6–8 (Van Nostrand Reinhold, 1983)
22. E.N. Lurch, *Fundamentals of Electronics*, 3rd edition, chapters 17–19 (Wiley, 1981)
23. S.A. Knight, *Electronics for Higher TEC*, chapter 8 (Granada, 1983)
24. D.C. Green, *Electronics for TEC Level IV*, chapter 5 (Pitman, 1981)

Tutorial questions

Note: Where applicable, answers correspond to rounding to 2 decimal places during calculation.

Linear op-amp circuits

7.1 For each of the following specifications, draw a suitable circuit employing a single op-amp. If the op-amp has input and output resistances of 1 MΩ and 100 Ω respectively, select suitable E24 resistance values (appendix D) in each case. Resistance values are to be implemented using a single component; series and/or parallel combinations to obtain non-preferred values are not allowed. Component selection tolerances may be ignored.

(a) Non-inverting amplification with a nominal voltage gain in the range 10 ± 0.5 per cent.

(b) Inverting amplification with the modulus of the nominal voltage gain in the range 15 ± 1 per cent; the input resistance of the circuit not to be less than 10 kΩ.

(c) Mixing of two signal voltages in the ratio 2:1, neither input presenting less than 15 kΩ to the signal source.

(d) Linear current-to-voltage conversion such that a sinusoidal signal current of amplitude 100 μA produced by a high-resistance transducer is converted to a voltage variation of amplitude 10 V.

(e) Subtraction of two voltage signals such that the output signal is ten times the difference.

[Answers:

(a) Circuit of figure 7.10c with R_1, R_F values of 9.1 kΩ, 82 kΩ; 8.2 kΩ, 75 kΩ; 7.5 kΩ, 68 kΩ; 6.2 kΩ, 56 kΩ; 4.7 kΩ, 43 kΩ; 3 kΩ, 27 kΩ or 2 kΩ, 18 kΩ. High values are preferred to keep the output loading low.

(b) Circuit of figure 7.11b with R_1, R_F values of 10 kΩ, 150 kΩ; 12 kΩ, 180 kΩ; 16 kΩ, 240 kΩ; 18 kΩ, 270 kΩ; 20 kΩ, 300 kΩ; 22 kΩ, 330 kΩ; 24 kΩ, 360 kΩ; etc. A high value of R_1 provides a high input resistance but an excessively high value of R_F causes non-ideal performance because of the low feedback current in comparison with the amplifier input current.
(c) Circuit of figure 7.11c with a ratio R_1/R_2 or R_2/R_1 of two, neither R_1 nor R_2 being less than 15 kΩ; for example, $R_1 = 15$ kΩ, $R_2 = 30$ kΩ or $R_1 = 18$ kΩ, $R_2 = 36$ kΩ. The overall gain is not specified and so R_F can be chosen at will; choosing $R_F = R_2$ gives gains of 2 and 1 for the two inputs.
(d) Circuit of figure 7.11a with $R_F = 100$ kΩ.
(e) Circuit of figure 7.12 with $R_2 = 10R_1$; for example, $R_1 = 10$ kΩ, $R_2 = 100$ kΩ]

7.2 A circuit is required to convert a 2 kHz square wave having a voltage range of ± 5 V to a sawtooth waveform of amplitude 20 V. Select suitable component values for a basic op-amp integrator, the resistance from the E12 series and the capacitance from the E6 series (appendix D). Calculate the percentage error in output voltage amplitude provided by the selected combination of preferred values compared with the specified required amplitude.

[Answers: Suitable combinations with corresponding errors: 10 nF, 6.8 kΩ, − 8.1 per cent; 6.8 nF, 10 kΩ, − 8.1 per cent; 4.7 nF, 12 kΩ, + 10.8 per cent; 3.3 nF, 18 kΩ, + 5.2 per cent; 2.2 nF, 27 kΩ, + 5.2 per cent; 1.5 nF, 33 kΩ, + 26.3 per cent]

7.3 Assuming the op-amps are ideal, show that the output of the circuit of figure 7.28a is $(v_1 + v_2)$ and that of figure 7.28b is $(v_3 + v_4) - (v_1 + v_2)$.

7.4 What is the input resistance of
(a) A unity-gain inverting op-amp circuit that employs 10 kΩ resistors and an op-amp having an input resistance of 10 MΩ.
(b) A non-inverting op-amp circuit that uses the same type of op-amp as in part (a) and 10 kΩ resistors.

[Answers: (a) 10 kΩ, (b) 10 MΩ]

7.5 Figure 7.29 shows an electronic analog voltmeter in which the microammeter, which has resistance R_m and a full scale deflection of 100 μA, is calibrated to read full scale when v is 10 V. Show that the circuit operation is independent of R_m and calculate the value of R.
[Answer: 100 kΩ]

The op-amp as a switch

See also tutorial questions 10.5–10.9 on op-amp astable and monostable circuits.

7.6 Select component values for the op-amp Schmitt trigger circuit of figure 7.16b that will provide input trigger levels of approximately ± 2 V and an output of approximately ± 12 V. The op-amp, which has input and output resistances of 1 MΩ and 100 Ω respectively, is powered from $\pm$ 18 V supplies; E24 (appendix D) resistance and reference diode voltage values are available.

[Answer: For symmetrical trigger levels about signal earth, the reference source v_R is not required. Back-to-back 11 V reference diodes across the output clamp v_O to approximately ± 11.7 V. V_U and V_L of ± 2 V require $R_2 = 5R_1$, allowing E24 values $R_1 = 15$ kΩ, $R_2 = 75$ kΩ to be selected in the 1–100 kΩ range centred on $\sqrt{R_I R_O}$.

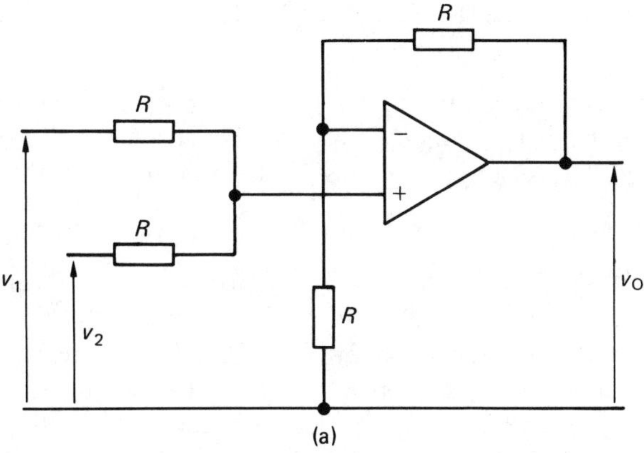

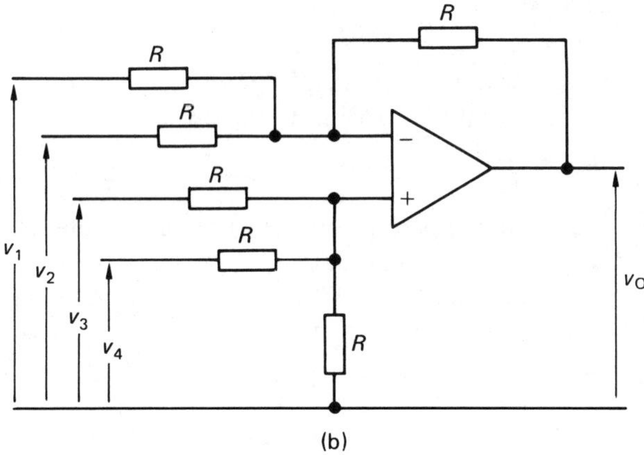

Figure 7.28

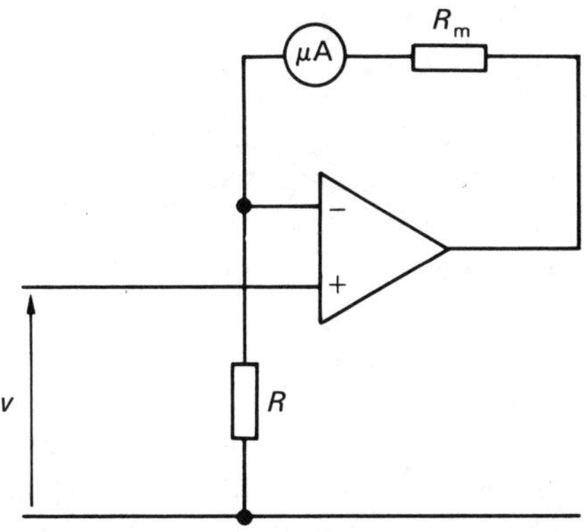

Figure 7.29

Combinations 10 kΩ, 51 kΩ; 11 kΩ, 56 kΩ; 12 kΩ, 62 kΩ and 16 kΩ, 82 kΩ would all be suitable]

7.7 Modify the circuit of question 7.6, using E24 components (appendix D), so that the circuit, operating from the same ± 18 V supplies, provides a nominal ± 10 V output with input trigger levels of approximately -0.5 V and $+5$ V.

[Hint: Let $R_2 = nR_1$ and solve for n and v_R for the required trigger levels]

[Answer: Circuit of figure 7.16b with $R_2 = 2.64R_1$, $v_R = 3.1$ V with back-to-back 9.1 V reference diodes across the output. Suitable choices of R_1, R_2 are 15 kΩ, 39 kΩ or 18 kΩ, 47 kΩ. The 3.1 V reference can be provided by a 3.0 V reference diode such as a BZX 79 C3V0 (appendix E, section E.2) with a reverse current of about 6 mA (from the static $I_Z - V_Z$ characteristic); this current can be supplied via a resistance of $(18\text{ V} - 3.1\text{ V})/6\text{ mA} = 2.48$ kΩ from the $+18$ V supply, select 2.4 kΩ]

Effects of non-ideal op-amp performance:
Finite parameters

7.8 The op-amp in the non-inverting circuit of figure 7.10c has open-loop gain A_{VD} and input resistance R_I; the output resistance is negligibly small. Show that the voltage gain v_O/v_1 is $\left(1 + \dfrac{R_F}{R_1}\right)\left(\dfrac{A_{VD}\beta}{A_{VD}\beta - 1}\right)$ where the feedback fraction β is $-(R_1 /\!/ R_F /\!/ R_I)/R_F$.
Hence show that the fractional gain error due to finite A_{VD} and R_I is the same as that for the corresponding inverting circuit as given by equation 7.97.
For $R_1 = 10$ kΩ, $R_F = 82$ kΩ and $A_{VD} = 10^4$, what is the minimum permissible input resistance R_I if the fractional gain error must not exceed 0.1 per cent?

[Answer: 103.95 kΩ]

Offsets

7.9 A basic inverting op-amp circuit (figure 7.11b) has a closed-loop gain of -7.5, the feedback resistance being 75 kΩ. If the input bias current of the op-amp is 80 nA and the input offsets are 2 mV and 20 nA, estimate the percentage offset error at the output when the static input voltage is 1 V. Mention any assumptions made.

[Answer: 0.31 per cent assuming op-amp output resistance is negligible and $I_{\overline{IB}} = I_{IB}$]

Slew-rate limiting

7.10 The input signal to a gain-of-10 op-amp inverter is a 100 kHz sinewave of rms value 200 mV. If the output must be free from distortion due to slew-rate limiting, what is the minimum permissible slew rate of the op-amp?

[Answer: 1.78 V/μs]

7.11 The sinusoidal output of a linear op-amp circuit has a peak-to-peak value of 5 V. As the signal frequency is increased, slew-rate limiting is just detectable at 20 kHz. What would be the output waveform if the input signal frequency were to be increased to 100 kHz? Assume that the input signal amplitude remains unchanged throughout.

[Answer: Triangular wave of peak-to-peak value 1.57 V]

Stability (frequency compensation)

7.12 The open-loop gain response of an uncompensated op-amp has breakpoints at 50 kHz, 1 MHz and 10 MHz, the gain at low frequency being 100 dB. Using 6 cycle log–lin graph paper, construct the gain and phase responses of the amplifier over the range 100 Hz to 100 MHz using the linearised construction technique.

(a) At what frequency does the gain of the open-loop amplifier become unity?

(b) At what frequency is the output signal out-of-phase with the differential input signal?

(c) If the amplifier is used as a voltage follower and the frequency of the input signal is progressively increased, at what frequency would the circuit become unstable? Explain why.

(d) The amplifier manufacturer wants to modify the response using basic lag compensation to shift the lowest breakpoint so as to produce a general-purpose amplifier that will be stable for all levels of resistive feedback. If a phase margin of 60° is required, to what frequency must the lowest breakpoint be shifted to meet this objective?

[Answers: 36 MHz; 3.2 MHz; 3.2 MHz, as at this frequency v_O lags v_I by 180° so that v_O is in phase with v^- resulting in positive feedback; 4.8 Hz]

7.13 An uncompensated op-amp has a dc gain of 80 dB and the open-loop response has breakpoints at 10 kHz, 500 kHz and 5 MHz. Lead-lag compensation is to be applied for an application requiring a closed-loop gain at low frequency of 20 dB; the phase margin is to be 60°. Using the linearised construction technique, plot the approximate phase response of the compensated amplifier above 10 kHz and estimate the frequency at which v_O lags v^- by 300°; hence calculate the required pole frequency. Select corresponding preferred-value components (E12 resistance, E6 capacitance; appendix D) for the compensating network assuming the series resistance at the compensating terminal is 9 kΩ.

[Answers: 230 kHz, 230 Hz; 220 Ω, 100 nF]

7.14 An op-amp having an open-loop dc gain of 120 dB has breakpoints at 10 kHz, 1 MHz and 10 MHz. Lead-lag compensation has been applied using a 330 nF capacitor. If the resistance in series with the compensating terminal is 15 kΩ, what is the correct value of resistance for the compensating network? What is the minimum closed-loop gain at which the amplifier may be used if the phase margin must not be less than 60°?

[Answers: 48 Ω, 37 dB]

7.15 Tests on an uncompensated op-amp show that the open-loop gain at very low frequency is 90 dB, that the gain is 3 dB below the low-frequency value at 50 kHz and that further breakpoints occur at 500 kHz and 10 MHz. It is required to introduce lead-lag compensation such that the amplifier has a phase margin of 60° when used to provide a gain of 30 dB at low frequency. The resistance in series with the compensating terminal is not known but it is found that when a single capacitor of 47 nF is connected from the compensating terminal to ground, the lowest breakpoint of the open-loop response is shifted to 250 Hz. Determine the value of the series resistance and select preferred-value components for the compensating network (E12 resistance, E6 capacitance; appendix D).

[Answers: 13.55 kΩ; 68 Ω, 47 nF]

7.16 An uncompensated op-amp having a lead compensation terminal is to be used to provide wideband linear amplification driving into an effective resistive load of 1 kΩ. The uncompensated response of the op-amp has breakpoints at 50 kHz, 500 kHz, 10 MHz and it is necessary to select suitable values for the parallel *CR* compensating network to be connected from the lead compensation terminal on the op-amp to the output. Choose suitable breakpoints for the compensating network and select corresponding E12 (appendix D) values for the network. Note that low-value capacitors are usually available in the E12 range.

[Answers: $f_x = 500$ kHz, $f_y = 2$ MHz; 39 kΩ, 8.2 pF]

8 Power Amplifiers

Coverage

- Consideration of the most significant aspects of power amplifiers; power efficiency and distortion.
- Classification of power stages according to mode of operation; classes A, B, AB, C, D and E.
- Analysis of class A and class B stages leading to the popular class AB circuit.
- Discussion of the operation and merits of class C, D and E stages.

A power amplifier is required to deliver substantial signal power to a load and this means that the operating point(s) of the transistor(s) must move over a large proportion of the 'length' of the load line (section 3.4.3) corresponding to wide swings of voltage and current. This type of amplifier is therefore termed a *large-signal amplifier* distinguishing this mode of operation from that of a small-signal amplifier (chapter 3) used to provide voltage *or* current amplification, but not both simultaneously. Strictly, power amplifiers should be referred to as power *stages* because it is usually only the output stage of a complete power amplifier that operates in large signal mode.

8.1 **Basics**

Power efficiency

In common with other amplifiers, the general principle of operation is that the degree of conduction of a transistor (BJT or FET) connected in series with the load controls the flow of energy from a dc power supply to the load in response to the input signal. This inevitably means that some power is dissipated in the transistor and the efficiency of conversion of dc input power to output signal power is of major importance because poor efficiency means high dissipation in the transistor with corresponding thermal problems. Two important performance parameters are therefore:

Power conversion efficiency, η

$$= \frac{\text{Average output signal power } P_{o(av)}}{\text{Average input power } P_{I(AV)}} \tag{8.1}$$

Average transistor dissipation

$$= \text{'Collector' dissipation } P_{\mathrm{C(AV)}} = \frac{1}{2\pi}\int_0^{2\pi} v_{\mathrm{CE}} i_{\mathrm{C}} \mathrm{d}(\omega t) \tag{8.2}$$

for a BJT

$$= \text{'Drain' dissipation } P_{\mathrm{D(AV)}} = \frac{1}{2\pi}\int_0^{2\pi} v_{\mathrm{DS}} i_{\mathrm{D}} \mathrm{d}(\omega t) \tag{8.3}$$

for a FET

Distortion

A consequence of the wide excursion of transistor operating point in power stages is that considerable distortion can be introduced because of the non-linear nature of the transistor characteristic (figure 3.14a). The non-linearity between input and output of a transistor is indicated by its transfer characteristic, $I_{\mathrm{C}} - V_{\mathrm{BE}}$ (or $I_{\mathrm{C}} - I_{\mathrm{B}}$) for a BJT and $I_{\mathrm{D}} - V_{\mathrm{GS}}$ for a FET; appendix E, sections E.6 and E.8 give data sheets of typical medium/high-power transistors. These transfer characteristics can be represented as a polynomial

$$i = I + av + bv^2 + cv^3 + \cdots \tag{8.4}$$

lower case symbols for current and voltage representing time-varying quantities, I being the constant value of current when $v = 0$.

If the applied voltage v is purely sinusoidal, the output (load) current is, from equation 8.4:

$$i = I + A \sin \omega t + B \sin^2 \omega t + C \sin^3 \omega t + \cdots \tag{8.5}$$

where $A \sin \omega t$ is the 'true' signal component and the higher-order terms are distorting harmonics which, using Fourier analysis (appendix A), can be written in terms of odd and even multiple-frequency terms.

Example 8.1: Distortion introduced by the non-linear transfer characteristic of a transistor

Show that large-signal operation of a JFET introduces second-harmonic distortion.

The transfer characteristic of a JFET may be represented by (equation 2.17)

$$I_{\mathrm{D(sat)}} \simeq I_{\mathrm{DSS}}\left(1 - \frac{V_{\mathrm{GS}}}{V_{\mathrm{P}}}\right)^2$$

$$\equiv I - aV_{\mathrm{GS}} + bV_{\mathrm{GS}}^2$$

corresponding to the first three terms of equation 8.4.

If the applied gate–source voltage signal is $V_{\mathrm{gsm}} \sin \omega t$, where V_{gsm} is the signal amplitude, the corresponding time-varying drain current will be

$$i_{\mathrm{D}} \simeq I - aV_{\mathrm{gsm}} \sin \omega t + bV_{\mathrm{gsm}}^2 \sin^2 \omega t$$

Using the trigonometrical relationship $\sin^2 \theta = (1 - \cos 2\theta)/2$, the drain current may be written

$$i_{\mathrm{D}} \simeq I' - A \sin \omega t - B \sin 2\omega t \tag{8.6}$$

where the constant component $I' = I + (bV_{\mathrm{gsm}}^2/2)$ and the coefficients A and B are aV_{gsm} and $bV_{\mathrm{gsm}}^2/2$ respectively.

Equation 8.6 shows the introduction of a 2ω term indicating second-harmonic distortion.

Classification

Power stage designs are classified according to the mode of operation of the transistor(s) as shown in table 8.1

Class A. The transistor is biased to a mid-range level of conduction and the operating point then moves along the load line about this Q-point as in a basic small-signal amplifier (chapter 3). However when used as a power stage the substantial quiescent power dissipation is a major disadvantage resulting in poor efficiency.
Transformer coupling improves efficiency but has the disadvantage of transformer cost, size and weight as well as worsened frequency response.

Table 8.1 Transistor conduction for the various classes of power stage operation.

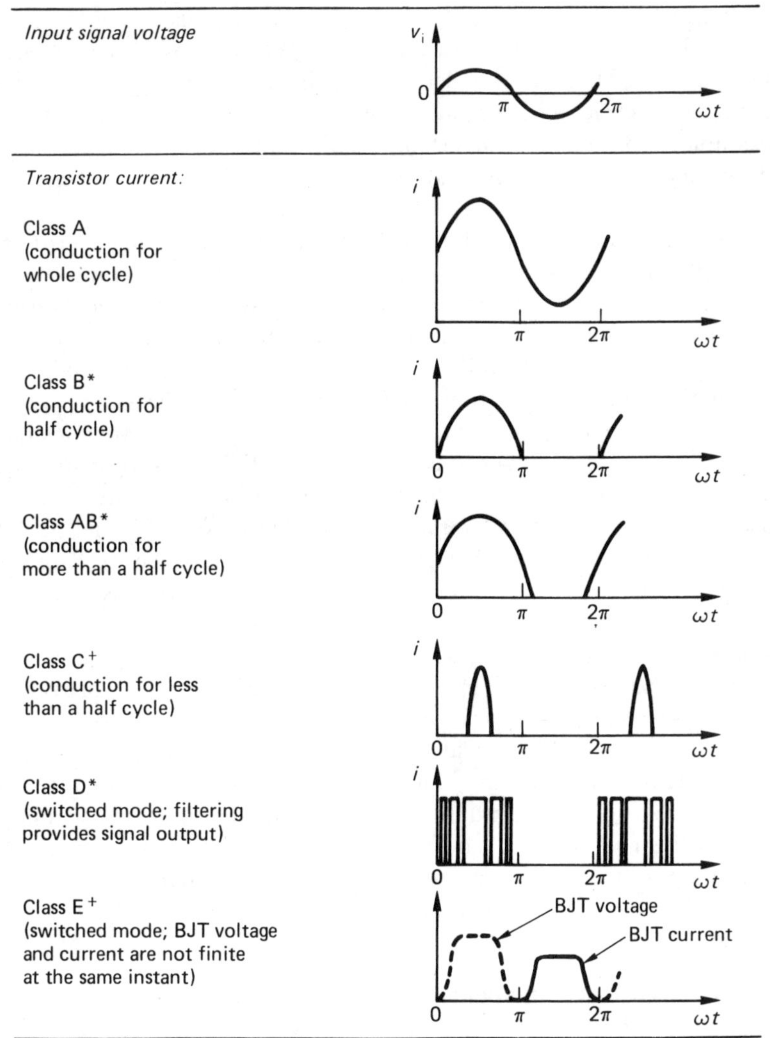

* For one transistor of a push-pull pair.

+ Load current maintained by tuned circuit.

Distortion performance can be improved by using two transistors operating in a *push–pull* configuration; the improvement is due to the cancellation of transistor-generated *even* harmonics.

Class B. Efficiency is improved by biasing the push–pull transistors to cut-off so that there is no quiescent current and therefore no static power dissipation. In this mode only one of the pair of transistors conducts at any instant; one transistor delivers power to the load for positive signal voltages while the other transistor operates when the signal is negative. Efficiency is good for this mode of operation but crossover distortion is introduced when conduction passes from one transistor to the other because of the non-linearity of the transistor transfer characteristic for low input voltage.

Class AB. If the transistors in a push–pull arrangement are biased just above cut-off, crossover distortion is greatly reduced with only a marginal reduction in efficiency. This is the most popular mode of operation for linear operation; it is termed class AB because it is between the class A and class B extremes.

Class C. High-efficiency special-purpose amplifiers are formed by biasing the transistor well into cut-off so that power is delivered to the load over only a small portion of the input signal cycle. Such amplifiers operate at a single frequency as is required, for example, to provide the carrier for a radio transmitter. The load is a tuned circuit which enables a continuous output to be obtained even though energy is supplied only in short bursts.

Classes D and E. Transistors are used as switches rather than in their linear mode. In the fully ON or fully OFF states either the voltage across the transistor is low or the current through it is low; in either case power dissipation is low resulting in high power conversion efficiency. In class D operation the signal is recovered from the resulting pulsed output while in class E, transistor dissipation is almost eliminated for single-frequency operation resulting in excellent efficiency.

The following consideration of power stages concentrates on bipolar versions but it must be emphasised that the work also applies to corresponding FET stages. It was not until the mid 1970s that high-power FETs became readily available and for this reason power stages were almost exclusively bipolar. The introduction of the VMOS power FET and the VJFET [1a], the latter also being termed a *static induction transistor* (SIT), each offering a high power dissipation capability, good frequency response and good linearity, has caused a growth in popularity of FET power stages although often a bipolar driver is retained. More recently a vertical DMOS structure has become popular for power applications, one version being the HEXFET from International Rectifier Incorporated. Reference [2] provides a detailed treatment of the types and uses of power FETs.

It is important to appreciate that the wide excursion of the operating point of the transistor(s) of a power stage means that small-signal models of the transistor performance such as the h, y and hybrid-π models (figures 3.9 and 3.10) cannot be used reliably in the analysis of these circuits as the transistor parameters vary with operating point because of the non-linearity of the characteristics. Analysis of power stages, particularly at 'high' power levels of above a few watts, frequently relies on graphical techniques.

8.2 Single-ended class A arrangements

The output stage of an amplifier can be represented in terms of its Thévenin model driving the load R_L. The arrangement corresponds to that of figure 3.4b with v_T being the generated signal voltage and R_T the output resistance R_o of the transistor with the load R_L being connected across AB. In operation, some of the signal power available from the source is dissipated as heat in the transistor, in R_o, reducing the efficiency of power transfer to the load. To minimise this power loss, the output resistance of the transistor should be as low as possible and so of the three configurations, common-emitter, common-base and common-collector (section 3.5), it is the common-collector (emitter-follower) with its low R_o (table 3.1) that is most useful as a power stage.

Figure 8.1a shows the essential features of a single transistor class A power stage with a direct-coupled load; input biasing is not shown. The circuit corresponds to the emitter-follower of figure 3.15c, the external load R_L being the emitter resistor. The term *single ended* is used to describe a single transistor power stage to distinguish it from two-transistor push–pull circuits.

The safe operating area (SOAR) for the BJT is bounded by the P_{tot}max hyperbola and the $I_C$max and V_{CEO}max ratings (section 2.3.3) as shown in figure 8.1b. To provide maximum allowable output signal power, the load line (sections 1.2.2 and 3.4.3) must be as 'long' as possible noting that it must not extend beyond the SOAR. The load line is therefore constructed, corresponding to the value of R_L, to be as close to the P_{tot}max hyperbola as possible without exceeding the $I_C$max and V_{CEO}max limits.

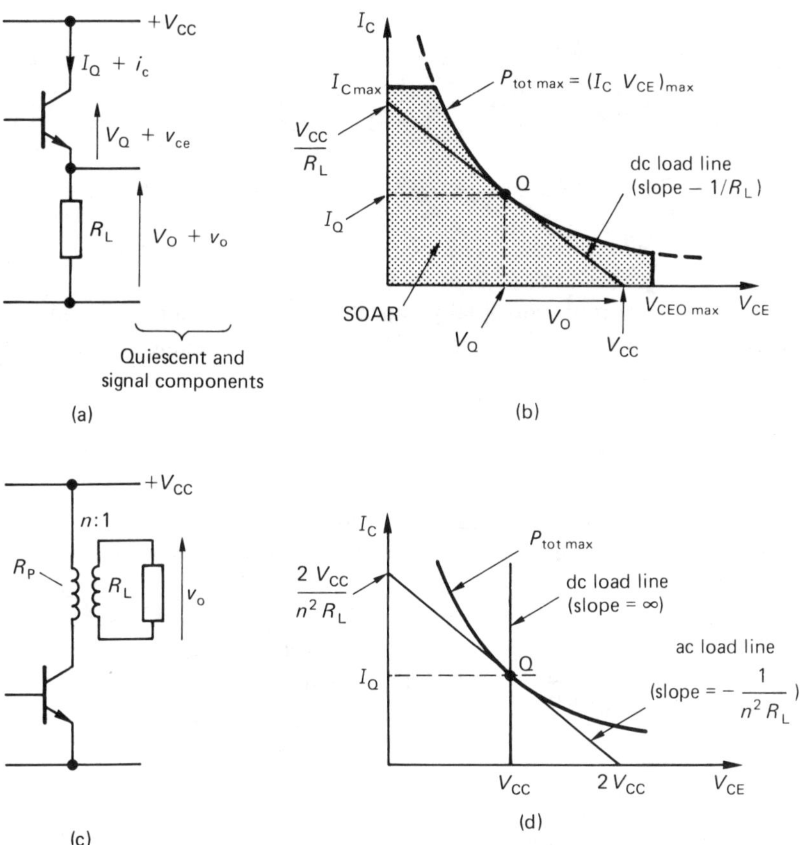

Figure 8.1 Single-ended class A power stages

For *maximum* output signal power, the excursions of the operating point of the BJT must be along the entire length of the load line from $V_{CE} = 0$, $I_C = V_{CC}/R_L$ on the verge of saturation, ignoring the small saturation voltage $V_{CE(sat)}$, to $V_{CE} = V_{CC}$, $I_C = 0$ on the verge of cut-off, ignoring leakage.

Consider the case where the sinusoidal input signal has sufficient amplitude to cause the operating point of the BJT to traverse the entire length of the load line. This condition allows maximum signal voltage and current amplitude for the length of load line considered and thus is the maximum output power condition. For equal-amplitude swings either side of Q, use of the entire load line means that Q must be positioned at the mid-point, thus

$$V_Q = \frac{V_{CC}}{2} \tag{8.7}$$

$$I_Q = \frac{V_{CC}}{2R_L} \tag{8.8}$$

Also, for use of the entire load line, the amplitudes V_{om} and I_{om} of the output (load) signal voltage and current are

$$V_{om}\max = V_{cem}\max = \frac{V_{CC}}{2} \tag{8.9}$$

$$I_{om}\max = I_{em}\max \simeq I_{cm}\max = \frac{V_{CC}}{2R_L} \tag{8.10}$$

The average output signal power developed in R_L is therefore

$$P_{o(av)} = V_{o(rms)} I_{o(rms)}$$

$$= \left(\frac{V_{om}}{\sqrt{2}}\right)\left(\frac{I_{om}}{\sqrt{2}}\right) \tag{8.11}$$

assuming v_o and i_o to be purely sinusoidal giving the $\sqrt{2}$ relationship between rms and peak values (note 11.1, chapter 11). The average signal power has a maximum value when the amplitudes V_{om} and I_{om} are a maximum from which

$$P_{o(av)}\max = \left(\frac{V_{om}\max}{\sqrt{2}}\right)\left(\frac{I_{om}\max}{\sqrt{2}}\right) = \frac{V_{CC}^2}{8R_L} \tag{8.12}$$

substituting for $V_{om}\max$ and $I_{om}\max$ from equations 8.9 and 8.10. Note that the assumption that the output waveshape is sinusoidal ignores any distortion introduced by the non-linear transistor characteristics.

The input power to the stage is provided by the dc power supply. The supply voltage remains fixed at V_{CC} while the current, ignoring that drawn by the input bias circuit, is the *total* collector current i_C $(= I_Q + i_c)$ which fluctuates about the average value I_Q. Thus the average input power $P_{I(AV)}$ is

$$P_{I(AV)} = V_{CC} I_Q = \frac{V_{CC}^2}{2R_L} \tag{8.13}$$

substituting for I_Q from equation 8.8.

The power conversion efficiency η of the circuit is the ratio of the average signal power delivered to the load to the average input power and has a theoretical maximum value

$$\eta_{max} = \frac{\text{Maximum average signal power to load}}{\text{Average input power}} = \frac{P_{o(av)}\text{max}}{P_{I(AV)}} = 0.25 \text{ or } 25 \text{ per cent} \quad (8.14)$$

using equations 8.12 and 8.13. This is the theoretical result for the single-ended class A arrangement of figure 8.1a ignoring the fact that the excursions of the operating point of the BJT cannot in reality be over the entire length of the load line because of saturation ($v_{CE}\text{min} = V_{CE(sat)}$) and cut-off ($i_C\text{min} = I_{CEO}$), and also ignoring power dissipation in the bias circuit. However, the result demonstrates the poor performance of this arrangement when used as a large-signal amplifier.

If the input signal is reduced so that the amplitudes of the output signal voltage and current are $kV_{om}\text{max}$ and $kI_{om}\text{max}$, $0 \leqslant k \leqslant 1$, the average output signal power falls to $k^2P_{o(av)}\text{max}$ and correspondingly the efficiency η falls to $0.25k^2$ or $25k^2$ per cent, showing that this arrangement has very poor power conversion efficiency at reduced signal amplitude.

It should be noted that the average power drawn from the V_{CC} supply is in fact constant at $V_{CC}^2/2R_L$ from equation 8.13. With zero input signal, the operating point of the BJT remains at Q and the power dissipated in the BJT, V_QI_Q, is equal to $V_{CC}^2/4R_L$ (using equations 8.7 and 8.8), showing that half the input power is dissipated in the BJT and half in the load R_L; both as static (dc) power under these conditions. As the input signal amplitude is increased, some of the power dissipated in both the BJT and the load appears as signal (ac) power and the static power components are reduced until at the maximum condition the four components of dissipated power (load signal power, load static power, BJT signal power, BJT static power) are each 25 per cent of the total average input power drawn from the V_{CC} supply. The power dissipated in the BJT, often termed the *collector dissipation* $P_{C(AV)}$, remains constant at half the average input power. From equation 8.13, $P_{C(AV)}$ for this circuit is therefore $V_{CC}^2/4R_L$ and so the ratio of maximum average signal power delivered to the load, $P_{o(av)}\text{max}$ (equation 8.12), to the maximum collector dissipation is 0.5. This ratio can be used as a figure-of-merit for an output stage and indicates, for this circuit, that the BJT must be capable of safely dissipating power of at least twice the value of designed maximum average output signal power.

Example 8.2: Power conversion performance of a single-ended class A power stage

A single-ended class A emitter–follower power stage operates from a 40 V power supply and drives a 10 Ω load. What is the power conversion efficiency when the load signal amplitude is half the theoretical maximum? What is the minimum allowable power rating of the BJT? Mention any simplifying assumptions or approximations made during the analysis.

From the load line construction of figure 8.1b, biasing for maximum possible signal amplitude requires $I_Q = V_{CC}/2R_L = 40\text{ V}/2(10\,\Omega) = 2\text{ A}$. Therefore, neglecting power drawn by the input bias circuit, the average input power $P_{I(AV)} = 40\text{ V} \times 2\text{ A} = 80\text{ W}$.
Maximum output signal voltage amplitude $V_{om}\text{max}$ is half the 'voltage length' of the load line $= V_{CC}/2 = 20\text{ V}$.
Maximum output signal current amplitude $I_{om}\text{max}$ is half the 'current length' of the load line $= V_{CC}/2R_L = 2\text{ A}$.
At half maximum amplitude, $V_{om} = 20\text{ V}/2 = 10\text{ V}$ and $I_{om} = 2\text{ A}/2 = 1\text{ A}$.

Assuming the output is sinusoidal:

$$V_{o(rms)} = \frac{V_{om}}{\sqrt{2}} = \frac{10\ \text{V}}{\sqrt{2}} \text{ and } I_{o(rms)} = \frac{I_{om}}{\sqrt{2}} = \frac{1\ \text{A}}{\sqrt{2}}$$

giving an average output signal power $P_{o(av)}$ of $\left(\frac{10}{\sqrt{2}}\right)\left(\frac{1}{\sqrt{2}}\right) = 5\ \text{W}$. Thus the power conversion efficiency under these conditions is

$$\eta = \frac{P_{o(av)}}{P_{I(AV)}} = \frac{5\ \text{W}}{80\ \text{W}} = 6.25 \text{ per cent}$$

Power dissipation in the BJT ($P_{C(AV)}$) is half the average input power whatever the output signal amplitude and so the minimum power rating of the BJT

$$(P_{tot}\max)\min = \frac{P_{I(AV)}}{2} = 40\ \text{W}$$

Notice the required high power rating for the BJT compared with the output signal power.

Efficiency improvement using transformer coupling

Although the relatively high output resistance of the CE stage is a major disadvantage as regards power transfer to a low impedance load, the arrangement can be used effectively using transformer coupling to provide impedance transformation (section 2.4.3).

In the basic arrangement of figure 8.1c, the static resistance in series with the BJT is the primary resistance of the transformer R_P which is normally very low. The slope of the dc load line is therefore very high and the Q-point is selected in relation to V_{CC} and $P_{tot}\max$ as shown in figure 8.1d. As far as the signal is concerned, the effective load in the collector circuit is n^2R_L (equation 2.46), where n is the primary-to-secondary turns ratio of the transformer, and so the ac load line is drawn through Q with a slope $-1/n^2R_L$. To make most effective use of the available active region of the BJT, values should be chosen to allow the ac load line to intercept the V_{CE}-axis at $2V_{CC}$, allowing equal maximum swings about Q. Under these conditions, with a slope of $-1/n^2R_L$, the ac load line intercepts the I_C-axis at $2V_{CC}/n^2R_L$ and the quiescent current I_Q is selected at half this value, making the Q-point

$$V_Q = V_{CC},\ I_Q = \frac{V_{CC}}{n^2R_L} \tag{8.15}$$

Notice that, because of energy storage in the transformer, the BJT collector is able to swing from 0 to $2V_{CC}$, allowing a maximum signal amplitude of V_{CC}, whereas for the direct-coupled circuit of figure 8.1a the maximum amplitude is $V_{CC}/2$.

At the maximum amplitude condition, the signal voltage waveforms across the transformer primary and collector–emitter terminals of the BJT each have an amplitude of V_{CC} (the variations being 180° out-of-phase with each other) and, for sinusoidal operation, the corresponding rms value is $V_{CC}/\sqrt{2}$ (note 11.1, chapter 11). With I_Q as given in equation 8.15, the maximum amplitude of the sinusoidal signal current in the primary is V_{CC}/n^2R_L with a corresponding rms value of $V_{CC}/(\sqrt{2})n^2R_L$ (note 11.1). The maximum average signal power delivered to the primary is therefore

$$\left(\frac{V_{CC}}{\sqrt{2}}\right)\left(\frac{V_{CC}}{(\sqrt{2})n^2R_L}\right)=\frac{V_{CC}^2}{2n^2R_L} \tag{8.16}$$

and assuming no power losses in the transformer this is equal to the maximum average signal power delivered to the load, $P_{o(av)}$max.

As far as the input power is concerned, the supply voltage remains fixed at V_{CC} while the current fluctuates sinusoidally about I_Q (equation 8.15) and so the average input power is

$$P_{I(AV)}=V_{CC}I_Q=\frac{V_{CC}^2}{n^2R_L} \tag{8.17}$$

The maximum power conversion efficiency for the transformer-coupled single-ended arrangement is therefore

$$\eta_{max}=\frac{P_{o(av)}\text{max}}{P_{I(AV)}}=0.5 \text{ or } 50 \text{ per cent} \tag{8.18}$$

If the output amplitudes are reduced, the efficiency falls. With amplitudes k times the maxima ($0 \leqslant k \leqslant 1$), the rms values of the signal voltage and current in equation 8.16 become k times their maximum values so that

$$P_{o(av)}=\frac{k^2V_{CC}^2}{2n^2R_L} \tag{8.19}$$

The average input power remains fixed as in equation 8.17 and so the conversion efficiency becomes

$$\eta=0.5k^2 \text{ or } 50k^2 \text{ per cent} \tag{8.20}$$

Transformer action ensures that no static power is delivered to the load and furthermore, as R_P is very low, static dissipation in the primary is very low. Thus the average power dissipated in the BJT (collector dissipation $P_{C(AV)}$) is the difference between the input power $P_{I(AV)}$ given by equation 8.17 and the output signal power to the load $P_{o(av)}$ (equation 8.19) from which

$$P_{C(AV)}=\frac{V_{CC}^2}{2n^2R_L}(2-k^2) \tag{8.21}$$

With no signal applied ($k=0$) the average power dissipated in the BJT is therefore a maximum at V_{CC}^2/n^2R_L, corresponding to $P_{I(AV)}$. As the signal amplitude increases, signal power is delivered to the load and the power dissipated in the BJT falls. Equation 8.16 gives the theoretical maximum average signal power delivered to the load $P_{o(av)}$max and the ratio $P_{o(av)}\text{max}/P_{C(AV)}\text{max}$ is therefore 0.5, the same as for the direct-coupled circuit of figure 8.1a.

It should be noted that the reflected load n^2R_L is in parallel with the magnetising reactance of the primary [3] and so for efficient power transfer to the load the primary reactance must be $\gg n^2R_L$; further, as inductive reactance falls with decreasing frequency, this requirement must be met at the *minimum* operating signal frequency. This condition establishes the minimum number of primary turns for satisfactory operation.

Compared with the direct-coupled circuit of figure 8.1a, the transformer-coupled arrangement provides a higher power conversion efficiency and it requires only half the value of power supply voltage V_{CC} to provide the same maximum output amplitude. However, although transformer-coupled arrangements were once popular, this technique is now largely obsolete because of the cost, bulk and poor frequency response of the transformer and, more significantly, because of the improved performance provided by other arrangements such as the complementary class AB circuit (section 8.5).

8.3 **Push–pull class A power stage**

Class A power stage performance can be improved by using two transistors in a push–pull configuration in place of the single-ended arrangement of figure 8.1a.

If the BJTs in the basic push–pull complementary stage of figure 8.2a are biased to a mid-range level of conduction (class A operation), the load voltage is proportional to the difference of the two emitter currents $(i_{E_1} - i_{E_2})$. Assuming perfect symmetry, the static components of these currents cancel in the load but the signal components i_{e_1} and i_{e_2}, being out-of-phase such that $i_{e_1} = -i_{e_2}$ at any instant, are additive, producing a finite output voltage. Figure 8.2b shows that although the signal components i_{e_1} and i_{e_2} are out-of-phase, their second harmonic distorting components $i_{e_{12}}$ and $i_{e_{22}}$ are in-phase and therefore these cancel in the load; this cancelling occurs for all even harmonics generated by the BJTs. Odd harmonics are out-of-phase at the load and are therefore additive but as the most serious distortion introduced by the power stage, that due to the non-linearity of the transfer characteristics of the transistors, is second harmonic as in example 8.1, push–pull operation can provide improved distortion performance. Note that the cancelling of even harmonics only applies to those *generated by the BJTs*; push–pull operation does not cancel distortion present in the drive signals. Also for maximum improvement, the two push–pull transistors must be matched so that they each introduce the same degree of even harmonic distortion.

The maximum current through each of the BJTs in figure 8.2a, when they are on the verge of saturation, is V_{CC}/R_L and so the quiescent current must be established at the mid-range value $V_{CC}/2R_L$. The power drawn from the $\pm V_{CC}$ supplies is therefore

$$P_{I(AV)} = (2V_{CC})\left(\frac{V_{CC}}{2R_L}\right) = \frac{V_{CC}^2}{R_L} \tag{8.22}$$

For a collector current swing of $kV_{CC}/2R_L$ $(0 \leqslant k \leqslant 1)$ about the Q-point for each BJT, the amplitude of the signal current in the load is kV_{CC}/R_L, assuming the transistor gains are sufficiently high for the emitter and collector currents to be considered equal, since the two signal currents add in the load. The rms value of the sinusoidal load signal current is therefore $kV_{CC}/(\surd 2)R_L$ (note 11.1, chapter 11) and the corresponding average signal power delivered to the load is

$$\begin{aligned} P_{o(av)} &= I_{o(rms)}^2 R_L \\ &= \left(\frac{kV_{CC}}{(\surd 2)R_L}\right)^2 R_L = \frac{k^2 V_{CC}^2}{2R_L} \end{aligned} \tag{8.23}$$

The power conversion efficiency of the ideal class A push–pull arrangement is then

$$\eta = \frac{P_{o(av)}}{P_{I(AV)}} = 0.5k^2 \text{ or } 50k^2 \text{ per cent} \tag{8.24}$$

indicating a two-fold increase compared with the direct-coupled single-ended stage of section 8.2.

With no signal applied, $I_C = I_Q = V_{CC}/2R_L$ and $V_{CE} = V_Q = V_{CC}$, and so the power dissipated in *each* BJT is $V_Q I_Q = V_{CC}^2/2R_L$ which is half $P_{I(AV)}$. The maximum collector dissipation

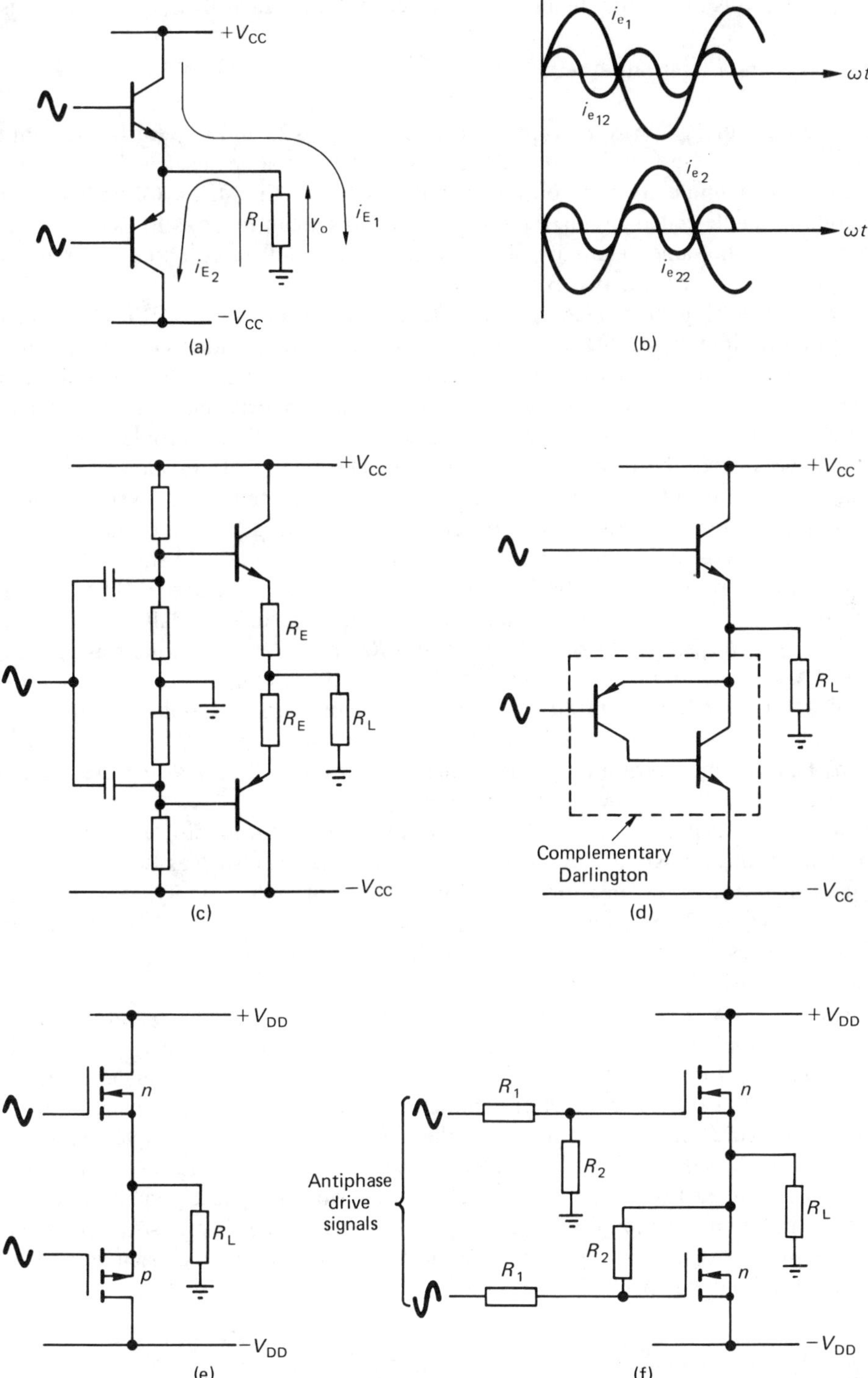

Figure 8.2 Push–pull class A power stages

$P_{C(AV)}$max, which is the minimum allowable power rating for each BJT (P_{tot}max)min, is thus

$$P_{C(AV)}\text{max} = (P_{tot}\text{max})\text{min} = \frac{V_{CC}^2}{2R_L} \tag{8.25}$$

and the merit factor $P_{o(av)}$max/$P_{C(AV)}$max, from equations 8.23 and 8.25 for $k = 1$, is unity for the push–pull circuit, showing that the BJTs must each be capable of safely dissipating power equal to the maximum average output signal power for the stage. Compared with the corresponding single-ended circuit, the push–pull arrangement requires BJTs of only half the power rating for the same maximum output signal power, but the resulting cost reduction is offset by the requirement for two BJTs in place of one.

A practical complementary class A power stage is shown in figure 8.2c. The resistor chain provides the required biasing while low-value resistors R_E are included for stability purposes. Bias stabilisation at moderate to high power dissipation is always an important consideration in linear BJT circuits because of the escalating interaction between temperature rise and current level, leading ultimately to thermal runaway and failure. This problem does not arise with FETs because of the positive temperature coefficient of FET resistance [1b]. Usually multistage dc feedback is applied within the complete amplifier to provide overall stabilisation while the negative feedback due to the emitter resistors provides local stabilisation within the power stage. Analysis of the thermal stability of this type of circuit [4] shows that the value of R_E needs to be proportional to both V_Q and the thermal resistance of the BJT from junction to ambient $R_{th(j\text{-}amb)}$, taking account of any heatsink that is used. The analysis gives a suitable value of R_E as $V_Q R_{th(j\text{-}amb)}/400$ for V_Q in volts and R_{th} in °C/W; thus if the stage is powered from ±15 V supplies and each BJT, with its heatsink, has a thermal resistance of 10°C/W, values of R_E of 0.33 Ω or 0.47 Ω should provide adequate thermal stability.

The single BJTs of the basic complementary stage can be replaced by corresponding (npn and pnp) Darlingtons (section 6.5). The higher current gain of the Darlingtons reduces the current drive capability required of the driver stage.

In some situations it may not be possible to obtain matched transistor or Darlington pairs and in such circumstances the *quasi*complementary arrangement, such as that shown in figure 8.2d, requiring *matched* transistors (or Darlingtons) of only one type, can be useful. A complementary Darlington combination (section 6.5) using high-power npn and low-power pnp BJTs provides high-power pnp BJT properties and therefore avoids the need for a single high-power pnp BJT.

Figures 8.2e,f show complementary and quasicomplementary stages based on FETs that have become popular with the availability of high-power enhancement-type VMOSTs. As with the BJTs in figure 8.2a, the e-MOSTs in the complementary arrangement of figure 8.2e must be biased to a mid-range level of conduction and input coupling capacitors would be required as in figure 8.2c to avoid upsetting the bias levels. The quasicomplementary circuit of figure 8.2f uses two e-MOSTs of the *same* type, n-channel in this case, and push–pull operation is obtained by driving the two transistors with antiphase signals which can be provided either by a differential stage (section 6.4) or by the single transistor phase-splitter circuit of figure 3.25 (see also tutorial question 3.19). In either case, capacitive coupling to the power stage may be required.

8.4 Class B power stage

The class A push–pull stage gives poor power conversion efficiency, particularly at low output signal amplitude, because of the mid-range bias levels of the BJTs whereby substantial power is drawn from the supplies regardless of the signal level. If the BJTs are biased to cut-off as in figure 8.3a they conduct only in response to the input signal; T_1 conducts when v_i is positive, T_2 when v_i is negative (figure 8.3b), no power being drawn from the supplies under quiescent conditions, thereby improving efficiency. This mode of operation, termed class B, is discussed in detail in section 6.6.

Analysis centres on the *composite* characteristics of figure 8.3c which are formed by aligning the V_{CE}-axes of the output characteristics of T_1 and T_2 to make the Q-points of the two BJTs ($V_{CE_1} = |V_{CE_2}| = V_{CC}$) coincide. The ac load line of slope $-1/R_L$ then extends from $V_{CE_1} = 0$, $I_{C_1} = V_{CC}/R_L$ for T_1 fully conducting, through Q, to $V_{CE_2} = 0$, $|I_{C_2}| = V_{CC}/R_L$ for T_2 fully conducting.

If v_i is sinusoidal, the two collector currents are half-wave rectified sinusoids (section 11.2.2) of amplitude kV_{CC}/R_L, $0 \leqslant k \leqslant 1$, where the $k = 1$ case is the maximum amplitude condition corresponding to the maximum 'current length' of the load line for each BJT. Using the $1/\pi$ relationship between maximum and average values of a half-wave rectified sinusoid (note 11.2, chapter 11), the *average* current drawn from *each* supply is $kV_{CC}/\pi R_L$ and the corresponding average power drawn from *each* supply is $V_{CC}I_{C(AV)} = kV_{CC}^2/\pi R_L$. The total average input power $P_{I(AV)}$ is that drawn from both supplies which is therefore double this amount giving

$$P_{I(AV)} = \frac{2kV_{CC}^2}{\pi R_L} \tag{8.26}$$

Assuming the gains of the BJTs are sufficiently high for the difference between emitter and collector currents to be ignored, the two half-wave collector currents combine to form a purely sinusoidal load signal current of the same amplitude, kV_{CC}/R_L from above. Thus the rms signal current in the load is $kV_{CC}/(\surd 2)R_L$ (note 11.1, chapter 11). Correspondingly, the rms signal voltage across the load is $kV_{CC}/\surd 2$ as the 'voltage length' of the load line for each BJT is V_{CC} (figure 8.3c). The average signal power developed in the load is therefore

$$P_{o(av)} = V_{o(rms)} I_{o(rms)}$$

$$= \left(\frac{kV_{CC}}{\surd 2}\right)\left(\frac{kV_{CC}}{(\surd 2)R_L}\right) = \frac{k^2 V_{CC}^2}{2R_L} \tag{8.27}$$

Combining equations 8.26 and 8.27, the power conversion efficiency of the class B stage is

$$\eta = \frac{P_{o(av)}}{P_{I(AV)}} = \frac{\pi k}{4} \text{ or } 78.5k \text{ per cent} \tag{8.28}$$

giving a maximum of 78.5 per cent at the theoretical maximum signal amplitude. This is a considerable improvement compared with the maxima of 50 per cent and 25 per cent for the push–pull and direct-coupled single-ended class A arrangements of sections 8.2 and 8.3. Note also that $\eta \propto k$ for class B whereas $\eta \propto k^2$ for class A stages, showing that the efficiency for class B does not degrade for low signal amplitudes as much as for class A stages. For example, if the signal amplitude is 20 per cent of the theoretical maximum, $k = 0.2$ giving efficiencies of 15.7 per cent for class B (equation 8.28) but only 2 per cent for class A push–pull (equation 8.24) and 1 per cent for direct-coupled class A (following equation 8.14).

Because the average current drawn from the supply varies with signal amplitude, it follows that the average input power for class B operation is not constant as it is for class A. Therefore for class B it is not as straightforward to determine the peak collector dissipations, and hence the required ratings, of the BJTs.

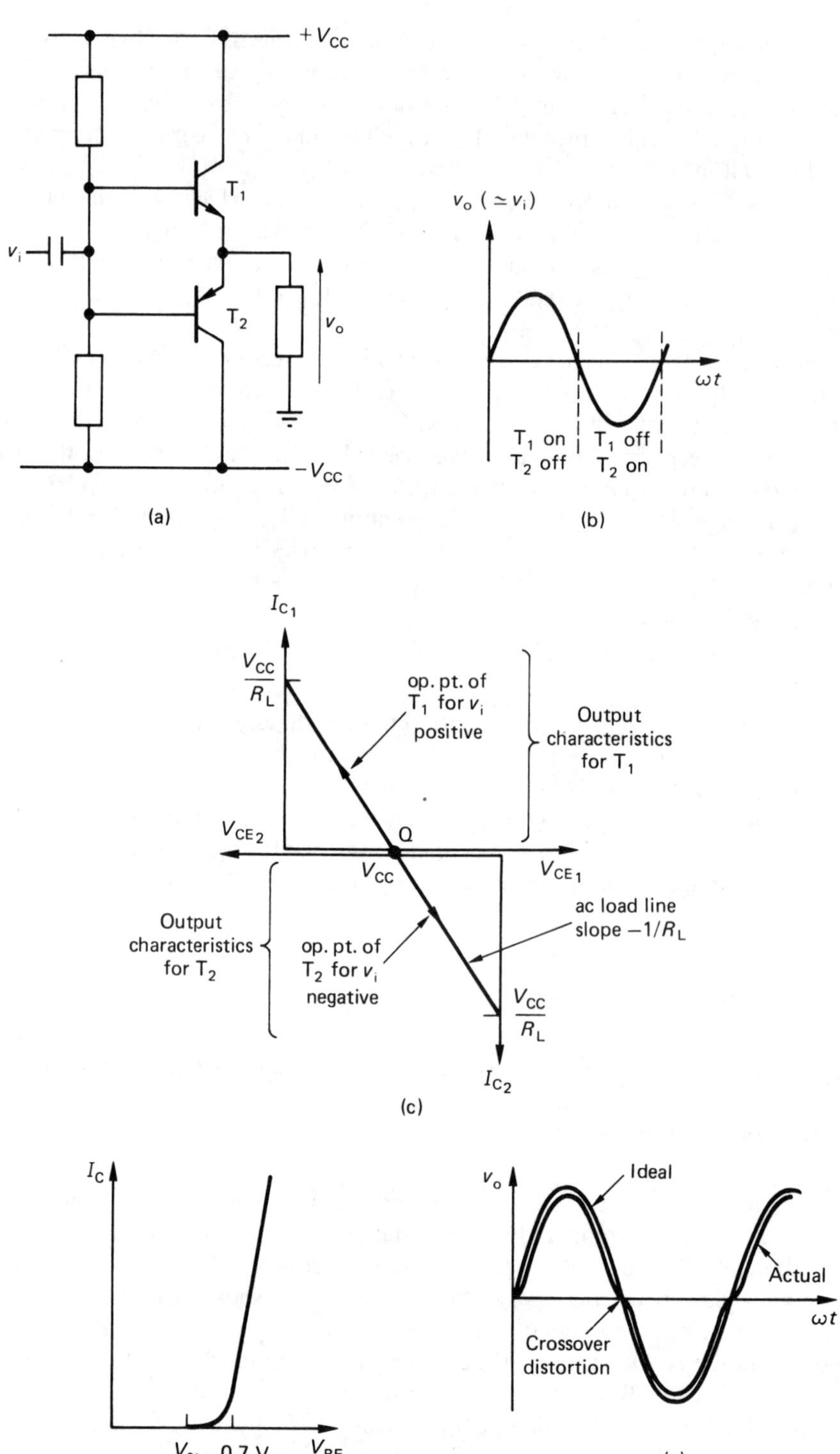

Figure 8.3 Push–pull class B power stage

The BJTs dissipate power only during their conduction half-cycles (they are OFF during the other half-cycles), during which time

$$v_{CE} = V_{CC} - v_o$$
$$\simeq V_{CC} - i_C R_L, \text{ assuming } i_E \simeq i_C \qquad (8.29)$$

and the instantaneous power dissipated in each BJT, the instantaneous collector dissipation p_C, is then

$$p_C = v_{CE} i_C$$
$$\simeq (V_{CC} - i_C R_L) i_C \qquad (8.30)$$

But the amplitude of the collector current is kV_{CC}/R_L from above and so i_C can be written (kV_{CC}/R_L) sin ωt, which, combined with equation 8.30, gives

$$p_C \simeq \frac{kV_{CC}^2}{R_L}(\sin \omega t - k \sin^2 \omega t) \qquad (8.31)$$

For each BJT, p_C, as given by equation 8.31, applies only during the conduction half-cycle, during the other half-cycle $i_C = 0$ giving $p_C = 0$, thus the average collector dissipation for each BJT is

$$P_{C(AV)} = \frac{1}{2\pi}\int_0^{\pi} p_C \mathrm{d}(\omega t)$$

$$= \frac{kV_{CC}^2}{2\pi R_L}\int_0^{\pi}(\sin \omega t - k \sin^2 \omega t)\, \mathrm{d}(\omega t)$$

$$= \frac{kV_{CC}^2}{2\pi R_L}\int_0^{\pi}\left(\sin \omega t - \frac{k}{2} + \frac{k}{2}\cos 2\omega t\right) \mathrm{d}(\omega t), \text{ using } \sin^2 \omega t = (1 - \cos 2\omega t)/2$$

$$= \frac{kV_{CC}^2}{2\pi R_L}\left[-\cos \omega t - \frac{k\omega t}{2} + \frac{k}{4}\sin 2\omega t\right]_0^{\pi}$$

$$= \frac{V_{CC}^2}{2\pi R_L}\left(2k - \frac{k^2\pi}{2}\right) \qquad (8.32)$$

Differentiation of this expression with respect to k shows that $P_{C(AV)}$max occurs when $k = 2/\pi = 0.637$, so that power dissipation in the BJTs is a maximum when the collector current is 63.7 per cent of its maximum value V_{CC}/R_L and from equation 8.32 this maximum is

$$P_{C(AV)}\max = \frac{V_{CC}^2}{\pi^2 R_L} \qquad (8.33)$$

which is the minimum rating $(P_{tot}\max)$min for each BJT.

Combination of equations 8.27 and 8.33 gives the $P_{o(av)}\max/P_{C(AV)}\max$ merit factor for class B operation as $\pi^2/2$ (= 4.93) showing a vast improvement compared with push–pull class A operation (= 1) and the direct-coupled single-ended class A arrangement (= 0.5). For the class B circuit, the merit factor of almost 5 shows that the power ratings of the BJTs need only be about one-fifth of the designed maximum average output power of the stage.

Example 8.3: Performance of a class B power stage

A class B power stage operates from ± 30 V supplies and drives a 3 Ω load. What is the average signal power supplied to the load when the amplitude of the load current is 3 A? What is the power conversion efficiency under these conditions?
What is the minimum allowable power rating for the BJTs?

With $V_{CC} = 30$ V and $R_L = 3\,\Omega$, maximum theoretical amplitudes of the load current and voltage (V_{CC}/R_L and V_{CC}) are 10 A and 30 V respectively.

When the load current amplitude is 3 A, which is 30 per cent of maximum, $k = 0.3$, the load voltage amplitude is therefore $30\text{ V} \times 0.3 = 9$ V. The corresponding rms load signal current and voltage are $3\text{ A}/\sqrt{2}$ and $9\text{ V}/\sqrt{2}$, giving an average signal power supplied to the load of $(3\text{ A}/\sqrt{2})\,(9\text{ V}/\sqrt{2}) = 13.5$ W.

Assuming high BJT gain ($i_E \simeq i_C$), when the load current amplitude is 3 A the peak collector currents for each BJT must be approximately 3 A, giving an average value of $3\text{ A}/\pi$ (note 11.2, chapter 11) for *each* BJT. The average power drawn from *each* supply is therefore $(30\text{ V})(3\text{ A}/\pi)$ W and the total average input power

$$P_{I(AV)} = 2(30\text{ V})(3\text{ A}/\pi) \simeq 57.3\text{ W}$$

giving a power conversion efficiency for these operating conditions of

$$\eta = \frac{13.5\text{ W}}{57.3\text{ W}} \simeq 23.6 \text{ per cent}$$

Although the circuit is not operating under conditions of peak collector dissipation, the rating of the BJTs must allow for peak dissipation which, from equation 8.33, gives the minimum rating as

$$(P_{tot}\text{max})\text{min} = P_{C(AV)}\text{max} = \frac{V_{CC}^2}{\pi^2 R_L} = \frac{(30\text{ V})^2}{\pi^2(3\,\Omega)} = 30.4\text{ W}$$

Compared with the corresponding class A circuit, a class B power stage has the advantages of higher efficiency and a lower transistor rating requirement, but the class B stage suffers from the major disadvantage of crossover distortion. It has been assumed that the two half-wave rectified variations supplied by the two transistors combine at the load to reproduce faithfully the waveshape of the drive voltage. In practice, however, the transfer characteristic $I_C - V_{BE}$ of a BJT is non-linear (figure 8.3d) corresponding to the input characteristic of figure 2.3c; below a base-emitter threshold voltage V_γ ($\simeq 0.5$ V for a silicon BJT), very little conduction occurs. Therefore the collector currents of the push-pull BJTs in the class B stage do not faithfully follow the variation of drive voltage v_i until the input voltage is greater than about 0.7 V, resulting in *crossover distortion* (figure 8.3e) as conduction passes from one transistor to the other. Unfortunately, this type of distortion introduces odd harmonics which is not cancelled by push–pull action (section 8.3).

Class B stages based on e-MOSTs suffer from the same problem of non-linear conduction for low level input as e-MOSTs do not conduct until the gate–source voltage exceeds the threshold voltage (figure 2.4c) of typically 1–3 V.

8.5 Class AB operation

To overcome the problem of crossover distortion experienced in class B operation (section 8.4) it is usual to bias each transistor just above the turn-on threshold using level-shifting diodes as in figure 8.4a. With the (silicon) diodes forward-biased by the power supplies, the quiescent potential of T_1 base is approximately 0.7 V above signal earth while that of T_2 base is 0.7 V below earth. As v_i increases positively, the operating point of T_1 moves into its approximately linear region (figure 8.3d) supplying power to the load while T_2 moves down to cut-off. With v_i negative, the roles of the BJTs are reversed.

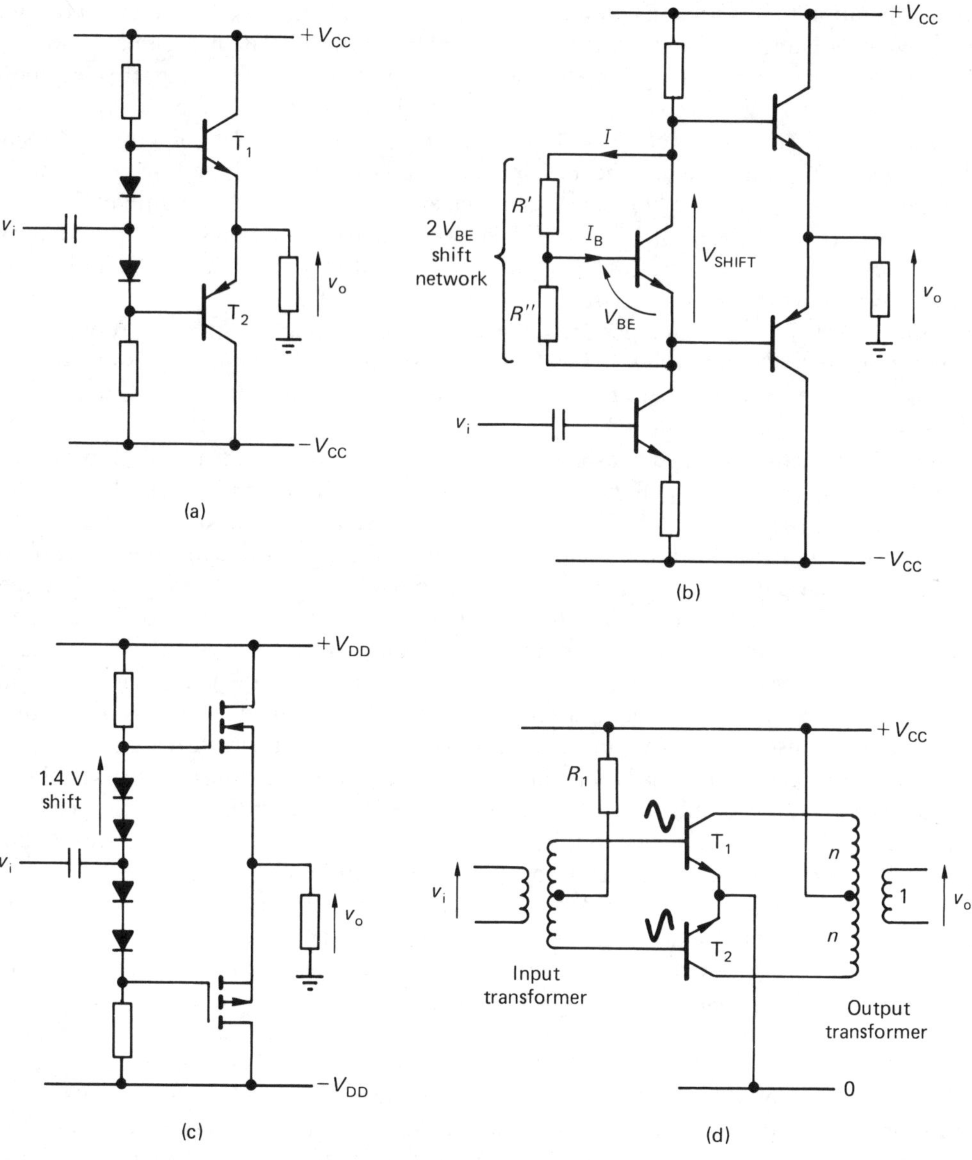

Figure 8.4 Class AB power stages

This mode of operation is termed class AB (table 8.1) because the conduction interval is between those of the class A and class B cases, whole cycle and half-cycle respectively. For *very* small input amplitudes the class AB circuit in fact operates in class A mode as both BJTs are able to conduct all the time but, as the signal amplitude increases, operation becomes essentially class B as the small bias becomes negligible; hence the use of the term *sliding* AB to describe this mode of operation.

The power conversion efficiency for class AB is lower than for class B because of the finite quiescent flow which increases the average power drawn from the supplies; however, as the bias is small, the loss in efficiency is also small for practical signal amplitudes. The major advantage of class AB operation is that while providing an efficiency almost equal to that of class B, the problem of crossover distortion is practically eliminated and hence it is the AB mode of operation that is used in commercial linear power stages. Note that in all BJT power stages, low-value emitter resistors are required for stability as in the class A circuit of figure 8.2c.

Figure 8.4b shows the use of a BJT shift network in place of a diode string; this technique is often favoured for integrated amplifiers. If the BJT has high gain so that $I \gg I_B$, the shift voltage $V_{SHIFT} = I\,(R' + R'')$, but $IR'' = V_{BE}$ and so $V_{SHIFT} = V_{BE}\,[1 + (R''/R')]$ giving a shift of $2V_{BE}$ for $R' = R''$. A further modification included in the circuit of figure 8.4b is to combine the drive transistor in the bias branch, a technique employed in the 741 op-amp of figure 7.5 in which T_{13}, T_{21} and the T_{18}, T_{19}, R_8 shift network provide dual bias and drive roles. In the 741, the R_9 and R_{10} emitter resistors provide the dual roles of stabilisation and output current sensing for protection purposes.

The same level-shifting techniques are incorporated in FET power stages to provide class AB operation as shown in figure 8.4c in which diode strings providing multiples of 0.6–0.7 V (depending on the bias current) are used to compensate for the turn-on threshold of the e-MOSTs.

Although complementary and quasicomplementary stages are now the rule for most output power stages, formerly push–pull circuits incorporated an output transformer. A basic class AB stage of this type utilising a centre-tapped input transformer to produce antiphase drive signals is shown in figure 8.4d. By tracing each 'half' of the output circuit from V_{CC} through one half of the output transformer primary and one of the BJTs to ground, it can be seen that the stage is effectively two single stages (figure 8.1c) combined. Power is delivered to the load via T_1 and the upper half of the output transformer primary when the drive signal is positive, T_2 being OFF, while T_2 and the lower half of the primary are active when the signal is negative. The small quiescent bias current for T_1 and T_2 to provide class AB operation is supplied via R_1. Instead of using an input transformer, the antiphase drive signals for the output transistors can be provided by a differential stage or a single-transistor phase-splitting circuit as used in a quasicomplementary stage (section 8.3). Even harmonic distortion generated by the output transistors and the output transformer cancels because the corresponding magnetic flux components in the transformer core are in antiphase.

The analysis of transformer-coupled stages is the same as that for complementary versions except that the effective ac load, as far as each output transistor is concerned, is the *reflected* value n^2R_L, as for the single-ended transformer-coupled case of section 8.2, where the centre-tapped output transformer turns ratio is n, n:1.

Because of the size, cost, weight and relatively poor frequency response of the transformer, the use of transformer coupling is now virtually obsolete except for certain special-purpose applications. They do however offer flexibility in matching to the load simply by a change of transformer turns ratio. A particular application in which such techniques are still used is in public-address systems where the number of loudspeakers to be driven, and hence the effective load, may not be fixed.

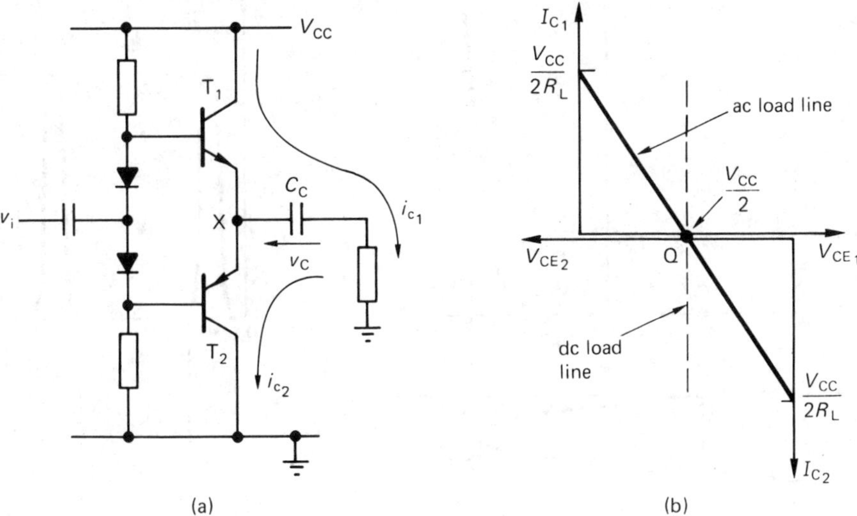

Figure 8.5 Single-supply complementary stage

Complementary stages discussed thusfar have operated from balanced ($\pm V_{CC}$) supplies but in many situations it is more convenient to operate from a single supply. Figure 8.5a shows a class AB stage modified for single-supply operation with the corresponding composite characteristic load line construction given in figure 8.5b. The quiescent potential of node X is $V_{CC}/2$ and with the load capacitively coupled (open circuit to dc) the dc load line is as shown dashed. With v_i positive T_1 is ON, T_2 OFF, signal current flows to the load and C_C charges up to $v_C = V_{CC}/2$. When v_i is negative with T_1 OFF and T_2 ON, C_C provides the charge to supply the load current.

8.6 **Class C power stage**

Class C operation is specialised in the sense that it can only be usefully applied to amplification of a constant frequency signal as required, for example, in carrier generation for an RF communication system (section 9.2.4). Such an application requires a low-distortion constant-amplitude sinusoidal waveform to be produced at a high power level of typically tens of kilowatts. The frequency stability required can most conveniently be provided by a resonant (tuned) circuit which is energised intermittently. By biasing the driving transistor well into cut-off, application of a sinusoidal drive signal causes conduction over only a limited portion of each cycle (figure 8.6) during which energy is supplied to the tuned circuit.

The amplitude of the v_{be} drive signal must be sufficiently high to raise v_{BE} above the conduction threshold V_γ, allowing a current pulse to flow into the tuned circuit. For the remainder of the input signal cycle the transistor is OFF, the output being maintained by oscillation within the tuned circuit. Although the pulsed form of the *current* variation introduces severe harmonic distortion, the fact that the tuned circuit has a high impedance at the operating frequency but a low impedance at harmonic frequencies means that the distortion of the output *voltage* waveform can be low. The average power drawn from the dc supply is relatively small, leading to a high power conversion efficiency (>80 per cent). A further application of

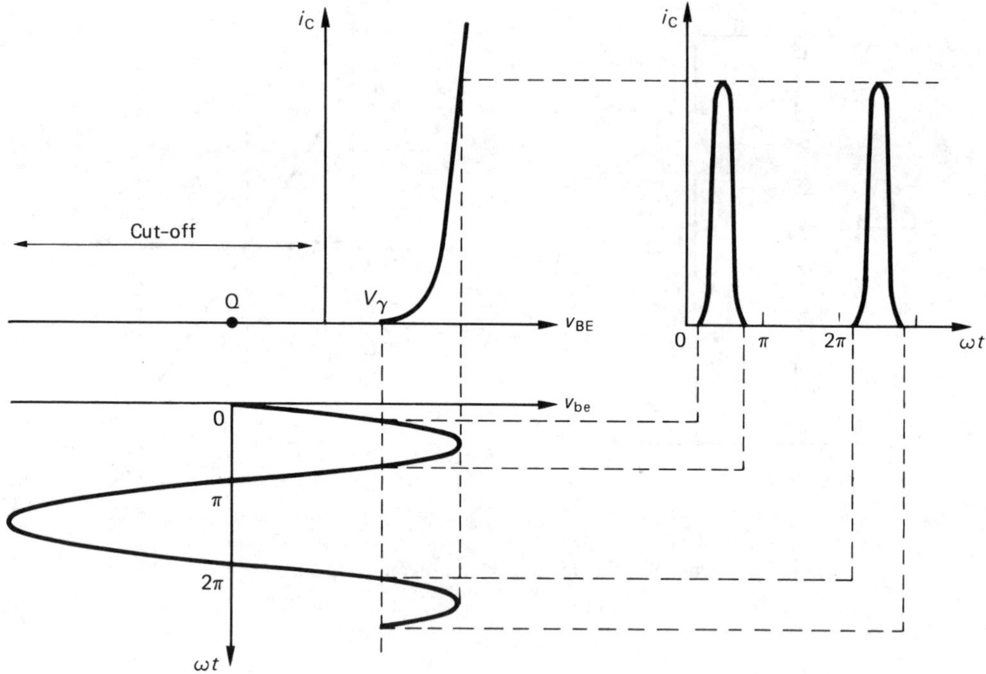

Figure 8.6 Class C operation

this arrangement is as a *frequency multiplier* whereby the resonant circuit is tuned to a harmonic of the input frequency; the pulsed current causes harmonic generation and the resonant circuit effectively selects one of the harmonics.

8.7 Switched-mode power stages: classes D and E

Power dissipation in the control transistor reduces efficiency and causes thermal problems for operation in classes A, B, AB and C. Class D operation improves efficiency by operating the transistors, BJTs or FETs, as power switches so that they are either fully ON, when the voltage across them is very low, or fully OFF, when the current through them is very low. In each of these cases the power dissipated in the transistors is very low and so, provided they are switched rapidly between states, the efficiency is high.

The signal v_s is converted to a pulse-width modulated (PWM) waveform using a comparator (figure 8.7a) and the PWM waveform is then used to drive the push–pull complementary pair of transistors to deliver power to the load (figure 8.7b). The comparator is most simply provided by an open-loop op-amp (figure 7.15a); the output switching to $+V_{CC}$ when the *net* input is positive and to $-V_{CC}$ when the *net* input is negative. By applying the signal v_s to the non-inverting input of the op-amp and a high-frequency sawtooth reference waveform v_r to the inverting input, the output of the op-amp switches rapidly between $+V_{CC}$ and $-V_{CC}$ depending on whether $(v_s - v_r)$ is positive or negative, thus producing a pulse-coded (modulated) version of the input signal. If this waveform is then applied to the complementary T_1, T_2 pair (figure 8.7b), T_1 is ON, T_2 OFF when the PWM waveform is positive while the

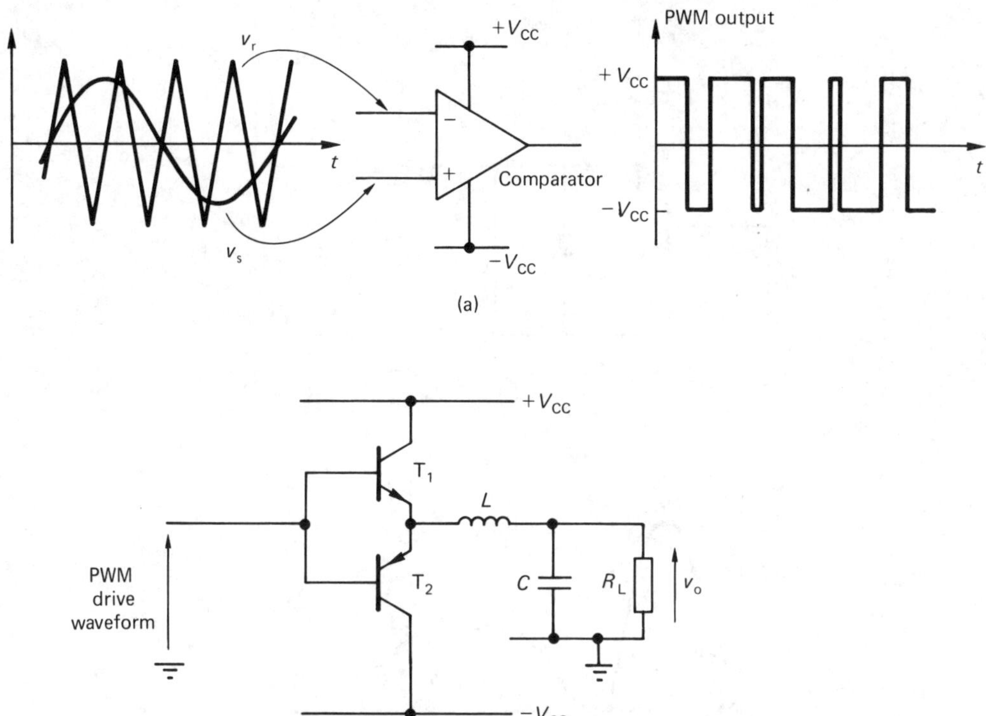

Figure 8.7 Class D switched-mode stage

converse is true when the drive waveform is negative. Such operation would cause v_o to switch between $+V_{CC}$ and $-V_{CC}$, neglecting $V_{CE(sat)}$ for the BJT in each case, and the load would draw a corresponding current depending on its value. However, if the load is driven via a low-pass filter, as provided by the *LC* network in figure 8.7b, which removes the high-frequency components associated with v_r, the load voltage becomes the mean value of the switched output waveform which corresponds to the signal variation. Clearly, the cut-off frequency of the filter must allow the highest harmonics of v_s (in the case of a complex signal waveform) to pass and the frequency of the sawtooth reference v_r must be high (much higher than is shown diagrammatically in figure 8.7a) so that the harmonics associated with it can be removed without distorting the signal components. The fact that the transistors operate as switches means that power dissipation is low, leading to power conversion efficiencies of over 90 per cent, most of the power drawn from the V_{CC} supply being delivered to the load; the only losses are in the comparator and the power contained in the high-frequency harmonics of the switched output waveform that are removed by the filter.

The low transistor loss obtainable in switched-mode operation has also been used to provide very high power conversion efficiency for single-frequency amplification, notably in the RF range. The technique is to arrange circuit operation principally by the selection of suitable component values so that the voltage across the control transistor has fallen to zero before the transistor is switched ON and that the transistor is switched OFF only when the current through it has fallen to zero. This mode of operation, which has become known as class E,

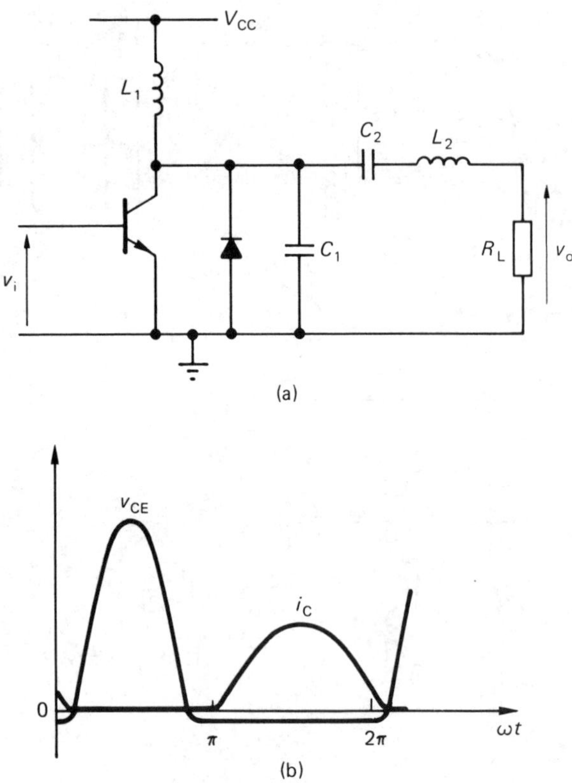

Figure 8.8 Tuned class E amplifier

ensures that the instantaneous power dissipated in the transistor is kept to an absolute minimum.

Figure 8.8a shows the basic class E circuit arrangement [5] in which v_i is the RF input signal. L_1 acts as a radio frequency choke (RFC) having high reactance at the operating frequency enabling the constant V_{CC} supply to be applied directly to the BJT but allowing the collector potential to fluctuate. C_2, L_2 and R_L form a tuned circuit incorporating the load so that a sinusoidal output can be obtained from the non-sinusoidal transistor output in a similar way as for the class C tuned amplifier of section 8.6. The C_2, L_2 combination is sometimes described as a (series) resonant *tank* circuit, the term 'tank' referring to the analogy of energy storage in the circuit with that associated with fluid stored in a traditional tank. Capacitor C_1 ensures that v_{CE} remains low until i_C has fallen to zero; C_1 effectively delays the rise of v_{CE}. The low damping of the variation of v_{CE} as provided by a high effective load Q-factor (appendix B, section B.3) is necessary to ensure that v_{CE} rapidly falls to zero, but this can damage the transistor because of the high C–E reverse bias caused by the corresponding overshoot. Damage is avoided by incorporating a 'commutating' diode (figure 8.8a) so clamping the negative excursion of v_{CE} to about -0.9 V. Typical current and voltage waveforms for the transistor are shown in figure 8.8b; note that large values of i_C and v_{CE} do not occur at the same instant, thereby keeping power dissipation very low. Efficiencies exceeding 95 per cent have been reported for this type of RF power amplifier.

References and further reading

1. M.E. Goodge, *Semiconductor Device Technology* (Macmillan, 1985)
   (a) section 2.3.7,
   (b) sections 2.2.21 and 2.3.7
2. E.S. Oxner, *Power FETs and their Applications*, chapter 7 (Prentice-Hall, 1982)
3. R.J. Smith, *Circuits, Devices and Systems*, 4th edition, chapter 21 (Wiley, 1984)
4. G.C. Haas, 'Design Factors and Considerations in Full Complementary Symmetry Audio Power Amplifiers', *J. Audio Eng. Soc.*, **16**, no. 3, July 1968.
5. N. O. Sokal and A. D. Sokal, 'Class E: A New Class of High-Efficiency Tuned Single-Ended Switching Power Amplifiers', *IEEE J. Solid-State Circuits*, **SC-10**, no. 3, June 1975.
6. R.J. Maddock and D.M. Calcutt, *Electronics: A Course for Engineers*, chapter 5 (Longman, 1988)
7. P.M. Chirlian, *Analysis and Design of Integrated Electronic Circuits*, 2nd edition, chapter 15 (Harper and Row/Wiley, 1987)
8. C.J. Savant, M.S. Roden and G.L. Carpenter, *Electronic Circuit Design*, chapter 6 (Benjamin/Cummings, 1987)
9. T.L. Floyd, *Electronic Devices*, 2nd edition, chapter 10 (Merrill, 1988)
10. A.S. Sedra and K.C. Smith, *Microelectronic Circuits*, 2nd edition, chapter 10 (Holt, Rinehart and Winston, 1987)
11. T.F. Bogart, *Electronic Devices and Circuits*, chapter 15 (Merrill, 1986)
12. J. Millman and A. Grabel, *Microelectronics*, 2nd edition, chapter 17 (McGraw-Hill, 1988)
13. C.L. Alley and K.W. Atwood, *Microelectronics*, chapter 15 (Prentice-Hall, 1986)
14. M.S. Ghausi, *Electronic Devices and Circuits*, chapter 6 (Holt-Saunders, 1985)
15. R.A. Colclaser, D.A. Neamen and C.F. Hawkins, *Electronic Circuit Analysis*, chapter 15 (Wiley, 1984)
16. S.A. Knight, *Electronics for Higher TEC*, chapter 4 (Granada, 1983)
17. M. Cirovic, *Basic Electronics*, 2nd edition, chapter 12 (Prentice-Hall, 1979)
18. C.A. Holt, *Electronic Circuits*, chapter 16 (Wiley, 1978)

Tutorial questions

Note: Where applicable, answers correspond to rounding to 2 decimal places during calculation.

Class A power stages

8.1 A direct-coupled single-ended class A power stage drives an 8 Ω load. The circuit operates from a 24 V dc supply and has been designed so that the Q-point of the BJT is at 12 V, 1.5 A. Working from basic principles, calculate the theoretical maximum value of average signal power that this arrangement is capable of developing in the load. What is the power conversion efficiency obtained when the signal amplitude at the load is 50 per cent of its theoretical maximum value?

[Answers: 9 W, 6.25 per cent]

8.2 It is necessary to replace the transistor in the single-ended transformer-coupled output stage of an audio power amplifier. Neither the turns ratio of the transformer nor the loudspeaker resistance is known, but prior to failure it was found that when the output signal amplitude was half its theoretical maximum the power delivered to the loudspeaker was 1 W. Calculate the minimum acceptable power rating for the replacement transistor. If the circuit operates from a 25 V supply and drives a 3 Ω loudspeaker, what must be the turns ratio of the transformer?

[Answers: 8 W, 5.1:1]

8.3 A 5 Ω load is directly driven from a complementary amplifier operating in class A from balanced 15 V dc supplies. Calculate
(a) the theoretical maximum average signal power that can be developed in the load.
(b) the power conversion efficiency when the amplitude of the output signal voltage is 70 per cent of the theoretical maximum,
(c) the minimum power rating of each of the transistors.
To what value would the supply voltages need to be raised to enable the maximum average signal power in the load to be increased to 30 W for the same arrangement?

[Answers: 22.5 W, 24.5 per cent, 22.5 W, ± 17.32 V]

Class B power stages

8.4 A class B complementary amplifier is directly coupled to a 15 Ω load. If the amplifier is powered from ± 40 V supplies, what is the average power drawn from the supplies when the output signal amplitude is at its theoretical maximum? What is the minimum acceptable power rating for each of the output transistors?

[Answers: 67.91 W, 10.81 W]

8.5 Show that when a complementary class B stage is driven by a sinusoidal input and the output signal amplitude is half the theoretical maximum, the power conversion efficiency is 12.5π per cent, this result being independent of supply voltage and load resistance.

Class AB power stage

8.6 A class AB transformer-coupled power stage drives a 3 Ω load. If the output transformer is 5,5:1 and the circuit operates from a 40 V supply, what is the maximum signal power that may be delivered to the load if transformer losses can be neglected? If the quiescent power drawn from the supply is negligible, what is the power conversion efficiency achieved when the output signal amplitude is 80 per cent of the theoretical maximum?

[Answers: 10.67 W, 62.83 per cent]

9 Analog Signal Generation and Processing

Coverage

- Analysis and design of the various types of *CR* and *LC* linear oscillators: phase-shift, Wien-bridge, Colpitts, Clapp, Hartley and crystal oscillators.
- Consideration of some techniques used to process signals: amplitude limiting, level clamping, precision rectification, filtering, shaping, modulation and demodulation.

The 'input' to most electronic systems is an information-carrying electrical signal. If the signal is not provided by a transducer, such as the piezoelectric cartridge in a phonographic system, which converts a non-electrical variation into an electrical signal, the initial voltage variation must be generated. Electronic circuits that generate a repetitively varying electrical voltage are called *oscillators* and those providing a sinusoidal signal are termed *linear oscillators* distinguishing them from switching oscillators that generate a pulsed output, such as the astable circuits of sections 10.1.4 and 10.2.1. This chapter considers the various types of linear oscillator.

9.1 Signal generation: linear oscillators

Figure 9.1 represents the feedback amplifier considered in section 5.1, the closed-loop (overall) gain v_o/v_s (equation 5.6) being

$$A_{cl} = \frac{A}{1 - A\beta} \tag{9.1}$$

where the product $A\beta$ ($= v_f/v_i$) is the *loop gain.*

When $|1 - A\beta| < 1$, the feedback is termed *positive* and the modulus of the closed-loop gain $|A_{cl}|$ is greater than $|A|$. If the gain and phase associated with A and β are such that $(1 - A\beta)$ is zero, corresponding to $A\beta = 1$, equation 9.1 indicates that A_{cl} would be infinite which, if true in practice, would mean that linear operation was not possible as the amplifier output would saturate. However, very high gain causes a large output amplitude and as all electronic systems are non-linear for large-signal operation (section 8.1), $A\beta$ changes as A_{cl} rises, causing A_{cl} to be finite thereby constraining the output.

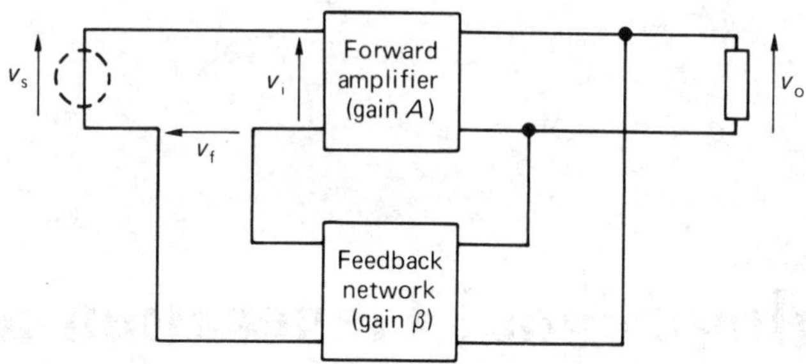

Figure 9.1 Feedback amplifier

At the $A\beta = 1$ condition $v_f = v_i$ (figure 5.1) so that, with the external signal source v_s removed, the circuit provides its own input via the feedback loop. Under these conditions the circuit is said to be *self- sustaining* meaning that an output is generated with no externally-applied input; the circuit is an *oscillator*.

The $A\beta = 1$ condition indicates that for oscillations to be sustained

(1) the modulus of the loop gain $|A\beta|$ must be unity, and

(2) the phase shift around the loop $\angle A\beta$ must be zero

which is written

$$A\beta = 1 \angle 0^\circ \qquad (9.2)$$

and termed the *Barkhausen condition* for oscillation.

A linear oscillator is therefore an amplifier with positive feedback for which the Barkhausen condition is satisfied at a particular frequency.

An obvious question is that as the circuit has no externally-applied input, how do the oscillations build up initially? At switch ON when the power supply voltage V_{CC} (V_{DD}) is applied to the circuit, the collector (drain) potentials fall as the transistor currents rise. These variations are fed back to the amplifier input and, provided $A\beta > 1$ at some frequency, oscillations will commence. If $A\beta \gg 1$, the waveshape of v_o will be controlled by severe non-linearities such as transistor saturation and cut-off whereby the output waveform will be severely distorted. If $A\beta$ is only slightly greater than unity, after the initial transient response [1a], the circuit will settle down to a steady-state at which v_o is sinusoidal. The frequency of the sinusoid will be that at which $A\beta$ is just equal to unity. Mild non-linearities such as the non-linear transfer characteristic for saturation region operation of a JFET (figure 2.4b) cause the circuit to change its frequency of oscillation until the Barkhausen condition is satisfied.

With reference to figure 9.1, the requirement for $\angle A\beta = 0^\circ$ could be met by

(1) The forward block A being a CE or CS amplifier with an *even* number of stages, providing $\angle A = 0^\circ$ at mid frequencies, with β being a passive resistive network such as a potential divider giving $\angle \beta = 0^\circ$. The frequency of oscillation would then be that frequency at which $|A\beta| = 1$.

(2) Both A and β could be inverting amplifiers $\angle A = -180^\circ$ and $\angle \beta = -180^\circ$ giving $\angle A\beta = -360^\circ$ or 0°. This in fact is the same as (1) except that half of the amplifier stages in (1) are considered here to form the feedback network, the only difference being the port in the loop that is treated as the output.

(3) Block A could be an inverting amplifier $\angle A = -180^\circ$ with a feedback phase shift $\angle \beta = -180^\circ$ provided by a CR or LC passive network.

Arrangement (3) is popular because the values of the passive components can be readily calculated to determine the frequency of oscillation; additionally, by using variable passive components, a variable frequency output can be produced. Because of the required component values, CR oscillators are popular for the audio frequency (AF) range up to a few tens of kilohertz, while LC circuits are used at higher frequencies into the radio frequency (RF) range up to hundreds of megahertz. Note that a piezoelectric crystal is an electromechanical device having energy storage properties analogous to those of an electrical RLC circuit, and so the inclusion of such a crystal in the feedback loop of an amplifier can also form an oscillator of this general type. In circuits employing an op-amp, a limiting factor can also be the slew rate of the amplifier (section 7.4.4).

9.1.1 *CR oscillators*

Phase-shift oscillator

Consideration of the sinusoidal response of basic CR networks (section 4.1) shows that they introduce a phase shift between zero and $\pm 90^\circ$ depending on the applied frequency and the time constant CR: $\tan^{-1}(1/2\pi fCR)$ for the 'case 1' circuit (figure 4.2a) from equation 4.1 and $-\tan^{-1}(2\pi fCR)$ for the 'case 2' circuit (figure 4.2b) from equations 4.4 and 4.7. Notice that for a single CR circuit, the phase shift is less than 90°.

The phase-shift oscillator uses an inverting amplifier with a CR feedback network. To satisfy the Barkhausen phase condition of $\angle A\beta = 0^\circ$, the phase shift provided by the feedback network must be 180° at the required frequency of oscillation of the circuit, which, when combined with the $\pm 180^\circ$ shift due to the inverting amplifier, results in zero phase shift around the loop. Because the phase shift provided by one CR circuit is $< 90^\circ$, three cascaded circuits are required (figure 9.2). For oscillations to be sustained, the Barkhausen gain condition $|A\beta| = 1$ must also be satisfied so that the gain of the amplifier must compensate for the attenuation of the passive feedback network to provide unity gain around the loop.

Analysis requires the determination of the transfer function v_f/v_o of the β feedback network. Since each CR circuit loads the previous CR circuit, the transfer function cannot be taken as simply the product of the individual (unloaded) transfer functions of the three CR sections. Various methods can be used to determine the v_f/v_o relationship; the one employed here is to work backwards from the output of the feedback network, summing the voltages across the circuit elements eventually to find v_o as a function of v_f.

Assuming that the input resistance of the amplifier is sufficiently high that loading of the feedback network by the amplifier input can be taken as negligible, that is the amplifier input current $i_i \simeq 0$, then, from figure 9.2:

$$v_f = Ri_1 \tag{9.3}$$

Voltage v_2 is then $v_{c_1} + v_f$ but, assuming ideal capacitors and *sinusoidal* signals:

$$v_{c_1} = \frac{i_{c_1}}{j\omega C} \tag{9.4}$$

using equation 2.27 where $1/j\omega C$ is the operational reactance of C, $\omega(=2\pi f)$ being the angular frequency of the sinusoidal signal currents and voltages.

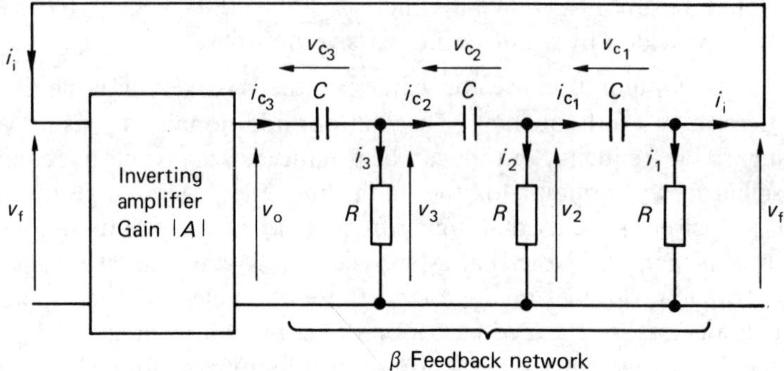

Figure 9.2 Basic phase-shift oscillator

For $i_i = 0$, $i_{c_1} = i_1$ and combining equations 9.3 and 9.4 gives

$$v_2 = v_{c_1} + v_f$$

$$= \frac{i_{c_1}}{j\omega C} + v_f$$

$$= \frac{i_1}{j\omega C} + v_f$$

$$= \frac{v_f}{j\omega CR} + v_f$$

$$= \left(\frac{1 + j\omega CR}{j\omega CR}\right) v_f \tag{9.5}$$

Having found v_2, the current $i_2 = v_2/R$ and noting $v_{c_2} = i_{c_2}/j\omega C$ (corresponding to equation 9.4) where $i_{c_2} = i_{c_1} + i_2 = i_1 + i_2$

$$v_{c_2} = \frac{i_1 + i_2}{j\omega C}$$

$$= \frac{v_f + v_2}{j\omega CR}$$

as $i_1 = \dfrac{v_f}{R}$ from equation 9.3.

Substituting for v_2 from equation 9.5 gives

$$v_{c_2} = -\left(\frac{1 + j2\omega CR}{\omega^2 C^2 R^2}\right) v_f \tag{9.6}$$

Continuing using the same procedure:

$$v_3 = v_{c_2} + v_2$$

$$= \left(\frac{\omega^2 C^2 R^2 - j3\omega CR - 1}{\omega^2 C^2 R^2}\right) v_f \tag{9.7}$$

using equations 9.5 and 9.6.

Then voltage $v_{c_3} = i_{c_3}/j\omega C$ where $i_{c_3} = i_{c_2} + i_3 = i_1 + i_2 + i_3$, thus

$$v_{c_3} = \frac{i_1 + i_2 + i_3}{j\omega C}$$

$$= \frac{v_f + v_2 + v_3}{j\omega CR} \tag{9.8}$$

Substituting for v_2 and v_3 from equations 9.5 and 9.7

$$v_{c_3} = \frac{v_f + \left(\dfrac{1 + j\omega CR}{j\omega CR}\right)v_f + \left(\dfrac{\omega^2C^2R^2 - j3\omega CR - 1}{\omega^2C^2R^2}\right)v_f}{j\omega CR}$$

$$= \left[\frac{-4\omega CR - j(3\omega^2C^2R^2 - 1)}{\omega^3C^3R^3}\right]v_f \tag{9.9}$$

The amplifier output v_o is then

$$v_o = v_{c_3} + v_3$$

$$= \left[\frac{-4\omega CR - j(3\omega^2C^2R^2 - 1)}{\omega^3C^3R^3}\right]v_f + \left(\frac{\omega^2C^2R^2 - j3\omega CR - 1}{\omega^2C^2R^2}\right)v_f$$

$$= \left[\frac{(\omega^3C^3R^3 - 5\omega CR) - j(6\omega^2C^2R^2 - 1)}{\omega^3C^3R^3}\right]v_f \tag{9.10}$$

from which the gain of the feedback network

$$\beta = \frac{v_f}{v_o} = \frac{\omega^3C^3R^3}{(\omega^3C^3R^3 - 5\omega CR) - j(6\omega^2C^2R^2 - 1)} \tag{9.11}$$

The phase difference between v_f and v_o is then

$$\angle\beta = \tan^{-1}\left(\frac{6\omega^2C^2R^2 - 1}{\omega^3C^3R^3 - 5\omega CR}\right) \tag{9.12}$$

which is the required 180° when the ( ) term is zero, that is, at a frequency ω_o at which

$$6\omega_o^2C^2R^2 - 1 = 0$$

from which

$$f_o = \frac{\omega_o}{2\pi} = \frac{1}{2\pi(\sqrt{6})CR} \tag{9.13}$$

Note that the ( ) term in equation 9.12 is zero when $\angle\beta$ is 0° or 180° but the $\angle\beta = 0°$ case is not a practical solution as v_f can only be in-phase with v_o for the *CR* cascade when the frequency approaches infinity.

Substituting $\omega = \omega_o = 1/(\sqrt{6})CR$ from equation 9.13 into 9.11 shows that the gain of the feedback network at this frequency

$$|\beta(\omega_o)| = \frac{1}{29} \tag{9.14}$$

To meet the Barkhausen gain criterion $|A\beta(\omega_o)| = 1$ therefore, the gain of the amplifier at frequency ω_o, $|A(\omega_o)|$, must be 29. In practice, to ensure that oscillations build up rapidly at switch ON, the amplifier is designed so that its gain modulus at ω_o is about 3–5 per cent larger than the limiting value of 29; a design value of about 30 is suitable, larger values would possibly result in distortion.

The phase-shift network used in the above example has been based on the 'case 1' lead network of figure 4.2a; if the positions of *C*s and *R*s in figure 9.2 are interchanged, effectively using 'case 2' lag networks (figure 4.2b), similar analysis gives the frequency of oscillation as

$$f_o = \frac{\sqrt{6}}{2\pi CR} \tag{9.15}$$

The required amplifier gain is the same in either case.

Examples of implementation of a phase-shift oscillator using the lead network are shown in figure 9.3. In the op-amp version (figure 9.3a) the basic inverting amplifier of figure 7.11b is used as the forward amplifier, a gain modulus of 30 being obtained by making $R_F = 30R_1$. Previous theoretical analysis assumes the input resistance of the amplifier is sufficiently high not to load the β network. The input resistance of the inverting amplifier for small-signal operation $R_{i(cct)}$ is equal to R_1 (corresponding to equation 7.67). By arranging that R_1 is the same value as the resistances in the β network (R), $R_{i(cct)}$ provides the resistance across the output of the feedback network (figure 9.3a) thereby avoiding loading inaccuracies.

The design procedure is to select a value of R, taking account of R_I and R_O of the op-amp (section 7.5); as the feedback resistance is required to be $30R$, R should be selected towards the lower end of the $0.1\sqrt{R_I R_O}$ to $10\sqrt{R_I R_O}$ range. Having selected R, the corresponding value of C can be calculated to give the required frequency of oscillation. Preferred-value components are then selected, often series and/or parallel combinations being necessary to obtain f_o within the specified range; the capacitors are low-loss polyester, polycarbonate or polystyrene types (section 2.4.2).

Example 9.1: Selection of component values for an op-amp phase-shift oscillator

Select components for the circuit of figure 9.3a (E24 resistances, E6 capacitance; appendix D) based on a 741 op-amp to provide a sinusoidal output of 10 kHz ±5 per cent.

From appendix E, section E.9, the 741 op-amp typically has $R_I = 2$ MΩ and $R_O = 75$ Ω, giving a geometric mean of approximately 12 kΩ and a corresponding 'ideal' range for external resistances of 1.2 kΩ to 120 kΩ.

With R_F required to be $30R_1$, suitable combinations are 1.2, 36; 1.3, 39; 1.5, 47; 1.6, 51; 1.8, 56; 2, 62; 2.2, 68; 2.4, 75; 2.7, 81; 3, 91; 3.3, 100; 3.6, 110; 3.9, 120 kΩ, giving gains of 30, 30, 31.3, 31.9, 31.1, 31, 30.9, 31.3, 30, 30.3, 30.3, 30.6, 30.8 respectively.

The mid-range combination of 2.2 kΩ, 68 kΩ is provisionally chosen.

From equation 9.13, $C = 1/2\pi(\sqrt{6})f_o R$ which, for $f_o = 10$ kHz and $R = 2.2$ kΩ requires $C = 2953$ pF which can be approximated by a parallel combination of two 1500 pF capacitors (3000 pF). With $R = 2.2$ kΩ and $C = 3000$ pF, f_o (equation 9.13) is 9.84 kHz.

If ±1 per cent tolerance components are used, resulting in a possible frequency spread of ±2 per cent, because of the *CR* product, the output frequency will be in the range 9.84 kHz ±2 per cent, that is 9.65 kHz to 10.04 kHz (all values rounded to 2 decimal places).

This range is well within the specification of 10 kHz ±5 per cent (9.5 kHz to 10.5 kHz) and is therefore adequate; had this not been the case, other combinations of values would need to be considered.

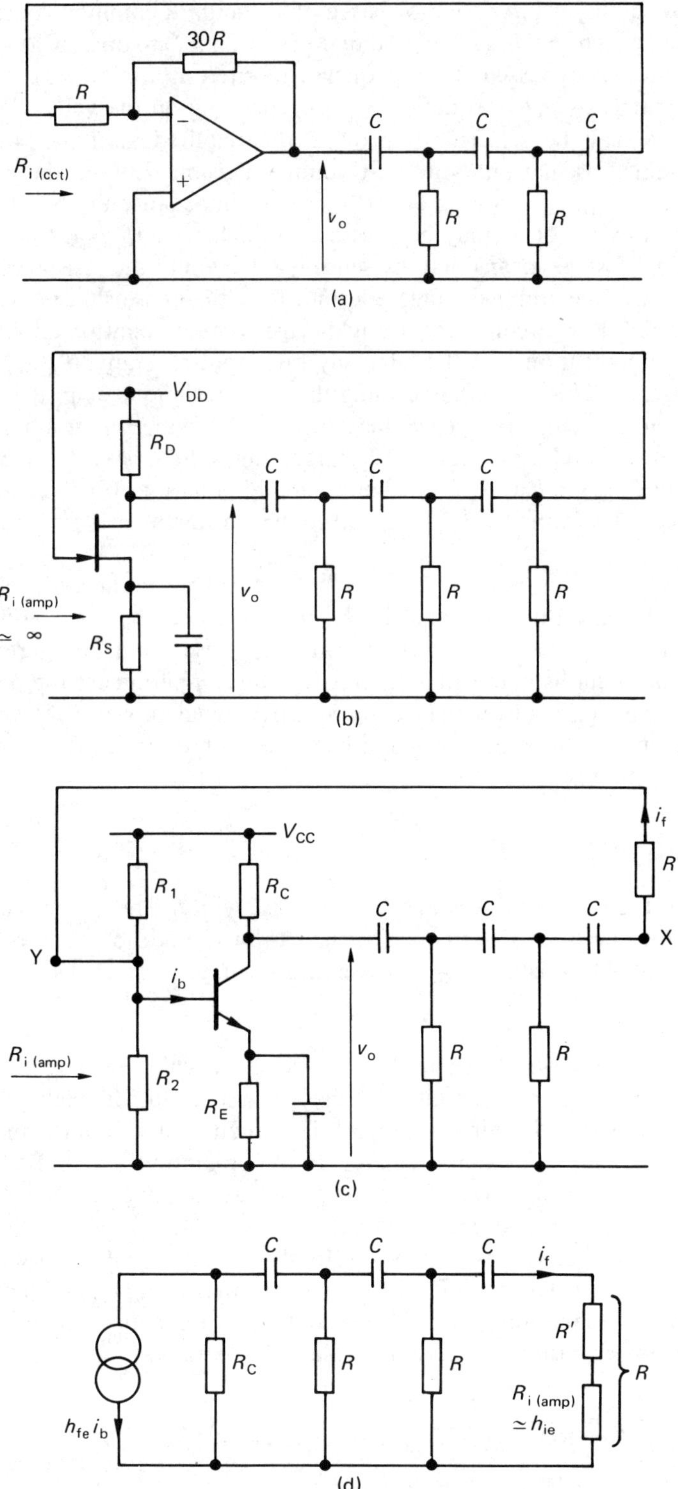

Figure 9.3 Phase-shift oscillators

Figure 9.3b shows a phase-shift oscillator based on a standard common-source FET stage as the forward amplifier. The FET is self biased by R_S (section 3.2) to operate as a linear amplifier and with R_S adequately bypassed at the frequency of interest (section 3.3), the ac gain of the stage is approximately $-g_{fs}R_D$ (equation 3.88). Depending on the value of g_{fs} for the FET at its Q-point, R_D can be selected to provide the required gain modulus greater than 29 to allow sustained oscillation. Note that voltage division between the output resistance of the FET stage ($\simeq R_D$, equation 3.91) and the input impedance of the CR cascade means that a gain well in excess of 29 may be necessary to achieve $|A\beta| = 1$. The very high input resistance of the FET stage means that, by sensible selection of the resistance value for the β network ($R \ll R_{i(amp)}$), the amplifier stage does not load the phase-shift network.

The corresponding BJT circuit using a single-stage common-emitter amplifier (figure 9.3c) suffers from the complication that the relatively low input resistance $R_{i(amp)}$ (equation 3.79) loads the CR cascade. This is overcome using the same technique as in the op-amp version (figure 9.3a), the circuit being arranged so that the input resistance of the amplifier stage forms part of the β network. Thus in figure 9.3c, assuming values have been chosen to make $R_{i(amp)} < R$, where $R_{i(amp)} \simeq R_1 /\!/ R_2 /\!/ h_{ie}$ (figure 3.8 and equation 3.79), resistance R' is then included in the feedback loop ($R' = R - R_{i(amp)}$) so that the β network is effectively terminated in R.

Assuming that $R_1 /\!/ R_2 \gg h_{ie}$ so that $R_{i(amp)} \simeq h_{ie}$ for simplicity, if the feedback loop is broken at Y and the feedback path terminated by h_{ie} to ground so that resistance levels are not changed, small-signal operation of the circuit can be represented as in figure 9.3d. Note that as operation of the circuit is in the audio frequency range, h-parameter representation of BJT small-signal performance is adequate (section 3.4.2). A signal current i_b flowing into the BJT base then results in a fedback current i_f and from the loop current gain expression i_f/i_b, the frequency of oscillation is

$$f_o = \frac{1}{2\pi CR\sqrt{[6 + 4(R_C/R)]}} \tag{9.16}$$

corresponding to the frequency at which i_f is in phase with i_b, the $\angle A\beta = 0°$ condition.

For oscillation to occur at this frequency, the $|A\beta| \geqslant 1$ condition must be satisfied which corresponds to $h_{fe} \geqslant 44.54$ from $|i_f/i_b| \geqslant 1$. See also tutorial question 9.4.

Wien-bridge oscillator

The balance condition of the Wien bridge, one form of which is shown in figure 9.4a, is frequency dependent and the circuit is therefore useful for frequency or capacitance measurement. Used as the β feedback network in conjunction with an amplifier, the bridge forms an audio frequency sinusoidal oscillator. In the op-amp version of figure 9.4a, positive feedback via Z_1, Z_2 determines the frequency of oscillation while negative feedback via R_F, R_1 sets the gain of the non-inverting amplifier.

Redrawing the arrangement as in figure 9.4b shows the circuit in forward amplifier A, feedback network β form. The amplifier is the basic non-inverting type of figure 7.10c having gain $A = 1 + (R_F/R_1)$ (equation 7.51) and very high input resistance (equation 7.46); loading of the feedback network is therefore negligible. The voltage transfer function of the β network is

$$\beta = \frac{v^+}{v_o} = \frac{Z_2}{Z_1 + Z_2} = \frac{R /\!/ (1/j\omega C)}{R + (1/j\omega C) + [R /\!/ (1/j\omega C)]}$$

$$= \frac{\omega CR}{3\omega CR - j(1 - \omega^2 C^2 R^2)} \tag{9.17}$$

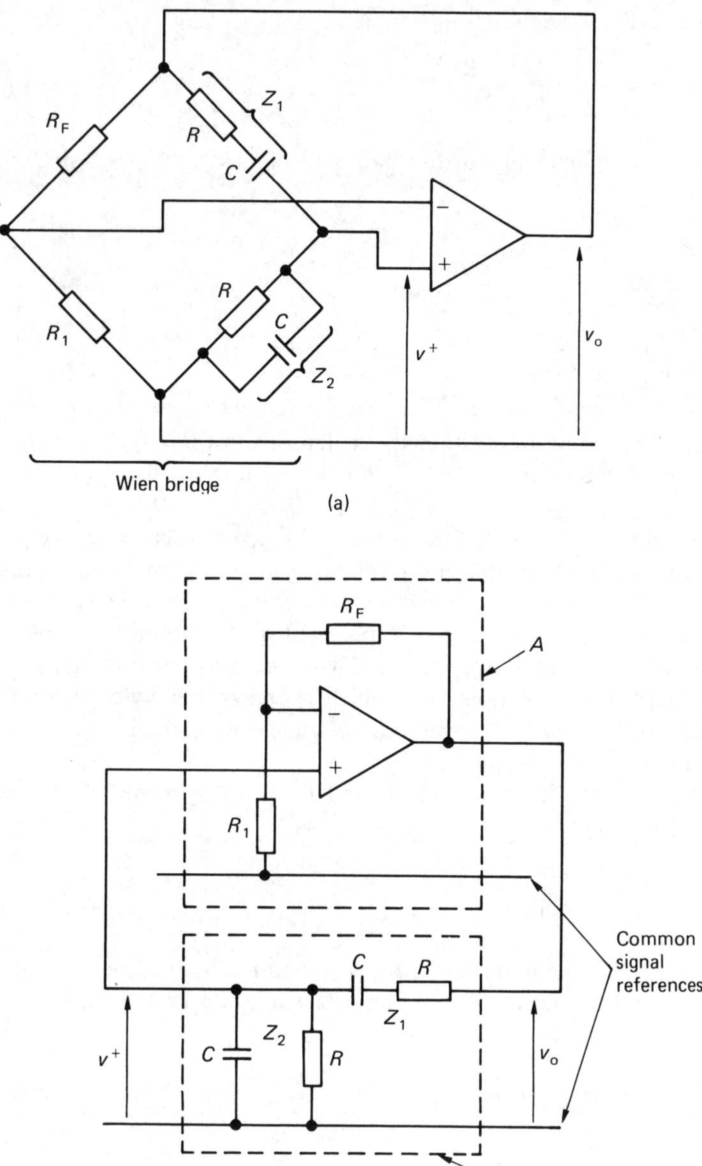

Figure 9.4 Wien-bridge oscillator

and the loop gain is therefore

$$A\beta = \left(1 + \frac{R_F}{R_1}\right)\left[\frac{\omega CR}{3\omega CR - j(1 - \omega^2 C^2 R^2)}\right] \tag{9.18}$$

The conditions for oscillation (equation 9.2) are zero phase shift around the loop $\angle A\beta = 0°$ and, at the frequency of oscillation, the modulus of the loop gain $|A\beta|$ is unity.

From equation 9.18

$$\angle A\beta = -\tan^{-1}\left(\frac{1-\omega^2C^2R^2}{3\omega CR}\right) \tag{9.19}$$

which is zero at a frequency ω_o corresponding to $(1-\omega_o^2C^2R^2)=0$, since $\tan 0° = 0$, giving

$$f_o = \frac{1}{2\pi CR} \tag{9.20}$$

At this frequency

$$|A\beta| = \left(1+\frac{R_F}{R_1}\right)\left(\frac{1}{3}\right) \tag{9.21}$$

from equation 9.18, and for sustained oscillations, $|A\beta|=1$, the gain of the amplifier $[1+(R_F/R_1)]$ must therefore be 3, which, for the op-amp oscillator of figure 9.4b means that R_F must be $2R_1$.

As with the phase-shift oscillator, rapid build up of oscillations requires a loop gain slightly >1. In addition, the selection tolerance of the components must be taken into account, that is, $R_F$min must be slightly greater than $2R_1$max. For example, choosing $R_F = 22\text{ k}\Omega \pm 1$ per cent, $R_1 = 10\text{ k}\Omega \pm 1$ per cent gives $R_F\text{min} = 21.78\text{ k}\Omega$ and $2R_1\text{max} = 20.2\text{ k}\Omega$ which would be suitable; even at the worst case corresponding to $R_F$min and R_1max the gain $1+(21.78\text{ k}\Omega/10.1\text{ k}\Omega)$ is 3.156 which is approximately 5 per cent greater than the limiting condition. This would ensure rapid build up of oscillations even for worst-case component values.

If the Z_1, Z_2 networks have different C and R values such that Z_1 comprises C_1, R_1 and Z_2 is C_2, R_2, analysis gives

$$f_o = \frac{1}{2\pi\sqrt{(C_1C_2R_1R_2)}} \tag{9.22}$$

and sensitivity to component variation due to tolerance, temperature variation or ageing can be determined by differentiation of equation 9.22. For example, the sensitivity of f_o to variation of C_1 is

$$\frac{\partial f_o}{\partial C_1} = \frac{1}{2\pi}\frac{\partial}{\partial C_1}[(C_1C_2R_1R_2)^{-\frac{1}{2}}] = \frac{-f_o}{2C_1} \tag{9.23}$$

the negative sign indicating that f_o decreases as C_1 increases and vice versa.

Continuous variation of output frequency can be obtained by simultaneous variation of the resistances or capacitances; ganged potentiometers or variable capacitors are the most basic, voltage-controlled components (FETs or diodes), being more sophisticated.

The op-amp circuit is but one version of Wien-bridge oscillator. Circuits using BJT or FET amplifier stages can be devised. Notice however that in contrast to the phase-shift oscillator, the amplifier in the Wien circuit must be non-inverting. Discrete Wien-bridge oscillators can therefore be based on two-stage CE BJT or CS FET amplifiers with the Z_1, Z_2 network connected as a frequency-dependent potential divider across the amplifier output, the common node between Z_1 and Z_2 providing the fedback signal to the amplifier input. In the BJT case the circuit is designed so that the amplifier input resistance $R_{i(amp)}$ forms part of the Wien-bridge network to avoid loading problems.

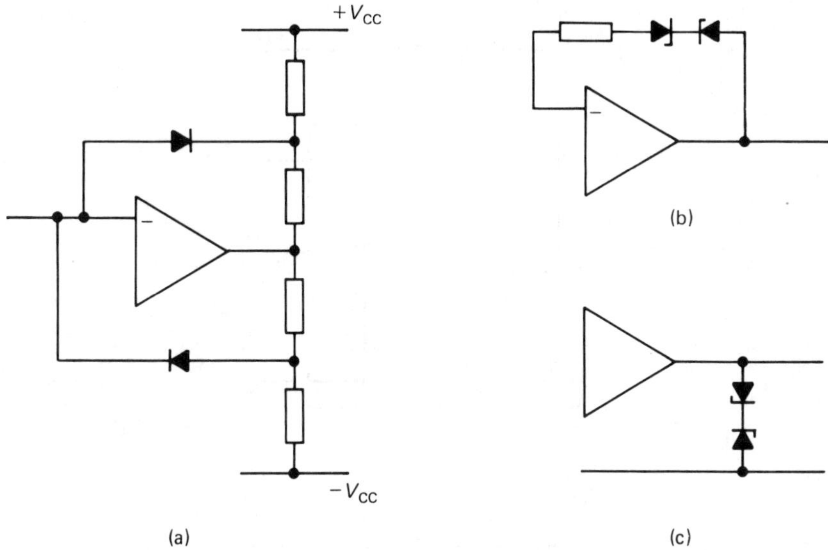

Figure 9.5 Amplitude stabilisation

Amplitude stabilisation

Although it is necessary for $|A\beta|$ to be slightly greater than unity at the frequency of oscillation to ensure rapid build up of oscillations at switch ON, this would cause the output amplitude to increase until severe non-linearity such as amplifier saturation limited the output voltage resulting in severe distortion. To ensure $|A\beta|$ reduces to unity, the steady-state oscillation condition, before the output is severely distorted and so stabilise the output amplitude, non-linear gain reduction is included. Various techniques can be used such as gain limiting (figures 9.5a, b) or a soft output voltage clamp (figure 9.5c), the term 'soft' describing the progressiveness of the clamp as the reverse-biased diode breaks down. Alternatively a FET acting as a voltage-controlled resistor can be used to shunt a circuit resistor so reducing the gain as the voltage rises.

9.1.2 *LC oscillators*

Figure 9.6a gives the general form of an *LC* oscillator, the feedback network comprising impedances Z_1, Z_2, Z_3. If the performance of the forward amplifier is represented by its *y*-parameter model [2a], the circuit may be represented as in figure 9.6b. Parameter y_{11} is the small-signal input admittance of the amplifier and y_{21} is its small-signal forward transadmittance (gain) which is the ratio of output signal current to input signal voltage. It has been assumed for simplicity that the output admittance of the amplifier y_{22} and internal feedback *within* the amplifier can be neglected.

The effective load at the amplifier output is then Z_3 in parallel with the series combination of Z_1 and $Z_2/\!/(1/y_{11})$. As admittances in parallel add directly, it is convenient here to work in admittances; thus if $Y_1 = 1/Z_1$, $Y_2 = 1/Z_2$ and $Y_3 = 1/Z_3$, the admittance of the Z_3, Z_1, Z_2, $1/y_{11}$ combination is $Y_3 + \left[\dfrac{Y_1(Y_2 + y_{11})}{Y_1 + Y_2 + y_{11}}\right]$ and then

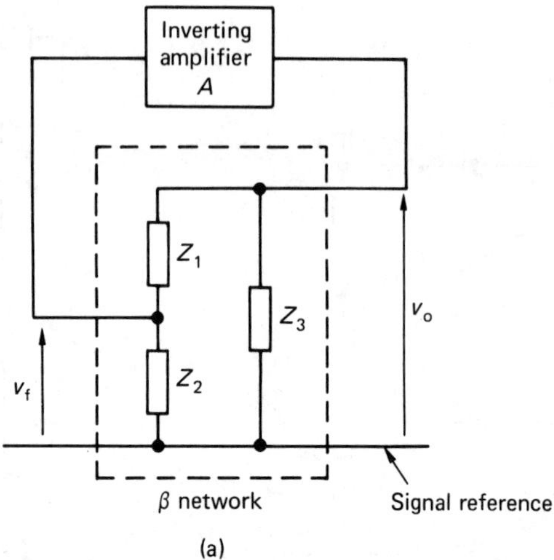

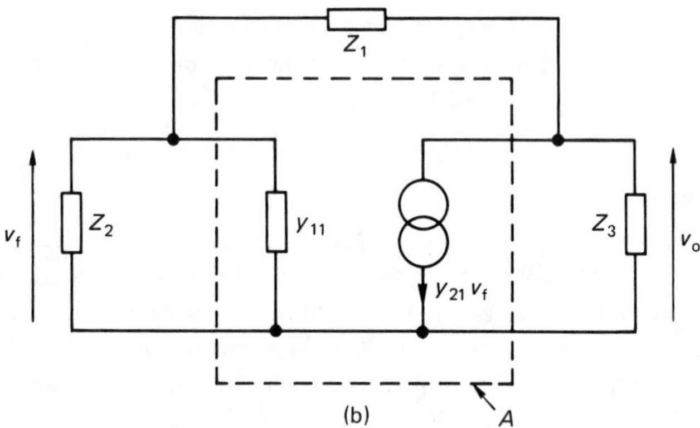

Figure 9.6 General *LC* oscillator

$$v_o = \frac{-y_{21} v_f}{Y_3 + \left[\dfrac{Y_1(Y_2 + y_{11})}{Y_1 + Y_2 + y_{11}}\right]}$$

from which

$$A = \frac{v_o}{v_f} = \frac{-y_{21}}{Y_3 + \left[\dfrac{Y_1(Y_2 + y_{11})}{Y_1 + Y_2 + y_{11}}\right]} \tag{9.24}$$

The feedback network provides v_f from v_o by potential division between Y_1 and the $(Y_2 + y_{11})$ combination, giving

$$\beta = \frac{v_f}{v_o} = \frac{Y_1}{Y_1 + Y_2 + y_{11}} \tag{9.25}$$

Combining equations 9.24 and 9.25, the loop gain is

$$A\beta = \frac{-y_{21} Y_1}{Y_3(Y_1 + Y_2 + y_{11}) + Y_1(Y_2 + y_{11})} \tag{9.26}$$

Investigation of the conditions for oscillation ($\angle A\beta = 0°$ and $|A\beta| = 1$) requires knowledge of the form of the admittances Y_1, Y_2 and Y_3. It is assumed that they are ideal reactances such that, in general, $Y = 1/jX$ where $X = \omega L$ for an inductive reactance and $X = -1/\omega C$ in the capacitive case. Note from equations 2.39, 2.26 and 2.27 that the operational reactances of an inductor and a capacitor, which includes the phase relationship between voltage and current as required here, are $j\omega L$ and $-j/\omega C$ respectively. Substituting $Y_1 = 1/jX_1$, $Y_2 = 1/jX_2$ and $Y_3 = 1/jX_3$ in equation 9.26 gives

$$A\beta = \frac{-y_{21} X_2 X_3}{y_{11}(X_1 X_2 + X_2 X_3) - j(X_1 + X_2 + X_3)} \tag{9.27}$$

The phase shift around the loop $\angle A\beta$ is therefore $-180° - \tan^{-1}[-(X_1 + X_2 + X_3)/(y_{11}(X_1 X_2 + X_2 X_3))]$ which is zero as required for oscillation when

$$X_1 + X_2 + X_3 = 0 \tag{9.28}$$

and at the frequency ω_o at which this occurs the loop gain, from equation 9.27, is

$$[A\beta]_{\omega_o} = \frac{-y_{21} X_3}{y_{11}(X_1 + X_3)} = \frac{y_{21} X_3}{y_{11} X_2} \tag{9.29}$$

as $X_1 + X_3 = -X_2$ from equation 9.28.

For $A\beta$ to be positive at ω_o as required for oscillation (equation 9.2), it follows from equation 9.29 that X_2 and X_3 must be of the same sign which means that X_2 and X_3 must be the same type of reactance, either both capacitive or both inductive, for oscillation to occur. Further, to meet the condition given by equation 9.28, reactance X_1 must be of the other type (termed the *dual*) to that of X_2 and X_3.

In either case, X_1 inductive and X_2, X_3 capacitive or X_1 capacitive and X_2, X_3 inductive, from equation 9.29, for oscillations to be maintained $A\beta$ at ω_o must be equal to $+1$, giving

$$\frac{y_{21} X_3}{y_{11} X_2} = 1$$

that is

$$X_2 = X_3\left(\frac{y_{21}}{y_{11}}\right) \tag{9.30}$$

which is termed the *maintenance condition*. Having satisfied equation 9.30, the frequency of oscillation is given by equation 9.28.

Colpitts oscillator

The Colpitts version of *LC* oscillator has an inductor as Z_1 (figure 9.6) while Z_2 and Z_3 are both capacitors. Corresponding to the general case discussed above, assuming ideal components $X_1 = \omega L$, $X_2 = -1/\omega C_2$ and $X_3 = -1/\omega C_3$, the maintenance condition from equation 9.30 is

$$C_3 = C_2\left(\frac{y_{21}}{y_{11}}\right) \tag{9.31}$$

and the frequency of oscillation, from equation 9.28, is

$$\omega_o L - \frac{1}{\omega_o C_2} - \frac{1}{\omega_o C_3} = 0$$

giving

$$f_o = \frac{\omega_o}{2\pi} = \frac{1}{2\pi}\sqrt{\frac{C_2 + C_3}{LC_2C_3}} \tag{9.32}$$

Figure 9.7 shows various practical Colpitts circuits. In the FET version of figure 9.7a, based on a common-source stage, the JFET is biased for mid-range conduction as discussed in section 3.2, a radio frequency choke (RFC) being used in place of the drain load R_D. The choke (inductor) has a low resistance to static (bias) current flow but a very high impedance at the frequency of operation of the circuit f_o which is in the RF range. The choke therefore enables the V_{CC} supply to be applied to the drain of the JFET for bias purposes but also allows the drain voltage to vary. The advantage of using a RFC in place of a resistive load R_D is that loading on the transistor output is reduced and almost all the output signal current flows into the feedback network. The coupling capacitor C_C is included as a dc block (section 3.3) to prevent a large static current flow through L due to the different static voltage levels at the gate and drain of the transistor. The value of C_C must be selected so that its impedance at the operating frequency f_o is low, thereby not reducing the loop gain of the circuit. Equation 9.31 gives the maintenance condition for the circuit, y_{21} being y_{fs} ($\simeq g_{fs}$) for the JFET and $y_{11} \simeq 1/R_G$, thus

$$\frac{C_3}{C_2} \geqslant g_{fs} R_G \tag{9.33}$$

As with other types of oscillator circuit, values are selected to provide a loop gain 3–5 per cent higher than the limiting value of unity to allow rapid build up of oscillations at switch ON. The operating frequency is given by equation 9.32.

A basic BJT Colpitts circuit using a common-emitter stage is given in figure 9.7b (without C'), C_C providing dc blocking as in the JFET circuit discussed above. At the high operating frequency of this type of oscillator it is necessary to use a HF model to represent BJT performance such as the HF hybrid-π model of figure 3.9b, although some simplifications such as neglecting $r_{bb'}$, $r_{b'c}$ and r_{ce} are usually permissible. Also the relatively low input impedance of the CE stage means that the shunting effect of $R_{i(amp)}$ ($\simeq R_1 /\!/ R_2 /\!/ r_{b'e}$) and $C_{i(amp)}$ ($= C_{b'c} + C_{b'c}(1 - A_{v(amp)})$ ignoring strays, see also figures 4.6a, b) may need to be taken into account.

Relating the general maintaining condition (equation 9.31) to the BJT circuit of figure 9.7b, C_2 is shunted by $C_{i(amp)}$ and so C_2 in equation 9.31 becomes $(C_2 + C_{i(amp)})$ in this case. Also, if v_i is the input signal voltage to the BJT and i_i, i_o are the input and output signal currents, $y_{21} = i_o/v_i$ and $y_{11} = i_i/v_i$ so that the ratio $y_{21}/y_{11} = i_o/i_i$ which is the small-signal current gain h_{fe} of the BJT, assuming high value bias resistances R_1, R_2 so that $i_i \simeq i_b$. Also, if the bias resistances are sufficiently high that $R_{i(amp)}$ may be taken as $r_{b'c}$ ($= 1/y_{11}$), the maintenance condition, from equation 9.31, is

$$C_3 = (C_2 + C_{i(amp)})h_{fe} \tag{9.34}$$

In practice values are chosen, as in other cases, to make $A\beta$ 3–5 per cent higher than the theoretically required value of unity. Equation 9.32 gives the output frequency if C_2 is replaced by $(C_2 + C_{i(amp)})$.

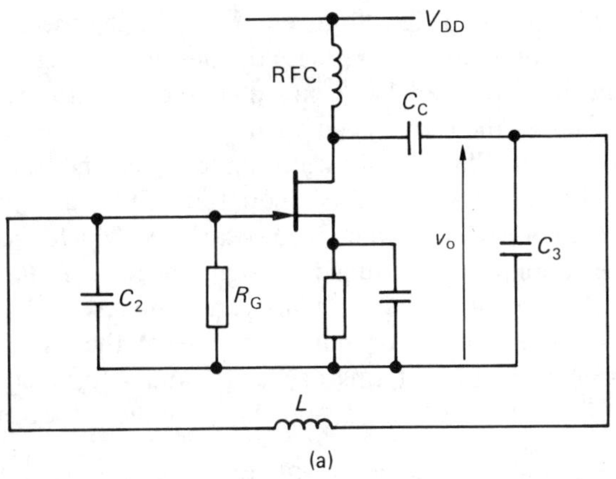

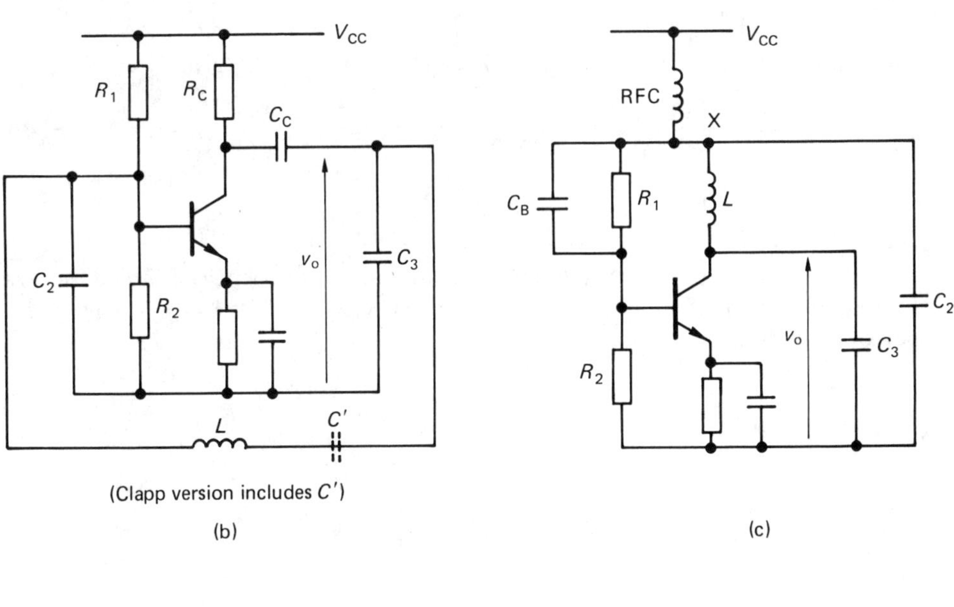

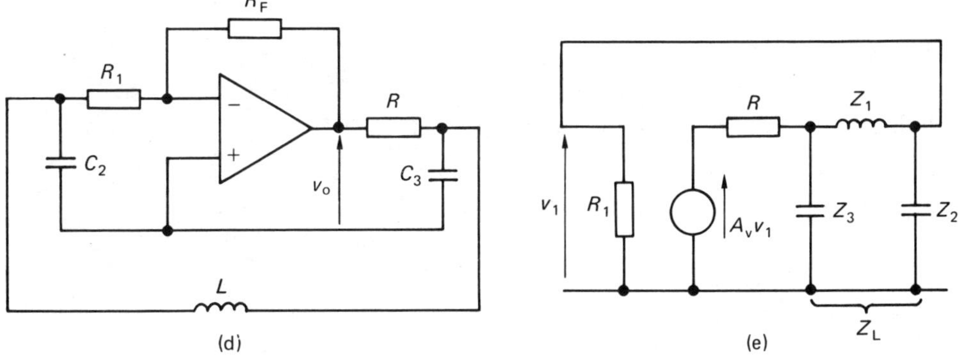

Figure 9.7 Colpitts oscillators

Figure 9.7c shows an alternative BJT Colpitts circuit where the use of a RF choke in place of R_C, as in the JFET circuit of figure 9.7a, reduces the output loading. By including a bypass capacitor across R_1, the inductor can be included in the collector circuit, node X being connected to the base as far as the signal is concerned.

An op-amp based Colpitts oscillator is shown in figure 9.7d. The basic inverting circuit of figure 7.11b, having voltage gain $-R_F/R_1$ (equation 7.65) and input resistance R_1 (equation 7.67), provides the forward amplifier. Resistance R, which effectively increases the output resistance of the amplifier, is included so that the ratio L/R is small, giving low damping. For analysis purposes, circuit performance can be represented by the model of figure 9.7e in which $A_v = -R_F/R_1$ and the output resistance of the circuit is included in R. Representing the feedback network in terms of Z_1, Z_2 and Z_3, which impose an effective load Z_L $(=Z_3/\!/(Z_1+Z_2))$ on the output of the amplifier, the gain of the forward amplifier is $A_v\left(\dfrac{Z_L}{R+Z_L}\right)$ and the feedback fraction is $\left(\dfrac{Z_2}{Z_1+Z_2}\right)$ giving a loop gain $A_v\left(\dfrac{Z_L}{R+Z_L}\right)\left(\dfrac{Z_2}{Z_1+Z_2}\right)$.

Substituting for Z_L together with $Z_1 = jX_1$, $Z_2 = jX_2$ and $Z_3 = jX_3$ gives

$$A\beta = \frac{A_v X_2 X_3}{X_3(X_1+X_2) - jR(X_1+X_2+X_3)} \tag{9.35}$$

where $X_1 = \omega L$, $X_2 = -1/\omega C_2$ and $X_3 = -1/\omega C_3$.

$\angle A\beta$ is therefore $\angle A_v - \tan^{-1}[-R(X_1+X_2+X_3)/(X_3(X_1+X_2))]$, and assuming $\angle A_v$ to be $-180°$, the amplifier stage providing inversion, at the frequency of oscillation, $\angle A\beta$ is 0° (as required for oscillation, equation 9.2) when $R(X_1+X_2+X_3)=0$. This gives the frequency of oscillation as

$$\omega_o L - \frac{1}{\omega_o C_2} - \frac{1}{\omega_o C_3} = 0$$

from which

$$f_o = \frac{\omega_o}{2\pi} = \frac{1}{2\pi}\sqrt{\frac{C_2+C_3}{LC_2C_3}} \tag{9.36}$$

Substituting $X_1+X_2+X_3=0$ back in equation 9.35 gives

$$[A\beta]_{\omega_o} = \frac{A_v X_2}{X_1+X_2} \tag{9.37}$$

which must be $\geqslant 1$ for oscillation to occur, hence, at ω_o:

$$\frac{A_v X_2}{X_1+X_2} = 1$$

but $X_1+X_2+X_3=0$ and so

$$A_v = \frac{-X_3}{X_2} \tag{9.38}$$

Substituting for A_v $(=-R_F/R_1)$ and X_2, X_3 gives the limiting condition for oscillations to be maintained as

$$|A_v| = \frac{R_F}{R_1} = \frac{C_2}{C_3} \tag{9.39}$$

Clapp oscillator

Variation of capacitances C_2 and C_3 due, for example, to changing temperature, causes the frequency of oscillation of the basic Colpitts circuit to drift. Improved frequency stability can be obtained by the addition of C' (figure 9.7b) effectively replacing L by the L, C' tuned circuit. Analysis of the circuit with C', called a Clapp oscillator, shows that if $C' \ll C_2$ and C_3, f_o is approximately equal to $1/2\pi\sqrt{(LC')}$ with little dependence on C_2 and C_3. Implementation of C' as a parallel combination of capacitors with negative and positive temperature coefficients can provide C' almost independent of temperature over a relatively wide range, thereby providing improved stability in this respect. Notice that the crystal oscillator of section 9.1.3 uses the same principle, the resonant crystal replacing the LC' tuned circuit in the Clapp oscillator.

Another advantage of the Clapp circuit is that with C' being smaller than $C_2C_3/(C_2 + C_3)$ (equation 9.32), the value of L required for a certain output frequency is larger in the Clapp case than for the basic Colpitts circuit. This can be important because of the lower limit of practical values of L that can be used and also because the forward transadmittance y_{21} of available transistors is limited which has implications for the maintenance condition (equation 9.31).

Hartley oscillator

The Hartley circuit is the dual of the Colpitts oscillator in that Z_1 in the general form of figure 9.6 is a capacitor and Z_2, Z_3 are inductors. Thus with $X_1 = -1/\omega C$, $X_2 = \omega L_2$ and $X_3 = \omega L_3$, the maintenance condition (from equation 9.30) is

$$L_2 = L_3\left(\frac{y_{21}}{y_{11}}\right) \tag{9.40}$$

while from equation 9.28, the frequency of oscillation is

$$-\frac{1}{\omega_o C} + \omega_o L_2 + \omega_o L_3 = 0$$

giving

$$f_o = \frac{1}{2\pi\sqrt{[C(L_2 + L_3)]}} \tag{9.41}$$

both results assuming no mutual coupling between L_2 and L_3. In practice, the two coils are often formed as the single tapped coil in which case the mutual coupling M [3a] between the two sections must be taken into account. This complication, together with the fact that for the typical values required here, inductors are more costly than capacitors, makes the Hartley circuit less popular than the Colpitts version. Figure 9.8 shows two BJT Hartley circuits. The basic arrangement of figure 9.8a uses a standard common-emitter stage, capacitors C_C providing dc blocking so that the inductors, which have low impedance at dc, do not upset the bias conditions. In the simpler, component-efficient version of figure 9.8b, the bypass capacitor C_B connects L_2 across the amplifier input while the low impedance signal path provided by the V_{CC} supply effectively connects L_3 across the amplifier output.

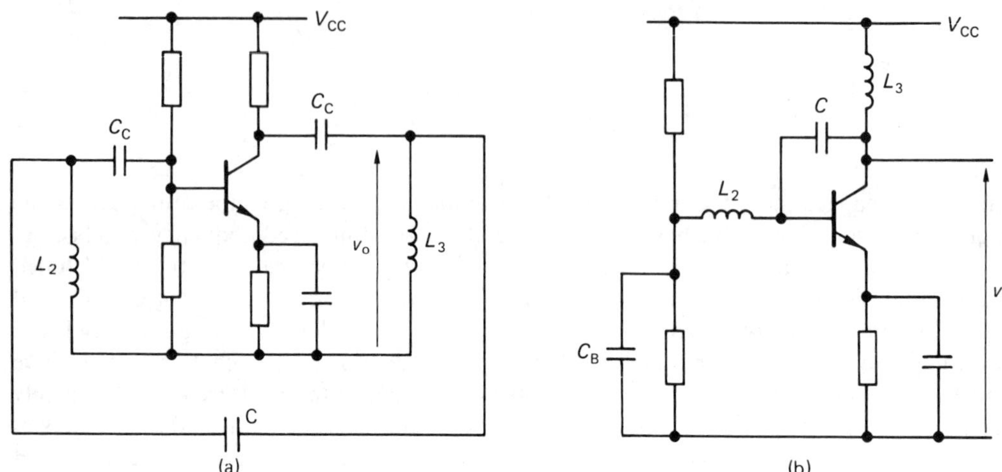

Figure 9.8 Hartley oscillators

9.1.3 **Crystal oscillators**

The atomic structure of some crystalline materials is such that at equilibrium with no external voltage applied there is a spatial separation of positive and negative charges within the material, forming what are termed *dipoles*. When a voltage is applied across such a material, the dipoles tend to rotate to align themselves with the applied electric field and this causes mechanical stress within the material, resulting in physical deformation. This property is called the *piezoelectric* effect and is found in several materials, notably quartz, a form of silicon dioxide. The effect is reversible in that an applied mechanical stress results in an electric field and hence a voltage across the material due to dipole movement.

The link between the electrical and mechanical properties of such a material makes it a useful electromechanical transducer. Also if such a crystal is put under stress, either mechanically or electrically, and the force suddenly removed, mechanical and electrical oscillations result that are very lightly damped. The crystal thus behaves as an *LCR* tuned circuit as far as the piezoelectric effect is concerned. For use as a lightly-damped (high Q, appendix B, section B.3) tuned circuit in an electronic system, the crystal must have electrodes on opposite faces to allow electrical connection. Figure 9.9a shows the circuit symbol of a piezoelectric crystal while the model of figure 9.9b represents its small-signal performance, C_p being the inter-electrode capacitance.

The frequency response of this type of crystal is as shown in figure 9.9c, a *series* resonance occurring at frequency $\omega_s(=1/\surd(LC))$ and a *parallel* resonance at $\omega_p(=1/\surd(LC''))$, where $C''=CC_p/(C+C_p)$. The resonant frequencies and Q-factor of a crystal depend on its physical size, particularly its thickness, and crystals with resonant frequencies from a few tens of kilohertz to tens of megahertz are readily available. Higher frequency resonances are possible by selecting a harmonic of the fundamental resonance; this is usually achieved by using the crystal in conjunction with an LC tuned circuit which selects operation at the harmonic frequency. Typical parameters for a 10 MHz crystal are $L=10$ mH, $C=0.025$ pF, $R=6\,\Omega$, $C_p=10$ pF and Q $(=\omega_o L/R$, equation B.35, appendix B$)\simeq 10^5$. Since $C_p \gg C$ it follows that $C''\simeq C$ and hence $\omega_s \simeq \omega_p$; usually the series and parallel resonant frequencies are within

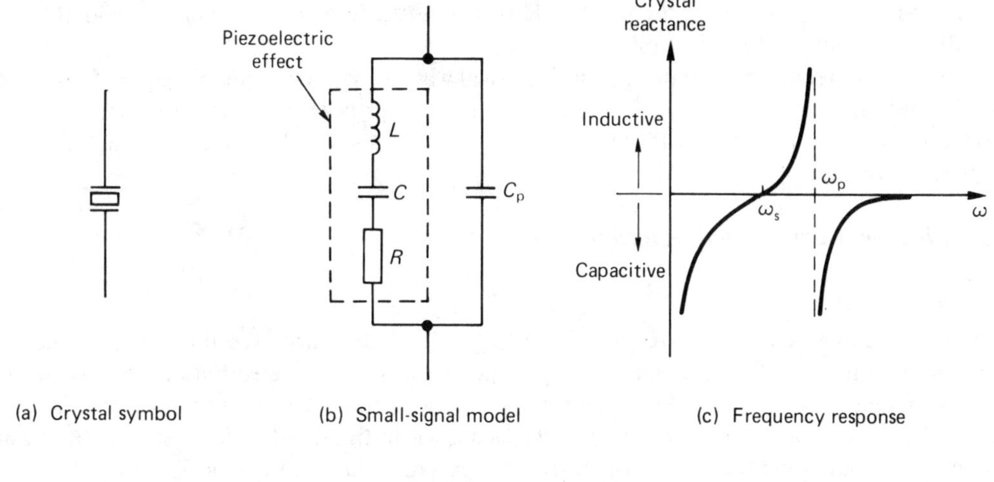

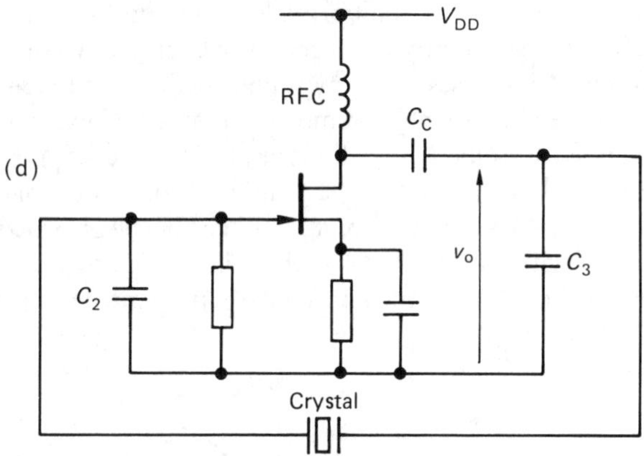

Figure 9.9 Crystal oscillator

1 per cent of each other. In operation, the crystal resonates either at ω_s or ω_p, depending on the impedance of the associated circuit.

Figure 9.9d shows a crystal oscillator, termed a Pierce oscillator, derived from the Colpitts circuit of figure 9.7a. Notice that the crystal version is essentially the same as the Clapp circuit, the crystal replacing the LC' tuned circuit.

Several versions of crystal oscillator are possible, the crystal providing either Z_1 or Z_2 in the general representation of figure 9.6. In the Pierce version, in which the crystal provides Z_1, capacitors C_2 and C_3 may not be required. A popular configuration uses the crystal as Z_2, a tuned circuit as Z_3, forming the collector (drain) load, and utilises the internal capacitance of the transistor to provide Z_1.

9.2 **Analog signal processing**

Electronic systems manipulate the flow of energy in electrical form to convey information (section 1.1). In some cases the information-carrying electrical signal is created by a transducer, such as a piezoelectric pick-up in audio reproduction equipment, alternatively the system may use a repetitively varying voltage as a *carrier* which is then used to convey information by superimposing a variation on the carrier. This technique, termed *modulation*, is widely used in radio-frequency communications.

In all these systems, manipulation of the electrical waveform to perform the required function satisfactorily is termed *signal processing* and the remainder of this chapter considers some of the basic techniques used, in addition to amplification considered in detail in chapters 3–8, to process signals.

9.2.1 *Limiting, clamping and rectification*

Limiting circuits

A limiter or clipper circuit ensures that a varying voltage does not exceed a certain value. In the passive limiter of figure 9.10a, $v_O = v_1$ while the diode is reverse biased, that is, while $v_1 < V_R$. When $v_1 > V_R$ the diode switches ON and, neglecting the small voltage drop across the diode, the output is fixed at the value V_R as shown in figure 9.10b for a sinusoidal input signal. During the time the limit is operative, the voltage difference $v_1 - V_R$ is dropped across the series resistor. In practice, this passive circuit provides a *soft* limit which means that during the limiting interval v_O does change slightly because of the changing voltage drop across the diode as the current through it increases, corresponding to the characteristic of figure 2.2c for V positive. With $V_R = 0$, the circuit simply removes the positive excursions of the signal providing a half-wave rectified output. If the diode and V_R reference are reversed, similar limiting occurs for v_1 negative. Combined parallel limiting branches enable v_O to be limited to a positive–negative range. In practice, the reference voltage may be provided by a breakdown diode, in fact by comparison with the model of such a diode (figure 11.15c, see also figure 1.5f) it can be seen that the diode, V_R branch in figure 9.10a can be implemented using a voltage-reference diode.

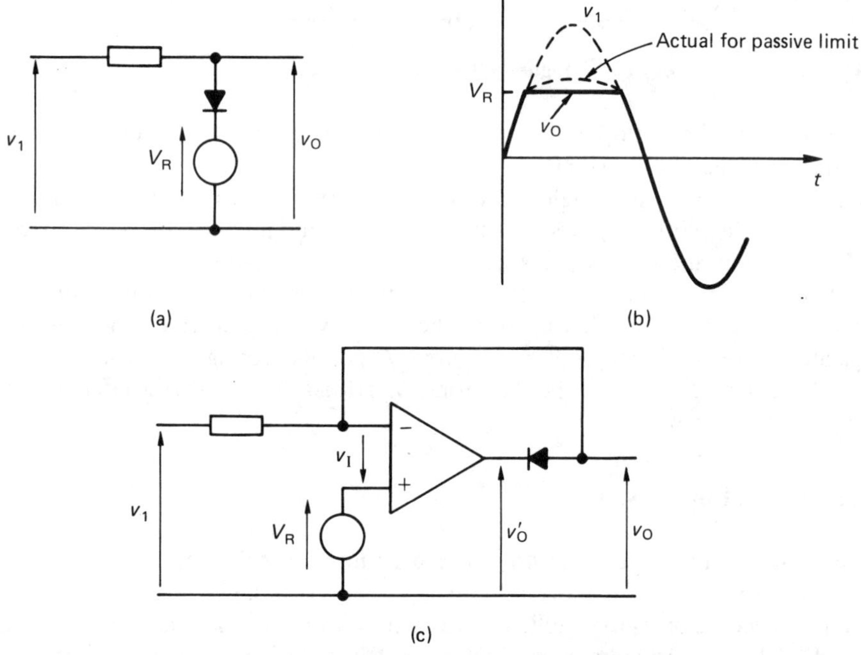

Figure 9.10 Signal limiting

A more precise limit, termed a *hard* limit, is provided by the active arrangement of figure 9.10c. With $v_1 < V_R$, the differential input voltage to the op-amp v_I is positive which makes v'_O positive whereby the diode is reverse-biased (open circuit) and $v_O = v_1$. When $v_1 > V_R$, v_I tends to be negative, making v'_O negative so that the diode conducts and the feedback becomes operative. The high gain of the op-amp causes v_O to rise to such a value to make $v_I = 0$ (section 7.1) which occurs when $v_O = V_R$ so that the output is clamped at the limit value. Because the feedback is from the output of the circuit, rather than the output of the op-amp, the circuit compensates for the voltage drop across the diode, v'_O rising to a higher value than v_O so that when fed back $v_O = V_R$ gives the equilibrium condition $v_I = 0$. Notice that when the limit is operative, the circuit operates as a voltage follower (figure 7.10a), the effective input voltage then being the V_R reference; the $v_1 - V_R$ difference then being dropped across the series resistor in the input branch.

Signal clamping

Section 3.3 explains the use of a series dc blocking capacitor to remove the static (constant, dc) component of a varying voltage. In some situations it is necessary to reintroduce a static component, termed *dc restoration*, which involves *clamping* the mean level of the ac signal to a finite voltage value.

Consider the circuit of figure 9.11a with $V_R = 0$ and v_1 sinusoidal. At switch ON, the first negative half cycle of v_1 causes the diode to conduct and the capacitor charges up to the peak value V_{1M} of v_1. Assuming the load connected across the circuit output draws negligible current, that is, it has very high input resistance, there is no discharge path for the capacitor and it therefore remains charged at $v_C = V_{1M}$. The output voltage $v_O = v_1 + v_C$ and so, for $V_R = 0$, the circuit adds a static component to the waveform equal to the amplitude of v_1 whereby the output voltage fluctuation becomes positive for all time, the negative peaks being clamped to zero voltage as shown in figure 9.11b. Clamping at levels other than V_{1M} can be achieved by adding a reference voltage V_R so that the capacitor charges to $V_R + V_{1M}$ when the diode conducts initially.

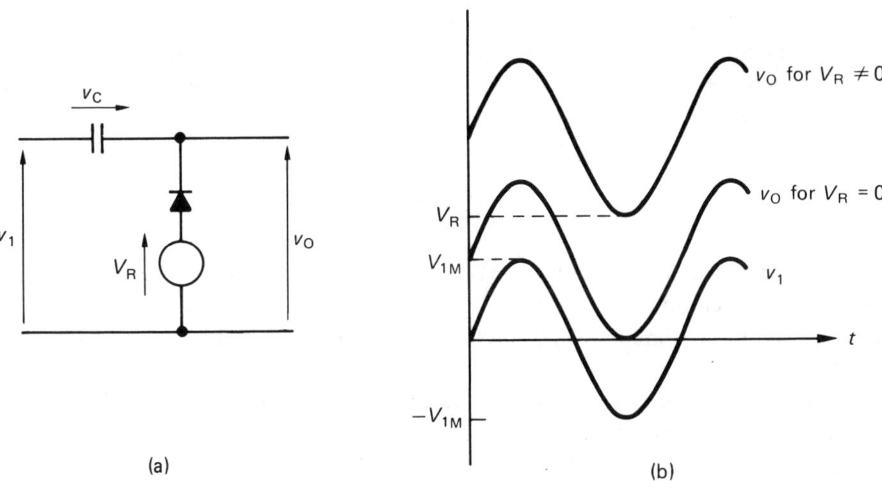

Figure 9.11 Signal clamping

Precision rectification

Half- or full-wave rectification to produce a unidirection voltage from an alternating source can be readily achieved using passive diode circuits for power supply applications as discussed in section 11.2.2. In such cases the forward voltage drop across the diode(s) is of little consequence; in a basic linear power supply, the number of turns on the secondary winding of the transformer is increased to provide a slightly higher output voltage to compensate. However in some rectification applications such as in measurement circuits, the input circuit of a DMM (digital multimeter) for ac ranges, for example, such a voltage loss cannot be tolerated and more precise rectification is required.

The circuit of figure 9.12a provides precise half-wave rectification, the op-amp compensating for the diode drop when v_1 is positive as in the limiter of figure 9.10c, by virtue of feedback from the output. With v_1 negative, v_O' is negative so that the diode is OFF and $v_O = 0$. When v_1 is positive, v_O' is positive, the diode conducts and because of the high gain of the op-amp v_O follows v_1 so that $v_I = 0$ at any instant (section 7.1) resulting in precise half-wave rectification (figure 9.12b).

The arrangement within the dashed box of figure 9.12c also provides precision half-wave rectification but with the advantage of a gain > 1 in the ON condition. With v_1 negative, v_O'' is positive so that D_1 is ON and D_2 OFF whereby $v_O' = 0$. For v_1 positive, v_O'' is negative, D_1 is OFF, D_2 ON, turning the circuit into an analog inverter (as figure 7.11b) providing $v_O' = -(R_F/R_1)v_1$.

By combining the half-wave circuit with an inverting mixer (figure 7.11c) having appropriate gains for each input, as in the complete circuit of figure 9.12c, precise full-wave rectification can be obtained. When v_1 is negative, the output of the half-wave circuit v_O' is zero as in the previous paragraph and the circuit output v_O is $-(R_F/R_1)v_1$ provided by the mixer. For v_1 positive, the half-wave circuit provides $v_O' = -(R_F/R_1)v_1$ and the circuit output, $v_O = -\left(\frac{R_F}{R_1}v_1 + 2v_O'\right)$, corresponding to equation 7.71 with $R_2 = R_F/2$ and $v_2 = v_O'$, is therefore $+(R_F/R_1)v_1$. The corresponding waveforms for a sinusoidal input are then as shown in figure 9.12d. The circuit is also termed a *modulus* or *absolute-value* circuit since $v_O = |v_1|$ at any instant.

Note that a suitable-value capacitor connected across the output of the full-wave circuit, providing basic capacitance smoothing (section 11.2.3), converts the circuit into a precision *peak detector* having an output as shown dashed in figure 9.12d. Such a circuit provides demodulation of an amplitude-modulated carrier (section 9.2.4), the output of the peak detector follows the waveform envelope.

9.2.2 ***Filtering***

In many signal processing applications it is necessary to select or reject a range of frequency components from a complex waveform. Typical examples are

(1) the removal of low-frequency interference such as that induced from ac mains, commonly termed *hum*,
(2) the removal of high-frequency interference induced from high-speed switching circuits,
(3) the directing of particular frequency ranges to specific equipment such as in the use of a *crossover* network in an audio reproduction system that directs high-frequency components of the audio signal to a HF loudspeaker and low-frequency components to a LF loudspeaker,

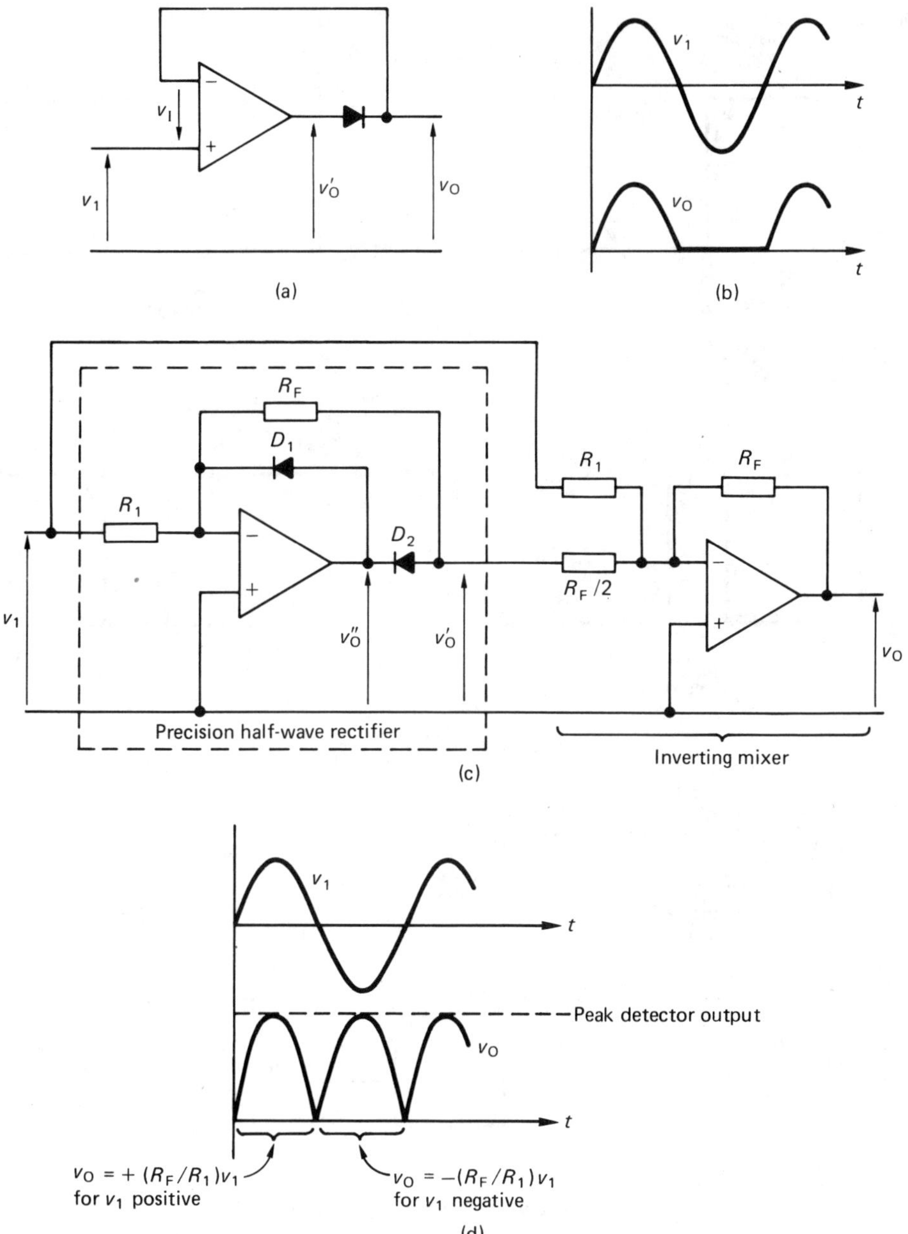

Figure 9.12 Precision rectification

(4) selection of a particular frequency component from a complex waveform such as that received by a radio aerial.

Such frequency selection or rejection is termed *filtering*.

Filters are classified as low pass, high pass, band pass and band stop according to their |gain|–frequency response. Idealised characteristics are shown in figure 9.13 with corresponding practical responses represented by dashed lines. A range of high-frequency

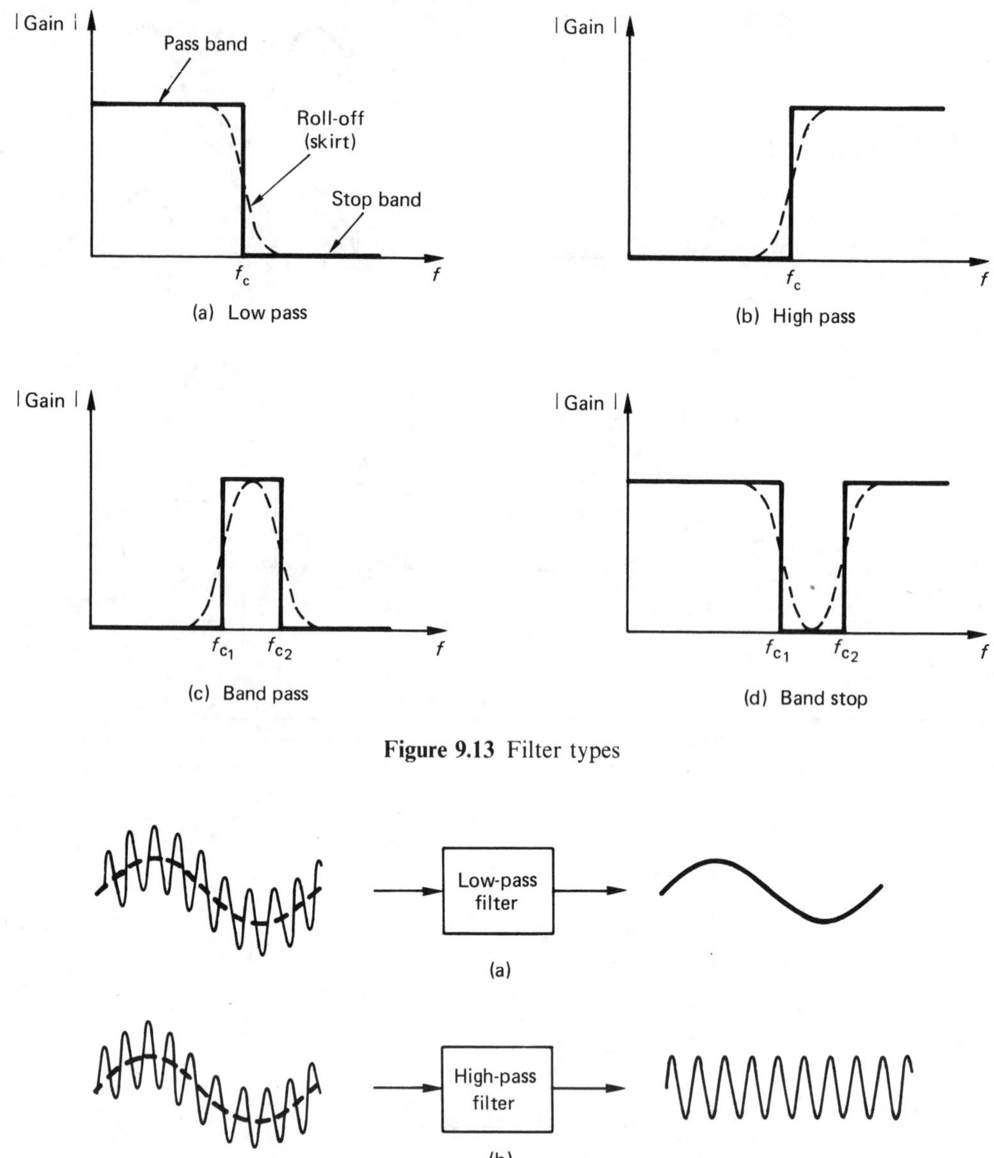

Figure 9.13 Filter types

Figure 9.14 Filter performance

interference can be removed using a low-pass filter (figure 9.14a), the cut-off frequency f_c being selected above the range of the required signal components but below the lowest frequency of the unwanted interference. Similarly, low-frequency interference such as mains hum can be removed using a high-pass filter (figure 9.14b), the cut-off being above the frequency of the interference but below the lowest frequency of the signal components. Where a narrow band of interference frequencies occurs *within* the range of signal frequencies, a sharp *notch* or band-stop filter is useful to remove the interference with only minimal effect on the range of signal components. A band-pass filter is useful in selecting a narrow band of frequency components from a complex signal such as that received in a communication system. An audio crossover network can be implemented using low- and high-pass filters each routing frequency components to the appropriate loudspeaker. In all cases the sharpness of the response at the cut-off frequency is of fundamental importance because it determines the selective quality of the filter.

Before the development of low-cost, high-performance op-amps, filters comprised passive *CR* or *LC* networks. Section 4.1 shows that basic *CR* circuits provide low- and high-pass responses, the gain being 3 dB down (that is, 3 dB below the gain in the pass band) at the breakpoint f_{lo} or f_{hi}, which correspond here to f_c, while the roll-off of the filter 'skirt' is ± 20 dB/decade. This gentle roll-off does not provide adequate selectivity for most practical cases; increased sharpness can be achieved by cascading a number of *CR* sections although because of the loading of one section on another, inter-stage buffering is required using, for example, op-amp voltage followers (figure 7.10a), resulting in a cascade of circuits of the type shown in figure 9.15a. This would provide a low-pass response which has a cut-off frequency

$$f_c = \frac{1}{2\pi C_1 R_1} \tag{9.42}$$

corresponding to equation 4.3. For a high-pass response the positions of the capacitors and resistors in the cascade are interchanged, the cut-off frequency still being given by equation 9.42 corresponding to equation 4.8. Such cascades, having n sections, provide a roll-off slope of $\pm 20n$ dB/decade so that n can be selected to provide the required skirt slope, but the arrangement has the disadvantage that as n is increased the gain at the cut-off frequency is progressively reduced resulting in a more 'rounded' knee in the response.

Performance is improved by introducing feedback as in the arrangement of figure 9.15b which is the basic form of the popular Sallen and Key *active filter* named after its originators. Feedback is provided by connecting the capacitor of the input *CR* section to the filter output instead of to signal earth as it is in the basic *CR* cascade. This circuit is a second-*order* filter ($n = 2$) as it has two *CR* time constants or *poles* [1b, 3b] resulting ultimately in a -40 dB/decade skirt slope. Higher order filters can easily be formed; a third-order version is produced by adding a *CR* section at the input of the second-order circuit as in figure 9.15c, while fourth- and fifth-order types are formed respectively by cascading two second-order circuits and third- and second-order circuits, and so on. Practical applications sometimes require filters of up to tenth order.

In addition to the skirt slope of $\pm 20n$ dB/decade, other important filter parameters are
(1) sharpness of the knee,
(2) pass band ripple,
(3) phase response.

Different values of resistances and capacitances in an active filter that incorporates feedback result in slightly different responses even for the same cut-off frequency. These responses, the most important of which are termed Chebyshev, Butterworth and Bessel, each optimise one of the above performance parameters. Figure 9.15d compares the responses for a fifth-order case; note that the ultimate skirt slope is the same in each case, $-20(5) = -100$ dB/decade.

Positive feedback via the feedback capacitor in the Chebyshev version causes a peak in the response near f_c which cancels the reduced gain at this frequency because of the multiple *CR* sections providing a very sharp knee; however, this is accompanied by ripple in the pass band. In the Butterworth type, pass band ripple is minimised but the knee is not as sharp as with the Chebyshev filter; the Butterworth response is described as having a *maximally flat pass band*. In section 4.6 it is shown that to avoid phase distortion, a system must have a linear

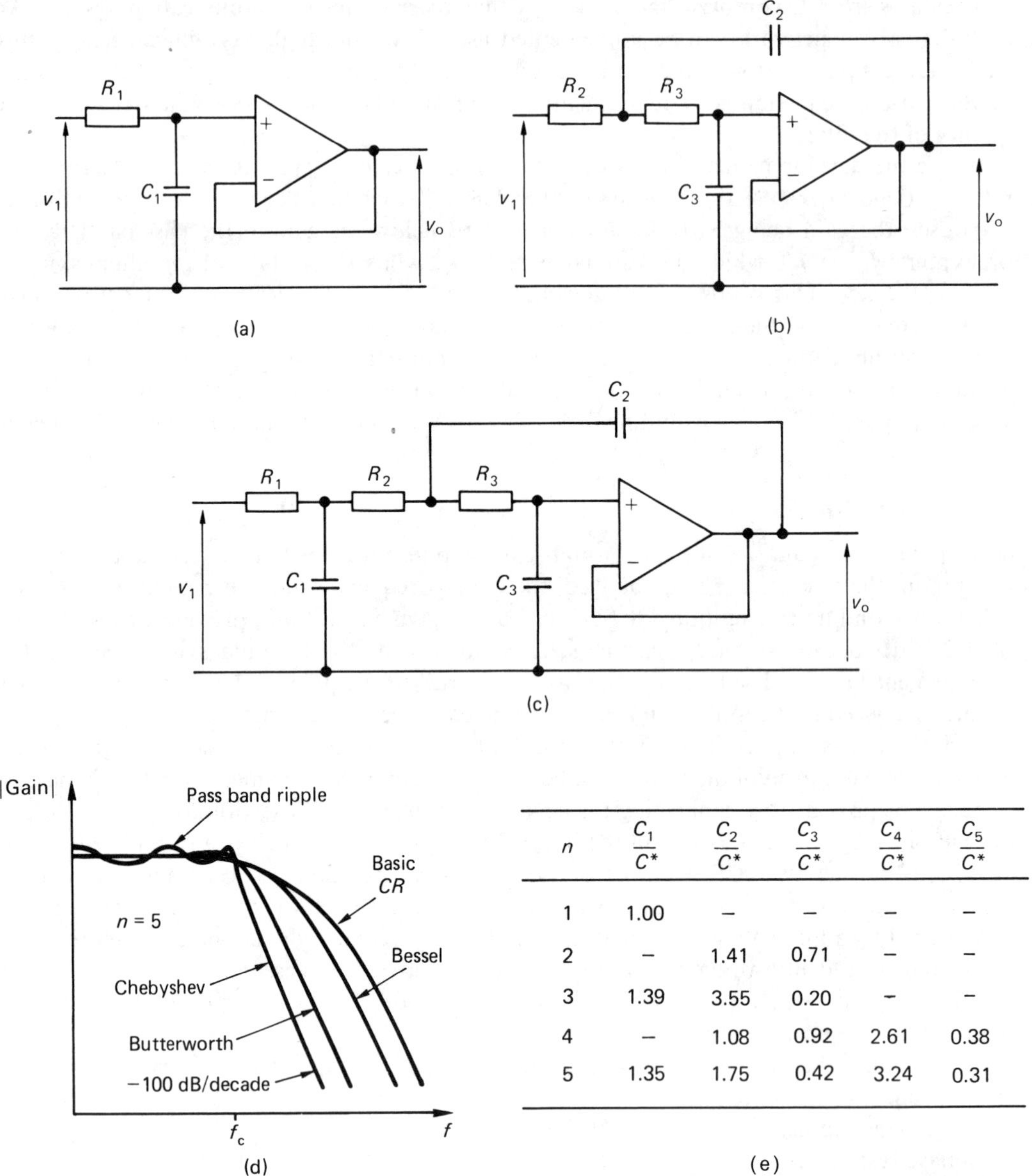

n	$\frac{C_1}{C^*}$	$\frac{C_2}{C^*}$	$\frac{C_3}{C^*}$	$\frac{C_4}{C^*}$	$\frac{C_5}{C^*}$
1	1.00	–	–	–	–
2	–	1.41	0.71	–	–
3	1.39	3.55	0.20	–	–
4	–	1.08	0.92	2.61	0.38
5	1.35	1.75	0.42	3.24	0.31

Figure 9.15 Active filters

phase–frequency response and the filter that most closely provides this feature is the Bessel type, but this is achieved at the expense of knee sharpness. The type of response selected for a particular application depends on which of these aspects of filter performance is most significant in the case concerned.

Texts concerned with the detailed design of active filters [4, 5] provide tables that greatly simplify the selection of component values to provide a particular type of response. In order to represent the general case, normalised values are normally quoted; a representative section of such a table for low-pass Butterworth responses of up to fifth order is given in figure 9.15e.

Values are normalised in this case to the value of capacitance C^* for the first-order circuit of figure 9.15a, which, from equation 9.42, gives

$$C^* = \frac{1}{2\pi f_c R} \tag{9.43}$$

where R is the selected resistance value. Having chosen the skirt slope, and hence the filter order, to meet the required specification, a suitable value of R is selected (section 7.5) and C^* can then be calculated using equation 9.43 for the particular cut-off frequency f_c required. Actual capacitance values are then calculated by multiplying the appropriate normalised values in the table by C^*. For example, if a second-order Butterworth response is required having $f_c = 5$ kHz, the second-order circuit of figure 9.15b would be selected and making $R_2 = R_3 = R = 10\,\mathrm{k\Omega}$, C^* is 3.18 nF from equation 9.43. From the table of figure 9.15e, a second-order Butterworth response requires $C_2/C^* = 1.41$ and $C_3/C^* = 0.71$, giving component values $C_2 = 1.41 \times 3.18\,\mathrm{nF} = 4.48\,\mathrm{nF}$ and $C_3 = 0.71 \times 3.18\,\mathrm{nF} = 2.26\,\mathrm{nF}$.

The fourth- and fifth-order filters, formed by cascading two second-order circuits and third- and second-order circuits respectively, columns 4 and 5 in the table, refer to capacitors in the second-order section, R_4, C_4, R_5, C_5 corresponding to R_2, C_2, R_3, C_3 in figure 9.15b.

Example 9.2: Filter design

A communications circuit receives signals up to 10 kHz with a signal strength of 100 mV; any induced high-frequency noise must be at least 40 dB below the signal level. In a particular application a 20 mV, 20 kHz noise signal is induced at the input of the circuit. Design a suitable Butterworth filter to overcome this problem.

The requirement is for a low-pass filter that has a pass band up to 10 kHz (f_c) with a skirt slope that will attenuate the 20 mV, 20 kHz noise signal sufficiently.

A voltage ratio of -40 dB is a numerical ratio of $10^{\frac{-40}{20}} = 1/100$, so that the filter must attenuate the noise voltage to 1/100th of the signal voltage, that is, $100/100 = 1$ mV.

Reduction of the noise voltage from 20 mV to 1 mV is an attenuation of 26 dB and so the filter response must fall from 0 dB at 10 kHz (f_c) to -26 dB at 20 kHz.

The frequency range 10 kHz–20 kHz is $\log(20/10) \simeq 0.3$ decade, and so the minimum required skirt slope is -26 dB/0.3 decade $= -86.7$ dB/decade. As the skirt slope of an nth-order low-pass filter is $-20n$ dB/decade, it follows that a fifth-order filter is required in this case.

This can be implemented by cascading the third-order circuit of figure 9.15c with a second-order circuit (figure 9.15b, with components R_2, C_2, R_3, C_3 relabelled R_4, C_4, R_5, C_5 respectively).

Choosing equal-value resistors ($10\,\mathrm{k\Omega}$), section 7.5, a value of $f_c = 10$ kHz requires $C^* = 1.59$ nF, equation 9.43, and from the normalised capacitance values for $n = 5$ (figure 9.15e), $C_1 = 1.35 \times 1.59\,\mathrm{nF} = 2.15\,\mathrm{nF}$, $C_2 = 1.75 \times 1.59\,\mathrm{nF} = 2.78\,\mathrm{nF}$, $C_3 = 0.42 \times 1.59\,\mathrm{nF} = 0.67\,\mathrm{nF}$, $C_4 = 3.24 \times 1.59\,\mathrm{nF} = 5.15\,\mathrm{nF}$ and $C_5 = 0.31 \times 1.59\,\mathrm{nF} = 0.49\,\mathrm{nF}$.

The above work concerned with low-pass filters can be applied to the corresponding high-pass case if resistors and capacitors in the circuits of figure 9.15 are interchanged. In the high-pass case, the values given in figure 9.15e are normalised resistances R^*/R_n where R^*, from equation

9.42, is

$$R^* = \frac{1}{2\pi f_c C} \tag{9.44}$$

C being the selected capacitance value. The design procedure is therefore to select a suitable value for all the capacitors in the filter and then to calculate the normalising resistance value R^* for the required cut-off frequency. The required resistance values $R_1, R_2, \ldots R_n$ can then be determined by dividing R^* by the corresponding values quoted in the table.

A band-pass response can be obtained by cascading low-pass and high-pass filters while parallel connection provides a band-stop filter. It should be emphasised however that although this section has concentrated on the popular Sallen and Key circuit, there are many different designs [4, 5], some of which yield solutions that are more component efficient than the Sallen and Key version for certain responses.

The main attraction of active filters is that all types of filter responses can be achieved without the need for inductors which are generally unpopular because of their bulk, cost and lossy performance (section 2.4.3). Note that the resonant performance once utilised in passive LC filters is now achievable via positive feedback in active CR circuits (see tutorial question 9.10). Determination of the input impedance of some active CR circuits shows that they display inductive properties for certain component values (see tutorial question 9.12). This feature explains how responses that can only be achieved using inductors in passive circuits can be implemented without inductors using active circuits.

In some applications, an active filter is used for its phase shifting properties rather than as a frequency selector. Consider the circuit of figure 9.16a; analysis follows the same procedure as for the subtractor of section 7.3.1: first the input potentials v^+ and v^- are determined, then, knowing that $v_I = 0$ for linear operation (section 7.1), v^+ and v^- can be equated to determine the transfer function v_o/v_1. For the circuit of figure 9.16a:

$$v^+ = \left[\frac{1/j\omega C}{R + (1/j\omega C)}\right] v_1 = \frac{v_1}{1 + j\omega CR} \tag{9.45}$$

and

$$v^- = \frac{v_1 + v_o}{2} \tag{9.46}$$

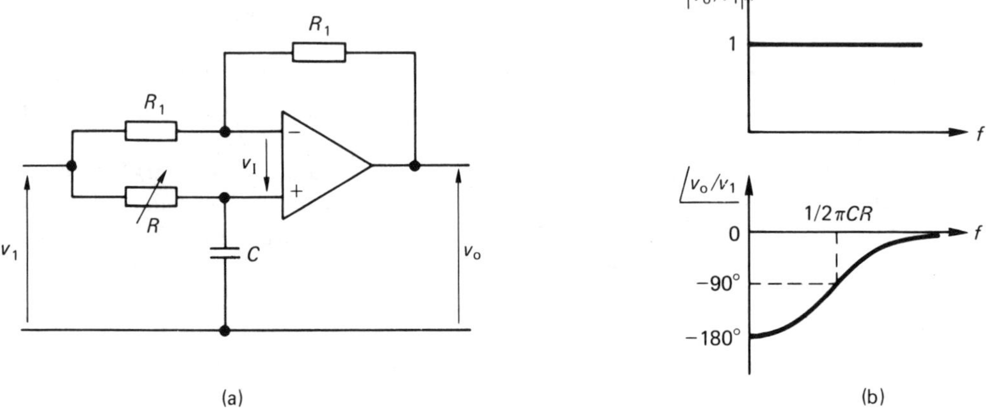

Figure 9.16 All-pass active filter

The latter relation corresponds to equation 7.74 with input signal v_1 and equal-value input and feedback resistances. Equating expressions 9.45 and 9.46 gives

$$\frac{v_o}{v_1}=\frac{1-j\omega CR}{1+j\omega CR} \tag{9.47}$$

indicating that the gain $|v_o/v_1|$ is unity (independent of frequency), hence the term *all-pass* to describe this type of filter, and the phase response is

$$\begin{aligned}\angle v_o/v_1 &= \tan^{-1}(-\omega CR)-\tan^{-1}(\omega CR)\\ &= -2\tan^{-1}(2\pi fCR)\end{aligned} \tag{9.48}$$

since $\tan(-\theta)=-\tan\theta$.
Within the bandwidth limitation of the op-amp, the circuit thus has a flat gain response and is therefore not frequency selective. A phase lag is however introduced between v_1 and v_o producing a time delay which makes the circuit useful in delay equalisation.

9.2.3 *Shaping*

It is sometimes necessary to modify the transfer (output/input) characteristic of a system; this process is termed *shaping* and a circuit providing the modification is called a *shaper*. A common application is in *linearisation* where the system transfer characteristic is non-linear but the requirement is for an output that is proportional to the input, possibly to drive a display. By cascading the system with a shaper having a suitable transfer characteristic, the latter can compensate for the system non-linearity, thereby linearising the response as considered in example 9.3.

A piecewise-linear (PWL) shaper approximates a non-linear characteristic by a number of linear *segments*. Figure 9.17a shows a two-segment representation, the change from one segment to the other occurring at *breakpoint* voltage V_B. In this example, the characteristic is of current against voltage and so the slope of each segment represents $\Delta I/\Delta V$ which is the reciprocal of *slope resistance*. For $0 \leqslant V \leqslant V_B$, the PWL approximation represents the system as a slope resistance r_1, while for $V > V_B$ the system approximates to slope resistance r_2.

The PWL approximation of figure 9.17a can be implemented by the network of figure 9.17b. Assuming the diode to be ideal (no forward voltage drop and no reverse leakage), when $0 \leqslant V \leqslant V_B$ the diode is switched OFF, no current flows through R_2 and I is given simply by V/R_1. By selecting R_1 equal to slope resistance r_1, the network has the same transfer characteristic as segment 1 in figure 9.17a. When V exceeds V_B, current flows through both R_1 and R_2, given by

$$\begin{aligned}I &= \frac{V}{R_1}+\frac{V-V_B}{R_2}\\ &= \left(\frac{R_1+R_2}{R_1R_2}\right)V-\frac{V_B}{R_2}\end{aligned} \tag{9.49}$$

Equation 9.49 shows the I–V relationship for $V > V_B$ to be linear (compare with the standard straight line form $y = mx + C$) having gradient $\left(\frac{R_1+R_2}{R_1R_2}\right)$ and I-axis intercept $\frac{-V_B}{R_2}$ as shown in figure 9.17c. Note that as V_B/R_2 is not $f(V)$, the differential relationship $\Delta I/\Delta V$ is

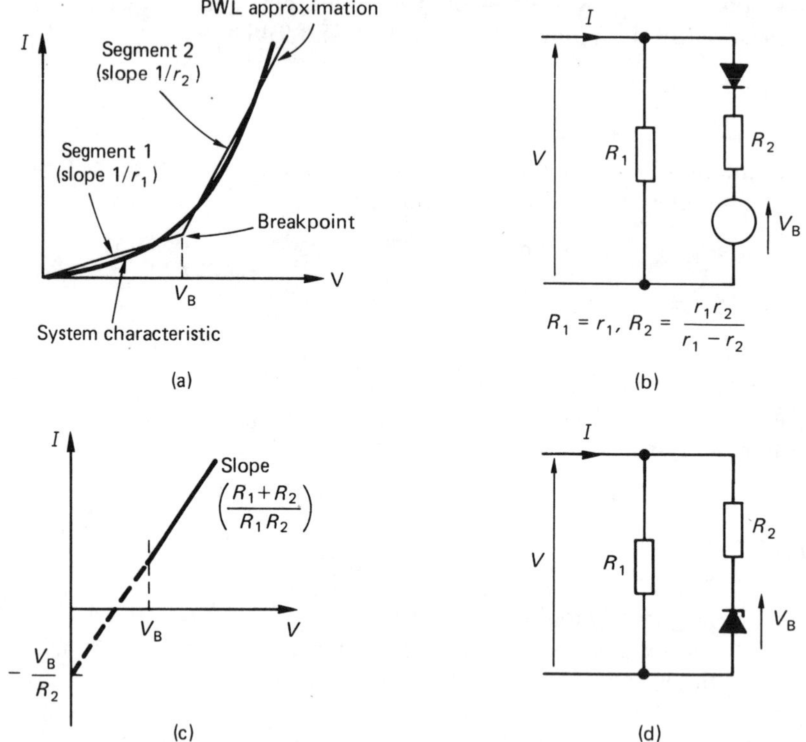

Figure 9.17 Principles of piecewise-linear representation

$\frac{R_1 + R_2}{R_1 R_2} = \frac{1}{R_1 /\!/ R_2}$ where // signifies 'in parallel with'. Thus *as far as the change of I with V* is concerned, R_1 and R_2 are effectively in parallel. If R_2 is selected so that $\frac{R_1 R_2}{R_1 + R_2} = r_2$, the circuit of figure 9.17b implements the PWL approximation of figure 9.17a. As $R_1 = r_1$, it follows that $R_2 = \frac{r_1 r_2}{r_1 - r_2}$. Figure 11.15c shows that the reverse characteristic of a voltage-reference diode can be modelled as a series diode–resistor–dc supply branch which corresponds to the R_2 branch in figure 9.17b. Thus this branch can be replaced by a voltage-reference diode as in figure 9.17d; if the slope resistance r_z of the reference diode is significant, the value of R_2 must be reduced accordingly though often r_z is negligible. Further consideration of PWL representation can be found in reference [2b].

In most applications it is a voltage transfer characteristic (v_O against v_I) that requires shaping, not a current–voltage relationship. The current–voltage *shaper network* (figure 9.17d) can be used to produce a shaped voltage–voltage characteristic using an op-amp. Consider replacement of resistor R_1 in the non-inverting amplifier of figure 7.10c by the shaper network as in figure 9.18a; input voltage v_I is applied across the shaper network as $v_I \simeq 0$ for linear operation (equation 7.3) and so for $v_I < V_B$ the resistance of the shaper network is R_1 while for $v_I > V_B$ the effective resistance is $R_1 /\!/ R_2$. The voltage gain of the basic circuit (figure 7.10c) is $\left(1 + \frac{R_F}{R_1}\right)$ (equation 7.51) and so the gain of the shaper circuit (figure 9.18a) is $\left(1 + \frac{R_F}{R_1}\right)$

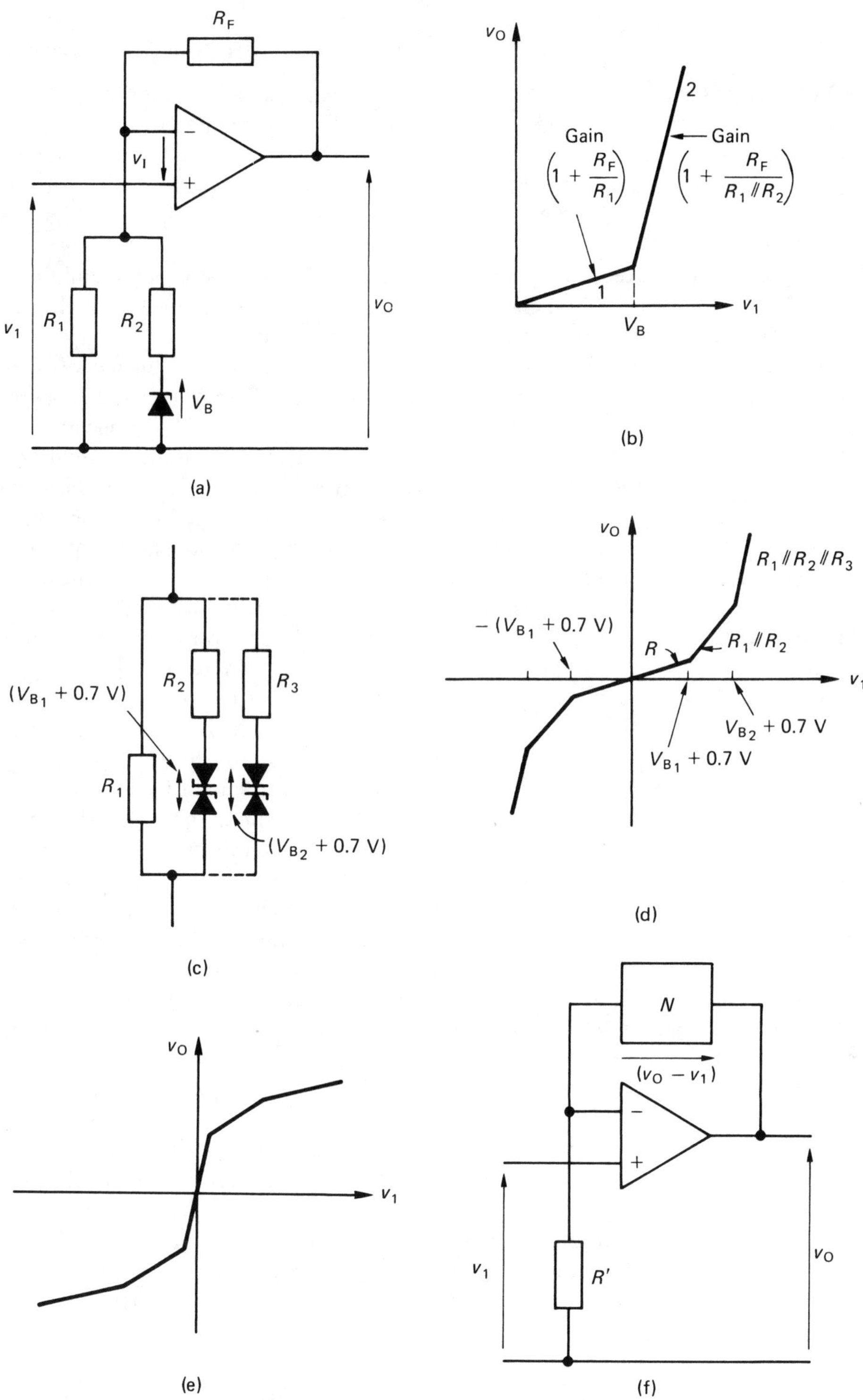

Figure 9.18 Piecewise-linear shaping

for $v_1 < V_B$ and $\left(1 + \frac{R_F}{R_1 /\!/ R_2}\right)$ for $v_1 > V_B$, resulting in the transfer characteristic of figure 9.18b. Note that as $R_1 /\!/ R_2 < R_1$, the slope of segment 2 is greater than that of segment 1.

A characteristic with symmetry about the origin can be obtained by the use of back-to-back reference diodes as in figure 9.18c. For either polarity of v_1 beyond the breakpoint, one of the back-to-back diodes will be at breakdown while the other is forward-biased with a voltage drop of about 0.7 V across it and the breakpoints are therefore $\pm(V_B + 0.7\,\text{V})$ for the symmetrical characteristic.

Shaping can be improved by using more segments in the PWL representation which corresponds to adding more branches to the shaper network (figure 9.18c); the resulting three-segment approximation is then as shown in figure 9.18d.

For the circuit arrangement of figure 9.18a, as v_1 increases more branches of the shaper network conduct and the resistance from the − input of the op-amp to ground progressively reduces, resulting in a *rising type* characteristic (figures 9.18b, d). If the application requires a *saturating type* characteristic (figure 9.18e) one possible implementation would be to use the shaper network N as the feedback branch replacing R_F in the basic circuit, instead of R_1, as in figure 9.18f whereby increasing voltage causes the effective feedback resistance R_F to reduce hence reducing the gain (equation 7.51). This arrangement has the practical disadvantage that the voltage across the shaper network is $(v_O - v_1)$ and therefore the breakpoint voltages do not appear directly on the transfer characteristic, they must be calculated. Noting in addition that the breakpoint voltage values that can be used in practice are restricted to available components (see example 9.3), it can be seen that this is a major complication. Fortunately this difficulty can be avoided by basing the shaper on the inverting amplifier of figure 7.11b which conveniently provides a *saturating* characteristic when R_F is replaced by the shaper network N (figures 9.19a, b) although inversion is introduced between v_1 and v_O. In cases where the source of v_1 is 'floating', that is, neither terminal is connected to signal earth, this is not a problem since the input connections can simply be reversed to provide a characteristic in quadrants 1 and 3. If one side of the v_1 source is grounded, the polarity of the input signal must first be inverted using an analog inverter (figure 7.11b with $R_F = R_1$ so that $A_{CL} = -1$, equation 7.65) before it is applied to the shaper. In this arrangement the voltage across the shaper network is v_O (figure 9.19a, $v_I \simeq 0$, equation 7.3) and so the breakpoint values are read from the v_O-axis of the characteristic (figure 9.19b). If the shaper network is included in the input branch of the inverting amplifier (figure 9.19c), an inverted rising type characteristic results and as v_1 appears across the network the breakpoint values are read from the v_1-axis (figure 9.19d).

If the input to the shaper is made proportional to time (a ramp or sawtooth waveform), a shaper can be used as a waveform generator. A multi-function generator providing square, sawtooth and sinusoidal outputs could be implemented using an astable switching circuit (figure 10.5a) to produce a square wave which, applied to an integrator, would provide a sawtooth waveshape (figure 7.13). The sawtooth could then drive a PWL shaper to generate an approximate sinusoidal output, although this last operation could alternatively be provided by a filter. Note that, in all these applications, the slew rate of the op-amps (section 7.4.4) must be adequate taking account of the maximum value of dv_O/dt to avoid increased distortion.

Design procedure for a PWL shaper

(1) Plot the required transfer characteristic *accurately* on squared paper. The plot should be reasonably large, such as A4 size, for good accuracy. Where a symmetrical characteristic is required, only one quadrant need be constructed.

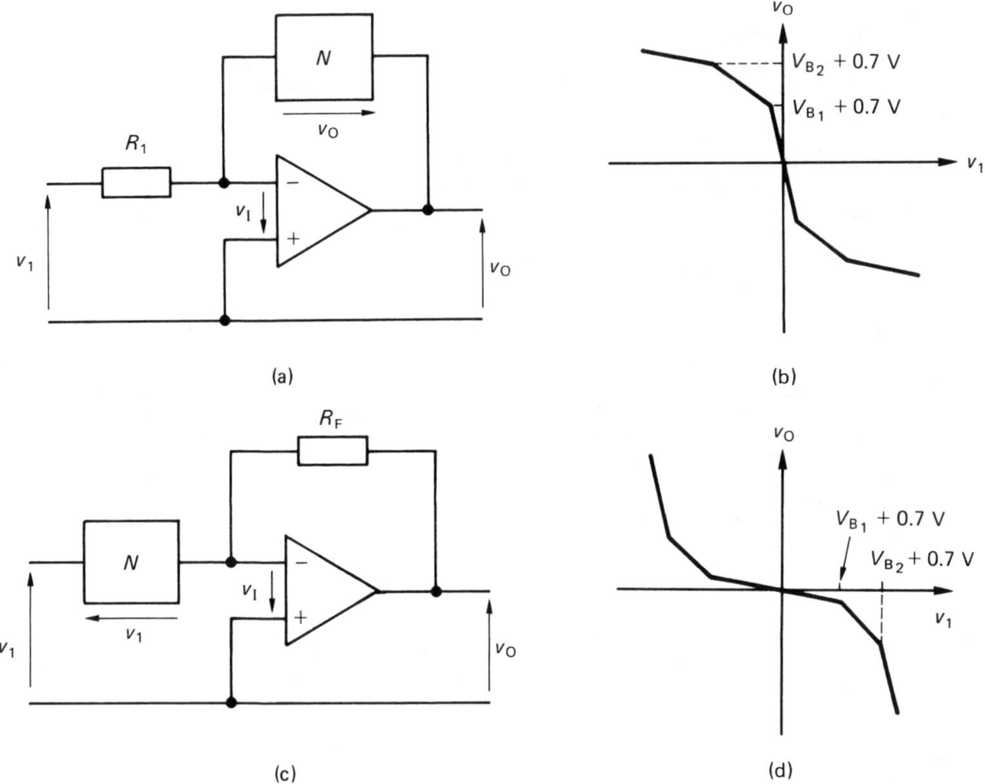

Figure 9.19 Inverting PWL shapers

(2) Identify the circuit configuration required taking account of the quadrant(s) and form (rising or saturating) of the characteristic (figures 9.20a, b, c). Note the complication of using a type 1 circuit to provide a saturating characteristic as regards the breakpoint voltage values (described above); in this case it is usually more convenient to use a type 2 circuit with the input inverted.

(3) For the chosen circuit, ascertain whether the switching points of the diodes in the shaper network N are controlled directly by the input or output voltage of the circuit.

(4) Mark on the v_1 or v_O axes of the characteristic, as appropriate, the breakdown voltages V_B of available voltage-reference diodes such as the type BZX 79 series (appendix E, section E.2). Such diodes are available with values of V_B in the E24 series (appendix D) between 2.4 V and 75 V. Note that for a symmetrical characteristic, 0.7 V must be added to each of the breakdown values to allow for the forward drop across one diode of the back-to-back pair (figure 9.18c). Low-value breakpoints below about 2.5 V can be implemented using forward-biased general-purpose diodes, n diodes connected in series giving a voltage drop of $0.7n$ V, or stabistors [2c]. Note that for these low-value breakpoints, back-to-back connections to produce a symmetrical characteristic cannot be used, instead separate parallel branches are required for $\pm v_1$.

(5) Linear segments are then drawn between the available breakpoints to represent adequately the required characteristic (figure 9.20d), long segments representing approximately linear regions, short segments being used in regions of widely varying slope. The best

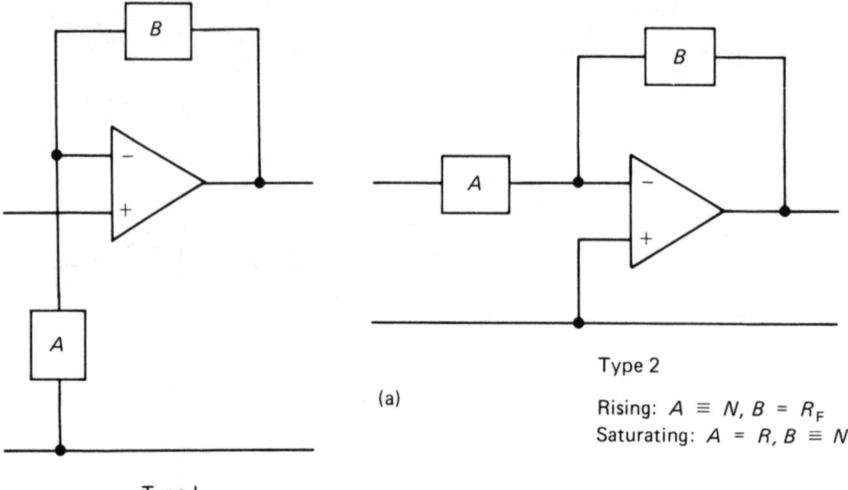

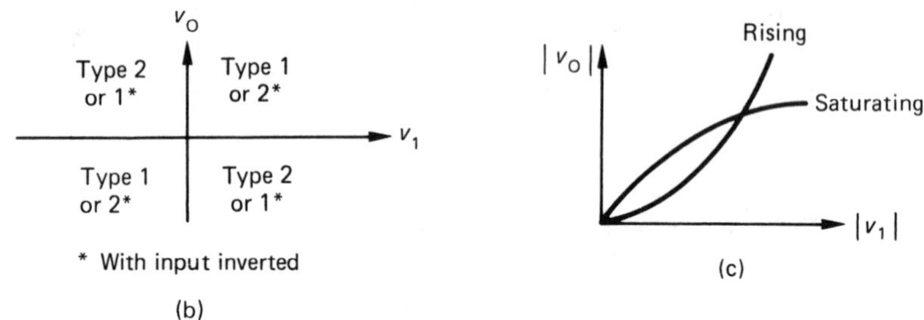

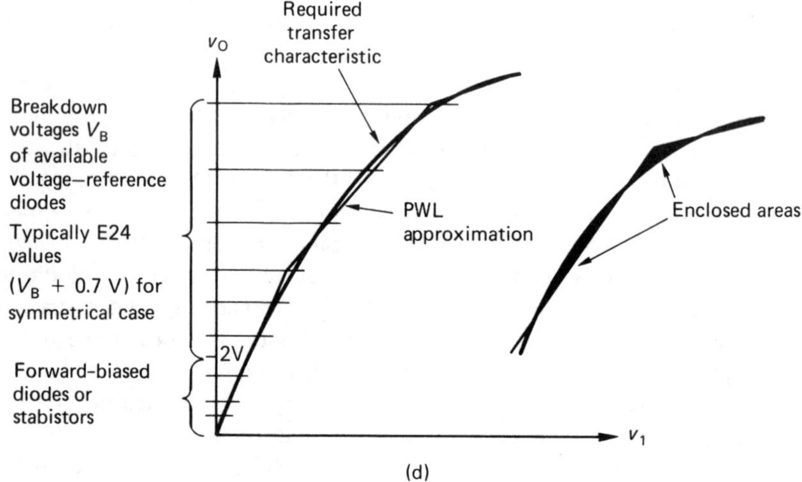

Figure 9.20 PWL shaper design

approximation using a small number of segments usually requires the segments to cross the 'true' characteristic; the objective is to minimise the 'enclosed areas' (figure 9.20d) and approximately to equalise the areas enclosed above and below the characteristic.

(6) The slopes of the chosen segments then give the incremental gains required, from which the resistances for the various branches of the shaper network N can be calculated. Since the network involves parallel branches, it is usually easier to work in conductances as parallel-connected conductances are directly additive. Usually series/parallel combinations of close-tolerance (preferred) resistance values are required to implement the design (example 9.3).

Example 9.3: PWL shaper design

The output voltage v of a transducer varies with input parameter θ according to:

θ (units)	0	1	2	3	4	5
v (mV)	0	40	95	180	300	500

with a corresponding symmetrical response of negative v for negative θ, the transducer having a floating output. Design a three-segment shaper that, when cascaded with the transducer, provides an output v_O that is linear with θ such that as $|\theta| = 0–5$ units, $|v_O| = 0 - 15$ V.

The proposed arrangement is shown in figure 9.21a. From the θ, v values given above, it can be seen that the v/θ characteristic of the transducer has a rising form and so the v_O/v characteristic of the shaper must be a saturating type to produce an overall linear relationship between v_O and θ.

Addition to the required variation of v_O to the table as in figure 9.21b enables the required v_O/v characteristic for the shaper to be constructed as in figure 9.21c which, as expected, is of the saturating type.

Because of the difficulties outlined above in the use of the type 1 circuit (figure 9.20a) to produce a saturating response, it is decided to use a type 2 arrangement here, but as this is an inverting amplifier it is necessary to invert the input to provide positive v_O for positive θ. In this example the transducer output is known to be floating, neither of the transducer output connections being earthed, and so inversion of the shaper input is easily achieved by reversing the input connections as in figure 9.21e.

The change of slope of the required shaper characteristic is reasonably uniform and so segments of approximately equal length are chosen. For the inverting circuit, a saturating characteristic is obtained with the shaper network N as the feedback element (figure 9.19a) in which case it is v_O that directly controls the breakpoints. The appropriate range of E24 voltage-reference diode breakdown voltages, augmented by 0.7 V as a symmetrical response is required, that is, from 4.7 V + 0.7 V to 12.0 V + 0.7 V, is included along the v_O-axis (figure 9.21c). Breakpoints at v_O = 5.8 V and 10.7 V, using 5.1 V and 10 V diodes, are considered most suitable providing the PWL characteristic ABCD.

$$\text{Slope of segment 1} = \frac{5.8\ \text{V}}{0.088\ \text{V}} = 65.91$$

$$\text{Slope of segment 2} = \frac{10.7\ \text{V} - 5.8\ \text{V}}{0.243\ \text{V} - 0.088\ \text{V}} = 31.61$$

$$\text{Slope of segment 3} = \frac{15.4\ \text{V} - 10.7\ \text{V}}{0.500\ \text{V} - 0.243\ \text{V}} = 18.29$$

These slopes are the incremental gains of the circuit for the three regions of operation $0 \leqslant v_O \leqslant 5.8$ V, $5.8 \text{ V} \leqslant v_O \leqslant 10.7$ V, and $10.7 \text{ V} \leqslant v_O \leqslant 15.4$ V.

For $v_O \leqslant 5.8$ V, the gain modulus of the circuit (figure 9.21d) is R_1/R' since none of the diodes is conducting.

Choosing $R' = 1$ kΩ so that $R_1 = 65.91R' = 65.91$ kΩ is within the ideal range 1–100 kΩ for

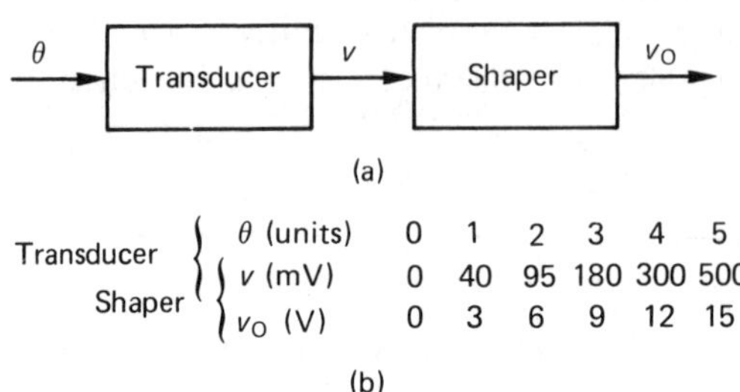

(a)

Transducer	θ (units)	0	1	2	3	4	5
Transducer / Shaper	v (mV)	0	40	95	180	300	500
Shaper	v_O (V)	0	3	6	9	12	15

(b)

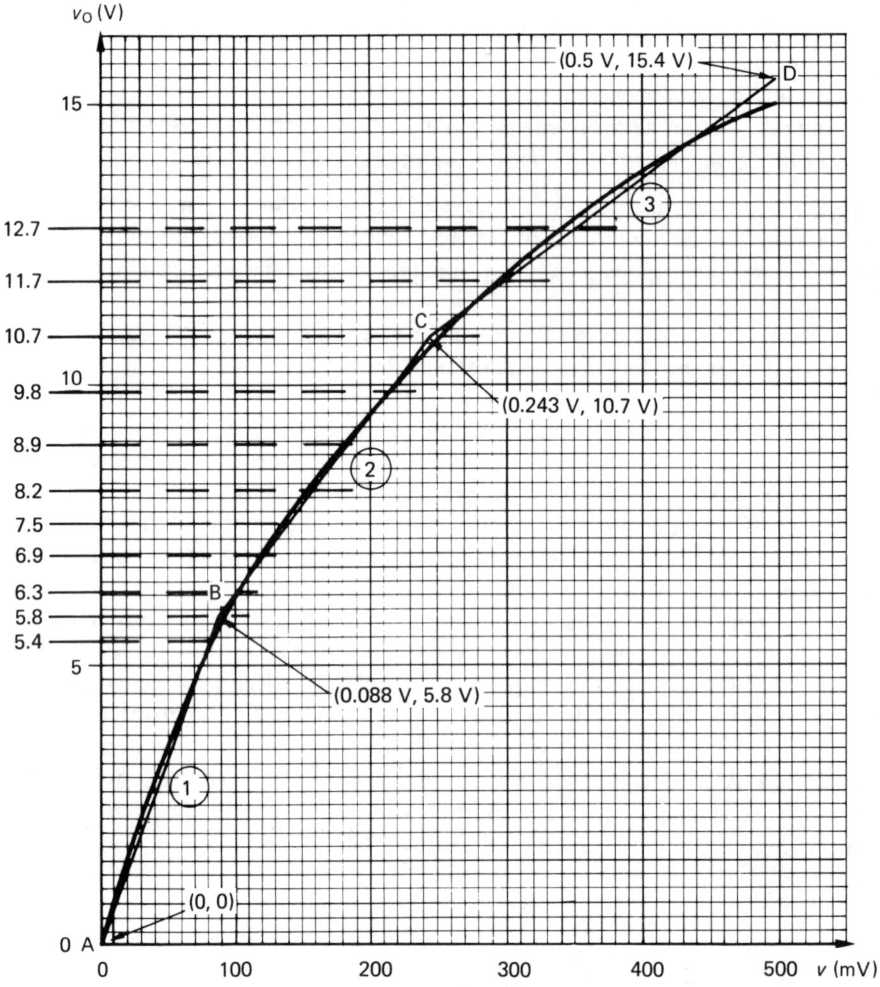

(c)

Figure 9.21 PWL shaper design example

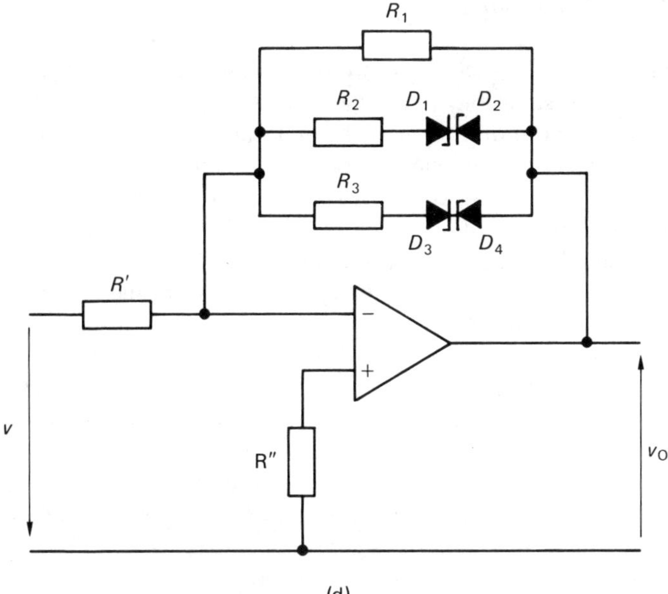

(d)

Figure 9.21 *continued*

a typical op-amp (section 7.5) enables R_1 to be implemented using 62 kΩ + 3.9 kΩ preferred E24 resistance values.

With D_1 and D_2 both 5.1 V diodes, the incremental gain of the circuit for $5.8\text{ V} \leqslant v_O \leqslant 10.7\text{ V}$ is $(R_1 /\!/ R_2)/R'$ which is $G'/(G_1 + G_2)$ in terms of conductances. $G' = 1/R' = 1/(1\text{ k}\Omega) = 1\text{ mS}$, $G_1 = 1/R_1 = 1/(65.9\text{ k}\Omega) = 15.17\ \mu\text{S}$, hence

$$\frac{G'}{G_1 + G_2} = \frac{1\text{ mS}}{15.17\ \mu\text{S} + G_2} = 31.61 \text{ (slope 2)}$$

from which

$$G_2 = 16.47\ \mu\text{S}$$

giving

$$R_2 = 1/(16.47\ \mu\text{S}) = 60.72\text{ k}\Omega$$

R_2 can therefore be implemented as 56 kΩ + 4.7 kΩ using preferred values.

D_3 and D_4 are both 10 V diodes and for $v_O \geqslant 10.7$ V the incremental gain is $(R_1 /\!/ R_2 /\!/ R_3)/R'$ or $G'/(G_1 + G_2 + G_3)$. Substituting the above values for G', G_1 and G_2 gives $G_3 = 23.03\ \mu\text{S}$ ($R_3 = 1/(23.03\ \mu\text{S}) = 43.42\text{ k}\Omega$) for an incremental gain of 18.29 (slope 3). R_3 could therefore be implemented using a single 43 kΩ resistor.

With the effective feedback resistance changing with v_O, calculation of a value for the offset minimising resistor R'' (section 7.4.2) cannot be precise. Usually the parallel combination of the first segment value R_1 and R' is taken as a compromise, in which case $(R_1 = 65.9\text{ k}\Omega) /\!/ (R' = 1\text{ k}\Omega) \simeq 1\text{ k}\Omega$ would be suitable.

The final design therefore is the circuit of figure 9.21d with: D_1 and $D_2 = 5.1$ V diodes, D_3 and $D_4 = 10$ V diodes, $R_1 = 62\text{ k}\Omega + 3.9\text{ k}\Omega$, $R_2 = 56\text{ k}\Omega + 4.7\text{ k}\Omega$, $R_3 = 43\text{ k}\Omega$ and $R' = R'' = 1\text{ k}\Omega$.

9.2.4 *Modulation and demodulation*

Fundamental signal processing activities in most communication systems are *modulation* at the sending end of the system and the dual process of *demodulation* at the receiving end. In analog communications, modulation is the shifting or *translation* of the frequency of a signal to make it suitable for transmission over the communication system. Direct transmission of the signal is not practical in most cases because of the frequency of the signal and the range of frequencies usually involved; a typical music signal, for example, has a frequency range of 20 Hz–20 kHz. The length of the transmitting and receiving aerials of a radio link is related to the frequency of the signal to be transmitted and, apart from the extremely long aerial that would be required to transmit signals at the lower end of the music spectrum, the *range* of frequencies would also create a major difficulty. If however transmission is based on a high frequency *carrier* on which the signal is superimposed, the communication system operates at the carrier frequency which, being high, avoids the need for excessively large aerials and so avoids the problem created by a wide range of frequency. The signal information is conveyed by varying a feature of the carrier, such as its amplitude, frequency or phase; *modulation* is the variation of a feature of the carrier in proportion to the signal. Figure 9.22 illustrates the case of amplitude modulation where the signal information is contained in the *envelope* of the modulated waveform. At the receiver, the signal must be extracted from the complex modulated waveform; this process is termed *demodulation.*

An additional major advantage of the use of modulation is that it enables *multiplexing* of the communication channel whereby many signals can be transmitted simultaneously over the same link. For example, by using a number of different carrier frequencies, each one being modulated by a separate signal, and transmitting the combined complex waveform, the individual signals can be detected at the receiver by using band-pass filters (section 9.2.2) to

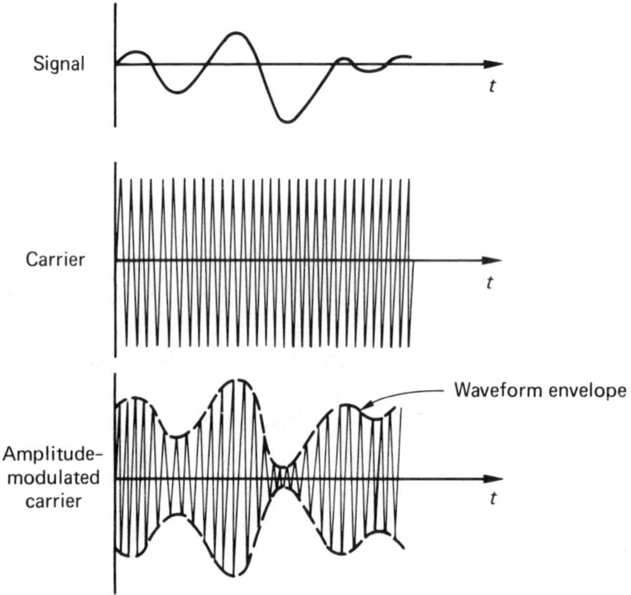

Figure 9.22 Amplitude modulation

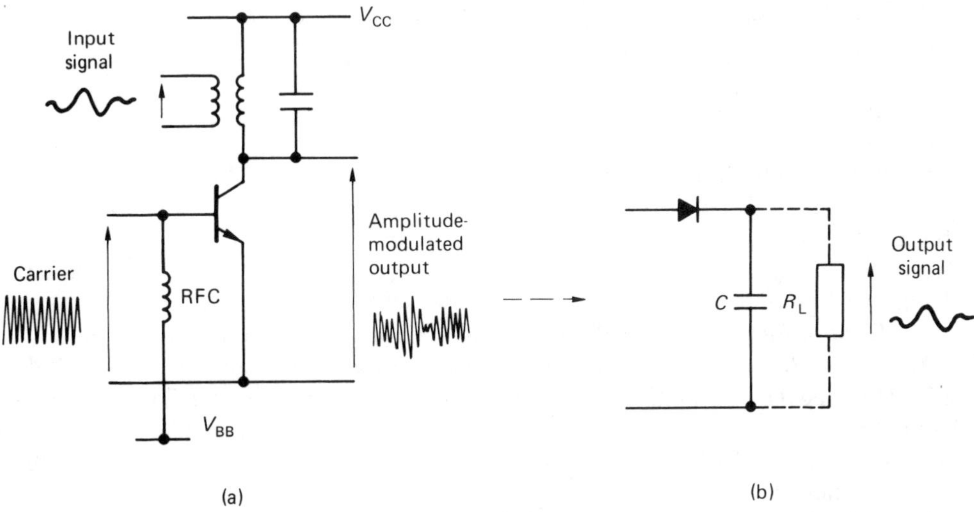

Figure 9.23 Modulator and demodulator for amplitude modulation system

select particular carrier frequencies prior to demodulation. This method of multiple use of a communication channel is called *frequency division multiplexing*. Detailed treatment of modulation and multiplexing techniques can be found in texts devoted to communication engineering such as references [6], [7] and [8].

Modulation involves multiplication. In the case of amplitude modulation (AM), the multiplication is between the signal and carrier waveforms; for frequency and phase modulation, the multiplication process is more involved. There are many versions of modulator; figure 9.23a shows one type of amplitude modulator based on the class C amplifier of section 8.6. The signal is superimposed on the power supply voltage V_{CC} using the transformer in the collector circuit so that the collector potential varies with the signal. Class C operation results in the BJT being repetitively driven to saturation so that the output voltage varies at the carrier frequency but has an amplitude proportional to the signal, thus providing an AM output.

At the receiver, the AM waveform can be demodulated using the peak detector circuit of figure 9.23b. The received voltage fluctuation is half-wave rectified by the diode and this is applied to a capacitor which charges to the peak value of the waveform. As the envelope voltage rises and falls, the capacitor voltage follows although to allow the capacitor to charge and discharge sufficiently rapidly to follow changes in the envelope voltage, the time constant CR_L must be sufficiently low in relation to the maximum signal frequency component. More detailed treatment of modulators and demodulators can be found in reference [9].

References and further reading

1. W.H. Hayt and J.E. Kemmerly, *Engineering Circuit Analysis*, 4th edition (McGraw-Hill, 1987)
   (a) chapter 5,
   (b) chapter 13

2. M.E. Goodge, *Semiconductor Device Technology* (Macmillan 1985)
   (a) appendix A2,
   (b) appendix A1,
   (c) section 2.1.3,
   (d) section 2.2.26
3. R.J. Smith, *Circuits, Devices and Systems*, 4th edition (Wiley, 1984)
   (a) chapter 8,
   (b) chapter 4
4. C.J. Savant, M.S. Roden and G.L. Carpenter, *Electronic Circuit Design*, chapter 13 (Benjamin/Cummings, 1987)
5. A.B. Williams, *Electronic Filter Design Handbook* (McGraw-Hill, 1981)
6. R.A. Williams, *Communication Systems Analysis and Design*, chapter 4 (Prentice-Hall, 1987)
7. J. Dunlop and D.G. Smith, *Telecommunications Engineering*, chapter 2 (Van Nostrand Reinhold, 1984)
8. D. Roddy and J. Coolen, *Electronic Communications*, 3rd edition, chapters 8 and 10 (Prentice-Hall, 1984)
9. G.M. Miller, *Modern Electronic Communication*, 2nd edition, chapters 2–6 (Prentice-Hall, 1983)
10. J. Millman and A. Grabel, *Microelectronics*, 2nd edition, chapters 2, 15 and 16 (McGraw-Hill, 1988)
11. F.H. Mitchell, *Introduction to Electronics Design*, chapters 13 and 14 (Prentice-Hall, 1988)
12. R.J. Maddock and D.M. Calcutt, *Electronics: A Course for Engineers*, chapters 5 and 6 (Longman, 1988)
13. T.L. Floyd, *Electronic Devices*, 2nd edition, chapters 15 and 16 (Merrill, 1988)
14. C.J. Savant, M.S. Roden and G.L. Carpenter, *Electronic Circuit Design*, chapters 1, 11, 12 and 13 (Benjamin/Cummings, 1987)
15. P.M. Chirlian, *Analysis and Design of Integrated Electronic Circuits*, 2nd edition, chapter 18 (Harper and Row/Wiley, 1987)
16. A.S. Sedra and K.C. Smith, *Microelectronic Circuits*, 2nd edition, chapters 5 and 13 (Holt, Rinehart and Winston, 1987)
17. T.F. Bogart, *Electronic Devices and Circuits*, chapter 14 (Merrill, 1986)
18. C.L. Alley and K.W. Atwood, *Microelectronics*, chapters 14 and 17 (Prentice-Hall, 1986)
19. G.M. Glasford, *Analog Electronic Circuits*, chapters 7 and 9 (Prentice-Hall, 1986)
20. M.S. Ghausi, *Electronic Devices and Circuits*, chapters 1, 9 and 10 (Holt-Saunders, 1985)
21. S.A. Knight, *Electronics for Higher TEC*, chapter 9 (Granada, 1983)
22. P. Horowitz and W. Hill, *The Art of Electronics*, chapters 3 and 4 (Cambridge, 1982)
23. D.C. Green, *Electronics for TEC Level IV*, chapter 7 (Pitman, 1981)

Tutorial questions

Note: Where applicable, answers correspond to rounding to 2 decimal places during calculation.

CR linear oscillators

9.1 The phase-shift oscillator of figure 9.3a is required to provide a 3 kHz sinusoidal output. If the input and output resistances of the op-amp are 1 MΩ and 100 Ω respectively, select suitable component values for the circuit, assuming E24 resistance and E12 capacitance values (appendix D) are available. What is the percentage error in the output frequency for the chosen component values compared with the required value? What would be the output frequency range if the selection tolerances of the chosen capacitance value is ± 10 per cent and that of the resistance value ± 2 per cent?

[Answers: Choose R within the range 1–100 kΩ; for $R = 10$ kΩ, C chosen as 2.2 nF; frequency error -1.67 per cent; frequency range 2.60–3.30 kHz]

9.2 Show that if the resistor and capacitor positions are interchanged in each of the three sections of the phase-shift network in figure 9.2, the transfer function (v_f/v_o) of the network is $[(1 - 5\omega^2C^2R^2) + j(6\omega CR - \omega^3C^3R^3)]^{-1}$. Hence confirm that the frequency of oscillation of the corresponding oscillator is $(\sqrt{6})/2\pi CR$ and that at this frequency the modulus of the gain of the network is 1/29.

9.3 Select components (E12 resistors and E6 capacitors) for a phase-shift oscillator, using a single JFET amplifying stage, that will provide a nominal 5 kHz sinusoidal output. The circuit is to operate from a 15 V dc supply and a suitable Q-point for the JFET may be taken as $I_{D(sat)} = 1$ mA, $V_{GS} = -2$ V, g_{fs} being 4.5 mS. For the component values selected, what will be the percentage error in the nominal output frequency compared with the specified value? Note that the gain of a basic CS stage is $-g_{fs}R_D$ where R_D is the drain resistance (table 3.2).

[Specimen answers: Circuit of figure 9.3b with $R = 82$ kΩ, $C = 150$ pF, $R_D = 6.8$ kΩ, $R_S = 1.8$ kΩ, $C_S = 1\ \mu$F; frequency error + 5.6 per cent]

9.4 By representing the small-signal performance of the phase-shift oscillator circuit of figure 9.3c as in figure 9.3d, show that the transfer function (i_f/i_b) is

$$\frac{-h_{fe}}{\left(3 + \dfrac{R}{R_C} - \dfrac{1}{\omega^2C^2R^2} - \dfrac{5}{\omega^2C^2RR_C}\right) + j\left(\dfrac{1}{\omega^3C^3R^2R_C} - \dfrac{6}{\omega CR_C} - \dfrac{4}{\omega CR}\right)}$$

giving a frequency of oscillation of $\left[2\pi CR\sqrt{\left(6 + \dfrac{4R_C}{R}\right)}\right]^{-1}$. By determining $|i_f/i_b|$ at the frequency of oscillation, what is the minimum value of h_{fe} of the BJT for oscillation to occur? Note that differentiation of the expression for h_{fe} with respect to (R_C/R) shows that minimum h_{fe} corresponds to $R_C/R = 2.69$.

[Answer: 44.54]

9.5 Select suitable component values (± 2 per cent E12 resistances and ± 10 per cent E6 capacitances, appendix D) for the Wien-bridge oscillator circuit of figure 9.4 to give a nominal output frequency of 1 kHz. The input and output resistances of the op-amp are 1 MΩ and 100 Ω respectively. What is the output frequency for the values selected?

[Specimen answers: $R = 10$ kΩ + 560 Ω, $C = 15$ nF; $R_F, R_1 = 22$ kΩ, 10 kΩ; 27 kΩ, 12 kΩ; 33 kΩ, 15 kΩ; 39 kΩ, 18 kΩ; 47 kΩ, 22 kΩ; 82 kΩ, 39 kΩ or 100 kΩ, 47 kΩ within the range 10–100 kΩ; 1004.77 Hz ± 12 per cent]

LC linear oscillators

9.6 A Colpitts oscillator is based on a common-emitter single-stage amplifier as in figure 9.7b. Using a simplified version of the hybrid-π model of the BJT (ignoring $r_{bb'}$, $r_{b'c}$ and

r_{ce}), draw a network model representing the ac performance of the circuit. Hence show that the frequency of oscillation is given by $1/2\pi\sqrt{(LC)}$ where C is the series combination of C_3 and $(C_2 + C_{i(amp)})$, $C_{i(amp)}$ being the effective input capacitance of the amplifier stage. Taking the BJT gain $h_{fe} = g_{fe} r_{b'c}$ [1d], what is the minimum value of h_{fe} for sustained oscillation assuming the effective bias resistance is much larger than $r_{b'c}$?

[Answer: $C_3/(C_2 + C_{i(amp)})$]

9.7 A JFET Hartley oscillator is formed by replacing C_2, C_3 and L in the Colpitts circuit of figure 9.7a by L_2, L_3 and C respectively, a coupling capacitor being added between L_2 and R_G. If $R_G = 1\ \text{M}\Omega$ and g_{fs} for the JFET is 10 mS, select suitable values for L_2, L_3 and C for a nominal 1 MHz output. Mention any assumptions made.

[Specimen answers: Assuming $y_{is}(\text{JFET}) \ll 1/R_G$, the maintenance condition gives $L_2 = 10^4 L_3$. Selecting $L_3 = 1\ \mu\text{H}$ as a practical low value, L_2 is required to be 10 mH and assuming no mutual coupling between L_2 and L_3, C is then required to be 2.5 pF for a 1 MHz output]

9.8 Show that the tuned-collector LC oscillator of figure 9.24 will oscillate only if L_1 is connected with the correct sense and $g_{fe}M/CR$ is greater than unity, where g_{fe} is the forward transconductance of the BJT and M is the mutual inductance between L and L_1.

[*Hint*: With reference to appendix B, section B.1, find the impedance of the collector load at resonance ($Z(\omega_o)$). Then from equation 3.65 with R_C replaced by $Z(\omega_o)$ determine

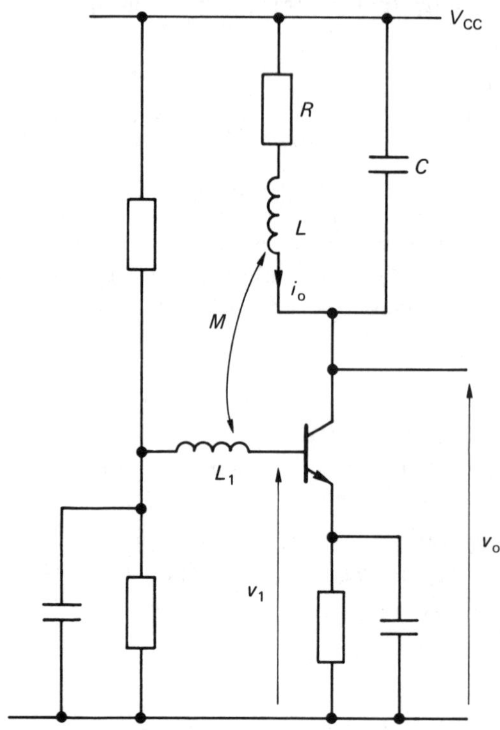

Figure 9.24 Tuned-collector LC oscillator

the voltage gain of the circuit at this frequency. Hence find i_o in terms of v_1 assuming the resistance of the inductor to be small, and finally determine the voltage v_1 induced in L_1 from $v_1 = \pm j\omega_o M i_o$]

Signal processing:
Limiting and precision rectification

9.9 A 5 V rms sinusoidal signal is applied to the circuits of figures 9.25a, b, where the diode label refers to the breakdown voltage of the diode in volts, the symbol *V* representing the decimal point. Sketch the output waveform in each case. If the same signal is applied to the circuit of figure 9.25c, what would be the output waveshape? If a large-value capacitor is connected across the output, what would be the value of v_O?

[Answers: (a) Sinewave with positive half cycles limited at 3.3 V.
(b) Sinewave with positive limit of 4 V and negative limit of 5.4 V.
(c) Negative-going half-wave rectified sinusoid; – 7.07 V with *C* connected]

Active filters

9.10 Show that the voltage gain v_o/v_1 of the second-order Sallen and Key active filter circuit of figure 9.15b is $[1 - \omega^2 C_2 C_3 R_2 R_3 + j\omega C_3(R_2 + R_3)]^{-1}$.
Notice that the negative term, which is due to the positive feedback, can cause a resonant peak in the response depending on the component values selected.

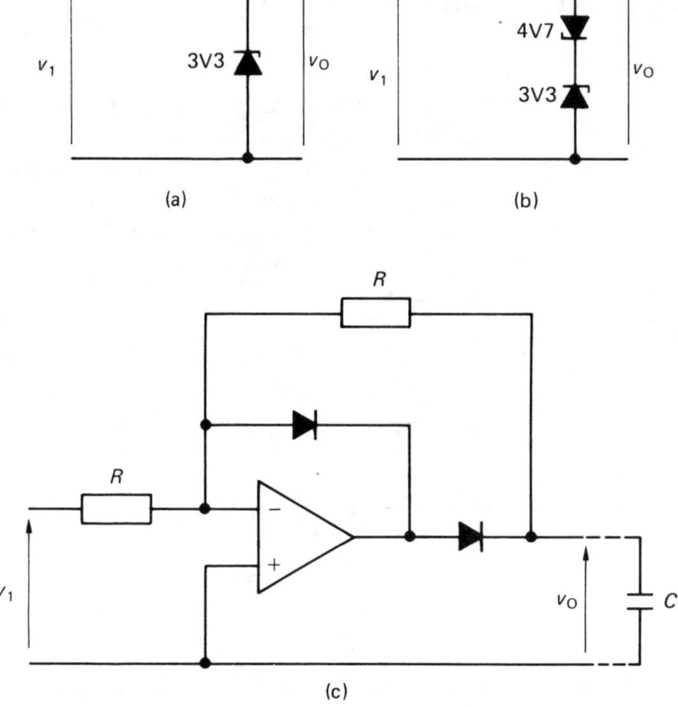

Figure 9.25 Signal processing

9.11 A cable link to the input of an amplifier carries analog signals above 250 Hz. Under worst-case conditions, the amplitude of 50 Hz mains hum induced in the cable is found to be half that of the signal. To meet the specification, the level of any superimposed noise must be at least 30 dB below that of the signal.
What type of filter is required to overcome this problem? What is the minimum skirt slope that will ensure the system is within specification? By adapting the table in figure 9.15e, select component values (E6 capacitance, E12 resistance; appendix D) for a suitable Butterworth filter based on the Sallen and Key circuit for this application.

[Answers: High pass with 250 Hz cut off; 34.26 dB/decade; 2nd-order circuit of figure 9.15b with R_2 and R_3 interchanged with C_2 and C_3 respectively; select $C_2 = C_3 = 68$ nF to give resistance values within the 1–100 kΩ ideal range with $R_2 = 6640\ \Omega$ and $R_3 = 13\,186\ \Omega$, allowing choice of $R_2 = 5.6\ \text{k}\Omega + 1\ \text{k}\Omega$ and $R_3 = 12\ \text{k}\Omega + 1.2\ \text{k}\Omega$]

9.12 Derive an expression for the input impedance Z_i of the circuit of figure 9.26 and hence show that the circuit behaves as a frequency-dependent inductor for $R_1 < R_2$. Give expressions for the inductance and Q-factor (equation B.10, appendix B) of the simulated inductor. If $R_1 = 1$ kΩ and $C_2 = 100$ nF, calculate the value of R_2 required to provide an inductance of 250 mH at 500 Hz. What would be the Q-factor of the simulated coil? Note that if the input of the circuit is shunted by a capacitor (C_1, figure 9.26), the arrangement simulates a tuned circuit.

[Answers: $L = C_2R_1(R_2 - R_1)/(1 + \omega^2C_2^2R_1^2)$;

$Q = \omega C_2(R_2 - R_1)/(1 + \omega^2C_2^2R_1R_2)$;

$R_2 = 3.75$ kΩ; $Q = 0.63$]

Piecewise-linear shapers

9.13 It is required to produce a two-segment shaper to approximate the relationship $v_O = -0.1v_I^2$ for $0 \leqslant v_I \leqslant +10$ V. The shaper specification requires $v_O = 0$ when $v_I = 0$ and it is known that in application v_I is *usually* > 4 V. The shaper output must always be within ± 0.5 V of the true value given by the squared relationship.
Choose a suitable circuit arrangement and select appropriate component values from the E24 ranges (appendix D) of resistances and diode breakdown voltages assuming component tolerances may be neglected.

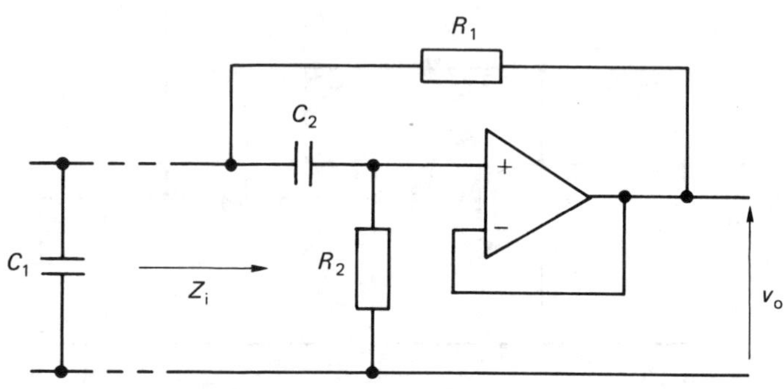

Figure 9.26 Simulated inductor

[Specimen answer: The specification indicates that the PWL approximation must be most accurate at $v_1 = 0$ and for $v_1 > 4$ V allowing the segments to be constructed accordingly, taking account also of the ± 0.5 V maximum tolerance in v_o. The circuit required is that of figure 9.19c with the two-segment network N being the R_1, R_2, V_B network from figure 9.18a. Choosing $R_F = 10$ kΩ requires $R_1 = 24$ kΩ, $R_2 = 8.2$ kΩ + 510 Ω and a 5.1 V breakdown diode]

9.14 Over the temperature range 0 to 50°C, a transducer produces a voltage v that is proportional to the square of the temperature such that $v(0°\text{C}) = 0$ and $v(50°\text{C}) = 2.5$ V. Design a three-segment PWL shaper, which, when cascaded with the transducer, produces a voltage output that is linear with transducer temperature providing 0 to 5 V for the temperature range 0 to 50°C. Output polarity is not specified. Resistance values and diode breakdown voltages should be selected from the E24 range (appendix D); the minimum available diode breakdown voltage is 2.7 V; forward-biased general-purpose diodes with a voltage drop of 0.7 V can be used for breakpoints < 2.7 V.

[Specimen answer: Circuit of figure 9.19a with an input resistance of 10 kΩ and a three-segment network N as in figure 9.18c. As operation is in only one quadrant, back-to-back diodes are not required; V_{B_1} is selected as 1.4 V using two general-purpose diodes in series while V_{B_2} is selected as a 3.0 V breakdown diode. For these breakpoints, the network N resistances are $R_1 = 82$ kΩ, $R_2 = 33$ kΩ and $R_3 = 27$ kΩ]

9.15 It is required to produce a three-segment PWL shaper that will convert a 5 V peak-to-peak sawtooth waveshape to a 20 V peak-to-peak sinusoid. Design a suitable circuit using resistances and diode breakdown voltages from the E24 range (appendix D) ignoring component tolerances.
[Specimen answer: Circuit of figure 9.19a with an input resistance of 10 kΩ and a three-segment network N as in figure 9.18c. As two-quadrant operation is involved, back-to-back diodes are required. Choosing diodes $V_{B_1} = 6.8$ V, $V_{B_2} = 9.1$ V, giving breakpoints of 7.5 V and 9.8 V allowing for the 0.7 V forward drop across the conducting diode, suitable resistance values are $R_1 = 51$ kΩ + 6.8 kΩ, $R_2 = 51$ kΩ + 6.2 kΩ and $R_3 = 4.7$ kΩ + 1.3 kΩ]

10 Pulse Circuits

Coverage

- Consideration of transistors as switches with particular regard to the output voltage levels of basic inverters and switching speed.
- Analysis of performance and selection of component values for discrete and op-amp based bistable, monostable and astable pulse circuits.

Note that the op-amp circuits considered in this chapter are developed from the basic regenerative comparator (Schmitt trigger circuit) considered in section 7.3.2.

Pulse circuits use transistors as switches so that the output of these circuits can take only two levels, a HI level $\hat{v}_O$ or a LO level $\check{v}_O$. Although these are not analog circuits, they are rarely given component-level consideration in texts devoted to digital electronics and so this topic is included here for completeness as examples of circuit design.

10.1 Discrete-component pulse circuits

10.1.1 *Transistors as switches*

Initial consideration of the basic *transistor–load–dc supply* circuit in section 1.3 explains that if the input control voltage is varied over a sufficiently wide range, the transistor is driven to its fully conducting (ON) state or its fully non-conducting (OFF) state corresponding to the upper and lower extremes of the operating point on the load line (figure 1.8). Such operation does not require input biasing as is needed for linear operation (chapter 3 introduction) because the level of conduction of the transistor is controlled only by the level of the input signal. An important advantage of switching circuits is that the output voltage is more precisely defined than in linear circuits where the wide range of transistor parameters requires the use of stabilising feedback to produce closely defined performance (chapter 5 introduction).

In the BJT circuit of figure 10.1a, initially without R_B, if v_I is at its LO value ($\check{v}_I$) such that $V_{BE} < 0.5$ V, $I_B = 0$, the BJT is OFF. The operating point is then at A on the load line in figure 10.1b, the collector current being the leakage value I_{CEO} (equation 2.12). In this condition the voltage drop across the collector load is $R_C I_{CEO}$ and the output voltage is at the HI value

$$\hat{v}_O = \hat{v}_{CE} = V_{CC} - R_C I_{CEO} \qquad (10.1)$$

As I_{CEO} is small, typically less than 20 μA for a low-power silicon BJT at room temperature

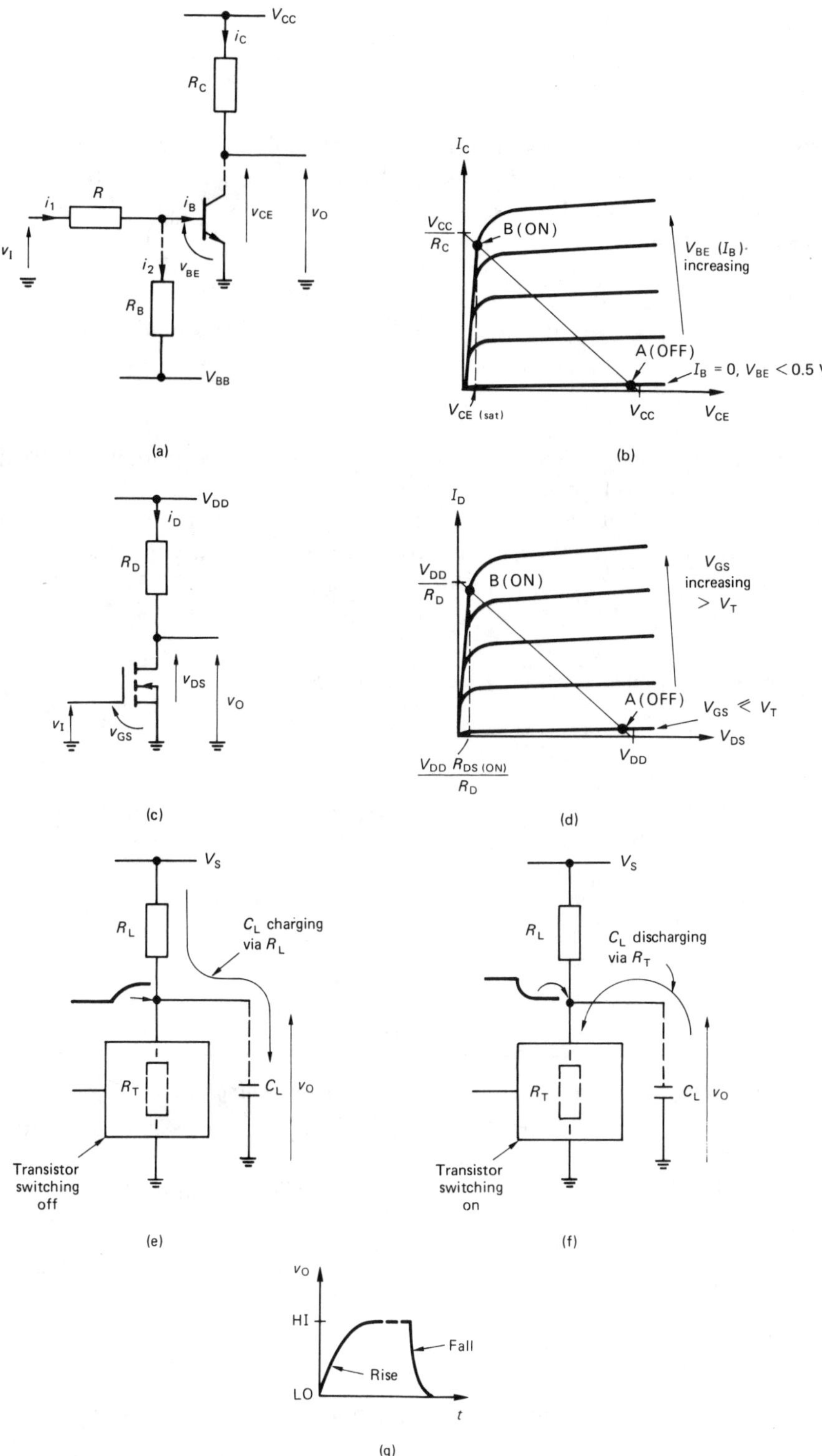

Figure 10.1 Transistors as switches

(see example 2.4), R_C only a few kilohms and V_{CC} several volts, the $R_C I_{CEO}$ term in equation 10.1 can often be neglected, giving

$$\hat{v}_O \simeq V_{CC} \tag{10.2}$$

This approximation corresponds to taking the cut-off point A as being on the V_{CE}-axis (figure 10.1b). If v_I is increased to the HI value ($\hat{v}_I$), i_B increases, i_C increases, the voltage drop across R_C increases and v_O falls. Provided i_C is able to increase sufficiently, v_O falls to its LO value which is the minimum value of v_{CE} for the BJT, $V_{CE(sat)}$, giving

$$\check{v}_O = V_{CE(sat)} \tag{10.3}$$

As the value of $V_{CE(sat)}$ is typically less than 200 mV for a low-power silicon BJT, the approximation

$$\check{v}_O \simeq 0 \tag{10.4}$$

can often be used in design calculations. This approximation corresponds to taking the saturation point B of the BJT (figure 10.1b) as being on the I_C-axis.

To ensure the switch to saturation when v_I is at its HI value $\hat{v}_I$, the base current must be sufficient, taking account of the gain h_{FE} of the BJT. The collector current in the fully ON state

$$\hat{i}_C = I_{C(sat)} = \frac{V_{CC} - V_{CE(sat)}}{R_C} \tag{10.5}$$

and the base current supplied, without R_B connected, is

$$\hat{i}_B = \frac{\hat{v}_I - V_{BE(sat)}}{R} \tag{10.6}$$

The corresponding minimum value of static CE current gain h_{FE}min for the BJT that will allow the BJT to be at saturation for the base current of equation 10.6 is therefore

$$h_{FE}\,\text{min} = \frac{\hat{i}_C}{\hat{i}_B} = \frac{R}{R_C}\left(\frac{V_{CC} - V_{CE(sat)}}{\hat{v}_I - V_{BE(sat)}}\right) \tag{10.7}$$

Example 10.1: Minimum transistor gain for a basic BJT switching circuit

The basic switching circuit of figure 10.1a (without R_B) has $V_{CC} = 5$ V, $R_C = 10$ kΩ and $R = 1$ MΩ. If the BJT must be driven to saturation when the input voltage is +5 V, what is the minimum allowable value of CE gain of the BJT assuming $V_{BE(sat)} = 0.8$ V and $V_{CE(sat)} = 0.2$ V?

At saturation, from equation 10.5:

$$\hat{i}_C = I_{C(sat)} = \frac{5\text{ V} - 0.2\text{ V}}{10\text{ k}\Omega} = 480\ \mu\text{A}$$

The maximum value of base current that can be supplied when $v_I = 5$ V is (equation 10.6):

$$\hat{i}_B = \frac{5\text{ V} - 0.8\text{ V}}{1\text{ M}\Omega} = 4.2\ \mu\text{A}$$

Thus

$$h_{FE}\min = \frac{480\ \mu A}{4.2\ \mu A} = 114.3$$

If h_{FE} is greater than the minimum value given by equation 10.7 such that the base current supplied is larger than the value required to drive the BJT to saturation, termed *overdriving*, the switch to the ON state is quicker because the higher base current establishes the necessary charge distribution in the base [1] more rapidly. This is clearly an advantage as far as switch ON is concerned, but the extra charge then stored in the BJT base slows the switch back to the OFF state because the collector current cannot fall until the base charge has been removed [1]. The switch OFF time can be reduced by applying a negative voltage to the base when v_I falls to its LO value, so accelerating the flow of charge out of the base. This is achieved by adding resistor R_B with V_{BB} negative (figure 10.1a) so that when $v_I = \check{v}_I$ the R, R_B potential divider makes v_{BE} slightly negative, given by

$$v_{BE} = \frac{\check{v}_I R_B + V_{BB} R}{R + R_B} \tag{10.8}$$

corresponding to the result of tutorial question 1.2.

The R, R_B divider thus determines the value of negative voltage applied to the base at switch OFF. However, at switch ON the current drain i_2 through R_B must not be excessive relative to the current i_1 supplied from the v_I source, otherwise i_B will not be adequate to saturate the BJT. From figure 10.1a, i_1 must be $\geqslant i_B\min$ (for saturation, $= I_{C(sat)}/h_{FE}) + i_2$, thus

$$\left(\frac{\hat{v}_I - V_{BE(sat)}}{R}\right) \geqslant \left(\frac{I_{C(sat)}}{h_{FE}}\right) + \left(\frac{V_{BE(sat)} - V_{BB}}{R_B}\right) \tag{10.9}$$

The values selected for R and R_B must satisfy equations 10.8 and 10.9. A degree of flexibility exists because the negative value of v_{BE} required in equation 10.8 need not be precise while in equation 10.9, provided $i_1 > i_B\min + i_2$, saturation is assured. The value of v_{BE} at switch OFF is selected typically in the range 20–40 per cent V_{BB}; the larger the value, the smaller the switch OFF time, but this involves a smaller R_B/R ratio which increases the relative current drain i_2 at switch ON; the 20–40 per cent range provides a reasonable compromise.

Example 10.2: Component selection for a BJT inverter

The BJT inverter of figure 10.1a, including R_B, is to operate from ± 5 V power supplies with input switching levels of 0 and $+5$ V. If the BJT has $h_{FE} = 200$, $V_{BE(sat)} = 0.8$ V, $V_{CE(sat)} = 0.2$ V and the ON state collector current is to be approximately 0.5 mA, select suitable E12 values (appendix D) for R_C, R_B and R.

$$\text{ON state } i_C = I_{C(sat)} = \frac{V_{CC} - V_{CE(sat)}}{R_C}$$

giving

$$R_C = \frac{+5\ V - 0.2\ V}{0.5\ mA} = 9.6\ k\Omega \tag{10.10}$$

which allows $R_C = 10\ k\Omega$ to be selected.

With $R_C = 10\,k\Omega$, the actual nominal value of $I_{C(sat)}$ is $(+5\,V - 0.2\,V)/10\,k\Omega = 480\,\mu A$ and the corresponding minimum value of base current to ensure saturation is

$$i_B \min = \frac{I_{C(sat)}}{h_{FE}} = \frac{480\,\mu A}{200} = 2.4\,\mu A$$

Using the relationship between the currents i_1, i_2 and i_B (equation 10.9),

$$\left(\frac{+5\,V - 0.8\,V}{R}\right) \geqslant 2.4\,\mu A - \left(\frac{0.8\,V - (-5\,V)}{R_B}\right)$$

from which

$$\frac{4.2\,V}{R} \geqslant 2.4\,\mu A + \frac{5.8\,V}{R_B} \qquad (10.11)$$

Determination of R from this relation requires an estimate of the R_B/R ratio. This ratio determines the OFF state value of v_{BE}, and making an initial choice of -1.5 V for this value (30 per cent of V_{BB}) enables the R_B/R ratio to be estimated from equation 10.8. Since v_I is at its LO value of zero in the OFF state:

$$\frac{R_B}{R} = \frac{V_{BB}}{v_{BE}} - 1 = \frac{(-5\,V)}{(-1.5\,V)} - 1 = 2.33 \qquad (10.12)$$

Substituting $R_B = 2.33R$ in relation 10.11

$$\frac{4.2\,V}{R} \geqslant 2.4\,\mu A + \frac{5.8\,V}{2.33R}$$

gives $R \leqslant 713\,k\Omega$. To allow an adequate margin for tolerance, the E12 value of $560\,k\Omega$ is chosen.

Although equation 10.12 allows R_B to be calculated from R, it is based only on the choice of OFF state v_{BE} which is nominal. To allow for component tolerances and a degree of overdriving to reduce switch ON time, it is important to restrict the i_2 current drain through R_B to allow sufficient base current to be supplied to the BJT in the ON state. With these factors in mind, an ON state base current *double* the $2.4\,\mu A$ minimum value will be allowed.

Having selected $R = 560\,k\Omega$, the nominal current (i_1) supplied from $\hat{v}_I$ is $(5\,V - 0.8\,V)/560\,k\Omega = 7.5\,\mu A$. Allowing the base current to be $2 \times 2.4\,\mu A = 4.8\,\mu A$, the maximum allowable drain through R_B is $7.5\,\mu A - 4.8\,\mu A = 2.7\,\mu A$ from which

$$R_B \geqslant \frac{V_{BE(sat)} - V_{BB}}{i_2} = \frac{0.8\,V - (-5\,V)}{2.7\,\mu A} = 2.15\,M\Omega$$

allowing the preferred value $2.7\,M\Omega$ to be selected.

A check of actual nominal conditions for the selected values $R = 560\,k\Omega$ and $R_B = 2.7\,M\Omega$ using $v_{BE} = V_{BB}/[(R_B/R) + 1]$ from equation 10.12 and $\hat{i}_B = (4.2V/R) - (5.8V/R_B)$ from relation 10.11 shows that the OFF state value of v_{BE} is -0.86 V while the ON state base current is $5.35\,\mu A$, indicating satisfactory operation.

Note: Examination of the above design procedure will reveal that a wide range of values of R, R_B will produce a working circuit. If the OFF state value of v_{BE} is made more negative, the R_B/R ratio is reduced as are the calculated values of R and R_B from relation 10.11. However the ratio cannot be too low otherwise i_1 will not be sufficiently large compared with i_2 to allow adequate base current. Also, reduced resistance values correspond to increased current levels thereby increasing the load on the v_I source and increasing wasteful power dissipation in the circuit. The design presented above is a compromise between circuit switching speed and power consumption.

Figures 10.1c, d show a basic FET switching circuit and corresponding load line on the output characteristics based, for example, on an e-MOST. The principle of operation is similar to that of the BJT circuit of figure 10.1a in that the transistor is OFF when $v_I(=v_{GS})$ is LO ($<$threshold voltage V_T) such that $v_O(=v_{DS})\simeq V_{DD}$, point A on the load line, while with v_I HI the operating point is at B, v_O then being at its LO value $V_{DD}R_{DS(ON)}/R_D$. Note that the circuit operates as a potential divider, the upper branch being the fixed drain resistance R_D while the lower branch is the channel resistance of the FET which is switched from a HI value, when only leakage current flows, to a LO value $R_{DS(ON)}$. Circuit design is simpler than in the BJT case because, being voltage controlled, there is no requirement to supply input current to the FET in its ON state as there is for the BJT. However gate current does need to flow during the switching transition corresponding to the change of the state of charge of the gate–channel capacitance and, as in the BJT case, the switching speed is limited by the rate at which this charge can be supplied/removed.

The above reference to switching speed in both the BJT and FET cases concentrates on the effect of *transistor* capacitance. In practice the switching circuit usually drives an external load, which may be the input of another circuit, and often the speed limit is imposed by the load capacitance. In figures 10.1e, f representing a basic switching circuit at switch OFF and switch ON respectively, R_T is the effective transistor resistance and C_L is the load capacitance. C_L includes inter-track capacitance on printed circuit boards and wiring capacitance, often collectively referred to as *stray* capacitance. At switch OFF the transistor resistance is rising and the rise of output voltage v_O depends not only on the rate of rise of R_T but on the time constant $C_L R_L$ as C_L charges via R_L. Correspondingly at switch ON, with R_T falling, the rate of fall of v_O depends on how quickly C_L can discharge via R_T, that is, the fall time depends on the time constant $C_L R_T$. Because $R_L \gg R_{T(ON)}$, the rise time of v_O is longer than the fall time as represented in figure 10.1g.

10.1.2 *Discrete bistable circuits*

Figure 10.2a shows two BJT switching circuits (figure 10.1a) cross coupled (output 1 to input 2 and output 2 back to input 1). The resulting circuit has *two* stable states T_1 ON, T_2 OFF and T_1 OFF, T_2 ON, hence the name *bistable*; either collector can be considered as the output. In integrated form the bistable circuit is the basic cell of digital counters and static random access memories.

Considering the fundamental BJT bistable circuit of figure 10.2a, if T_1 is ON (saturated), that is, i_{B_1} is sufficiently high taking account of $h_{FE}(T_1)$, then v_{CE_1} is low ($V_{CE(sat)}$). Correspondingly v_{BE_2} is low via the R, R_B divider so that T_2 is OFF and v_{CE_2} is high enabling sufficient base current to be supplied to T_1 to keep it saturated; the condition T_1 ON, T_2 OFF is therefore a stable state. If a negative pulse is applied to the base of T_1 (or a positive pulse to the base of T_2), of adequate amplitude and duration to reduce the level of conduction of T_1 so that v_{CE_1} starts to rise (or to start T_2 conducting so that v_{CE_2} starts to fall), positive feedback causes a switch to T_1 OFF, T_2 ON which is also a stable state. Positive feedback, often termed regenerative action, occurs because as the state of conduction of one of the BJTs changes,

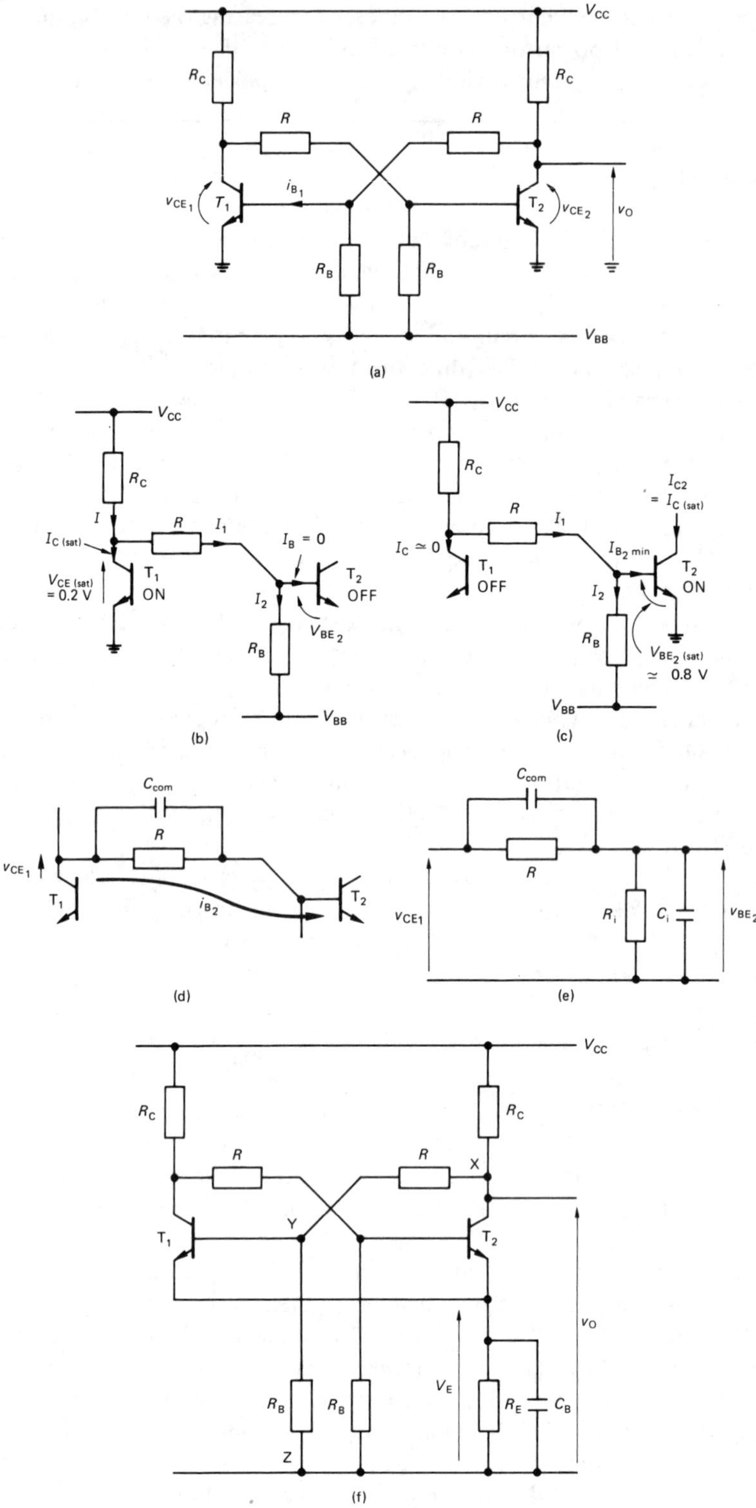

Figure 10.2 Discrete bistable switching circuit

the corresponding change of v_{CE}, applied to the base of the other BJT via the resistive coupling network, causes the state of conduction of the other BJT to change in the opposite sense ultimately causing one transistor to saturate and the other to cut-off, assuming circuit resistance values have been selected appropriately. The application of a pulse to initiate the change of state is termed *triggering*; the two triggering inputs to the circuit, one to each transistor, are called the SET and RESET control inputs. This switching action from one state to the other gives rise to the alternative name of *flip-flop* for this circuit.

Initial considerations in the circuit design are

(1) Selection of the positive and negative power supply voltages V_{CC} and V_{BB} respectively which may be constrained by other circuits in the complete system using the same supply(s).

(2) Selection of the collector current I_C for the saturated transistor noting that wasteful power dissipation increases with I_C but also that BJT gain h_{FE} reduces for low I_C.

(3) Knowledge of h_{FE}min at the chosen value for $I_{C(sat)}$ is required as this determines the minimum base current that must be supplied to ensure BJT saturation.

Having selected V_{CC}, V_{BB}, $I_{C(sat)}$ and h_{FE}min, the design involves selection of R_C, R and R_B for satisfactory operation. R_C is selected to allow $I_{C(sat)}$ to flow through the saturated BJT together with the current drawn by the R, R_B branch. The values for the R, R_B divider are chosen to provide sufficient base current to drive the BJT to saturation in the ON state and to provide a negative base–emitter voltage in the OFF state (section 10.1).

As the circuit is symmetrical, only one half need be considered. Circuit design follows a similar procedure as that for the basic switch in section 10.1 although the additional current drain via R, R_B must be considered. Figure 10.2b shows the half circuit in the T_1 ON, T_2 OFF state. From current division at T_1 collector, assuming T_1 to be saturated:

$$I = I_{C(sat)} + I_1$$

giving

$$\left(\frac{V_{CC} - V_{CE(sat)}}{R_C}\right) = I_{C(sat)} + \left(\frac{V_{CE(sat)} - V_{BB}}{R + R_B}\right) \tag{10.13}$$

noting that with T_2 OFF, $I_{B_2} \simeq 0$ so that $I_1 \simeq I_2$.

Theoretically, therefore, R_C depends on R and R_B, but in practice V_{BB} is only required to provide a negative base bias for T_2 to ensure a rapid switch to cut-off so that the current through R_B can be small, making the last term in equation 10.13 negligible. R_C can therefore be taken as

$$R_C \simeq \frac{V_{CC} - V_{CE(sat)}}{I_{C(sat)}} \tag{10.14}$$

Corresponding to equation 10.8, the bias applied to the base of T_2 is

$$V_{BE_2} = \frac{V_{CE(sat)} R_B + V_{BB} R}{R + R_B} \tag{10.15}$$

Unless R_B is chosen excessively large compared with R, the $V_{CE(sat)} R_B$ term in equation 10.15 can usually be neglected because $V_{CE(sat)} (\simeq 0.2\text{ V}) \ll V_{BB}$, giving

$$\frac{R_B}{R} \simeq \frac{V_{BB}}{V_{BE_2}} - 1 \tag{10.16}$$

where V_{BE_2} is chosen typically in the range 20–40 per cent V_{BB} (section 10.1). Selection of R and R_B also requires consideration of the base current to be supplied when T_2 is ON. Under these conditions (figure 10.2c) the collector current of T_1 is zero and so I_1 flows from V_{CC}, through R_C and R and then splits into I_{B_2} and I_2 so that, provided T_2 is saturated:

$$\left(\frac{V_{CC} - V_{BE(sat)}}{R_C + R}\right) = I_{B_2} + \left(\frac{V_{BE(sat)} - V_{BB}}{R_B}\right) \tag{10.17}$$

I_{B_2} must be greater than or equal to the minimum value required for saturation which corresponds to the maximum value for active operation (to which gain h_{FE} applies), thus

$$\begin{aligned} I_{B_2} &\geqslant I_{B_2}\text{min (for saturation)} \\ &= I_{B_2}\text{max (for active operation)} \\ &= \frac{I_{C_2}}{h_{FE}\text{min}} = \frac{I_{C(sat)}}{h_{FE}\text{min}} \end{aligned} \tag{10.18}$$

Combining equations 10.17 and 10.18:

$$\left(\frac{V_{CC} - V_{BE(sat)}}{R_C + R}\right) \geqslant \frac{I_{C(sat)}}{h_{FE}\text{min}} + \left(\frac{V_{BE(sat)} - V_{BB}}{R_B}\right) \tag{10.19}$$

Numerical values of all quantities in equations 10.16 and 10.19 are known, or have been selected, except R and R_B which can therefore be determined by elimination.

Example 10.3: Discrete bistable circuit design

Select E12 resistance values (appendix D) for the BJT bistable circuit of figure 10.2a for power supply voltages of ± 5 V and $I_{C(sat)}$ of 500 μA. The BJT has $h_{FE}\text{min} = 100$, $V_{BE(sat)} = 0.8$ V and $V_{CE(sat)} = 0.2$ V at $I_C = 500\ \mu$A.

From equation 10.14:

$$R_C \simeq \frac{V_{CC} - V_{CE(sat)}}{I_{C(sat)}} = \frac{+5\text{ V} - 0.2\text{ V}}{0.5\text{ mA}} = 9.6\text{ k}\Omega \tag{10.20}$$

allowing an E12 value of 10 kΩ to be selected which gives a nominal value of $I_{C(sat)}$ of $(+5\text{ V} - 0.2\text{ V})/10\text{ k}\Omega = 480\ \mu$A.

Choosing a mid-range target value of 30 per cent V_{BB} ($= -1.5$ V) for the base bias in the OFF state as in example 10.2 requires

$$\frac{R_B}{R} \simeq \frac{(-5\text{ V})}{(-1.5\text{ V})} - 1 = 2.33 \tag{10.21}$$

from equation 10.16.

In the ON state, with $I_{C(sat)} = 480\ \mu$A and $h_{FE}\text{min} = 100$, $I_B\text{min}$ from equation 10.18 is $480\ \mu\text{A}/100 = 4.8\ \mu$A and so to provide adequate base current, from equation 10.19:

$$\left(\frac{V_{CC} - V_{BE(sat)}}{R_C + R}\right) \geqslant 4.8\ \mu\text{A} + \left(\frac{V_{BE(sat)} - V_{BB}}{R_B}\right) \tag{10.22}$$

from which

$$\left(\frac{+5\text{ V} - 0.8\text{ V}}{10\text{ k}\Omega + R}\right) \geqslant 4.8\ \mu\text{A} + \left(\frac{0.8\text{ V} - (-5\text{ V})}{R_B}\right)$$

But R_B is required to be $\simeq 2.33R$ from equation 10.21 and so R must be selected to provide

$$\left(\frac{4.2\ \text{V}}{10\ \text{k}\Omega + R}\right) \geqslant 4.8\ \mu\text{A} + \left(\frac{5.8\ \text{V}}{2.33R}\right) \quad (10.23)$$

This relation is a quadratic in R:

$$R^2 - 346.40R + 5185.98 \leqslant 0 \quad (10.24)$$

for R in kilohms.

Solution gives $R \leqslant 330.72\ \text{k}\Omega$ or $R \leqslant 15.68\ \text{k}\Omega$. The latter value makes the current drain I_2 through $R_B \gg I_B$ which is both unnecessary and also invalidates the neglect of I_1 leading to equation 10.14; thus $R \leqslant 330.72\ \text{k}\Omega$ is required.

To allow for factors such as component selection tolerances, temperature variation and power supply fluctuation, R will be chosen considerably less than the threshold value of 330.72 kΩ to ensure that under worst-case conditions the minimum base current of 4.8 μA can be supplied; $R = 270\ \text{k}\Omega$ is chosen from the E12 range.

The corresponding value of R_B from equation 10.21 is 2.33 (270 kΩ) $\simeq$ 629 kΩ; 680 kΩ is selected. For the values selected, $R = 270\ \text{k}\Omega$, $R_B = 680\ \text{k}\Omega$ with $V_{CC} = +5\ \text{V}$, $V_{BB} = -5\ \text{V}$, $V_{BE(sat)} = 0.8\ \text{V}$ and $V_{CE(sat)} = 0.2\ \text{V}$, consideration of equation 10.17 in conjunction with figure 10.2c gives $I_1 = (V_{CC} - V_{BE(sat)})/(R_C + R) = 4.2\ \text{V}/280\ \text{k}\Omega = 15\ \mu\text{A}$ and $I_2 = (V_{BE(sat)} - V_{BB})/R_B = 5.8\ \text{V}/680\ \text{k}\Omega = 8.53\ \mu\text{A}$, allowing a nominal base current of $15\ \mu\text{A} - 8.53\ \mu\text{A} = 6.47\ \mu\text{A}$ which is approximately 35 per cent greater than the minimum of 4.8 μA to allow for tolerances and fluctuations.

In the OFF state, the base–emitter voltage is given, equation 10.15, as $\dfrac{(0.2\ \text{V})(680\ \text{k}\Omega) + (-5\ \text{V})(270\ \text{k}\Omega)}{270\ \text{k}\Omega + 680\ \text{k}\Omega} = -1.28\ \text{V}$, indicating a deviation from the nominal target value of -1.5 V but a satisfactory value nonetheless.

Note that I_1 ($= 15\ \mu\text{A}$) is small compared with $I_{C(sat)}$ ($= 480\ \mu\text{A}$) so that the simplification leading to equation 10.14 is valid.

The switching speed of the bistable circuit can be reduced, and hence the maximum operating (toggle) frequency increased, by the addition of *commutating* or *speed-up* capacitors across the coupling resistors (figure 10.2d). During the transition when T_1 switches OFF, causing v_{CE_1} to rise (denoted by $v_{CE_1}\uparrow$ in figure 10.2d), and T_2 switches ON, the switching speed depends on how quickly the input capacitance of T_2 can be charged by i_{B_2}. Addition of C_{com} allows a surge of charge to flow to T_2 as v_{CE_1} rises, thereby shortening the switch ON time.

The situation can be represented as in figure 10.2e where R_I and C_I are the effective input resistance and capacitance of T_2, C_I being mainly Miller capacitance (section 4.4). The transfer function v_{BE_2}/v_{CE_1} is then

$$\frac{v_{BE_2}}{v_{CE_1}} = \frac{R_I /\!/ (1/j\omega C_I)}{[R_I /\!/ (1/j\omega C_I)] + [R /\!/ (1/j\omega C_{com})]}$$

$$= \frac{R_I}{R_I + R\left(\dfrac{1 + j\omega C_I R_I}{1 + j\omega C_{com} R}\right)} \quad (10.25)$$

For the rate of rise of voltage at T_1 collector to be transmitted most effectively to the base of T_2, this transfer function must be frequency independent so that high-frequency components of the fast rise of v_{CE_1} are not attenuated, causing the rise of v_{BE_2} to be slowed. From equation 10.25, this frequency independence occurs when the time constants are equal

$$C_I R_I = C_{com} R \tag{10.26}$$

from which the value of commutating capacitor can be calculated. Typically C_{com} is in the range 10–500 pF. Note that this principle of time constant equalisation to provide faithful transmission of waveshape is applied in the use of an adjustable input probe with an oscilloscope. In that case, R_I, C_I are the input resistance and capacitance of the vertical deflection (Y) amplifier of the oscilloscope while R or C_{com} are adjustable within the probe, usually by rotating a ferrule. Such a probe is set by using it to monitor a fast-rise pulse waveform on the oscilloscope; such a waveform is usually provided at a test point on the front panel of the instrument. The probe is then adjusted until the rise time of the displayed waveshape is at a minimum but without any overshoot.

Single power supply operation of the bistable circuit can be achieved using a common emitter resistor to provide a positive emitter bias (figure 10.2f). R_E is chosen, depending on the selected value of $I_{C(sat)}$, so that V_E is in the range 20–40 per cent of V_{CC} and with the ratio $R_B/(R+R_B)$ selected so that the base potential is less than V_E, v_{BE} of the OFF BJT is negative as for the basic circuit of figure 10.2a. Corresponding to design example 10.3, for $V_{CC} = 5$ V and $I_{C(sat)} = 500\ \mu$A, a value of R_E of 3.9 kΩ would provide $V_E \simeq 2$ V, and if R, R_B are selected to make the base potential about 1 V, V_{BE} is 1 V − 2 V = −1 V for the OFF BJT, similar to the value for the circuit of example 10.3. For a symmetrical circuit, V_E is the same in either state but during switching, as the BJTs pass through the active region of operation, v_E changes. However if R_E is shunted by C_B, the time constant $C_B R_E$ being much greater than the switching time, v_E remains approximately constant and switching is guaranteed. Note that for the single-supply circuit the output levels are V_{CC} and $(V_E + V_{CE(sat)})$, the LO level being well above zero, so that level shifting may be necessary before connection to the next stage.

Integrated flip-flops are produced in a number of different versions commonly described as S–R, T, D and J–K types. The differences between these various types, which are mainly concerned with triggering, are considered in detail in texts devoted to digital electronics such as reference [2].

If C_B and the XY, YZ branches are removed from the single-supply bistable circuit of figure 10.2f and the base of T_1 is treated as the circuit input (with v_I applied), a discrete Schmitt trigger circuit is created in which the state of the output v_O depends on the value of v_I. As for the op-amp version (section 7.3.2), decisive switching based on regenerative feedback requires a loop gain greater than unity. This results in a hysteresis characteristic with upper and lower trigger levels and, for the discrete version of this circuit, this requires the collector load R_C to be greater than R/h_{FE} where R is the coupling resistance and h_{FE} the static CE gain of the BJTs.

10.1.3 *Discrete monostable circuits*

By replacing one of the R, R_B coupling networks in the basic bistable circuit (figure 10.2a) by a C, R charging network as in figure 10.3a the circuit has only one stable state, hence the term *monostable*, the other state being transitory, lasting for a time dependent on the time constant CR.

With reference to figure 10.3a, the stable state is T_1 OFF, its base being held slightly negative by the R, R_B divider as in the bistable circuit of section 10.1.2, and T_2 ON, base current being supplied from the V_{CC} supply via R'. In this state therefore $v_O = v_{CE_2} = V_{CE(sat)} \simeq 0.2$ V,

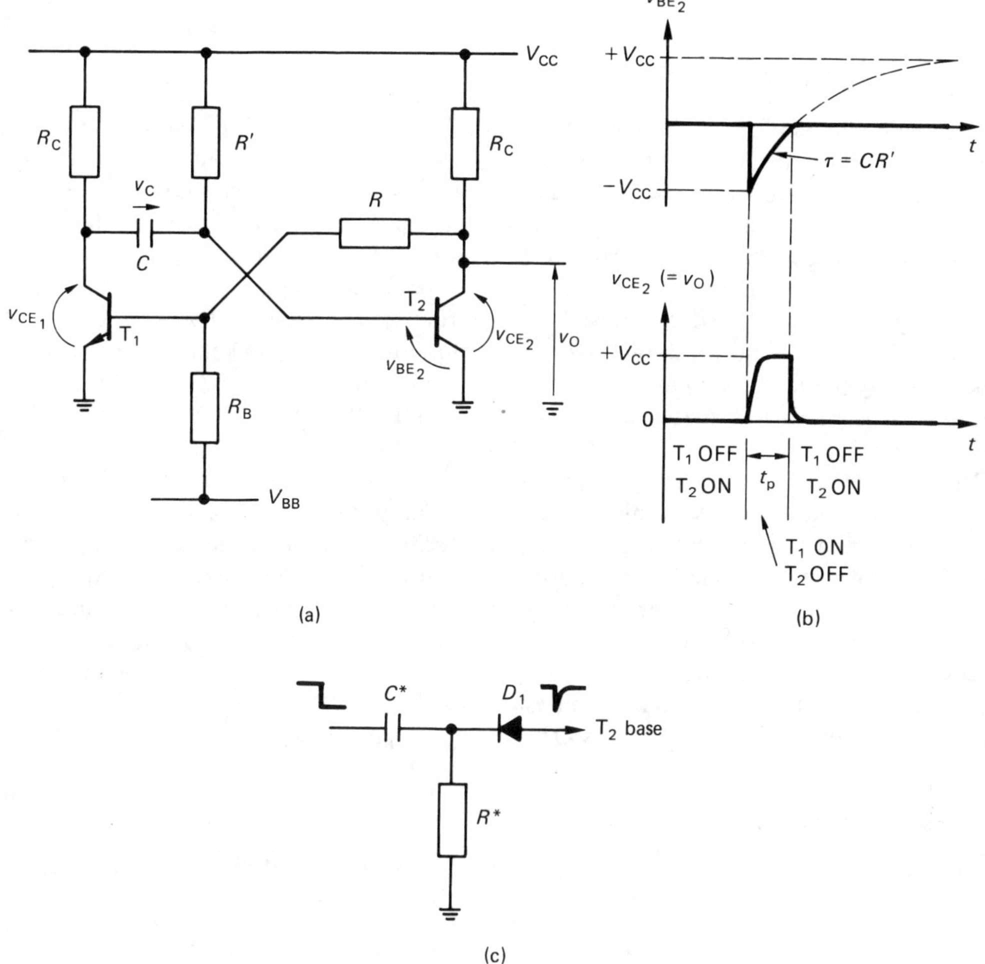

Figure 10.3 Discrete monostable switching circuit

$v_{BE_2} = V_{BE(sat)} \simeq 0.8$ V and $v_{CE_1} \simeq V_{CC}$. The capacitor voltage $v_C = v_{BE_2} - v_{CE_1} \simeq V_{BE(sat)} - V_{CC}$.

If the circuit is triggered into its unstable transitory state, often described as the quasistable state, by applying, for example, a negative pulse to the base of T_2 to switch T_2 OFF, T_1 switches ON and v_{CE_1} falls to $V_{CE(sat)}$. As the state of charge of C cannot change instantaneously, this sudden voltage fall is transmitted to the base of T_2 so that v_{BE_2} becomes $v_{CE_1} + v_C = V_{CE(sat)} + (V_{BE(sat)} - V_{CC}) \simeq -V_{CC}$. Note that with $v_{CE_1} = V_{CE(sat)} = 0$ in this condition, $v_{BE_2} \simeq v_C$. C then starts to charge via R' towards $+V_{CC}$ and so v_C, and hence v_{BE_2}, becomes progressively less negative (figure 10.3b) according to

$$v_{BE_2} \simeq v_C \simeq V_{CC} - 2V_{CC} \exp(-t/CR') \tag{10.27}$$

corresponding to the result given in equation 1.14 with 'aiming' value $V = V_{CC}$ and initial value $v_O(0) = -V_{CC}$.

When v_{BE_2} becomes slightly positive, just greater than the V_γ threshold (figure 2.3c), T_2 begins to conduct once again and regenerative action accelerates the switch back to the T_1

OFF, T_2 ON stable state. The output pulse width t_p during which v_O is at the HI level is therefore given by equation 10.27 with $v_{BE_2}(t_p) = V_\gamma \simeq 0$ which gives

$$t_p = CR' \ln 2 = 0.69CR' \tag{10.28}$$

If the circuit is to be triggered from a pulse, the differentiating network of figure 10.3c can be used to create a negative spike from a negative-going edge, the time constant C^*R^* controlling the effective duration of the spike. The diode in the trigger circuit removes positive-going spikes that occur when the input waveform is repetitive. The charge supplied by the trigger spike to initiate the switch ON of a BJT, or the charge removed if a negative spike is applied to initiate switch OFF, must be sufficient to commence the regenerative process. This charge is given by the area enclosed by the spike waveform and is therefore dependent on C^*R^*. Theoretical analysis requires knowledge of the amplitude of the spike and the transistor capacitance required to be charged or discharged. In practice an allowable value of time constant is selected, less than the output pulse width, R^* being chosen from loading considerations.

The monostable circuit therefore provides a single output pulse of width $0.69CR'$ following triggering and is useful in providing a gating waveform or a delay; it is alternatively called a *one-shot* circuit. Triggering by positive-going pulses can be accomplished using the base of T_1 as the trigger input, diode D_1 in the trigger circuit of figure 10.3c being reversed, while a negative-going output pulse (from $+V_{CC}$ to zero) can be obtained by using the collector of T_1 as the output in place of T_2.

Circuit design involves selection of R_C, R and R_B as for the bistable circuit of section 10.1.2 dependent on V_{CC}, V_{BB}, $I_{C(sat)}$, $h_{FE}\text{min}$ and V_{BE} for the OFF BJT. R' must allow sufficient base current to be supplied to T_2 when it is ON ($= I_{C(sat)}/h_{FE}\text{min}$), so that

$$R' \leqslant \frac{V_{CC} - V_{BE(sat)}}{I_{C(sat)}/h_{FE}\text{min}} \tag{10.29}$$

Having selected R', C is then chosen to give the required pulse width using equation 10.28.

Example 10.4: Discrete monostable circuit design

The monostable circuit of figure 10.3a is required to provide 100 μs positive gating pulses when triggered by the negative-going edges of a 1 kHz square wave. Select suitable E12 resistance and capacitance values (appendix D) for the circuit if it is to operate from ± 5 V supplies with $I_{C(sat)}$ of 500 μA with BJT properties as given in example 10.3.

R_C, R and R_B are selected as 10 kΩ, 270 kΩ and 680 kΩ respectively as in example 10.3.

The minimum base current that must be supplied via R' when T_2 is ON is $I_{C(sat)}/h_{FE}\text{min} = 500\ \mu\text{A}/100 = 5\ \mu\text{A}$ and so the maximum value of R' is

$$\frac{V_{CC} - V_{BE(sat)}}{I_B\text{min}} = \frac{+5\text{ V} - 0.8\text{ V}}{5\ \mu\text{A}} = 840\text{ k}\Omega$$

$R' = 560$ kΩ is selected which provides a nominal base current of $4.2\text{ V}/560\text{ k}\Omega = 7.5\ \mu\text{A}$, allowing a 50 per cent margin over the limiting value of 5 μA to allow for component tolerances and parameter changes due to temperature variation.

Having chosen R', C is then selected using equation 10.28 to give $t_p = 100\ \mu s$, namely

$$C = \frac{t_p}{0.69R'} = \frac{100\ \mu s}{0.69(560\ k\Omega)} = 258.8\ pF$$

allowing E12 value 270 pF to be selected.

Since triggering from a negative-going edge is required, the differentiating trigger network of figure 10.3c can be used applied to the base of T_2, R^* being chosen as a suitably high value (100 kΩ, for example) to ensure efficient transmission of the spike to T_2. C^*R^* must be significantly less than the pulse width t_p, 20 μs being used, for example, here; C^* is then 20 μs/100 kΩ = 200 pF, allowing 220 pF to be selected although this takes no account of the amplitude of the trigger spike.

10.1.4 *Discrete astable circuits*

If both R, R_B coupling networks in the basic bistable circuit (figure 10.2a) are replaced by C, R charging networks as in figure 10.4a, with R_3 and T_3 initially omitted and the emitter of T_1 connected to signal earth, the circuit has no stable states; it is a free-running pulse generator called an *astable* circuit.

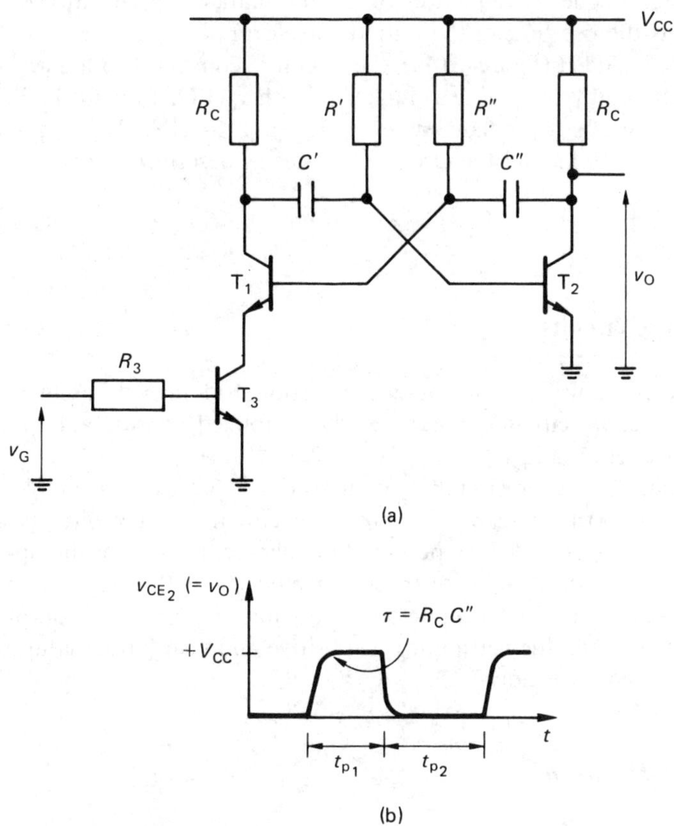

Figure 10.4 Discrete astable switching circuit

Analysis in each state follows the same procedure as that for the quasistable state of the monostable circuit in section 10.1.3. As one BJT switches OFF, its v_{CE} rises and that change is transmitted via the capacitive coupling to the other BJT causing that BJT to switch ON. The capacitor connected to the collector of the latter BJT then starts to charge from the V_{CC} supply, causing the base potential of the other BJT to rise until that transistor switches ON again and the process repeats. This mechanism, successive charging and discharging of the capacitors as the basis of operation of this circuit, gives rise to its alternative name, *relaxation oscillator*; the relaxation interval is the time the capacitor discharges from $-V_{CC}$ back to zero which defines the pulse width.

The output waveform is then as shown in figure 10.4b where the pulse widths, corresponding to equation 10.28 for the monostable circuit, are $t_{p_1} = 0.69C'R'$ and $t_{p_2} = 0.69C''R''$. The period T of the output waveform is then $t_{p_1} + t_{p_2}$ and so the output frequency is

$$f = \frac{1}{T} = \frac{1}{0.69(C'R' + C''R'')} \tag{10.30}$$

A square-wave output is provided when $C'R' = C''R''$.

Choice of component values follows a similar procedure to those for other circuits of this type, often collectively termed *multivibrators*. Collector resistors R_C are selected taking account of V_{CC} and $I_{C(sat)}$, equation 10.14. R' and R'' are chosen so that adequate base current can be supplied to allow the BJTs to saturate (equation 10.29) and then C' and C'' are selected to provide the required frequency (equation 10.30) and mark-to-space ratio (t_{p_1}:t_{p_2}). Note that choice of R_C affects the rise time of the output waveform.

With R_3 and T_3 included (figure 10.4a), the circuit is converted to a *gated astable*; circuit oscillation is controlled by the gating voltage v_G. With v_G LO, T_3 is OFF, T_1 cannot switch ON and the circuit does not oscillate. When v_G is HI, T_3 is ON, R_3 being chosen to ensure T_3 saturates (example 10.1), and the circuit oscillates as described above.

10.2 Op-amp pulse circuits

Although the discrete multivibrator circuits of section 10.1 provide useful examples of the basic design of switching circuits, design can be simplified considerably and performance improved by the use of op-amps.

The op-amp Schmitt trigger circuit used in section 7.3.2 as an example of an op-amp switching circuit forms the basis of this group of circuits. In the circuit of figure 7.16b, regenerative switching is provided by potential divider feedback from the op-amp output to the non-inverting (+) input. Bistable operation then occurs, with a degree of hysteresis, when the potential at the inverting (−) input of the op-amp is varied; the output switching to positive saturation $\hat{v}_O$ when the net input v_I is positive and to negative saturation $\check{v}_O$ when v_I is negative as discussed in section 7.3.2.

10.2.1 *Op-amp astable circuits*

Figure 10.5a shows an op-amp based astable circuit. Comparison with figure 7.16b shows that the astable circuit is basically a regenerative switch, with reference voltage $v_R = 0$, the input voltage v^- being provided from the op-amp output via the CR charging circuit instead of from an external source as in the Schmitt trigger circuit of figure 7.16b.

Assume, to start the explanation of operation, that the capacitor is discharged ($v^- = 0$) and, as a result of op-amp imbalances and the positive feedback via R_1, R_2, the amplifier output is at its positive maximum $\hat{v}_O$. Under these conditions, by potential division, the voltage at the + input is

$$v^+ = \left(\frac{R_1}{R_1 + R_2}\right)\hat{v}_O = \beta\hat{v}_O \tag{10.31}$$

where β is the feedback fraction (section 7.3.2 and chapter 5).

The capacitor charges via R towards $\hat{v}_O$ with time constant CR and so the voltage at the − input starts to rise. When v^- becomes slightly greater than v^+, the differential input voltage to the op-amp v_I changes sign from positive to negative, and the high voltage gain of the op-amp together with the regenerative feedback causes the output to switch rapidly to the negative maximum $\check{v}_O$. This causes v^+ to change instantly to

$$v^+ = \left(\frac{R_1}{R_1 + R_2}\right)\check{v}_O = \beta\check{v}_O \tag{10.32}$$

and the capacitor begins to charge towards the negative value $\check{v}_O$. Switch back to $\hat{v}_O$ occurs when v^- becomes slightly more negative than v^+ ($= \beta\check{v}_O$) when v_I becomes slightly positive and so the process continues, the relevant waveforms being shown in figure 10.5b.

During the 'space' time t_s when the output is at its LO value $\check{v}_O$, the capacitor voltage, which is equal to v^-, is given by

$$v^- = \check{v}_O + (\beta\hat{v}_O - \check{v}_O)\exp(-t/CR) \tag{10.33}$$

corresponding to equation 1.14 with initial voltage $\beta\hat{v}_O$ and 'aiming' voltage $\check{v}_O$. Switching occurs when v^- (equation 10.33) just equals v^+ (equation 10.31), so that t_s is given by

$$\check{v}_O + (\beta\hat{v}_O - \check{v}_O)\exp(-t_s/CR) = \beta\hat{v}_O \tag{10.34}$$

from which

$$t_s = CR\ln\left[\frac{\check{v}_O - \beta\hat{v}_O}{(1-\beta)\check{v}_O}\right] \tag{10.35}$$

Similarly, during the 'mark' time t_m:

$$v^- = \hat{v}_O + (\beta\check{v}_O - \hat{v}_O)\exp(-t/CR) \tag{10.36}$$

The initial voltage is $\beta\check{v}_O$ and the aiming voltage $\hat{v}_O$ with reference to equation 1.14, the mark interval being terminated when v^- (equation 10.36) equals v^+ (equation 10.32) giving

$$\hat{v}_O + (\beta\check{v}_O - \hat{v}_O)\exp(-t_m/CR) = \beta\check{v}_O \tag{10.37}$$

from which

$$t_m = CR\ln\left[\frac{\hat{v}_O - \beta\check{v}_O}{(1-\beta)\hat{v}_O}\right] \tag{10.38}$$

If the two output levels are symmetrical about signal earth, that is, if $\hat{v}_O = -\check{v}_O$, the mark and space times t_m and t_s are equal (equations 10.35 and 10.38) and the output waveform is

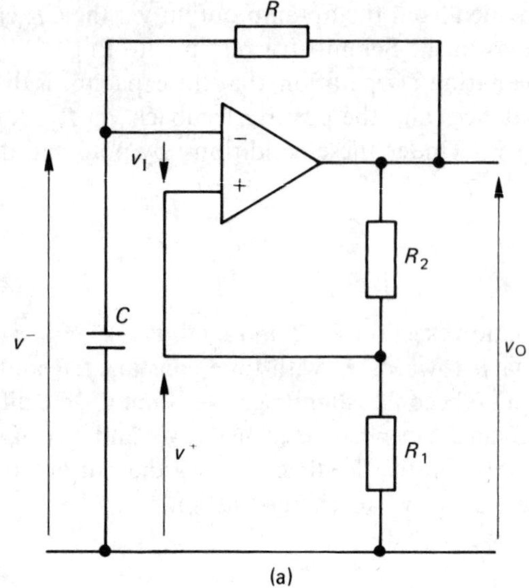

(a)

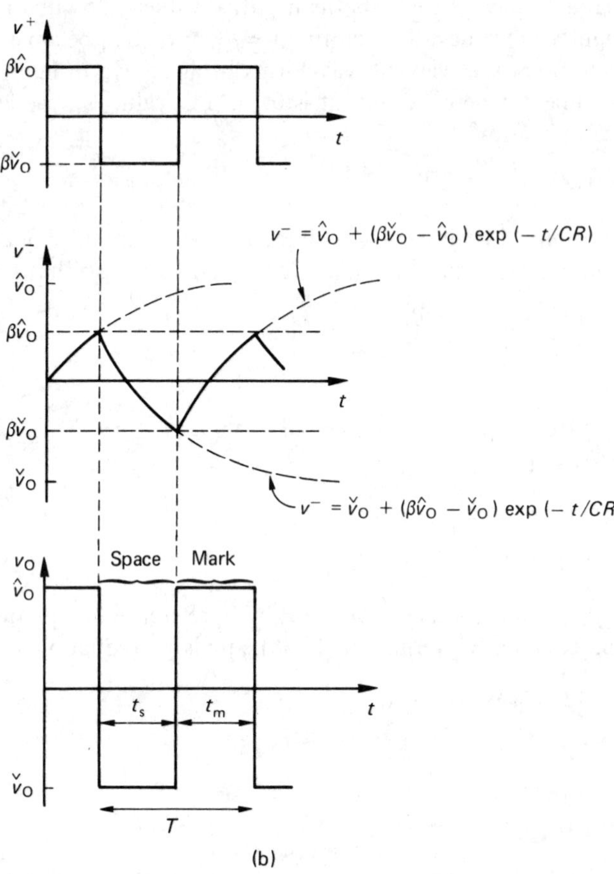

(b)

Figure 10.5 Op-amp astable switching circuit

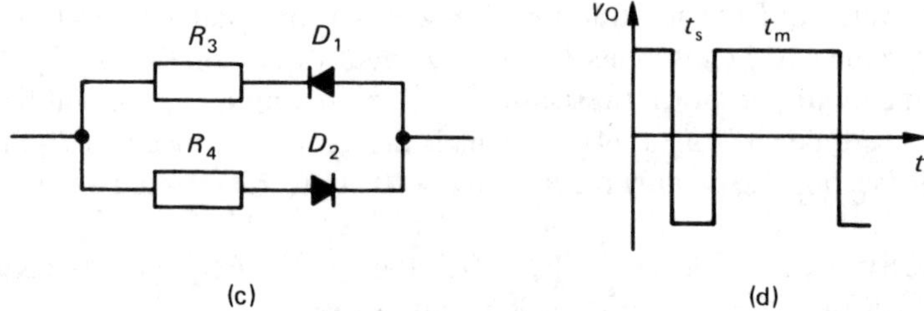

Figure 10.5 *continued*

a square wave. The period T of the square wave is

$$T = t_m + t_s$$

$$= 2t_m = 2CR \ln\left[\frac{\hat{v}_O - \beta\check{v}_O}{(1-\beta)\hat{v}_O}\right]$$

$$= 2CR \ln\left(\frac{1+\beta}{1-\beta}\right) \text{ as } \hat{v}_O = -\check{v}_O$$

$$= 2CR \ln\left[1 + (2R_1/R_2)\right] \text{ as } \beta = R_1/(R_1 + R_2) \quad (10.39)$$

The output frequency is therefore

$$f = 1/2CR \ln[1 + (2R_1/R_2)] \quad (10.40)$$

and for $R_1 = R_2$, giving a mid-range value of β of 0.5 providing reliable operation (section 7.3.2), the output frequency is

$$f = 1/2CR \ln 3 \simeq 1/2.2CR \quad (10.41)$$

If the timing resistor R in the circuit of figure 10.5a is replaced by the network of figure 10.5c, D_1 switches R_3 in circuit when v_O is positive giving time constant CR_3, D_2 being open circuit, while R_4 is effective, giving time constant CR_4, when v_O is negative. This enables an arbitrary mark-to-space ratio t_m:t_s to be obtained; if $R_3 > R_4$, t_m is greater than t_s and the output waveform is as shown in figure 10.5d. Note that the forward voltage drop V_F across the diode in the CR timing network affects the mark and space times, and hence the output frequency, because the aiming voltage as C is charging is reduced from $\hat{v}_O$ to $\hat{v}_O - V_F$ during the mark interval and from $\check{v}_O$ to $\check{v}_O + V_F$ during the space interval, V_F being about 0.6 V for a general-purpose silicon diode.

Example 10.5: Component selection for an op-amp astable circuit

Select E12 component values (appendix D) for the op-amp astable circuit of figure 10.5a to provide a 5 kHz square wave with output voltage levels of ± 7.5 V. The op-amp operates from ± 15 V supplies and the output waveform tolerance is ± 5 per cent.

As the required output voltage levels are different from the power supply voltages, output clamping is required as discussed in section 7.3.2 and demonstrated in figure 7.15c. Selection of back-to-back 6.8 V reference diodes limits the output to approximately ± 7.5 V, allowing for the voltage drop across the forward-biased diode.

A mid-range value of feedback fraction β is selected for reliable operation (section 7.3.2), the convenient value of 0.5 chosen here requiring equal values for R_1 and R_2. No information is given as to the input and output resistances of the op-amp and so it will be assumed to be a general-purpose type such as a 741 for which the geometric mean of R_I and R_O is of the order of 10 kΩ (section 7.5), allowing $R_1 = R_2 = 10\ \text{k}\Omega$ to be selected as suitable mid-range values.

With symmetrical output levels and $\beta = 0.5$, the output frequency is given by equation 10.41, from which the CR time constant is required to be

$$CR \simeq 1/2.2f = 1/2.2(5\ \text{kHz}) = 90.91\ \mu\text{s}$$

Preliminary selection of $R = 10\ \text{k}\Omega$ from $\sqrt{R_I R_O}$ requires

$$C = \frac{90.91\ \mu\text{s}}{10\ \text{k}\Omega} = 9.09\ \text{nF}$$

which allows use of a parallel combination of E12 values 6.8 nF and 2.2 nF to provide f well within the ± 5 per cent range. Alternatively combinations 2.7 kΩ, 33 nF; 3.3 kΩ, 27 nF; 27 kΩ, 3.3 nF and 33 kΩ, 2.7 nF all provide simple combinations satisfying the specification.

10.2.2 *Op-amp monostable circuits*

The op-amp astable of figure 10.5a can be readily converted to single-shot (monostable) operation by preventing the capacitor voltage changing sign using a diode as in figure 10.6a. With diode D_1 polarity as shown, the capacitor voltage and hence v^- cannot become positive, at least no more positive than the 0.6 V forward drop across the diode, and so the stable state of the circuit is v_O positive, making v^+ and hence v_I positive.

If a negative trigger pulse is applied to the + input causing v_I instantaneously to become negative, regenerative action causes a switch to the quasistable state with v_O switching to its negative saturation value $\check{v}_O$. The capacitor then starts to charge negatively aiming towards $\check{v}_O$ with time constant CR. When the capacitor voltage ($= v^-$) becomes just slightly more negative than v^+, which is $\beta\check{v}_O$ under these conditions where $\beta = R_1/(R_1 + R_2)$, v_I becomes positive once again, initiating a switch back to the $\hat{v}_O$ stable state. The corresponding voltage waveforms are shown in figure 10.6b.

Ignoring the 0.6 V drop across the capacitor in the stable state due to the forward-biased diode, the variation of capacitor voltage during the quasistable interval is

$$v_C = v^- \simeq \check{v}_O - \check{v}_O \exp(-t/CR) \tag{10.42}$$

corresponding to equation 1.14 with zero initial voltage and aiming voltage $\check{v}_O$. The end of the quasistable state, at time t_p, is when v_I changes sign which is when $v^- = v^+ = \beta\check{v}_O$ giving

$$\check{v}_O - \check{v}_O \exp(-t_p/CR) = \beta\check{v}_O \tag{10.43}$$

from which the output pulse width t_p is

$$t_p = CR \ln\left(\frac{1}{1-\beta}\right) = CR \ln\left(1 + \frac{R_1}{R_2}\right) \tag{10.44}$$

Note that immediately following the switch back to the stable state, the capacitor discharges from $\beta\check{v}_O$ back to zero (actually $+0.6$ V). During this discharge interval, XY on the v^-/t plot of figure 10.6b, the circuit cannot reliably be retriggered.

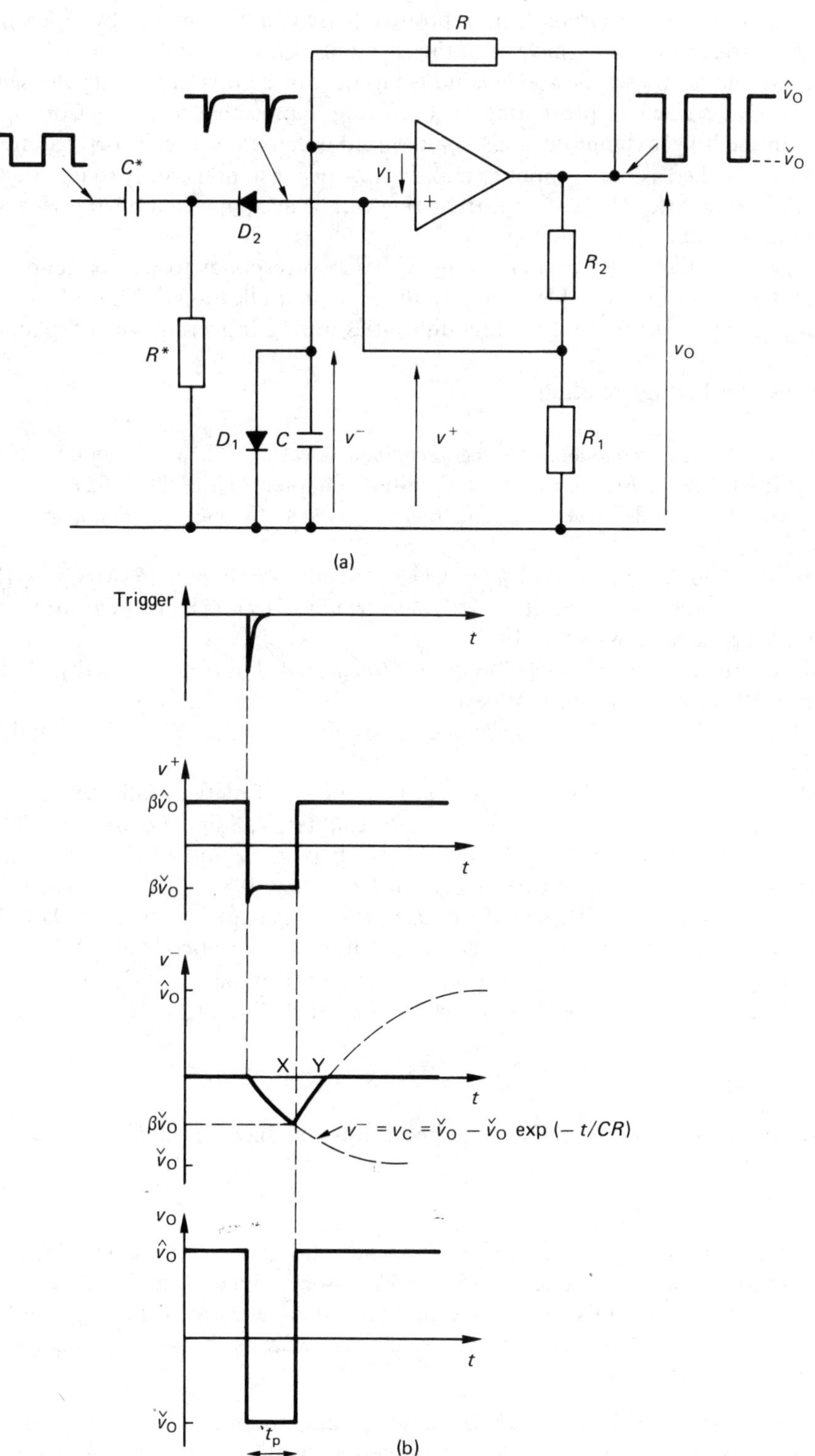

Figure 10.6 Op-amp monostable switching circuit

Triggering of the above circuit from a positive pulse can be achieved by reversing D_2 and applying the trigger to the $-$ instead of the $+$ input of the op-amp.

A positive output pulse, the stable state being $\check{v}_O$, can be obtained using the same circuit with diode D_1 reversed so preventing v^- becoming appreciably negative. Correspondingly, diode D_2 in the trigger circuit must also be reversed because the circuit then requires positive trigger pulses applied as the $+$ input to make v_1 positive instantaneously to initiate the switch to the quasistable state. Alternatively, triggering can be accomplished by applying a negative pulse to the $-$ input of the op-amp.

The trigger circuit C^*, R^* and D_2 in figure 10.6a corresponds to that of figure 10.3c used to trigger the discrete monostable circuit. In the current application, R^* must be selected very much larger than R_1 to prevent loading difficulties during triggering when D_2 conducts.

References and further reading

1. M.E. Goodge, *Semiconductor Device Technology*, section 2.2.13 (Macmillan, 1985)
2. T.L. Floyd, *Digital Fundamentals*, 2nd edition, chapter 7 (Merrill, 1982)
3. R.J. Maddock and D.M. Calcutt, *Electronics: A Course for Engineers*, chapter 6 (Longman, 1988)
4. J. Millman and A. Grabel, *Microelectronics*, 2nd edition, chapter 15 (McGraw-Hill, 1988)
5. A.S. Sedra and K.C. Smith, *Microelectronic Circuits*, 2nd edition, chapter 5 (Holt, Rinehart and Winston, 1987)
6. P.M. Chirlian, *Analysis and Design of Integrated Electronic Circuits*, 2nd edition, chapter 18 (Harper and Row/Wiley, 1987)
7. G.J. Ritchie, *Transistor Circuit Techniques*, 2nd edition, chapter 6 (Van Nostrand Reinhold, 1987)
8. G.M. Glasford, *Analog Electronic Circuits*, chapter 9 (Prentice-Hall, 1986)
9. T.F. Bogart, *Electronic Devices and Circuits*, chapters 4, 8 and 14 (Merrill, 1986)
10. M.S. Ghausi, *Electronic Devices and Circuits*, chapters 12 and 14 (Holt-Saunders, 1985)
11. T.Young, *Linear Integrated Circuits*, chapter 7 (Wiley, 1981)
12. S.S. Basi, *Semiconductor Pulse and Switching Circuits*, chapters 5, 6, 7 and 9 (Wiley, 1980)
13. M. Cirovic, *Basic Electronics*, 2nd edition, chapter 18 (Prentice-Hall, 1979)
14. S.A. Knight, *Electronics for Higher TEC*, chapter 9 (Granada, 1983)
15. D.C. Green, *Electronics for TEC Level IV*, chapter 8 (Pitman, 1981)

Tutorial questions

Note: Where applicable, answers correspond to rounding to 2 decimal places during calculation.

Discrete bistable circuits

10.1 Select suitable E24 resistance values (appendix D) for a basic discrete bistable circuit (figure 10.2a) required to operate from ± 6 V power supplies using BJTs with a minimum h_{FE} of 150 and an ON state collector current of 300 μA. Take $V_{BE(sat)} = 0.8$ V and $V_{CE(sat)} = 0.2$ V. For the preferred values chosen, what is the value of V_{BE} for the OFF state transistor?

[Answers: $R_C = 20$ kΩ, $R = 1.2$ MΩ, allowing an approximate 50 per cent margin above $I_B$min for saturation and $R_B = 6.2$ MΩ targeting for $V_{BE(OFF)} = -1$ V. Actual $V_{BE(OFF)}$ for these values is -0.8 V]

10.2 A discrete bistable circuit incorporates collector loads R_C of 15 kΩ, 470 kΩ coupling resistors and base bias resistors of 1.5 MΩ. The identical BJTs have $r_{b'e} = 5$ kΩ, $C_{b'c} = 5$ pF, $f_T = 250$ MHz and the ON state collector current is 500 μA. Noting that the voltage gain of a CE stage during active operation is $-g_{fe}R_C$ (table 3.1), g_{fe} is approximately $40I_C$ at 25°C (equation 3.63) and $C_{b'e} = (g_{fe}/2\pi f_T) - C_{b'c}$ (table 4.1), use the hybrid-π BJT model to determine the effective input resistance and input capacitance of each transistor stage for active operation during switching. Hence calculate the value of commutating capacitor required to optimise performance and select a suitable E12 (appendix D) value.

[Answers: 16.1 pF; select 18 pF]

Discrete monostable circuit

10.3 The circuit of question 10.1 is to be modified to provide negative pulses from V_{CC} to zero, of 50 μs duration, following the positive-going edges of a low frequency square wave. Describe the required modification, select appropriate E12 (appendix D) component values and explain the necessary triggering arrangement.

[Answers: Convert the circuit to monostable operation by removal of one of the R, R_B coupling networks and add a CR' timing circuit as in figure 10.3a. Select $R' = 1.5$ MΩ, providing a 74 per cent margin over $I_B$min, combined with $C = 47$ pF to provide the required pulse width. Form of output, stable state HI with negative pulse, requires the circuit output to be taken from T_1 collector. Triggering by positive edges requires the trigger circuit of figure 10.3c with D_1 reversed, applied to the base of T_1. Suitable trigger circuit values based on C^*R^* as 20 per cent of t_p, are $R^* = 100$ kΩ and $C^* = 100$ pF]

Discrete astable circuit

10.4 Design a discrete astable circuit operating from a 12 V supply that provides a 1 kHz square wave output and consumes no more than 5 mW. The BJTs have a minimum h_{FE} of 100, $V_{BE(sat)}$ is 0.8 V and $V_{CE(sat)}$ is 0.2 V; E12 component values (appendix D) are to be used.

[Answer: Circuit of figure 10.4a with R_3 and T_3 omitted. $R_C = 33$ kΩ gives $I_{C(sat)} = 357.6$ μA with power dissipation approximately $V_{CC}I_{C(sat)}$ of 4.3 mW. $R' = R'' =$ 2.2 MΩ provides a base current margin of approximately 42 per cent over the minimum value of 3.6 μA. $C' = C'' = 330$ pF, in conjunction with R', R'', provides a nominal 1 kHz output]

Op-amp astable circuits

10.5 In the circuit of figure 10.5a, R is replaced by the network of figure 10.5c with $R_3 = 47$ kΩ and $R_4 = 10$ kΩ. If $R_1 = R_2$, $C = 10$ nF and back-to-back 4.7 V reference diodes are connected across the output, what would be the frequency and mark-to-space ratio of the output waveform? The forward voltage drops across the general-purpose diodes may be ignored; the forward voltage drop across a voltage reference diode is 0.7 V.

[Answers: 1.60 kHz, 4.70:1]

10.6 An op-amp astable circuit operating from ± 15 V supplies is required to provide a nominal 500 Hz square wave output with voltage levels of ± 5 V; the allowable tolerance on frequency and voltage levels is ± 5 per cent. Select suitable E12 component values (appendix D), based on a typical op-amp of the 741 type, using a feedback fraction of 0.5.

[Answer: Circuit of figure 10.5a with 4.3 V back-to-back reference diodes across the output, $R_1 = R_2 = 10$ kΩ based on $\sqrt{R_I R_O} \simeq 10$ kΩ for a typical 741 op-amp, $R = 9.1$ kΩ and $C = 100$ nF]

10.7 Modify the circuit of question 10.6, retaining the feedback fraction of 0.5, to provide a 500 Hz output with a mark-to-space ratio of 3:1 with output voltage levels of $+5$ V and -2 V, all within a tolerance range of ± 10 per cent. Select resistors and reference diode voltages from the E24 range and capacitors from the E12 range (appendix D); forward voltage drops of 0.6 V for general-purpose diodes and 0.7 V for reference diodes are not to be ignored.

[Answer: Circuit of figure 10.5a with R replaced by the network of figure 10.5c, $R_1 = R_2 = 10$ kΩ. With $C = 100$ nF as for the circuit of question 10.6, R_3 and R_4 would be required to be 13.89 kΩ and 1.97 kΩ respectively. Although this would be satisfactory, the R_4 value is rather low and therefore it is suggested that C is reduced, for example, to 22 nF allowing E24 values 62 kΩ and 9.1 kΩ to be selected for R_3 and R_4. Output voltage limiting can be achieved using a back-to-back connection of a 4.3 V reference diode and a general-purpose diode to provide the nominal $+5$ V limit, with a parallel branch of three series general-purpose diodes to provide the nominal -2 V limit; note that the lowest available reference diode voltage is 2.4 V (appendix E, section E.2)]

Op-amp monostable circuit

10.8 The circuit of question 10.5 has a general-purpose diode connected across the capacitor, the anode of the diode being connected to signal earth. If a positive trigger pulse is applied to the + input of the op-amp, sketch the output waveform. How would the output voltage waveform be affected if the diode connections were reversed and negative trigger pulses applied?

[Answers: 516.35 μs positive pulse from -5.4 V to $+5.4$ V following the trigger. The output pulse would be inverted, the change being from $+5.4$ V to -5.4 V, and the pulse width reduced to 109.86 μs]

10.9 Using standard op-amp monostable circuits with $\beta = 0.5$, it is required to generate the pulse waveforms of figures 10.7a, b, c and d synchronised to a 1 kHz square wave as shown. The op-amp is a typical 741 type powered by ± 18 V supplies and the pulse width is required to be 50 μs in each case, the allowable tolerance on the output voltage levels being ± 20 per cent. Select suitable component values in each case, including the triggering circuit, using E24 resistors and reference diode voltages and E12 capacitors.

[Answers: Each circuit is based on that of figure 10.6a with $R_1 = R_2 = 10$ kΩ corresponding to $\sqrt{R_I R_O} \simeq 10$ kΩ for a type 741 op-amp. The pulse width of 50 μs requires a time constant of 72.135 μs; C is chosen to correspond to a mid-range value of R of the order of 10 kΩ; $C = 6.8$ nF and $R = 10$ kΩ + 620 Ω being selected. The C^*R^* time constant for the trigger network is chosen as 20 per cent t_p, 10 μs, R^* being chosen as 100 kΩ to be $\gg R_1$ and C^* is then 100 pF.

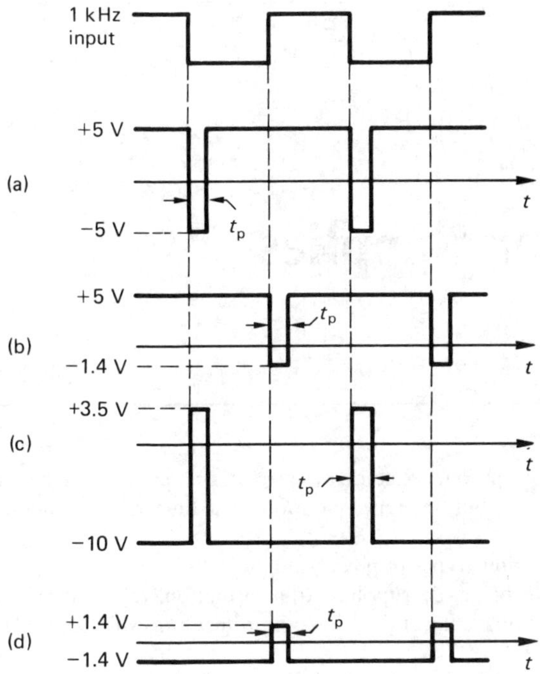

Figure 10.7 Pulse waveforms relating to tutorial question 10.9

(a) D_1 cathode to signal earth; 4.3 V back-to-back reference diodes across the output provide nominal 5 V clamping levels. A negative trigger is applied to the + input via D_2 with its anode connected to the + input.
(b) D_1 cathode to signal earth. Output clamping requires a back-to-back connection of a 4.3 V reference diode and a general-purpose diode to provide a nominal +4.9 V clamp in parallel with two series general-purpose diodes giving a −1.2 V clamp. A positive trigger is applied to the − input via D_2 with its cathode connected to the − input.
(c) D_1 anode to signal earth; 9.1 V and 2.7 V back-to-back reference diodes across the output provide nominal clamping levels of 9.8 V and 3.4 V. A negative trigger is applied to the − input via D_2 with its anode connected to the − input.
(d) D_1 anode to signal earth. Parallel clamping branches each comprising two series general-purpose diodes provide nominal ±1.2 V output levels. A positive trigger is applied to the + input via D_2 with its cathode connected to the + input]

See also tutorial questions 7.6 and 7.7 concerned with op-amp based Schmitt trigger circuits.

11 Power Supplies

Coverage

- The concept of *power*; primary electrical sources; dc and ac systems; the advantage of ac for long-distance power distribution; representation of a time-varying quantity; instantaneous, peak, average and rms values.
- Identification of the various types of power supplies.
- Detailed consideration of ac–dc supplies: transformation, rectification, smoothing circuits, linear stabiliser/regulator circuits, current limiting and protection, switched-mode techniques; performance indices, circuit design.
- Brief survey of dc–ac and dc–dc supplies, voltage multipliers and batteries.

Electrical power is produced by
(1) electromagnetic induction in *generators*,
(2) chemical reaction in *batteries* and *fuel cells*,
(3) photoelectric generation in *solar cells/panels*.
These are *primary* sources; in each case electrical equilibrium is disturbed causing a voltage to be established. When the external circuit is closed, a current flows attempting to restore the original equilibrium. While most sources provide a unidirectional flow termed *direct* current, dc, an alternator produces an oscillating output called *alternating* current, ac, which varies sinusoidally with time.

Power p is the rate of generation, transfer or dissipation of energy w, thus

$$p = \frac{dw}{dt} \tag{11.1}$$

Voltage is defined as the work done (energy transferred) per unit quantity of electricity (charge, q) passed and so:

$$v = \frac{dw}{dq} \tag{11.2}$$

while current is the rate of flow of charge:

$$i = \frac{dq}{dt} \tag{11.3}$$

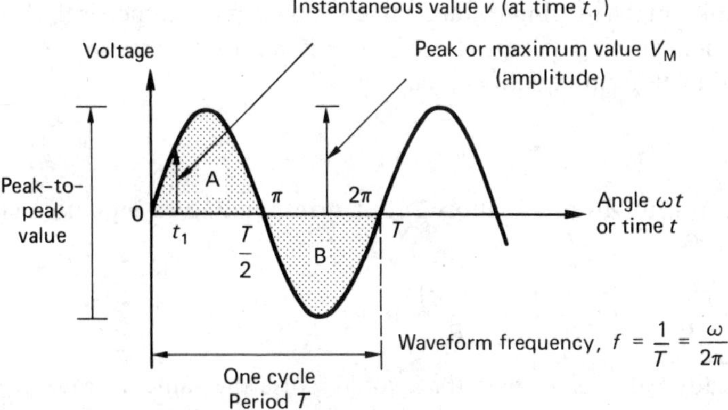

Figure 11.1 Sinusoidal voltage variation

Combining equations 11.1, 11.2 and 11.3, instantaneous electrical power is

$$p = \frac{dw}{dt} = \left(\frac{dw}{dq}\right)\left(\frac{dq}{dt}\right) = vi \tag{11.4}$$

A major loss in an electrical power distribution system is that due to the resistance of the power lines. This *ohmic* loss is proportional to the square of the current flow (substituting $v = Ri$, equation 2.20, into equation 11.4) and so efficiency can be improved by operating at a higher transmission voltage with a correspondingly reduced current flow. The voltage in an ac distribution system can be readily increased before transmission using a step-up transformer; voltage increase in a dc system is more complicated and costly, making the ac system the most popular for long-distance power distribution.

The 'value' of a time-varying voltage

The terms instantaneous, peak, peak-to-peak, average and root-mean-square are used to describe a time-varying voltage, or current, depending on which aspect of the variation is of interest.

Instantaneous value v is the value at any time instant, such as t_1 in figure 11.1; this value has little quantitative use.

Peak value V_M is the maximum value which is also referred to as the *amplitude* of the waveform. The peak-to-peak value is the total voltage difference between the positive and negative peaks.

The *average* value V_{AV} (see footnote *, next page), also called the *mean* value or *dc component*, is found by integrating the voltage variation over a complete cycle and dividing by the cycle 'length'. Note that as the voltage is a function of time and frequency, it is often convenient to use *angle* ωt as the independent variable; the cycle 'length' is the period T in terms of time or 2π radians (360°) in terms of angle. Then

$$V_{AV} = \frac{1}{T}\int_0^T v(t)\,dt \text{ or } \frac{1}{2\pi}\int_0^{2\pi} v(\omega t)\,d(\omega t) \tag{11.5}$$

Note that the average value of a variation that is symmetrical about the time (angle) axis is zero, corresponding to cancellation of the positive and negative areas A and B in figure 11.1 during integration over the complete cycle.

The *effective* value of the varying voltage as far as power is concerned is the root-mean-square value V_{RMS}*. If a time-varying voltage $v(t)$, or $v(\omega t)$, is applied to a resistor R, the instantaneous power dissipated in R, from equation 11.4, is

$$p = vi = \frac{v^2}{R} \tag{11.6}$$

as $i = v/R$ for a resistor from equation 2.20. Corresponding to equation 11.5, the average power dissipated P_{AV} is

$$P_{AV} = \frac{1}{T}\int_0^T \frac{v^2(t)}{R}\,dt \text{ or } \frac{1}{2\pi}\int_0^{2\pi} \frac{v^2(\omega t)}{R}\,d(\omega t) \tag{11.7}$$

If V_{RMS} is the steady value of voltage that would cause the same average power dissipation in R as the varying voltage v, then combining equations 2.22 and 11.7

$$P_{AV} = \frac{V_{RMS}^2}{R} = \frac{1}{2\pi}\int_0^{2\pi} \frac{v^2(\omega t)}{R}\,d(\omega t) \tag{11.8}$$

from which

$$V_{RMS} = \sqrt{\left[\frac{1}{2\pi}\int_0^{2\pi} v^2(\omega t)\,d(\omega t)\right]} \tag{11.9}$$

The quantity inside the square root is the *mean* (average) of the squared voltage and so the effective value of the time-varying voltage, as far as *power* is concerned, is the *R*OOT of the *M*EAN *S*QUARE value V_{RMS}.

Note 11.1: RMS value of a sinusoidal quantity

A sinusoidally varying voltage (figure 11.1) may be represented as

$$v = V_M \sin \omega t$$

where V_M is the amplitude and ω ($= 2\pi f$) the angular frequency. Substituting for v in the general relation of equation 11.9:

$$\begin{aligned} V_{RMS} &= \sqrt{\left[\frac{1}{2\pi}\int_0^{2\pi} V_M^2 \sin^2 \omega t\,d(\omega t)\right]} \\ &= \sqrt{\left[\frac{V_M^2}{4\pi}\int_0^{2\pi} (1-\cos 2\omega t)\,d(\omega t)\right]} \\ &= \sqrt{\left\{\frac{V_M^2}{4\pi}\left[\omega t - \tfrac{1}{2}\sin 2\omega t\right]_0^{2\pi}\right\}} \\ &= \sqrt{\left\{\frac{V_M^2}{4\pi}\left[(2\pi - 0) - (0 - 0)\right]\right\}} = \frac{V_M}{\sqrt{2}} \text{ or } 0.707V_M \end{aligned} \tag{11.10}$$

using the relationship $\sin^2\omega t = \frac{1}{2}(1 - \cos 2\omega t)$.

* *Symbol terminology.* Upper case symbols M (maximum, peak), AV (average, mean), RMS (root-mean-square) indicate values for a general *total* waveform comprising a dc component and time-varying (signal) component. If it is necessary to refer to the peak, average or rms value of only the signal component of the total waveform, lower case suffixes m, av and rms are used.

Note that if a time-varying voltage (or current) is specified simply as so many volts (or amps) with no other reference, such as peak or peak-to-peak value, then the quoted value refers to the rms value of the varying quantity. Thus '240 V mains' in the UK refers to an rms value of 240 V, the associated power flow being *as if* the voltage was constant at 240 V; the peak value V_M is $240\sqrt{2} \simeq 339$ V (equation 11.10)

11.1 **Types of supplies**

The most common primary sources are ac 'mains' (sinusoidal; 240 V rms, 50 Hz in the UK; 220 V rms, 50 Hz in Europe; 115 V rms 60 Hz in the US) for 'fixed' equipment and batteries for portable appliances. This chapter is concerned with a range of circuits, collectively described as *power supplies*, that convert voltage level and sometimes power form (ac or dc) from that supplied by a primary source to that required by the electrical/electronic equipment.

Power supplies may be classified as

(1) AC–DC types, usually mains driven, that provide a constant voltage, variable current supply for fixed equipment.

(2) DC–AC types that provide an ac output, usually at mains frequency, from a battery source. These are called *inverters* and are used as stand-by supplies for essential services, providing power during a mains failure as well as for vehicle, marine and general-outdoor applications.

(3) DC–DC types used to change the voltage level from that of the battery source to that required by the equipment. Step-down types are basically *regulators*; step-up types are usually called *converters*.

Some supplies are *embedded* within equipment, often termed *dedicated* supplies because they provide power for a specific load and can therefore be designed to meet the requirements of that particular load. Other supplies have a general-purpose role, being designed to handle a power throughput up to a specified maximum. Such supplies may include additional features such as variable output current limiting and overcurrent, including short circuit, protection.

11.2 **AC–DC supplies**

As represented in figure 11.2, a linear ac–dc supply comprises

(1) A *transformer* to change the amplitude of the ac input to a suitable value dependent on

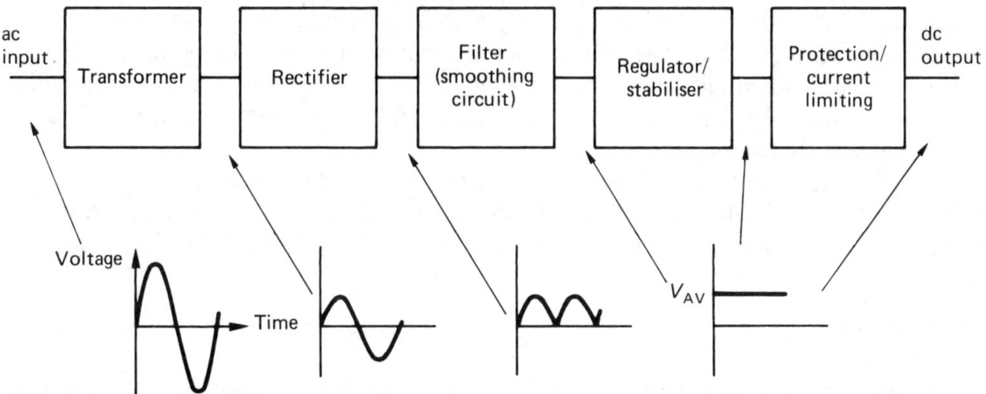

Figure 11.2 Block diagram representation of a linear ac–dc power supply

the required output voltage. The transformer also acts as a safety element in that it provides electrical isolation from the mains source.

(2) A *rectifier* to convert from the alternating input to unidirectional (fixed polarity) form.

(3) A *filter*, sometimes termed a *smoothing circuit* in this application, to remove the fluctuating component (ripple) from the unidirectional output from the rectifier to leave the steady (dc) value.

(4) For supplies required to drive a widely fluctuating load, a *regulator* stage is normally included to maintain the output voltage essentially constant as the load varies.

(5) In general-purpose supplies, the regulator usually incorporates current limiting to protect both the supply and the load from excessive current flow.

11.2.1 *Transformation*

The transformer is designed/selected on the basis of the required primary-to-secondary voltage ratio, the maximum secondary current to be supplied and the power throughput as outlined in section 2.4.3. The ratings of this type of transformer are quoted in terms of rms values assuming sinusoidal waveshapes, thus a transformer specification quoting a 240 V primary with a 30 V, 2 A secondary means that the VA rating of the core and winding wire gauges are such that when the primary is energised with a 240 V (rms) sinusoidal supply at mains frequency, the secondary will provide a 30 V (rms) output at a full-load output current of 2 A (rms).

An important performance index of a transformer in this context is its *voltage regulation* which is defined as

$$\text{Voltage reduction} = \frac{\text{No-load voltage} - \text{Full-load voltage}}{\text{No-load voltage}} \tag{11.11}$$

and is usually given as a percentage. Winding resistance causes the output (secondary) voltage of the transformer to fall as the output current is increased. The secondary voltage is thus a maximum on no-load (zero secondary current) and a minimum when the current drawn is at its rated maximum (full-load); typical values of regulation are in the range 5–15 per cent for ratings up to 1 kVA.

The regulation performance is important in cases where the load fluctuates over a wide range because if the regulation is poor the input voltage to the rectifier will fall significantly as the load current increases and correspondingly the load voltage will fall. In such cases the regulator/stabiliser circuit has to cope not only with a varying load but also with a varying input voltage (section 11.2.4). The transformer secondary must provide a sufficiently high voltage under full-load conditions so that, allowing for the voltage losses across the rectifier (section 11.2.2), the smoothing circuit (section 11.2.3) and the regulator (section 11.2.4), the required load voltage can be maintained.

Note that voltage regulation is also used as a merit factor for a complete power supply (sections 11.2.3 and 11.2.4, figures 11.14 and 11.18), the output resistance of the supply featuring in an exactly similar way to the winding resistance of the transformer in this respect.

11.2.2 *Rectification*

The unilateral conduction properties of the semiconductor diode (section 2.3.2) enable it to be used to convert the alternating output of the transformer into a unidirectional current, a

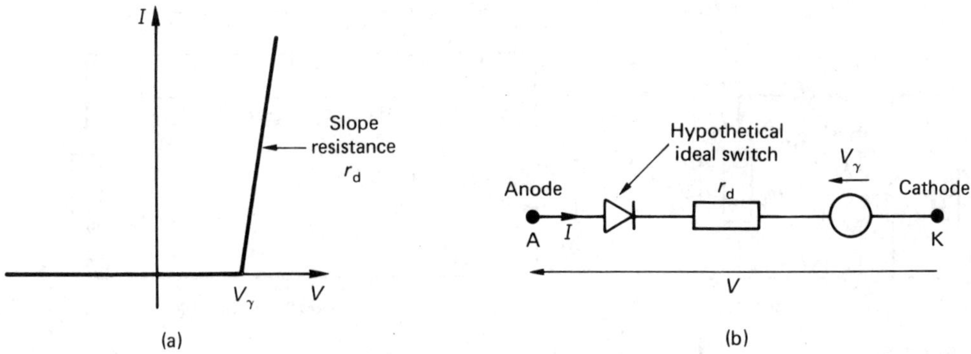

Figure 11.3 Diode characteristic and model

process termed *rectification.* Diodes designed specifically for this application are often called rectifiers.

Figure 11.3a shows a first-order approximation of the relevant portion of the $I-V$ characteristic of figure 2.2c. For applied voltages less than the threshold voltage V_γ ($\simeq 0.5$ V for a silicon junction diode) the diode approximates to an open circuit, while for $V > V_\gamma$ current increases rapidly with voltage, the diode exhibiting a slope resistance r_d ($= \Delta V/\Delta I$) of a few ohms. Figure 11.3b gives the corresponding network model in which the unblanked diode symbol represents a hypothetical ideal switch: open circuit for $V < V_\gamma$, short circuit for $V > V_\gamma$.

Half-wave rectification

The simplest rectification arrangement is to use a single diode in series with the ac supply as in figure 11.4a. For the diode direction shown, current flows through the load only when v_S is positive and greater than the diode threshold V_γ.

To analyse the circuit, the model of figure 11.3b is used to represent the conduction properties of the diode as in figure 11.4b. Current flow depends on whether v_S is $< V_\gamma$ or $> V_\gamma$:

(1) $v_S < V_\gamma$. The diode approximates to an open circuit, $i_L = 0$ and therefore $v_L = 0$.

(2) $v_S > V_\gamma$. The ideal switch in the diode model is short circuit, thus:

$$i_L = \frac{v_S - V_\gamma}{r_d + R_L} \tag{11.12}$$

from which

$$v_L = R_L i_L = \left(\frac{R_L}{r_d + R_L}\right) v_S - \frac{R_L V_\gamma}{r_d + R_L} \tag{11.13}$$

Thus v_L is zero except for $v_S > V_\gamma$ when v_L is a fraction $R_L/(r_d + R_L)$ of v_S less a fixed offset $R_L V_\gamma/(r_d + R_L)$ (equation 11.13) as shown in figure 11.4c for v_S sinusoidal. If the diode slope resistance r_d is small compared with load R_L, the ratio $R_L/(r_d + R_L)$ is approximately unity and v_L is then simply $v_S - V_\gamma$ for $v_S > V_\gamma$. Furthermore, if the amplitude V_{SM} of v_S is $\gg V_\gamma$, the voltage drop across the diode when it is conducting becomes insignificant so that $v_L \simeq v_S$ when v_S is positive. This is ideal *half-wave* rectification; literally half the input waveform is applied to the load so that although the load voltage varies, its polarity does not change (figure 11.4c: $v_L - \omega t$ plot).

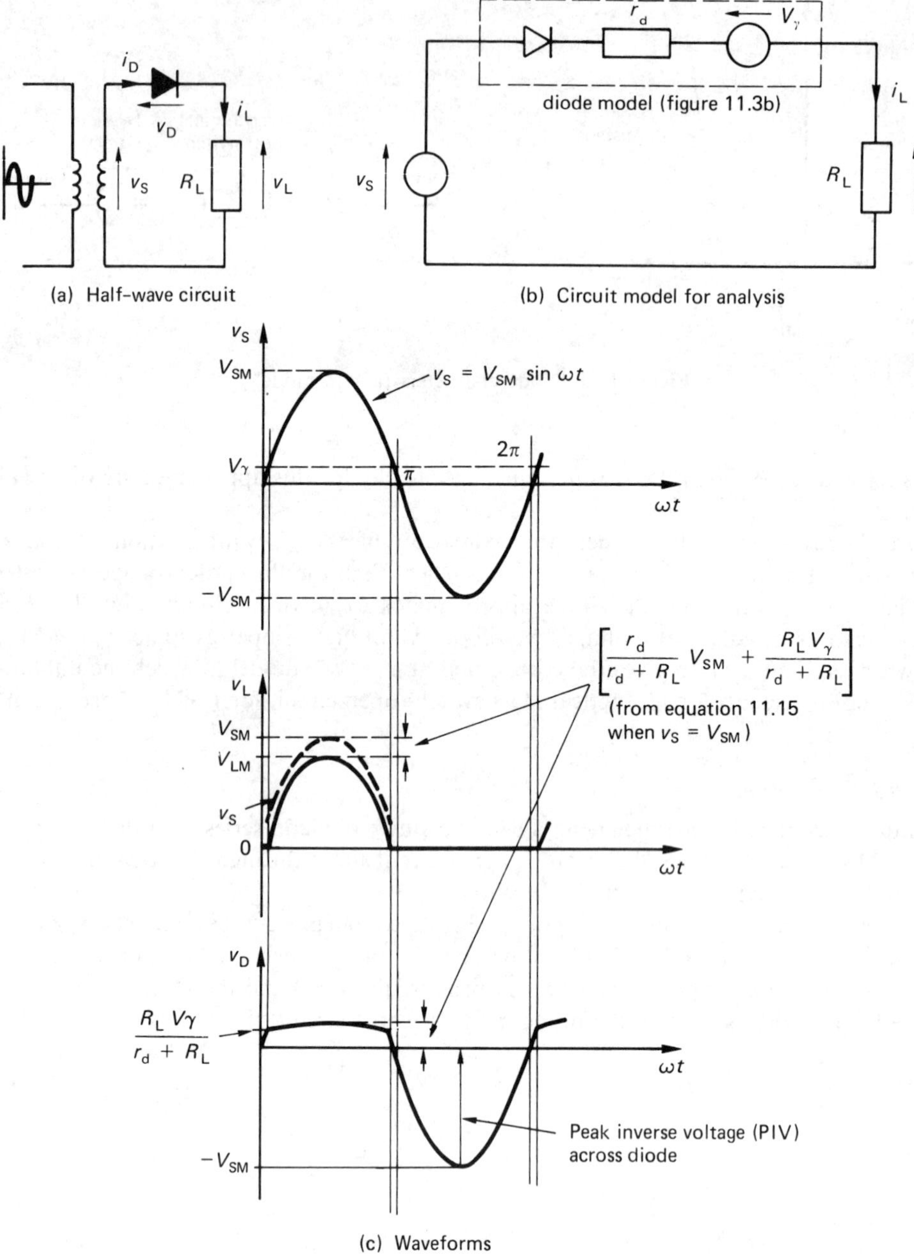

Figure 11.4 Half-wave rectification

The diode voltage v_D is $v_S - v_L$ (figure 11.4a), which, using equation 11.13, is

$$v_D = v_S - v_L \tag{11.14}$$

$$= \left(\frac{r_d}{r_d + R_L}\right) v_S + \frac{R_L V_\gamma}{r_d + R_L} \tag{11.15}$$

during the interval that the diode conducts; if $r_d \ll R_L$, v_D is approximately constant at V_γ.

When the diode is not conducting, $v_L = 0$ and, from equation 11.14, $v_D = v_S$ as shown in the $v_D - \omega t$ plot in figure 11.4c. The diode is therefore under maximum stress when v_S is at its negative maximum $- V_{SM}$, the *peak inverse voltage* (PIV) across the diode is therefore V_{SM}. Manufacturers normally specify the maximum allowable repetitive peak reverse voltage V_{RRM}max for a rectifier diode, and the user must choose a diode having $V_{RRM}\text{max} > \text{PIV}$ to avoid reverse breakdown and consequential failure.

Figure 11.5 shows the graphical construction of the load voltage waveform for the half-wave circuit of figure 11.4a. The transfer characteristic of the circuit, output v_L against input v_S, shows graphically that $v_L = 0$ for $v_S < V_\gamma$ while for $v_S > V_\gamma$, v_L is given by equation 11.13, the slope of the characteristic being $R_L/(r_d + R_L)$. Voltage axes have corresponding scales, as do the time axes of the v_S and v_L waveforms. The sinusoidal source voltage variation is superimposed on the v_S-axis of the transfer characteristic and the variation of v_L plotted corresponding to the movement of the operating point along the characteristic. For example, at a time corresponding to $\omega t = \pi/4$, v_S has a value given by point A on the $v_S - \omega t$ plot. Projecting up to the transfer characteristic and then across to the $v_L - \omega t$ graph enables point B (at $\pi/4$) to be plotted, and so on for other points to construct the complete waveform. Note that as v_S increases from zero, v_L remains at zero until the diode starts to conduct at $v_S = V_\gamma$, that is, point C on the v_S waveform. Notice also that linear representation of the diode characteristic above the conduction threshold V_γ results in a linear transfer characteristic for $v_S > V_\gamma$ whereby sinusoidal v_S maps to sinusoidal v_L above the threshold. In practice, the forward characteristic of the diode and hence the circuit transfer characteristic for v_S positive

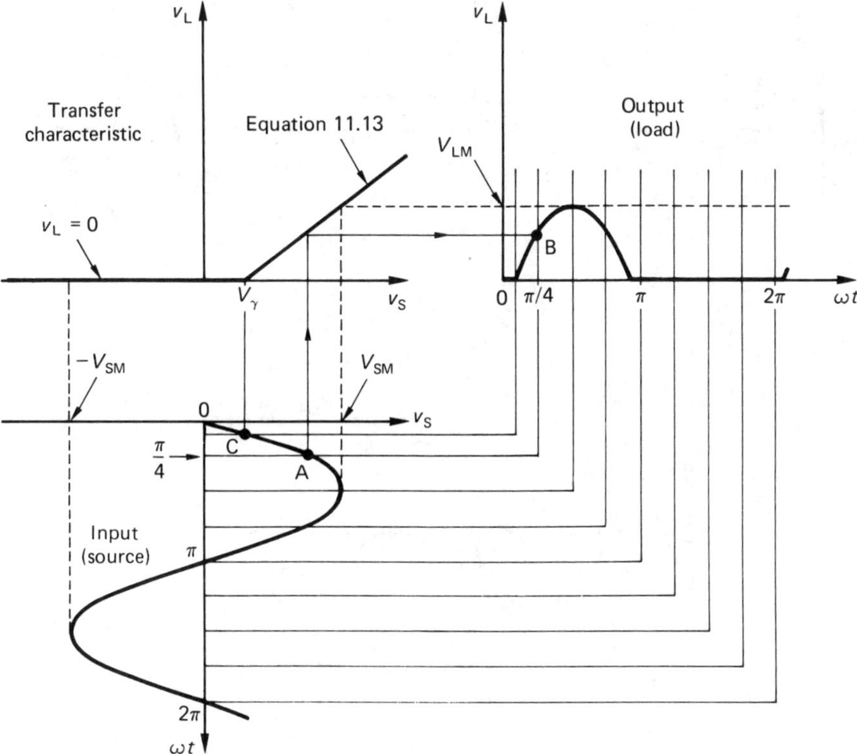

Figure 11.5 Graphical derivation of the load voltage waveform for a half-wave rectifier

are non-linear so that some distortion will appear in v_L. The lower the input amplitude V_{SM}, the more non-linear is the relevant portion of the diode characteristic and the greater the distortion introduced.

Mathematical representation of the half-wave rectified sinewave

Figure 11.6a shows an ideal half-wave rectified sinewave as the load voltage v_L in the circuit of figure 11.4a with its average value (dc component) $V_{L(AV)} = V_{LM}/\pi$ (note 11.2) and its effective value powerwise (rms value) $V_{L(RMS)} = V_{LM}/2$ (note 11.2). Note that the average value is that which makes the two shaded areas in figure 11.6a equal. The half-wave rectified sinewave (v_L)

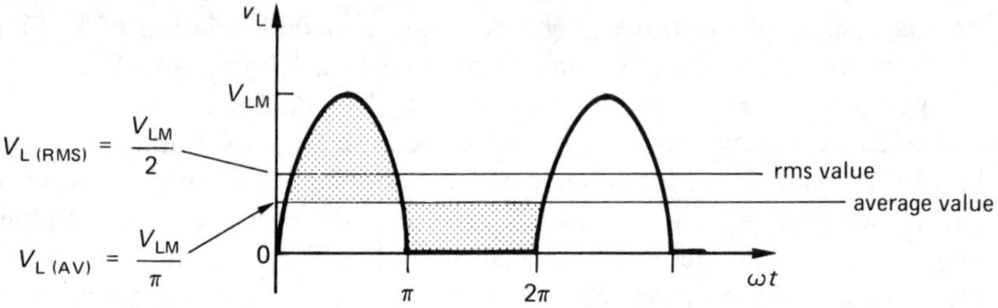

(a) Root-mean-square and average values

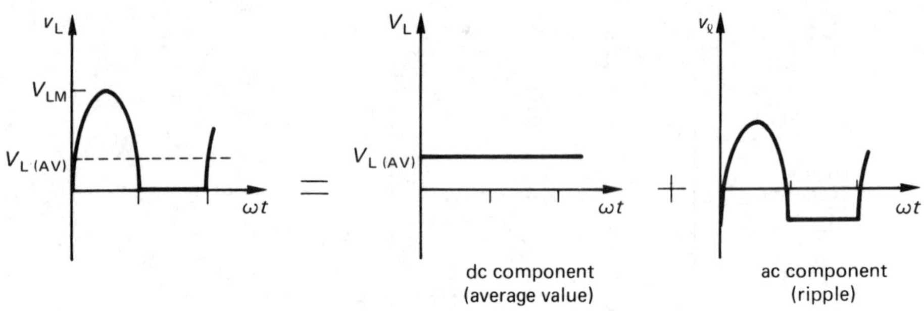

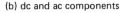

(b) dc and ac components

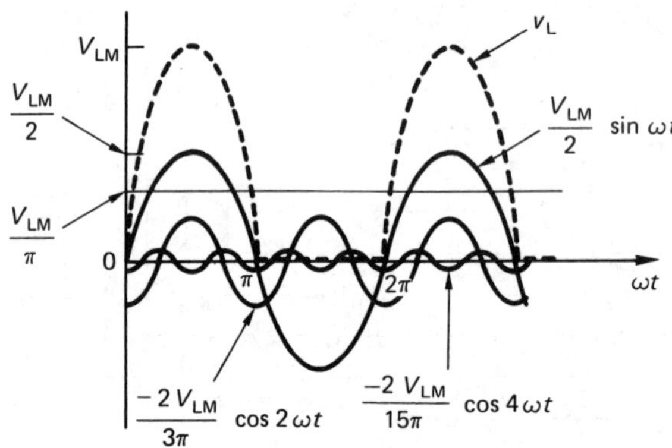

(c) Fourier representation (harmonic analysis)

Figure 11.6 Half-wave rectified sinewave

can be considered (figure 11.6b) to be made up of a dc component $V_{L(AV)}$ and an ac component v_l which, in the context of dc power supplies, is usually called *ripple*. Section 11.2.3 considers various methods to reduce the ripple to negligible proportions so as to leave the dc component as the output of the supply.

Note 11.2: Average and rms values of a half-wave rectified sinewave

Average value. Equation 11.5 gives the general definition of average value. In the half-wave case, $v_L = V_{LM}\sin\omega t$ for $\omega t = 0-\pi$ and $v_L = 0$ for $\omega t = \pi-2\pi$, thus

$$V_{L(AV)} = \frac{1}{2\pi}\left[\int_0^{\pi} V_{LM}\sin\omega t\,d(\omega t) + \int_{\pi}^{2\pi} 0\,d(\omega t)\right]$$

$$= \frac{V_{LM}}{2\pi}\Big[-\cos\omega t\Big]_0^{\pi}$$

$$= \frac{V_{LM}}{2\pi}[+1-(-1)] = \frac{V_{LM}}{\pi} \text{ or } 0.318V_{LM} \tag{11.16}$$

RMS value. Using the definition of equation 11.9:

$$V_{L(RMS)} = \sqrt{\left\{\frac{1}{2\pi}\left[\int_0^{\pi} V_{LM}^2\sin^2\omega t\,d(\omega t) + \int_{\pi}^{2\pi} 0\,d(\omega t)\right]\right\}}$$

$$= \sqrt{\left\{\frac{V_{LM}^2}{4\pi}\int_0^{\pi}(1-\cos 2\omega t)\,d(\omega t)\right\}}, \text{ using } \sin^2\omega t = \tfrac{1}{2}(1-\cos 2\omega t)$$

$$= \sqrt{\left\{\frac{V_{LM}^2}{4\pi}\left[\omega t - \tfrac{1}{2}\sin 2\omega t\right]_0^{\pi}\right\}}$$

$$= \sqrt{\left\{\frac{V_{LM}^2}{4\pi}\left[(\pi-0)-(0-0)\right]\right\}} = \frac{V_{LM}}{2} \tag{11.17}$$

Fourier analysis (appendix A) allows the half-wave rectified sinewave to be represented by the series

$$v_L = V_{LM}\left[\frac{1}{\pi} + \frac{1}{2}\sin\omega t - \frac{2}{3\pi}\cos 2\omega t - \frac{2}{15\pi}\cos 4\omega t \ldots - \frac{2}{(n^2-1)\pi}\cos n\omega t\right] \tag{11.18}$$

where $n = 2, 4, 6, \ldots \infty$. The first term ($V_{LM}/\pi$) is the dc component $V_{L(AV)}$ and the remainder of the series is the ripple. ($V_{LM}/2$)sin ωt is the *fundamental* as it has the same frequency as the original sinewave, and ($2V_{LM}/3\pi$)cos $2\omega t$ is the *second harmonic.* Note that, apart from the fundamental, this series contains only *even* harmonics, the $3\omega t$, $5\omega t$, ... terms are missing, or alternatively, can be considered to have zero amplitude. Note also that the amplitudes of the harmonics progressively reduce so that in many cases a reasonably accurate representation is provided by the first few terms of the infinite series. Figure 11.6c shows the first four terms of the series drawn approximately to scale. The validity of this representation can be checked to a limited accuracy by adding these components to obtain v_L. In the interval $\omega t = 0-\pi$, the components are mostly positive resulting in a positive v_L, but for $\omega t = \pi-2\pi$ it is not difficult to accept that the positive and negative components cancel, making v_L zero.

A figure-of-merit for a rectifier is the ratio of dc output power to ac input power, termed the *rectification efficiency* η_{rect}. The dc power developed in the load is $I^2_{\text{L(AV)}}R_{\text{L}}$ corresponding to equation 2.21, $I_{\text{L(AV)}}$ being the dc component of the load current, while the average power delivered from the ac source, which is dissipated in r_{d} and R_{L}, is $I^2_{\text{L(RMS)}}(r_{\text{d}}+R_{\text{L}})$ corresponding to equation 2.22, thus

$$\eta_{\text{rect}}=\frac{\text{dc output power}}{\text{ac input power}}=\frac{I^2_{\text{L(AV)}}R_{\text{L}}}{I^2_{\text{L(RMS)}}(r_{\text{d}}+R_{\text{L}})} \tag{11.19}$$

Assuming ideal rectification, that is source amplitude $V_{\text{SM}} \gg$ diode threshold V_γ, $I_{\text{L(AV)}}=I_{\text{LM}}/\pi$ and $I_{\text{L(RMS)}}=I_{\text{LM}}/2$ corresponding to the results of note 11.2 where I_{LM} is the peak load current. Substitution in equation 11.19 shows that η_{rect} for the half-wave rectifier is

$$\eta_{\text{rect(half-wave)}}=\frac{\dfrac{I^2_{\text{LM}}}{\pi^2}R_{\text{L}}}{\dfrac{I^2_{\text{LM}}}{4}(r_{\text{d}}+R_{\text{L}})}=\frac{4}{\pi^2}\left(\frac{R_{\text{L}}}{r_{\text{d}}+R_{\text{L}}}\right) \tag{11.20}$$

If $r_{\text{d}} \ll R_{\text{L}}$, $\eta_{\text{rect}}=4/\pi^2=40.5$ per cent, and so even for the ideal case of negligible r_{d} and V_γ only 40.5 per cent of the total input power appears at the load in dc form for the half-wave circuit. The remaining 59.5 per cent appears at the load still in ac form, as ripple.

Full-wave rectification

The poor ac-to-dc conversion efficiency of the half-wave arrangement is due mainly to the fact that power in only half the source waveform is utilised. Efficiency is doubled (equation 11.24) by *full-wave* rectification whereby both halves of the source waveform are used. Full-wave rectification must maintain the current flow through the load in the same direction, and hence keep the polarity of v_{L} unchanged, for both positive and negative v_{S}. Two arrangements are used

(1) Two half-wave circuits in parallel, one operating for positive v_{S}, the other for negative v_{S}.
(2) Bridge configuration using four diodes.

The two-diode arrangement (figure 11.7a) requires a transformer with a centre-tapped secondary; the two half-wave circuits are shown by full and dashed lines respectively. For positive v_{S}, diode D_1 conducts and D_2 is OFF, while for negative v_{S} current flows to the load via D_2, D_1 then being OFF. In each case i_{L} is in the same direction and so the polarity of v_{L} is the same (figure 11.7b); as in the single half-wave arrangement, the peak load voltage V_{LM} is less than the peak source voltage V_{SM} due to the diode drop. Figure 11.7b also shows the variation of diode voltage, v_{D_1} being shown, v_{D_2} has the same form but is phase-shifted by half a cycle relative to v_{D_1}. During the conduction half cycle v_{D_1} is simply the forward diode drop of D_1, but when switched off the inverse voltage rises to a peak value of $-(V_{\text{SM}}+V_{\text{LM}})$ which is almost $-2V_{\text{SM}}$; the diode PIV is therefore approximately $2V_{\text{SM}}$, twice the value for the single half-wave case (figure 11.4c). This is due to the fact that while D_1 is OFF, v_{S} is negative so that at the peak condition the anode of D_1 (point A, figure 11.7a) is at $-V_{\text{SM}}$ relative to the centre-tap (point C) and at the same time the cathode of D_1 (point B) has risen to $+V_{\text{LM}}$ because of current flow via D_2. At this instant, therefore, the voltage across D_1 is $v_{\text{S}}-v_{\text{L}}=-V_{\text{SM}}-(+V_{\text{LM}})=-(V_{\text{SM}}+V_{\text{LM}})$.

The bridge arrangement (figure 11.8a) provides full-wave rectification without the need for a centre-tapped transformer, although four diodes are required in place of the two for the dual half-wave circuit. Inspection of figure 11.8a shows that D_1 and D_2 are ON, D_3 and

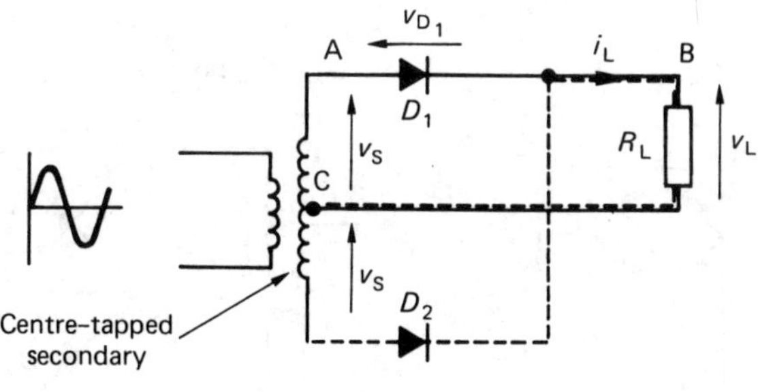

(a) Two half-wave circuits in parallel

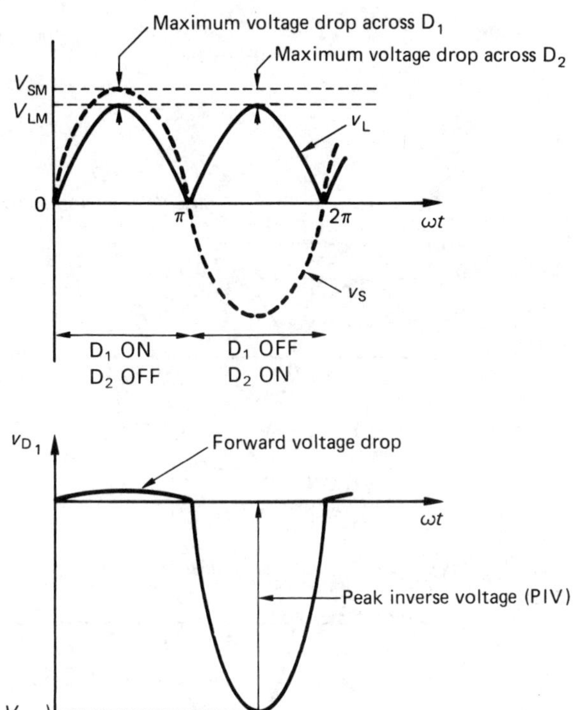

(b) Circuit waveforms

Figure 11.7 Two-diode full-wave rectifier

D_4 OFF when v_S is positive, while the converse is true for negative v_S; in each case the current through R_L is in the same direction. Note that there are always two conducting diodes in series with the load and so the rectification is marginally less ideal than for the two-diode circuit because of the combined resistances and threshold voltages of the diodes. Figure 11.8b shows the waveforms for the bridge circuit; the PIV for *each* of the bridge diodes is approximately half that of the diodes in the two-diode circuit. The simplified symbol of figure 11.8c is often used to represent a bridge rectifier.

Bridge rectifiers are produced in integrated form with a variety of ratings; appendix E, section E.4 gives data for a 4.8 A, 400 V type BY224–400. A bridge specification usually quotes

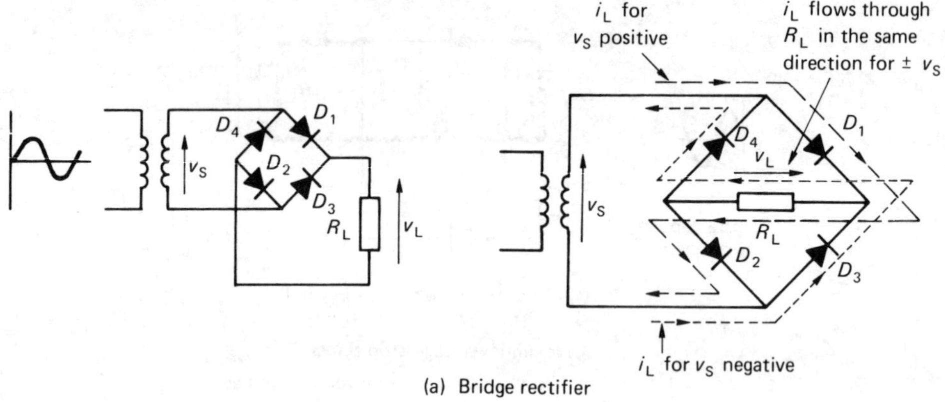

(a) Bridge rectifier

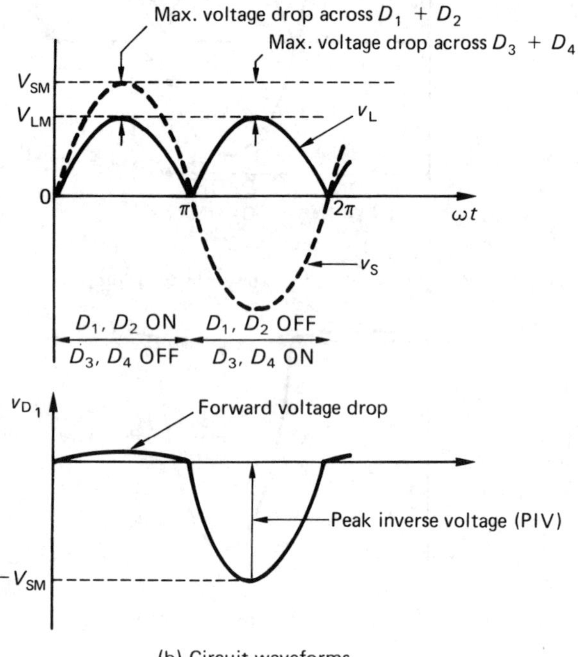

(b) Circuit waveforms

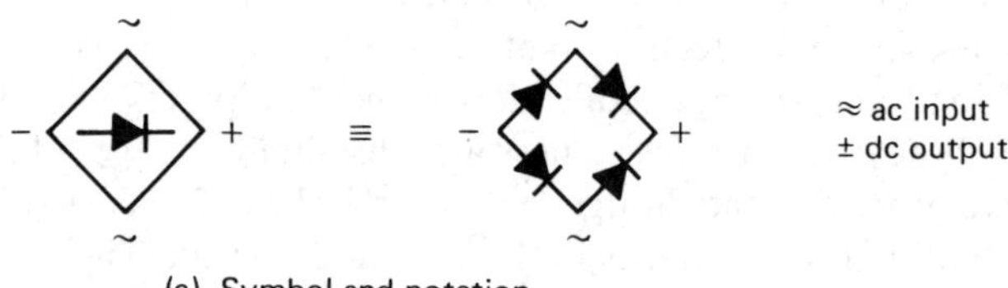

(c) Symbol and notation

Figure 11.8 Bridge full-wave rectifier

the maximum permissible value of average output current $I_{O(AV)}$max at a certain temperature, also termed the maximum average forward current ($I_{F(AV)}$max) or simply the 'current rating'. The input voltage limitation is often quoted in terms of the maximum permitted rms value of the input voltage $V_{I(RMS)}$max based on sinusoidal excitation taking account of the maximum PIV that the bridge diodes can withstand. However, some manufacturers simply quote the maximum permitted repetitive peak input reverse voltage V_{IRM}max, as in the BY224 designation above, and the user must ensure that the PIV does not exceed this value in operation. In most applications a smoothing/filter circuit is included between the rectifier and the load, usually incorporating a shunt capacitor. As discussed in section 11.2.3, the capacitor is recharged during short intervals when the input voltage to the bridge exceeds the capacitor voltage. Such an arrangement draws current in spikes (figure 11.11d) and the bridge diodes must be capable of carrying these surges. Various peak current ratings are used to describe the surge limitations of a bridge, namely the maximum repetitive peak output current I_{ORM}max, the maximum non-repetitive (that is, isolated surge) peak input current I_{ISM}max or the maximum non-repetitive peak forward current I_{FSM}max. The value of I_{FSM}max is typically 10 to 50 times the $I_{F(AV)}$max value. Manufacturers usually give the voltage drop V_F across the bridge, typically 1.2–2 V, at a specific forward current and the typical reverse leakage current at maximum reverse voltage, typically 5–20 μA for bridges having $I_{F(AV)}$max up to about 50 A. In consideration of use with capacitance smoothing, some specifications state the resistance required in series with the bridge, as a function of $V_{I(RMS)}$, to limit the peak current at switch ON, when the capacitor may be uncharged, for safe operation.

In summary, the two-diode full-wave circuit has the advantage of a lower diode voltage drop than the bridge circuit but it requires a larger, heavier, more costly centre-tapped transformer and the diodes are subjected to a higher PIV. The bridge circuit requires a cheaper basic transformer, the individual diodes have a lower PIV and bridges are conveniently available in integrated form, but there is the disadvantage of a higher diode voltage drop than for the two-diode circuit.

Mathematical representation of the full-wave rectified sinewave

An ideal full-wave rectified sinewave is shown in figure 11.9; note 11.3 shows the average and rms values to be $2V_{LM}/\pi$ and $V_{LM}/\sqrt{2}$ respectively. The average value is that which makes the two shaded areas in figure 11.9 equal. Notice that the average value of the full-wave rectified sinewave is double that of the half-wave case; this result is evident from comparison of the waveforms, the area enclosed from 0 to 2π in the full-wave case being double the half-wave value. Also the rms value of the full-wave rectified sinewave is the *same* as that for the original sinewave. Mathematically this is because the rms value depends on the square of the voltage and although the sinewave is negative for $\omega t = \pi$–2π, when squared, the two waveshapes are identical.

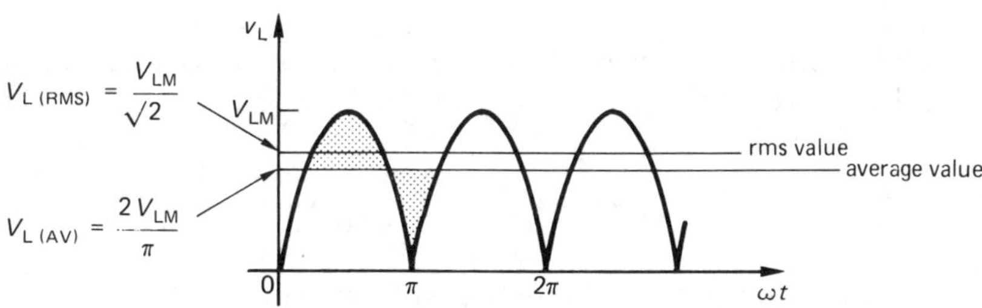

Figure 11.9 Full-wave rectified sinewave

Note 11.3: Average and rms values of a full-wave rectified sinewave
In the full-wave case, $v_L = V_{LM} \sin \omega t$ for $\omega t = 0-\pi$ and $v_L = -V_{LM} \sin \omega t$ for $\omega t = \pi-2\pi$ since the process of rectification inverts the sinewave during the second half cycle.

Average value. From equation 11.5:

$$V_{L(AV)} = \frac{1}{2\pi}\left[\int_0^{\pi} V_{LM} \sin \omega t \; d(\omega t) + \int_{\pi}^{2\pi} (-V_{LM} \sin \omega t) \; d(\omega t)\right]$$

But since the two half cycles are identical, the integration can be reduced, for simplicity, to

$$V_{L(AV)} = \frac{1}{\pi}\int_0^{\pi} V_{LM} \sin \omega t \; d(\omega t)$$

$$= \frac{V_{LM}}{\pi}\Big[-\cos \omega t\Big]_0^{\pi}$$

$$= \frac{V_{LM}}{\pi}\Big[+1-(-1)\Big] = \frac{2V_{LM}}{\pi} \text{ or } 0.637V_{LM} \tag{11.21}$$

RMS value. From equation 11.9:

$$V_{L(RMS)} = \sqrt{\left\{\frac{1}{2\pi}\left[\int_0^{\pi} V_{LM}^2 \sin^2 \omega t \; d(\omega t) + \int_{\pi}^{2\pi} (-V_{LM} \sin \omega t)^2 \; d(\omega t)\right]\right\}}$$

$$= \sqrt{\left\{\frac{1}{2\pi}\int_0^{2\pi} V_{LM}^2 \sin^2 \omega t \; d(\omega t)\right\}}$$

$$= \sqrt{\left\{\frac{V_{LM}^2}{4\pi}\int_0^{2\pi} (1-\cos 2\omega t) \; d(\omega t)\right\}}, \text{ using } \sin^2 \omega t = \tfrac{1}{2}(1-\cos 2\omega t)$$

$$= \sqrt{\left\{\frac{V_{LM}^2}{4\pi}\Big[\omega t - \tfrac{1}{2}\sin 2\omega t\Big]_0^{2\pi}\right\}}$$

$$= \sqrt{\left\{\frac{V_{LM}^2}{4\pi}\Big[(2\pi-0)-(0-0)\Big]\right\}} = \frac{V_{LM}}{\sqrt{2}} \text{ or } 0.707V_{LM} \tag{11.22}$$

Note that as in the calculation of the average value, because of waveform symmetry, $V_{L(RMS)}$ can be obtained by integrating $V_{LM}^2 \sin^2 \omega t$ from $0-\pi$ and averaging over the interval $0-\pi$.

Applying Fourier analysis (appendix A) enables the full-wave rectified sinewave to be represented by the infinite series

$$v_L = V_{LM}\left[\frac{2}{\pi} - \frac{4}{3\pi}\cos 2\omega t - \frac{4}{15\pi}\cos 4\omega t \ldots - \frac{4}{(n^2-1)\pi}\cos n\omega t\right] \tag{11.23}$$

$n = 2, 4, 6, \ldots \infty$, showing that it contains only even harmonics.

The rectification efficiency of the full-wave arrangement, assuming the diode threshold to be negligible, from equation 11.19, is

$$\eta_{\text{rect(full wave)}} = \frac{\dfrac{4I_{\text{LM}}^2}{\pi^2} R_{\text{L}}}{\dfrac{I_{\text{LM}}^2}{2}(r_{\text{d}} + R_{\text{L}})} = \frac{8}{\pi^2}\left(\frac{R_{\text{L}}}{r_{\text{d}} + R_{\text{L}}}\right) \tag{11.24}$$

using $I_{\text{L(AV)}} = 2I_{\text{LM}}/\pi$ and $I_{\text{L(RMS)}} = I_{\text{LM}}/\sqrt{2}$ from note 11.3. The efficiency thus has a maximum value of $8/\pi^2$ or 81 per cent when the diode resistance is negligible in comparison with R_{L}. This value is twice that for the half-wave circuit (equation 11.20) corresponding to utilisation of the power content of both half cycles of the source waveform.

11.2.3 *Smoothing*

Rectification (section 11.2.2) provides only partial conversion from ac to dc; the ripple must be reduced to an acceptably low level to provide an essentially dc output. Ripple reduction, *smoothing*, is achieved by

(1) Adding a component having a low impedance to the ac ripple (a capacitor) in parallel with the load so as to divert the ac components from the load (figure 11.10a).

(2) Adding a component having a high impedance to the ac ripple (an inductor) in series with the load to attenuate the ripple voltage (figure 11.10b).

(3) Combining the effects (1) and (2) as in the *LC* and *CLC* filters of figures 11.10c, d.

The following consideration of smoothing circuit performance is based on full-wave rectification which, with its higher rectification efficiency, is more popular than the half-wave case, however the work applies equally to half-wave excitation if the change in the period of the filter input (v_1) and the change in its harmonic content are taken into account.

It should be noted that this work is concerned with unregulated supplies in which the smoothing circuit provides *all* the smoothing. The reader should appreciate that in supplies incorporating a voltage regulator/stabiliser (section 11.2.4), the stabiliser circuit also provides

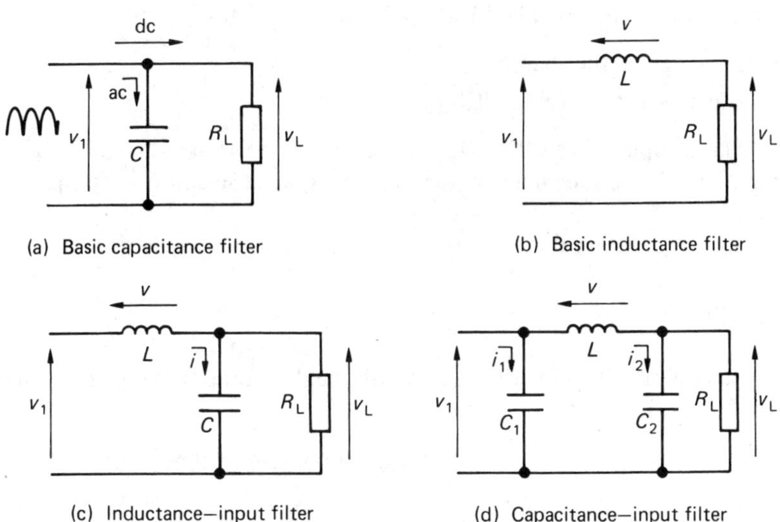

Figure 11.10 Smoothing circuits

a degree of smoothing in which case the performance requirement of the smoothing circuit can be eased.

Basic capacitance smoothing

This is the most widely used smoothing arrangement, providing a cost-effective solution particularly for low current supplies. Figure 11.11a shows the circuit arrangement. At switch ON, with C discharged, a pulse of current is drawn to charge the capacitor; the surge rating I_{FSM}max (or I_{ISM}max) of the bridge must be adequate to cope with this surge. Depending on the bridge rating, it may be necessary to include R_S to limit the current rise.

Once steady state has been reached the variation of load voltage v_L is as shown in figure 11.11b; for simplicity, voltage drops across the bridge diodes and the surge-limiting resistor R_S have been neglected, the peak load voltage V_{LM} being shown equal to the peak source voltage. The capacitor is fully charged at time t_1 (point A) and then during the interval t_1–t_2, v_S is less than the load (capacitor) voltage so the bridge is OFF. Therefore during this time the load is isolated from the source, the load current being supplied by the capacitor which is discharging, and v_L falls exponentially with time constant CR_L. At time t_2 the increasing source voltage becomes just greater than the capacitor voltage (v_L), the bridge switches ON and the capacitor is recharged to the peak value. The bridge diodes are therefore switched ON only for the short interval δ during which they pass a spike of current. The two sections of the bridge conduct on alternate half cycles of v_S and the corresponding current waveforms are as shown in figure 11.11d. The rise time of the diode current is short, depending on the internal properties of the diode, notably change of the state of charge of the diode capacitance giving a finite forward recovery time [1a], then, as the smoothing capacitor charges and v_L rises, the charging current falls.

The total excursion of v_L ($v_L$max − $v_L$min) is termed the *ripple voltage* Δv_L and is given, in this case, from figure 11.11b, by

$$\Delta v_L = V_{LM} - V_2 \tag{11.25}$$

V_{LM} and V_2 being the values of v_L at the start and end of the discharge interval.

A general figure-of-merit for the smoothing provided is the ratio of the ripple voltage to the average load voltage and is called the *ripple factor* F_r, thus

$$F_r = \frac{\text{ripple voltage at the load}}{\text{average load voltage}} = \frac{\Delta v_L}{V_{L(AV)}} \tag{11.26}$$

Ideally $\Delta v_L = 0$ (no ripple) giving $F_r = 0$; in practice, the permissible value of F_r depends on the application, 1 or 2 per cent may be required in some cases, in others, up to 10 per cent may be allowable.

During the discharge interval t_1–t_2, the load (capacitor) voltage varies as

$$v_L = V_{LM} \exp\left[-\left(\frac{t-t_1}{CR_L}\right)\right] \tag{11.27}$$

corresponding to equation 1.14 (example 1.2) with the discharge starting at t_1 instead of $t = 0$, $v_O = v_L$, $v_O(0) = V_{LM}$ and $V = 0$.

At $t = t_2$, $v_L = V_2$ and $t_2 - t_1 = \frac{T}{2} - \delta \simeq \frac{T}{2}$ for *good smoothing*, that is, low Δv_L, $\delta \ll T/2$, thus

$$V_2 \simeq V_{LM} \exp\left(-\frac{T}{2CR_L}\right) \tag{11.28}$$

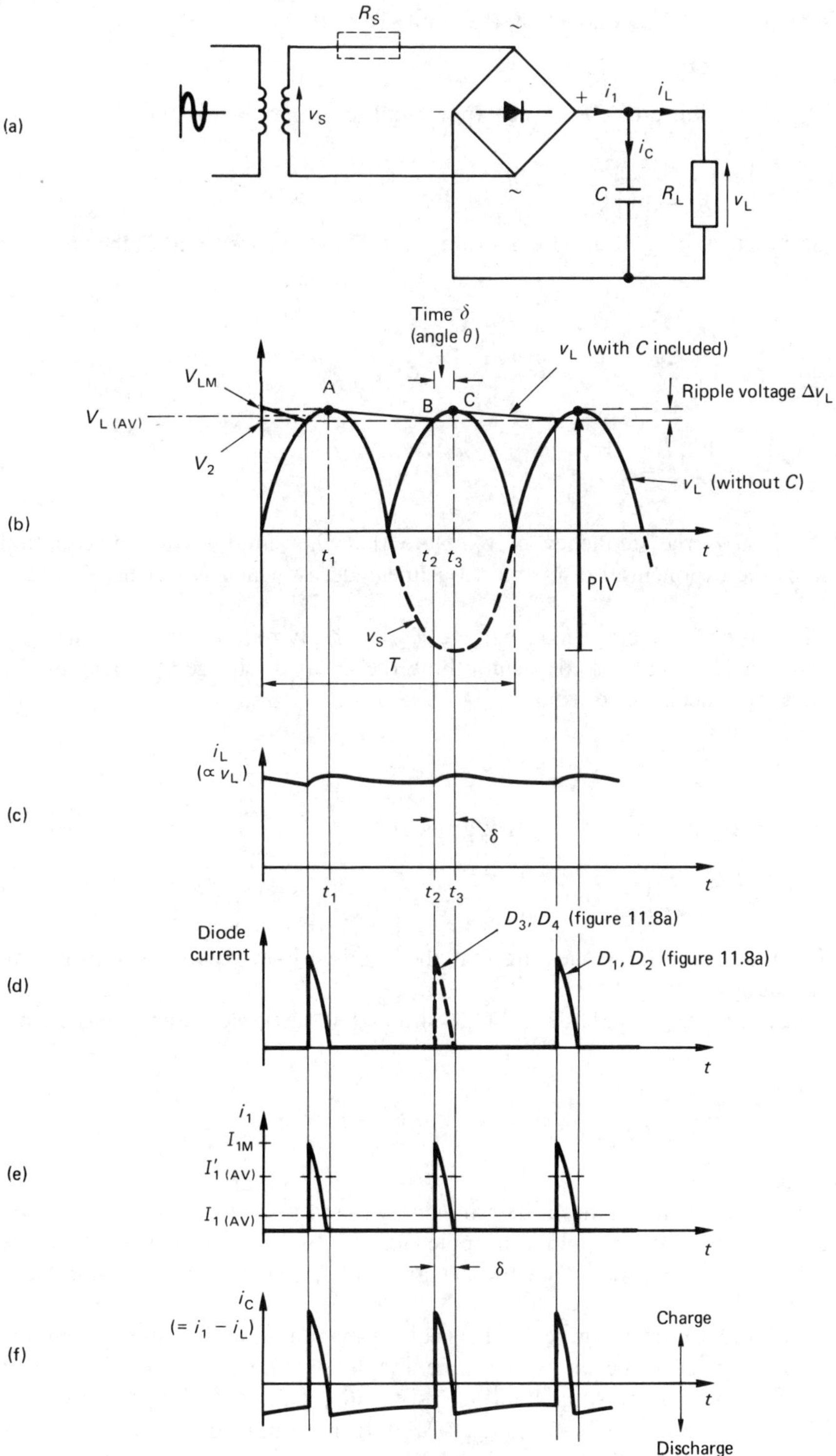

Figure 11.11 Basic capacitance smoothing

Combining equations 11.25 and 11.28, the ripple voltage is

$$\Delta v_L \simeq V_{LM}[1 - \exp(-T/2\tau)] \tag{11.29}$$

where τ is the time constant CR_L. The exponential term may be expanded as

$$\exp\left(-\frac{T}{2\tau}\right) = 1 - \frac{T}{2\tau} + \frac{T^2}{4\tau^2} - \cdots \tag{11.30}$$

and for the practical case of good smoothing, $\tau \gg T$, the squared and higher terms may be neglected giving

$$\exp\left(-\frac{T}{2\tau}\right) \simeq 1 - \frac{T}{2\tau} \tag{11.31}$$

leading to

$$\Delta v_L \simeq \frac{V_{LM} T}{2\tau} = \frac{V_{LM} T}{2CR_L} = \frac{V_{LM}}{2fCR_L} \tag{11.32}$$

where f $(= 1/T)$ is the frequency of v_S. Note that the simplification of equation 11.31 approximates the exponential discharge to a linear decay which is sufficiently accurate for low ripple.

Determination of the average load voltage $V_{L(AV)}$ strictly requires integration of v_L over a period (equation 11.5), but for good smoothing the linear discharge approximation enables $V_{L(AV)}$ to be simply determined from

$$V_{L(AV)} = V_{LM} - \frac{\Delta v_L}{2} \tag{11.33}$$

Substituting for Δv_L from equation 11.32 gives

$$V_{L(AV)} = V_{LM}\left(1 - \frac{T}{4\tau}\right) \simeq V_{LM} \tag{11.34}$$

as $\tau \gg T$ for good smoothing, showing that the nominal load voltage is approximately the peak voltage supplied by the rectifier.

Combining equations 11.26, 11.32 and 11.34 shows that the ripple factor for basic capacitance smoothing is

$$F_r = \frac{\Delta v_L}{V_{L(AV)}} \simeq \frac{T}{2\tau} = \frac{1}{2fCR_L} \tag{11.35}$$

noting that period $T = 1/f$.

Note that smoothing performance is determined by the ratio of the period of the v_S waveform to the CR_L time constant; for example, a ripple factor F_r better than 2 per cent (0.02) requires, from equation 11.35, $\tau = CR_L \geqslant T/0.04 = 25T$ and with T and R_L known, a suitable value of C can be selected.

Each pair of bridge diodes (figure 11.11a) is under maximum reverse stress when the source voltage is at its peak value, at which time the load voltage is at its peak value V_{LM} (figure 11.11b). Ignoring the surge-limiting resistor R_S, if present, the peak inverse voltage across each pair of diodes is therefore $(V_{SM} + V_{LM})$. If the voltage drop across the conducting diodes can be neglected, $V_{LM} = V_{SM}$ and the PIV across each pair of diodes is $2V_{SM}$. The V_{RRM} max rating of the bridge must therefore be $> 2V_{SM}$ for safety. Sometimes the bridge rating is given as the maximum rms input voltage $V_{I(RMS)}$max which must exceed the rms source voltage $V_{S(RMS)}$. Surge allowance is sometimes included by quoting $V_{I(RMS)}$max as a function of R_S, which includes the transformer secondary winding resistance, and the smoothing capacitance C. As charge supplied to C during the charge interval δ is released to the load during the remainder of the half cycle, there is no net current drain by the capacitor and the average bridge current is equal to the average load current:

$$I_{1(AV)} = I_{L(AV)} \tag{11.36}$$

The continuous-current rating of the bridge $I_{O(AV)}$max must therefore be greater than or equal to $I_{L(AV)}$.

Surge calculation

During the charging angle θ (figure 11.11b) the load voltage rises sinusoidally from value V_2 at point B which is given by

$$V_2 = V_{LM} \sin\left(\frac{\pi}{2} - \theta\right) = V_{LM} \cos\theta \simeq V_{LM}(1 - \tfrac{1}{2}\theta^2) \tag{11.37}$$

using $\cos\theta \simeq 1 - \frac{1}{2}\theta^2$ for small θ which is true in this case of good smoothing. But V_2 is also given by equation 11.28, which, using the linear discharge approximation (equation 11.31) and equation 11.35, gives

$$V_2 \simeq V_{LM}\left(1 - \frac{T}{2\tau}\right) \simeq V_{LM}(1 - F_r) \tag{11.38}$$

Comparing equations 11.37 and 11.38, the charging angle θ, in radians, is given by

$$\theta = \sqrt{2F_r} \tag{11.39}$$

During the charging interval the bridge current comprises two components, one recharging the capacitor, the other supplying the approximately constant load current. Taking $I'_{1(AV)}$ as the average value of bridge current during the charging interval (figure 11.11e), the charge supplied during this interval $I'_{1(AV)}\delta$ provides the load current during the discharge interval $\left(\frac{T}{2} - \delta\right)$, thus

$$I'_{1(AV)}\delta = I_{L(AV)}\left(\frac{T}{2} - \delta\right)$$

from which

$$I'_{1(AV)} \simeq \left(\frac{T}{2\delta}\right) I_{L(AV)} \tag{11.40}$$

as $\delta \ll T/2$ in practice. This shows the charging component of i_1 to be much greater than the load current component so that the surge current can be taken as approximately equal to the charging component, thus, during the charging interval:

$$i_1 \simeq i_C = C\frac{d}{dt}(V_{LM}\sin\omega t) = \omega C V_{LM}\cos\omega t \tag{11.41}$$

But from figure 11.11b, i_1 is a maximum at the start of the charging interval when the time rate of change of v_L, which is $\frac{d}{dt}(V_{LM} \sin \omega t)$, is a maximum, thus the peak bridge current is

$$I_{1M} \simeq \omega C V_{LM} \cos\left(\frac{\pi}{2} - \theta\right)$$

$$= \omega C V_{LM} \sin \theta$$

$$= 2\pi f C V_{LM} \sin(\sqrt{2F_r}) \tag{11.42}$$

using equation 11.39. The repetitive surge rating of the bridge I_{ORM}max must be equal to or greater than I_{1M} for surges.

The above analysis has considered the case of a resistive load; if the load is capacitive, bridge ratings must be reduced as recommended by the manufacturer to allow for the increased current stages.

Performance summary for basic capacitance smoothing

This is the simplest ripple reduction arrangement using a single, readily-available component which is cost effective if the capacitance value required is not excessive, that is, $< 10\,000\ \mu$F. For acceptably low ripple, the time constant CR_L must be $\gg T$ (equation 11.35) and for higher load currents, that is lower R_L, a higher value of C is required. Basic capacitance smoothing is therefore impractical for high load currents because of the excessively large value of C required.

A comparison of the performance of smoothing circuits is given in table 11.1.

Example 11.1: Basic capacitance smoothing

An unregulated ac–dc power supply employing a bridge rectifier and basic capacitance smoothing is driven from 240 V, 50 Hz mains and provides a load voltage of 20 V for load currents up to 100 mA. If the ripple factor must not exceed 5 per cent, select the lowest allowable E6 value capacitor (appendix D) noting that large-value electrolytic capacitors have a tolerance range of typically −20 per cent, +50 per cent. What is the worst-case ripple voltage at the load for the capacitor selected?
Determine the minimum acceptable continuous and surge current ratings for the bridge rectifier and assuming a 1.5 V voltage drop across the bridge at full-load current, what is the required turns ratio for the transformer?

Since the output of the supply is essentially dc, the quoted load voltage and current are *average* values, thus $V_{L(AV)} = 20$ V and $I_{L(AV)}\max = 100$ mA. Worst-case ripple ($F_r\max$ = 5 per cent = 0.05) occurs when the load current is a maximum, which is when the load resistance is a minimum, and so from equation 11.35:

$$C_{min} \simeq \frac{1}{2fF_r\max\ R_L\min} \tag{11.43}$$

$R_L\min = V_{L(AV)}/I_{L(AV)}\max = 20\ \text{V}/100\ \text{mA} = 200\ \Omega$, thus

$$C_{min} \simeq \frac{1}{2(50\ \text{Hz})(0.05)(200\ \Omega)} = 1000\ \mu\text{F}$$

Although the 1000 μF value is available in the E6 series, this is the *nominal* value; its *actual*

Table 11.1 Comparison of filter performance for linear unregulated ac–dc supplies

Type	*Average load voltage* $V_{L(AV)}$	*Ripple voltage* Δv_L	*Ripple factor* F_r	*Minimum continuous current rating of bridge* ($I_{O(AV)}$ max) min	*Minimum rep. surge current rating of bridge* (I_{ORM} max) min	*Application notes*
Basic C	$\simeq V_{IM}$	$\dfrac{V_{IM}}{2fCR_L}$	$\dfrac{1}{2fCR_L}$	$I_{L(AV)}$ max	$2\pi fCV_{IM}\sin(\sqrt{2F_r})$	Practical and cost effective for high load resistance (low load current) $V_{IM} = V_{LM} \simeq V_{L(AV)}$
Basic *L*	$\dfrac{2V_{IM}}{\pi}$	$\dfrac{R_L V_{L(AV)}}{3\pi fL}$	$\dfrac{R_L}{3\pi fL}$	$I_{L(AV)}$ max	Not applicable	Only practical for low load resistance (high load current). Lower $V_{L(AV)}$ than basic *C* type for same V_{IM}
LC $\left(\text{for } L \geqslant \dfrac{R_L}{6\pi f}\right)$	$\dfrac{2V_{IM}}{\pi}$	$\dfrac{V_{L(AV)}}{12\pi^2 f^2 LC}$	$\dfrac{1}{12\pi^2 f^2 LC}$	$I_{L(AV)}$ max	Not applicable	Practical for moderate load resistance for which basic smoothing is impractical. Lower $V_{L(AV)}$ than basic *C* type for same V_{IM} but better regulation
CLC	$\simeq V_{IM}$	$\dfrac{V_{L(AV)}}{16\pi^3 f^3 LC_1 C_2 R_L}$	$\dfrac{1}{16\pi^3 f^3 LC_1 C_2 R_L}$	$I_{L(AV)}$ max	Note (4)	Provides beffer F_r and higher $V_{L(AV)}$ than *LC* type for same V_{IM} but regulation is worse

Notes: (1) Expressions relate to supplies incorporating full-wave rectification with sinusoidal excitation.
(2) Negligible inductor coil resistance and negligible capacitor leakage is assumed.
(3) Application notes refer to mains driven (low frequency, 50/60 Hz) supplies; at the higher frequencies used in switched-mode systems (section 11.2.6), required component values are lower and the working range of basic *C* and basic *L* smoothing is extended.
(4) As for basic *C* type with $C = C_1$ and F_r corresponding to *L* and C_2 (figure 11.10d) being omitted.
(5) V_{IM} = peak voltage at rectifier output.
V_{LM} = peak load voltage.
f = frequency of input to rectifier.

value, allowing for the tolerance, may be as low as 1000 μF − 20 per cent = 800 μF which would not meet the specification. Thus a 1500 μF capacitor is selected (minimum value, 1500 μF − 20 per cent = 1200 μF) giving a worst-case ripple factor (equation 11.43) of

$$F_r \max \simeq \frac{1}{2fC_{min}R_L \min} = \frac{1}{2(50\text{ Hz})(1200\ \mu\text{F})(200\ \Omega)} = 0.0417 \text{ or } 4.17 \text{ per cent}$$

which is well within the specified 5 per cent maximum.
The worst-case ripple voltage, from equation 11.35, is therefore

$$(\Delta v_L)\max \simeq V_{L(AV)}F_r \max \simeq (20\text{ V})(0.0417) = 834\text{ mV}$$

Bridge ratings. The maximum value of average load current $I_{L(AV)}\max$ is specified as 100 mA and so the minimum acceptable continuous current rating of the bridge, $(I_{O(AV)}\max)\min$, must be 100 mA.

The surge current rating can be estimated using equation 11.42. It will be noted that I_{1M} increases with C and F_r but that F_r decreases as C increases. In fact it is the value of C that dominates here and $I_{1M}\max$ occurs when C is at its maximum value which, in this case, is 1500 μF + 50 per cent = 2250 μF. The ripple factor F_r corresponding to this value of capacitance is approximately 0.0222 from equation 11.35 and so the peak surge current is

$$\begin{aligned} I_{1M}\max &\simeq 2\pi f C_{max} V_{LM} \sin(\sqrt{2F_r}) \\ &= 2\pi(50\text{ Hz})(2250\ \mu\text{F})(20.22\text{ V}) \sin[\sqrt{(2 \times 0.0222)}] \\ &\simeq 3\text{A} \end{aligned}$$

noting that the peak load voltage

$$V_{LM} = V_{L(AV)} + \tfrac{1}{2}\Delta v_L = V_{L(AV)} + \tfrac{1}{2}F_r V_{L(AV)} = V_{L(AV)}(1 + \tfrac{1}{2}F_r) \qquad (11.44)$$

using equations 11.33 and 11.35. The minimum allowable repetitive surge rating of the bridge $(I_{ORM}\max)\min$ is therefore 3 A.

Transformer turns ratio. With reference to the circuit of figure 11.11a, the turns ratio of the transformer must be such that with 240 V (rms) mains applied to the primary, the *peak* value of the secondary voltage V_{SM} allows the required peak value of load voltage V_{LM} taking account of the voltage drops across R_S (if included) and the bridge.

Working with the nominal value of the selected capacitor (1500 μF), the ripple factor at full load ($R_L = 200\ \Omega$) is 0.0333 and the corresponding value of peak load voltage, from equation 11.44, is 20.33 V.

For a 1.5 V drop across the bridge and assuming R_S is not included, the peak secondary voltage V_{SM} must be 20.33 V + 1.5 V = 21.83 V, corresponding to an rms secondary voltage (equation 11.10) of $21.83V/\sqrt{2} = 15.44$ V. The required turns ratio is therefore 240 V (rms)/15.44 V (rms) $\simeq$ 15.54:1 using equation 2.44.

Basic inductance smoothing

At high load currents, basic capacitance smoothing is not practical *in an unregulated supply* because of the excessively large value of capacitance required to provide a reasonable quality output ($F_r < 5$ per cent). For example a 5 V, 10 A supply, for which $R_L = 5\text{ V}/10\text{ A} = 0.5\ \Omega$, driven by a 50 Hz input, would require a capacitance of 400 000 μF to provide a ripple factor of 5 per cent (equation 11.43).

In high load current applications, basic inductance smoothing (figure 11.12a) provides a

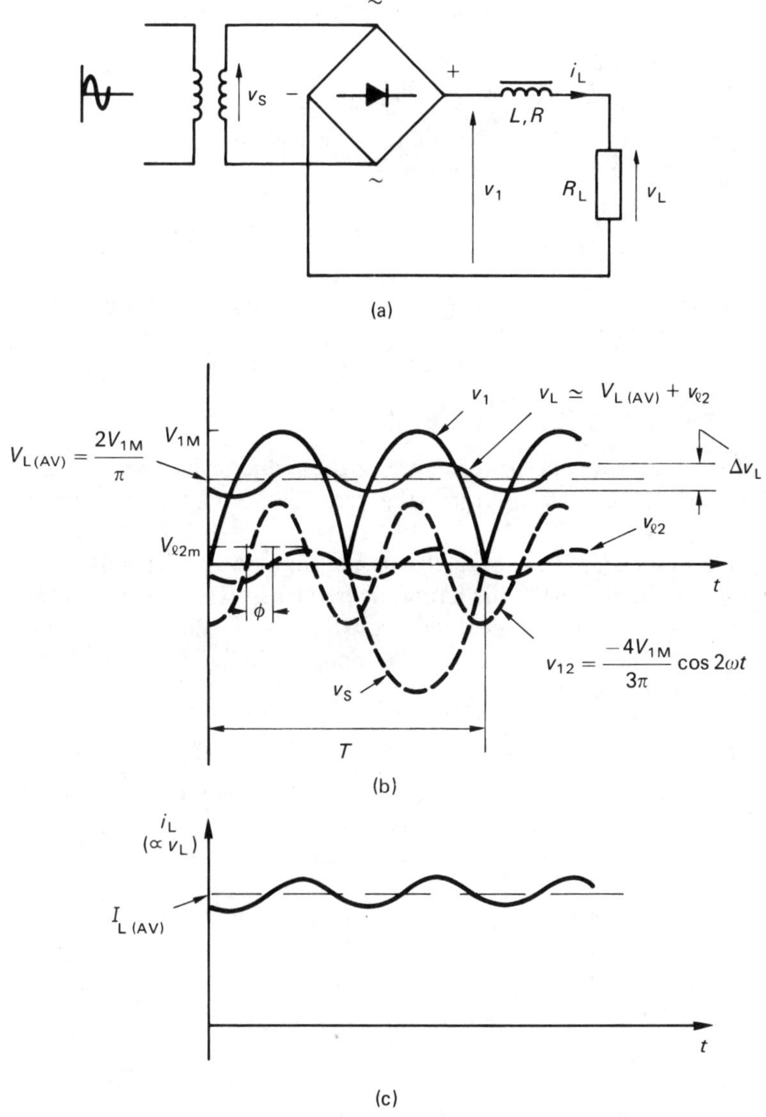

Figure 11.12 Basic inductance smoothing

practical solution. The inductor L and load R_L form a frequency-dependent potential divider such that the harmonics of v_1, which form the ripple, are attenuated thereby smoothing the output.

The input v_1 to the smoothing circuit is a full-wave rectified sinewave (figure 11.12b) which may be represented as an average value and a series of harmonics using Fourier analysis as given by equation 11.23 (replacing suffix L and 1 in this case). v_1 can therefore be represented as

$$v_1 = V_{1(AV)} + v_{12} + v_{14} + \cdots \tag{11.45}$$

where the dc component $V_{1(AV)} = 2V_{1M}/\pi$, the second harmonic $v_{12} = -(4V_{1M}/3\pi) \cos 2\omega t$, the fourth harmonic $v_{14} = -(4V_{1M}/15\pi) \cos 4\omega t$, and so on. For each of these components there is a corresponding component of the load voltage so that

$$v_L = V_{L(AV)} + v_{l2} + v_{l4} + \cdots \tag{11.46}$$

where $V_{L(AV)}$ depend on $V_{1(AV)}$, v_{l2} depends on v_{12}, and v_{l4} on v_{14}.

Assuming the inductor to be ideal, that is the coil has zero resistance, it provides no opposition to constant current flow so that

$$V_{L(AV)} = V_{1(AV)} = \frac{2V_{1M}}{\pi} \tag{11.47}$$

In practice, the inductor has resistance R and the potential divider formed by R and R_L causes $V_{L(AV)} < V_{1(AV)}$ according to

$$V_{L(AV)} = \left(\frac{R_L}{R + R_L}\right) V_{1(AV)} \tag{11.48}$$

Reduction of R to improve the performance of the inductor involves using thicker wire for the coil which may necessitate a larger core with the accompanying size, weight and cost penalties.

The reduction of the amplitude of the harmonic components depends on the reactance X_L of the inductor (equation 2.38) at the harmonic frequency. The operational impedance of the L, R_L combination, assuming an ideal inductor, is $R_L + jX_L$ and so the nth harmonic at the load v_{ln} is related to the nth harmonic at the input v_{1n} by

$$v_{ln} = \left(\frac{R_L}{R_L + jX_{Ln}}\right) v_{1n} \tag{11.49}$$

where X_{Ln} is the reactance of L *at the frequency of the* nth *harmonic*. Determination of ripple voltage at the load requires calculation of the amplitudes of the harmonic components at the load, phase relationships being of little interest here, thus equation 11.49 can be reduced to

$$V_{lnm} = \frac{R_L}{\sqrt{(R_L^2 + X_{Ln}^2)}} V_{1nm} \tag{11.50}$$

where V_{1nm} and V_{lnm} are the amplitudes of the nth harmonic components of the input and load voltages and $\sqrt{(R_L^2 + X_{Ln}^2)}$ is the modulus of the impedance of the series L, R_L combination at the frequency of the nth harmonic.

For the second harmonic, frequency 2ω where ω is the angular frequency of the mains input to the transformer, V_{12m} is $4V_{1M}/3\pi$ from the Fourier series (following equation 11.45) so that the amplitude of the second harmonic component at the load V_{l2m}, from equation 11.50, is

$$V_{l2m} = \frac{R_L}{\sqrt{(R_L^2 + 4\omega^2 L^2)}}\left(\frac{4V_{1m}}{3\pi}\right) \tag{11.51}$$

since $X_{L2} = (2\omega)L$.

Correspondingly the fourth harmonic component at the load, of frequency 4ω, is

$$V_{l4m} = \frac{R_L}{\sqrt{(R_L^2 + 16\omega^2 L^2)}}\left(\frac{4V_{1M}}{15\pi}\right) \tag{11.52}$$

since $X_{L4} = (4\omega)L$ and $V_{14m} = 4V_{1M}/15\pi$ from the Fourier series.

Noting that for the circuit to provide effective smoothing, the reactance of L must be much larger than R_L, comparison of the denominators of equations 11.51 and 11.52 shows that the fourth harmonic amplitude $V_{\ell 4m}$ is very much less than the second harmonic amplitude $V_{\ell 2m}$. Further, observation that the amplitude of the harmonics in the Fourier series (equation 11.23) progressively reduces with increasing harmonic number, coupled with the fact that the inductor exhibits a higher reactance at higher frequency, means that higher harmonics at the load are insignificant. For practical purposes, therefore, the ripple at the load can be attributed solely to the second harmonic so that the load voltage may be written

$$v_L \simeq V_{L(AV)} + v_{\ell 2}$$

$$= V_{L(AV)} - V_{\ell 2m} \cos(2\omega t - \phi) \tag{11.53}$$

where $V_{\ell 2m}$ is the amplitude given by equation 11.51 and ϕ $(= \tan^{-1} X_{L2}/R_L)$ is the phase shift between $v_{\ell 2}$ and v_{12}.

These components are shown in figure 11.12b from which it can be seen that the ripple voltage Δv_L, which is the total excursion of v_L, is given by the peak-to-peak value of the ripple component, that is, $2V_{\ell 2m}$. Thus from equation 11.51, the ripple voltage is

$$\Delta v_L = 2V_{\ell 2m} = \frac{8V_{1M}R_L}{3\pi\sqrt{(R_L^2 + 4\omega^2 L^2)}}$$

$$\simeq \frac{2R_L V_{L(AV)}}{3\omega L} \tag{11.54}$$

as, for effective smoothing, $2\omega L \gg R_L$ and, for an ideal inductor, $V_{1M} = \pi V_{L(AV)}/2$ (equation 11.47). From equation 11.54 the ripple factor F_r is

$$F_r = \frac{\Delta v_L}{V_{L(AV)}} \simeq \frac{2R_L}{3\omega L} = \frac{R_L}{3\pi f L} \tag{11.55}$$

since $\omega = 2\pi f$.

A design usually involves the determination of the required inductance so that the ripple factor F_r does not exceed a certain maximum for a specified range of load conditions. From equation 11.55, worst-case ripple $F_r$max corresponds to $R_L$max and so the minimum inductance to meet the specification is

$$L_{min} \simeq \frac{R_L \text{max}}{3\pi f F_r \text{max}} \tag{11.56}$$

Notice that worst-case ripple for basic inductance smoothing occurs when the load current is a *minimum*, corresponding to $R_L$max, which is in contrast to the basic capacitance smoothing case for which the worst case is *maximum* load current (at $R_L$min).

Also in contrast to the capacitance case, with basic inductance smoothing the bridge conducts continuously, the current fluctuating about the average value $I_{L(AV)}$ (figure 11.12c). This means that the bridge does not have to handle large current surges as it does for capacitance smoothing and so the surge rating of the bridge is not important. The minimum continuous current rating ($I_{O(AV)}$max)min is given by the maximum average load current $I_{L(AV)}$max which is $V_{L(AV)}/R_L$min. From figure 11.12b, maximum reverse bias across the bridge occurs when v_S peaks and so the peak inverse voltage across each *pair* of bridge diodes is $-(V_{SM} + V_{1M})$, which, neglecting the voltage drop across the bridge when conducting, is $\simeq -2V_{SM}$. The V_{RRM}max bridge rating must therefore be $> 2V_{SM}$ for safety.

Design of the smoothing inductor involves selection of a suitable core (material and size) that will accommodate the number of turns of appropriate gauge wire necessary to provide the required inductance. The smallest allowable gauge of wire, corresponding to the maximum average load current $I_{L(AV)}\max$, is found from published wire tables. As in the case of a transformer (section 2.4.3), minimum core size depends on the required VA rating to ensure that the material does not saturate in operation; this rating is $\pi f L I^2_{L(AV)}\max$*. The relationship between number of turns and inductance is given by equation 2.34 and if the core operates over the approximately linear part of its B–H (ϕ–I) characteristic, $d\phi/di$ may be taken as $\phi_m/I_{L(AV)}\max$ where ϕ_m is the core flux at the upper end of the linear range. Substituting for $d\phi/di$ in equation 2.34 gives the required number of turns as

$$N = \frac{LI_{L(AV)}\max}{\phi_m} = \frac{LI_{L(AV)}\max}{B_m A_m} \tag{11.57}$$

where B_m is the maximum flux density for the core material, avoiding saturation, and A_m is the cross-sectional area of magnetic material in the core 'limb'. Non-linearity of the B–H core characteristic causes L to vary with load current $I_{L(AV)}$. This variation can be reduced considerably by introducing a gap into the magnetic circuit in the form of a non-magnetic spacer which has the effect of improving the linearity of the characteristic. Core gapping has the additional advantage that introduction of the high reluctance (magnetic equivalent of resistance) section reduces the flux, enabling a smaller volume core to be used than in the ungapped case. Design using gapped cores is simplified by the use of Hanna curves, provided by core manufacturers, which allow selection of gap length and number of turns to provide a certain value of inductance. Note that selection of core size from VA requirement may not provide a large enough 'window' to accommodate the required number of turns using the required gauge of wire, in which case a larger core would be required, window size being the limiting factor instead of VA rating in that case. In addition, thicker wire than that dictated by $I_{L(AV)}\max$ may be selected to reduce the coil resistance and this may also necessitate a larger window core.

Performance summary for basic inductance smoothing

Equation 11.56 shows that the minimum inductance required increases with load resistance and so this smoothing technique is only practical for low values of R_L, that is, substantial load current.

Inductive smoothing provides a lower average load voltage $V_{L(AV)}$ than capacitance smoothing for the same input voltage.

Inductors are not readily available as off-the-shelf items and must be custom produced for, or by, the user for the particular application.

For mains-driven supplies, inductors are relatively large, heavy and costly. However for higher frequency operation as in switched-mode circuits (section 11.2.6), the value of inductance required is relatively low ($L_{min} \propto 1/f$, equation 11.56) making inductance smoothing more attractive.

Table 11.1 compares the performance of the various smoothing arrangements.

---

* *Core VA rating*. In contrast to the case of a transformer, the current through the smoothing inductor is approximately constant (figure 11.12c) and the voltage across the coil comprises only ripple and the ohmic drop due to coil resistance. Thus VA rating corresponding to the actual 'power' throughput cannot be found directly from $V_{rms}I_{rms}$ as in the transformer case, instead it must be estimated by comparison with the case of sinusoidal excitation which gives: core $VA = V_{rms}I_{rms} = (X_L I^2_{rms}) = 2\pi f L I^2_{rms} = \pi f L I^2_m$, using equations 2.38 and 11.10, where I_m is the peak current. In the inductor case, the peak current, assuming low ripple, is approximately $I_{L(AV)}\max$ and so the VA rating can be taken as $\pi f L I^2_{L(AV)}\max$. If the ripple is substantial, additional VA corresponding to the product of rms ripple voltage and rms ripple current must be added to avoid saturation.

Example 11.2: Basic inductance smoothing

An unregulated ac–dc power supply of the type shown in figure 11.12a provides a 20 V output to a resistive load which draws a current in the range 5 A to 10 A. If the supply is driven from 240 V, 50 Hz mains and the ripple factor at the load must not exceed 5 per cent, what is the minimum value of inductance required?
Assuming a voltage drop of 1.5 V across the bridge at full load, what is the required turns ratio for the transformer if the inductor coil resistance is 0.5 Ω? What are the relevant minimum ratings of the bridge rectifier?

For basic inductance smoothing, ripple voltage increases with load resistance (equation 11.54) and so worst-case ripple occurs when the load current is at its *minimum* value, 5 A in this case.

$V_{L(AV)} = 20$ V, $I_{L(AV)}\text{min} = 5$ A and so

$$R_L\text{max} = \frac{20\ \text{V}}{5\ \text{A}} = 4\ \Omega$$

Then, from equation 11.56, with $F_r\text{max} = 5$ per cent $= 0.05$ and $f = 50$ Hz:

$$L_{\text{min}} \simeq \frac{4\ \Omega}{3\pi(50\ \text{Hz})(0.05)} = 170\ \text{mH}$$

Transformer turns ratio. The resistance of the inductor coil causes $V_{L(AV)}$ to be less than $V_{1(AV)}$ (figure 11.12a) according to equation 11.48. Calculations are made at full-load current ($I_{L(AV)} = 10$ A) to ensure that $V_{L(AV)} = 20$ V can be maintained at full load which corresponds to $R_L\text{min} = V_{L(AV)}/I_{L(AV)}\text{max} = 20\ \text{V}/10\ \text{A} = 2\ \Omega$.
Thus, from equation 11.48, for $V_{L(AV)} = 20$ V, $V_{1(AV)}$ must be

$$V_{1(AV)} = \left(\frac{R + R_L}{R_L}\right)V_{L(AV)} = \left(\frac{0.5\ \Omega + 2\ \Omega}{2\ \Omega}\right)20\ \text{V} = 25\ \text{V}$$

and since v_1 is a full-wave rectified sinewave, its peak value V_{1M} must be $(\pi/2)V_{1(AV)} = (\pi/2)25\ \text{V} = 39.27$ V using the relationship between peak and average values given by equation 11.21.

Allowing for the 1.5 V drop across the bridge, the amplitude of the transformer secondary voltage V_{SM} must be $V_{1M} + 1.5$ V (figure 11.12a) $= 39.27\ \text{V} + 1.5\ \text{V} = 40.77$ V which corresponds to an rms value (equation 11.10) of $40.77\ \text{V}/\sqrt{2} = 28.83$ V.

The required turns ratio is then rms primary voltage/rms secondary voltage (equation 2.44) $= 240\ \text{V}/28.83\ \text{V} = 8.32{:}1$.

Bridge ratings. The minimum continuous current rating $(I_{O(AV)}\text{max})\text{min}$ is the maximum average load current that the supply is required to provide, which is 10 A in this case; the bridge does not have to cope with current surges in the case of inductance smoothing.

The minimum repetitive peak reverse voltage rating $(V_{RRM}\text{max})\text{min}$ is approximately $2V_{SM}$ which is 2×40.77 V (from above) $= 81.54$ V.

Inductance-input smoothing

Effective smoothing can be obtained with greatly reduced component values than those required for basic capacitance or basic inductance smoothing if the two types of smoothing circuit are cascaded forming an *LC* filter as in figure 11.13a.

As for basic inductance smoothing discussed above, the full-wave rectified sinewave v_1 is

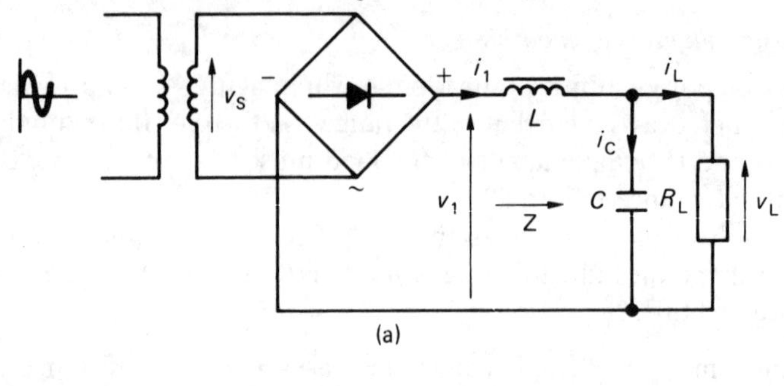

(a)

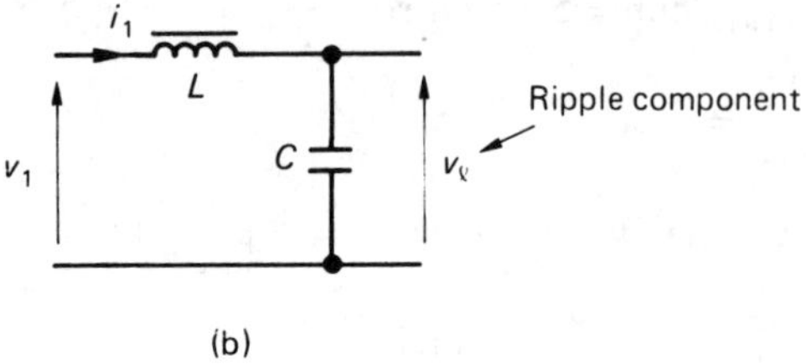

(b)

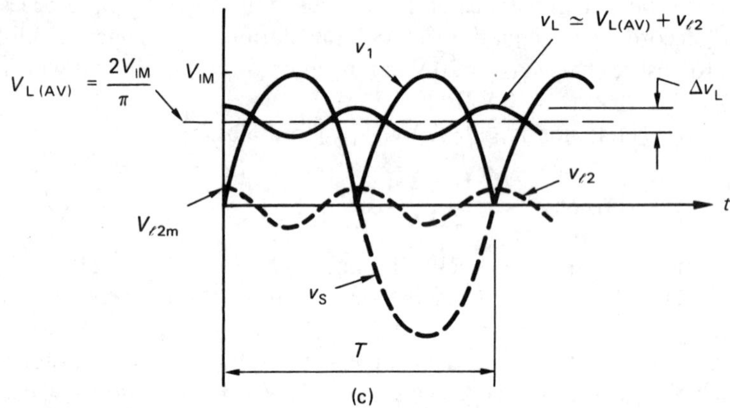

(c)

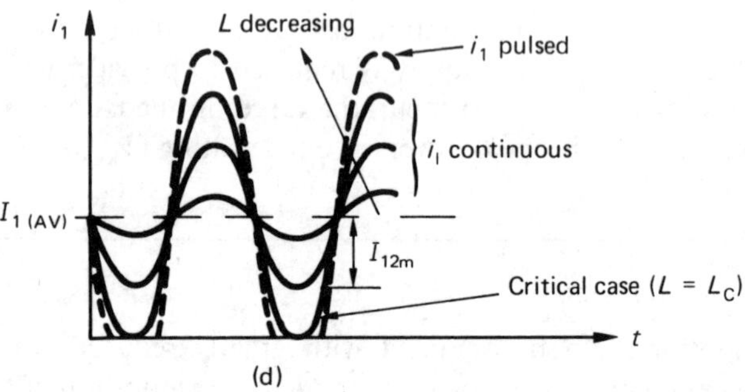

(d)

Figure 11.13 Inductance-input smoothing

considered in terms of its Fourier series (equation 11.23) and the corresponding constant and ripple components at the load evaluated to determine the ripple factor.

Assuming ideal components, for which capacitor leakage and inductor coil resistance are negligible, the constant component of v_1 is unaffected by the LC network and the average load voltage $V_{L(AV)}$ is

$$V_{L(AV)} = V_{1(AV)} = \frac{2V_{1M}}{\pi} \qquad (11.58)$$

Taking the coil resistance R into account but still assuming negligible capacitor leakage:

$$V_{L(AV)} = V_{1(AV)} - I_{L(AV)}R$$

$$= \left(\frac{R_L}{R + R_L}\right)V_{1(AV)} \qquad (11.59)$$

as $I_{L(AV)} = V_{1(AV)}/(R + R_L)$. Both results are the same as for the corresponding basic inductance cases (equations 11.47 and 11.48).

For the capacitor in the LC filter of figure 11.13a to provide effective smoothing, its reactance at the dominant ripple frequency (2ω, equation 11.23) must be low compared with R_L so as to divert most of the ripple current away from the load. Thus for effective smoothing

$$\frac{1}{2\omega C} \ll R_L \qquad (11.60)$$

Furthermore, for the inductor to be effective

$$2\omega L \gg R_L \qquad (11.61)$$

by comparison with the basic inductance case (equation 11.54).
Combining equations 11.60 and 11.61, it follows that for a practical LC smoothing circuit:

$$2\omega L \gg \frac{1}{2\omega C}$$

from which

$$4\omega^2 LC \gg 1 \qquad (11.62)$$

where $\omega(=2\pi f)$ is the frequency of the sinusoidal input to the rectifier.

Determination of the ripple at the load involves consideration of the L, C, R_L (figure 11.13a) circuit as a potential divider. Analysis is simplified by noting that equation 11.60 must be valid for satisfactory operation and so *as far as the ripple components are concerned* the circuit may be reduced to that of figure 11.13b since the ripple current through R_L is small compared with that through C. Then, assuming the inductor and capacitor to be ideal, the relationship between the input and output nth harmonic ripple components is

$$v_{ln} = \left(\frac{-jX_{Cn}}{jX_{Ln} - jX_{Cn}}\right)v_{1n} = \left(\frac{X_{Cn}}{X_{Cn} - X_{Ln}}\right)v_{1n} \qquad (11.63)$$

in terms of the operational reactances of equations 2.27, 2.38 and 2.39, X_{Cn} and X_{Ln} being the reactances of C and L at the frequency of the nth harmonic.

As in the basic inductance case, it is the second harmonic component of ripple, of frequency 2ω, that dominates and substituting $X_{C2} = 1/2\omega C$ and $X_{L2} = 2\omega L$ into equation 11.63 gives the second harmonic ripple at the load as

$$v_{\ell 2} = \left[\frac{1/2\omega C}{(1/2\omega C) + 2\omega L}\right] v_{12} = \left(\frac{1}{1 - 4\omega^2 LC}\right) v_{12} \tag{11.64}$$

Using relation 11.62, this reduces to

$$v_{\ell 2} \simeq -\left(\frac{1}{4\omega^2 LC}\right) v_{12} \tag{11.65}$$

the negative sign indicating that $v_{\ell 2}$ lags v_{12} by half a cycle.

From the Fourier series representing the full-wave rectified sinewave v_1 (equation 11.23 with suffix L replaced by 1), the second harmonic component v_{12} is $-(4V_{1M}/3\pi)\cos 2\omega t$ relative to the sinusoidal input and the corresponding ripple at the load, from equation 11.65, is

$$\begin{aligned} v_{\ell 2} &\simeq -\left(\frac{1}{4\omega^2 LC}\right)\left(-\frac{4V_{1M}}{3\pi}\right)\cos 2\omega t \\ &= \left(\frac{V_{1M}}{3\pi\omega^2 LC}\right)\cos 2\omega t \end{aligned} \tag{11.66}$$

The amplitude of this ripple component $V_{\ell 2m}$ (figure 11.13c) is therefore

$$V_{\ell 2m} \simeq \frac{V_{1M}}{3\pi\omega^2 LC} \tag{11.67}$$

and the ripple voltage Δv_L, which is the peak-to-peak voltage of the ripple component (figure 11.13c), is

$$\Delta v_L = 2V_{\ell 2m} \simeq \frac{2V_{1M}}{3\pi\omega^2 LC} \tag{11.68}$$

Combining equations 11.58 and 11.68, the ripple factor for LC smoothing is

$$F_r = \frac{\Delta v_L}{V_{L(AV)}} \simeq \frac{1}{3\omega^2 LC} \tag{11.69}$$

The effectiveness of the smoothing and the quality of the load voltage therefore depend on the product LC.

A feature of this type of smoothing circuit is that there is a minimum value of inductance below which the current through L becomes pulsed, whereby the smoothing effect provided by L is diminished and circuit performance reduces to that of the basic capacitance arrangement. Selection of values of L and C to meet a specification requires knowledge of the minimum (critical) value of inductance L_C (equation 11.73) so that a value $\geqslant L_C$ can be selected to ensure linear operation and then the corresponding value of C is calculated using equation 11.69 to provide the specified ripple factor.

Figure 11.13d shows the inductor current i_1 as having a steady component $I_{1(AV)}$ which is equal to $I_{L(AV)}$, assuming negligible leakage through the capacitor, and a second harmonic ripple component i_{12}. Thus, for ideal components:

$$I_{1(AV)} = I_{L(AV)} = \frac{V_{L(AV)}}{R_L} = \frac{2V_{1M}}{\pi R_L} \tag{11.70}$$

using equation 11.58.

As far as the ripple is concerned, if Z_2 is the impedance of the LCR_L circuit (figure 11.13a) at the second harmonic frequency 2ω:

$$i_{12} = \frac{v_{12}}{Z_2} = -\left(\frac{4V_{1M}}{3\pi Z_2}\right)\cos 2\omega t \tag{11.71}$$

using the expression for v_{12} from the Fourier series. From equations 11.60 and 11.61, it follows that Z_2 is made up almost entirely by the reactance of the inductor since $X_{L2} \gg R_L \gg X_{C2}$, thus $Z_2 \simeq j2\omega L$ giving i_{12}, from equation 11.71, as

$$i_{12} = -\left(\frac{2V_{1M}}{j3\pi\omega L}\right)\cos 2\omega t$$

$$= -\left(\frac{2V_{1M}}{3\pi\omega L}\right)\sin 2\omega t = -I_{12m}\sin 2\omega t \tag{11.72}$$

where I_{12m} is the amplitude of the ripple current through L.

Equation 11.72 shows that the amplitude of the ripple increases as L is reduced which is represented graphically in figure 11.13d. As i_1 is supplied by the rectifier, it cannot reverse direction and so if I_{12m} becomes greater than $I_{1(AV)}$, i_1 becomes pulsed and linear operation (for which the concept of reactance is meaningful) ceases. The limiting condition, which corresponds to the critical value of inductance L_C, is when the amplitude of the ripple I_{12m} is equal to the average value $I_{1(AV)}$, which, from equations 11.70 and 11.72 is when

$$\frac{2V_{1M}}{3\pi\omega L_C} = \frac{2V_{1M}}{\pi R_L}$$

which gives

$$L_C = \frac{R_L}{3\omega} = \frac{R_L}{6\pi f} \tag{11.73}$$

This is the minimum value of inductance that can be used; having selected $L \geqslant L_C$, C is then calculated from equation 11.69.

Note that the capacitor, in addition to providing sufficient capacitance and having an adequate working voltage rating, must also be capable of carrying the ripple current i_{12} without excessive heating. From equations 11.72 and 11.58 the peak ripple current I_{12m} is $V_{L(AV)}/3\omega L$ and since the ripple is sinusoidal (equation 11.72), the rms ripple current $I_{12(rms)}$ is $V_{L(AV)}/3(\sqrt{2})\omega L$. The minimum rms ripple current rating of the selected capacitor is therefore

$$I_{ripple(rms)} = \frac{V_{L(AV)}}{3(\sqrt{2})\omega L} \tag{11.74}$$

Performance summary for inductance-input smoothing

This provides effective smoothing for moderate-to-high current, unregulated supplies using modest values of L and C. Critical inductance increases with R_L (equation 11.73) so that this form of smoothing is less attractive for low load currents at which basic capacitance smoothing is perfectly satisfactory. The series inductance in the LC filter prevents surge loading of the rectifier. A comparison of the performance of the various smoothing circuits is given in table 11.1.

Example 11.3: Inductance-input smoothing

An LC smoothing circuit is required for an unregulated 30 V, 2 A supply which is driven from 50 Hz mains and employs full-wave rectification. Select suitable values of inductance and E6 (appendix D) capacitance if the ripple factor must not exceed 5 per cent.

$V_{L(AV)} = 30$ V, $I_{L(AV)} = 2$ A and so $R_L = 30\text{ V}/2\text{ A} = 15\,\Omega$.
From equation 11.73 the corresponding critical inductance is

$$L_C = \frac{15\,\Omega}{6\pi(50\text{ Hz})} \simeq 15.92\text{ mH}$$

A value of $L \geqslant 15.92$ mH can now be chosen, 20 mH being selected provisionally as a convenient value.

The corresponding value of C to provide $F_r \not> 5$ per cent is found from equation 11.69:

$$C_{min} \simeq \frac{1}{3\omega^2 L F_r \text{max}} \tag{11.75}$$

$$= \frac{1}{3(2\pi)^2(50\text{ Hz})^2(20\text{ mH})(0.05)} \simeq 3377\,\mu\text{F}$$

This has resulted in a relatively high value of C and since the values of L and C can be traded while keeping the product LC as required by equation 11.69, provided equations 11.60 and 11.61 are still valid, it is suggested in this case that L is increased to 100 mH giving C_{min} as approximately 675 μF. Thus, allowing for a -20 per cent tolerance in C, a 1000 μF capacitor can be selected. In fact, since the worst-case minimum value of this capacitor is 1000 μF $-$ 20 per cent $=$ 800 μF, the inductance value can be reduced to 85 mH while still providing $F_r \not> 5$ per cent. Note that at the second harmonic frequency, the reactances of the 85 mH inductor and 1000 μF capacitor are approximately 53 Ω and 1.6 Ω respectively, showing that the selected values satisfy equations 11.60 and 11.61, R_L being 15 Ω. The inductor must be capable of carrying 2 A continuously.

For $L = 85$ mH, the minimum rms ripple current rating of the capacitor, from equation 11.74, is

$$I_{ripple(rms)}\text{min} = \frac{V_{L(AV)}}{3(\sqrt{2})2\pi f L} = \frac{30\text{ V}}{3(\sqrt{2})(2\pi)(50\text{ Hz})(85\text{ mH})} \simeq 265\text{ mA}$$

Capacitance-input smoothing

Further improvement in smoothing performance and/or reduction of the values of smoothing components can be achieved by cascading basic C and LC filters, as in figure 11.10d, forming a CLC π-section filter commonly described as a capacitance-input filter.

Capacitor C_1 acts as a basic capacitance filter so that the waveshape of v_1 is similar to that of v_L for the basic C case (figure 11.11b); $V_{L(AV)}$, which is equal to $V_{1(AV)}$ if the resistance of the inductor is negligible, is therefore given by equation 11.34 where $\tau = C_1 R_L$, with V_{LM} replaced by V_{1M}. Analysis to determine the ripple voltage follows the same procedure as for the LC filter above except that the input v_1 is now the approximate negative sawtooth waveform across C_1 in place of the full-wave rectified sinewave in the LC case. Fourier analysis of the negative sawtooth of peak-to-peak value Δv_1 reveals that the amplitude of the dominant harmonic (frequency 2ω) is $\Delta v_1/\pi$. Making practical simplifications corresponding to effective smoothing, namely $(1/2\omega C_2) \ll R_L$, $2\omega L \gg (1/2\omega C_2)$ and $2\omega L \gg (1/2\omega C_1)$, leads to expressions for ripple voltage and ripple factor as quoted in table 11.1. Design of a *CLC* smoothing circuit involves selection of C_1 based on basic *C* filter design, neglecting the effects of *L* and C_2, to provide modest smoothing so that Δv_1 is 20–30 per cent of $V_{L(AV)}$. With C_1 selected, the product LC_2 is dictated by the required ripple factor and suitable component values can be selected knowing that $1/2\omega C_2$ must $\ll R_L$ and $2\omega L \gg (1/2\omega C_2)$ for satisfactory performance.

Regulation performance of non-stabilised ac–dc supplies

The average output voltage $V_{L(AV)}$ from a transformer–rectifier–filter circuit drops as the load current $I_{L(AV)}$ is increased because of the resistance of the secondary winding of the transformer (section 11.2.1), increased voltage drop across the rectifier and smoothing circuit performance.

For basic capacitance smoothing, $V_{L(AV)}$ reduces as $I_{L(AV)}$ increases (R_L reduces) because of reduction in the CR_L time constant causing increased discharge during each $T/2$ interval (figure 11.11b). In the basic inductance case, the ohmic drop $I_{L(AV)}R$ due to the coil resistance R increases with $I_{L(AV)}$ causing $V_{L(AV)}$ to fall. With *LC* and *CLC* smoothing, these two effects are combined.

Figure 11.14 compares the loading characteristics of the various smoothing configurations. As for a transformer, performance in this respect is described in terms of the *voltage regulation* (equation 11.11); the smaller the voltage reduction between no load ($I_{L(AV)} = 0$) and full load ($I_{L(AV)}$max), the better the regulation of the supply.

In general, inductance filters provide better regulation than capacitance types; notice that performance of the *LC* filter changes from essentially inductance type to capacitance type as R_L increases through the critical value corresponding to equation 11.73.

11.2.4 *Linear regulators*

Many applications require the load voltage $V_{L(AV)}$ to be maintained approximately constant as the load current $I_{L(AV)}$ varies with the changing load. This requires a circuit to be included between the filter and the load (figure 11.2) that compensates for the fluctuating output from the filter. Such circuits are called voltage *regulators* or *stabilisers*; they *regulate* against a

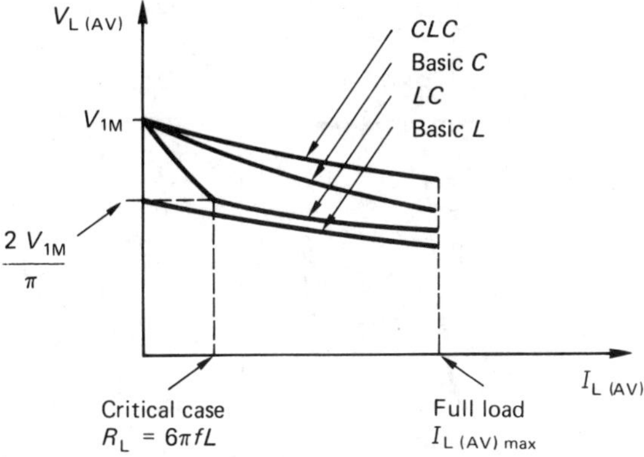

Figure 11.14 Regulation performance of non-stabilised ac–dc power supplies for various types of smoothing

changing load and *stabilise* against a varying input. The complete supply is described as a regulated or stabilised power supply.

Note that the action of the regulator in correcting for a changing filter output provides smoothing since the ripple constitutes a changing input voltage. In a regulated supply therefore, smoothing is provided by both the filter and the regulator stages and the filter specification can therefore be relaxed compared with that for a non-regulated supply. Usually basic capacitance smoothing is adequate in a regulated supply, even for relatively high load currents, the regulator stage contributing substantial smoothing.

Voltage reference diode

To provide correction for a changing input voltage, the regulator requires a voltage reference and this is usually provided by a reference diode held at breakdown, also called Zener and avalanche diodes [1b]. The symbol and reverse-bias characteristic of this type of diode are given in figures 11.15a, b; V_B is the nominal breakdown voltage at the 'knee' of the characteristic. Although at breakdown the voltage across the diode V_Z remains approximately constant while the current I_Z can vary over a relatively wide range, the variation of V_Z with I_Z in this region is represented by the slope resistance r_z ($=\Delta V_Z/\Delta I_Z$). Notice that V_Z and I_Z are defined in the 'reverse' direction relative to the directions of V and I for a general-purpose diode (figure 2.2); this is for convenience so that V_Z and I_Z can be quoted as positive numerical values. The reverse bias characteristic of the reference diode can be represented by the piecewise-linear model of figure 11.15c which corresponds to the model of figure 11.3b of the forward I–V characteristic of a diode. For applied voltages $V_Z > V_B$ the hypothetical ideal switch is a short circuit and the reference diode characteristic can be represented as resistance r_z in series with voltage source V_B.

Voltage reference diodes are available in a range of nominal breakdown voltages V_B and maximum power dissipation levels P_{max}. Appendix E, section E.2 gives information for the 400 mW BZX 79 range which provides V_B values according to the E24 series (appendix D) between 2.4 V and 75 V; a 4.7 V diode in this range is designated BZX 79 C4V7, C indicating a ± 5 per cent tolerance in the breakdown voltage and V being used in place of the decimal point to improve legibility. Appendix E, section E.3 provides data for the 1.3 W BZV 85 range (3.6 V to 75 V). Ranges with power ratings of 1, 2.5, 5 and 20 W are also readily available, in some cases the range of breakdown voltage extends up to 270 V.

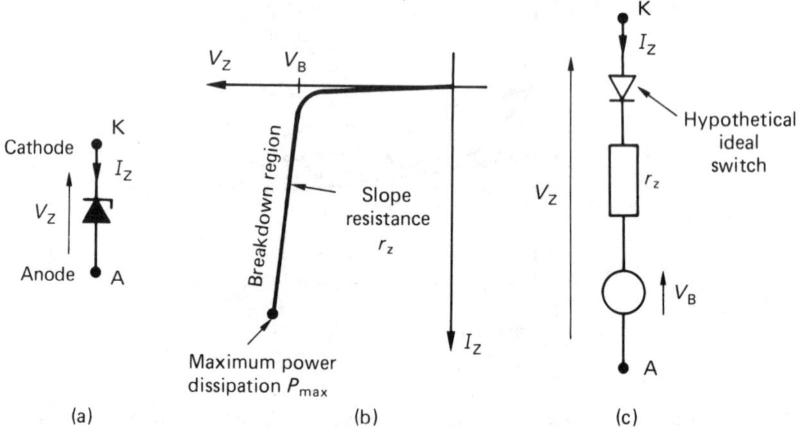

Figure 11.15 Voltage reference diode

Basic shunt diode regulator

The simplest regulating arrangement is that of figure 11.16a in which a reference diode is connected directly across (in shunt with) the load; the input v_I is the output of the smoothing stage. Provided the diode remains at breakdown, which depends on v_I, R_1 and R_L, the voltage v_Z across it remains approximately constant, hence the load voltage remains approximately constant as $v_L = v_Z$. Resistor R_1 must be included so that v_Z can be different from v_I, allowing v_Z to be almost constant while v_I varies.

If R_L falls, $I_{L(AV)}$ must rise correspondingly to maintain $V_{L(AV)}$. Over a limited range this increase in $I_{L(AV)}$ can be accommodated by a decrease in $I_{Z(AV)}$, thus as R_L fluctuates there is a 'see-saw' action between the load and diode currents, reducing the fluctuation in current $I_{I(AV)}$ drawn from the smoothing circuit and thus improving regulation. The small variation in load voltage is dependent on the slope of the breakdown characteristic of the diode which is described in terms of slope resistance r_z (figures 11.15b, c). The absolute limits to the range of $I_{L(AV)}$ for which this arrangement can provide regulation are given by

(1) $I_{L(AV)}$ being reduced and/or $V_{I(AV)}$ increasing to such a level that $I_{Z(AV)}$ reaches its maximum value corresponding to P_{max} for the diode, and

(2) $I_{L(AV)}$ increasing and/or $V_{I(AV)}$ reducing to such an extent that $I_{Z(AV)}$ falls to zero so that the diode comes out of breakdown and becomes non-conducting ($V_Z < V_B$, figure 11.15b). Under these conditions, regulation ceases and the circuit becomes a basic potential divider formed by R_1 and R_L (the diode being open circuit) whereby $V_{L(AV)}$ varies with R_L and $V_{I(AV)}$.

In practice, however, the working range is usually narrower than this absolute maximum range because of the specified upper and lower limits of $V_{L(AV)}$ ($= V_{Z(AV)}$) which restrict the range of I_Z (figure 11.17).

For specific circuit components, regulator performance can be analysed using either a graphical load line technique (section 1.2.2) or the piecewise-linear model of figure 11.15c (see also section 1.2.3). Using the graphical method, if the $V_{I(AV)}$, R_1 and R_L combination is reduced using Thévenin's theorem (note 3.1), the regulator can be represented in the classic source–load–non-linear device form of figure 11.16b which corresponds to the general case of figure 1.2a. Superimposing the load line corresponding to Thévenin resistance $R_T (= R_1 /\!/ R_L)$ on the diode characteristic (figure 11.16c) enables the diode operating point Q to be located and the average values of circuit currents and voltages to be obtained. Fluctuation of v_I and R_L causes the load line to move up and down so that the diode operating point moves along the characteristic; the change of $V_{L(AV)}$ therefore depends on the slope of the characteristic.

Using PWL modelling whereby diode performance is represented by the model of figure 11.15c, regulator performance is represented as in figure 11.16d, the diode being represented by r_z, V_B, the ideal switch in the model of figure 11.15c being a short circuit when the diode is at breakdown. The circuit model of figure 11.16d presents a linear network analysis problem which can be solved to find average current and voltage values using standard network analysis techniques. Provided the regulation of the drive circuit is known, that is the variation of $V_{I(AV)}$ with $I_{I(AV)}$, the model can be used to estimate the variation of $V_{L(AV)}$ with $I_{L(AV)}$. Reduction of the model to represent only voltage *changes* by removal of the *constant* source V_B, as in figure 11.16e, permits calculation of ripple reduction. If Δv_I and Δv_L are the peak-to-peak input and load ripple voltages then

$$\Delta v_L = \left[\frac{r_z /\!/ R_L}{R_1 + (r_z /\!/ R_L)}\right]\Delta v_I \simeq \left(\frac{r_z}{R_1 + r_z}\right)\Delta v_I \qquad (11.76)$$

for $r_z \ll R_L$.

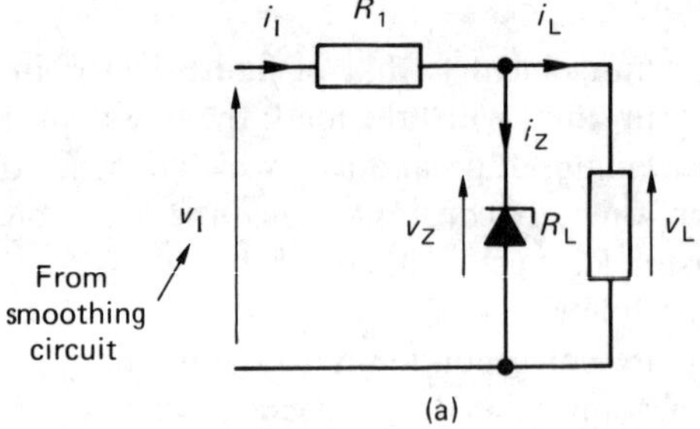

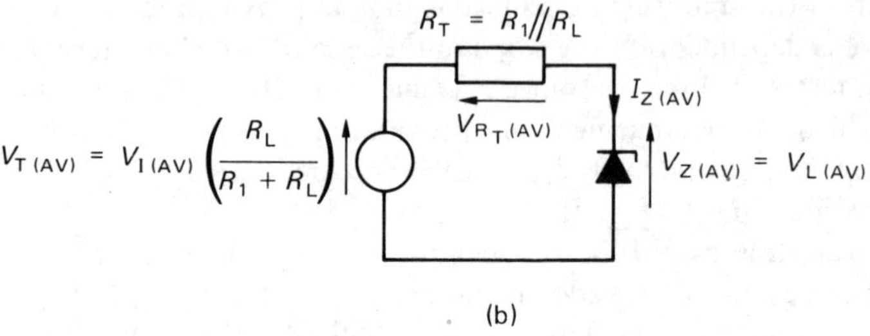

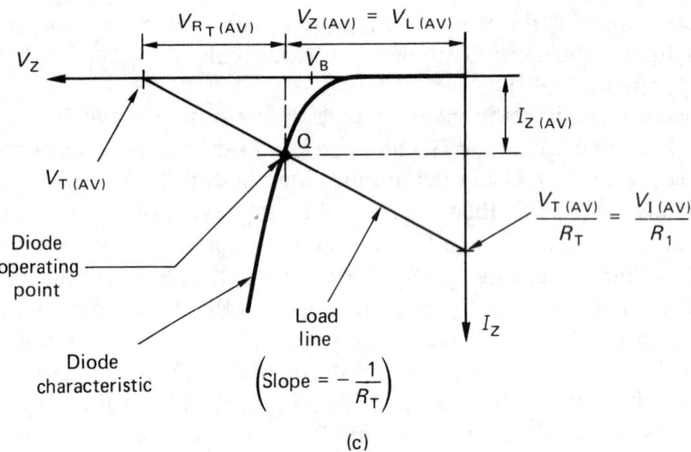

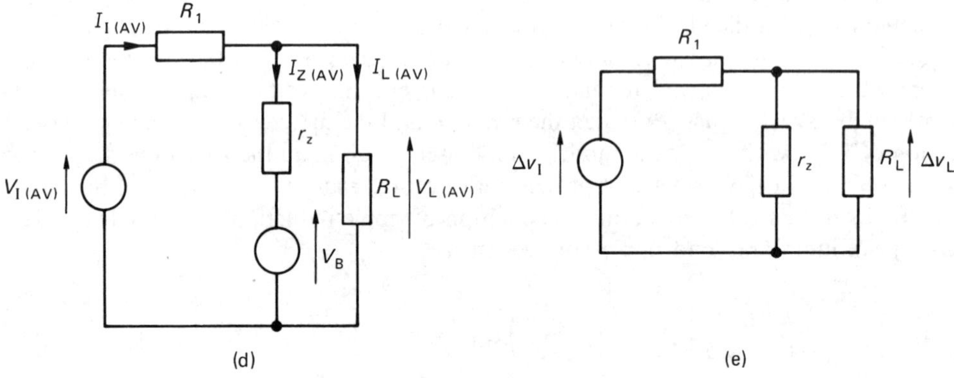

Figure 11.16 Shunt diode regulator analysis

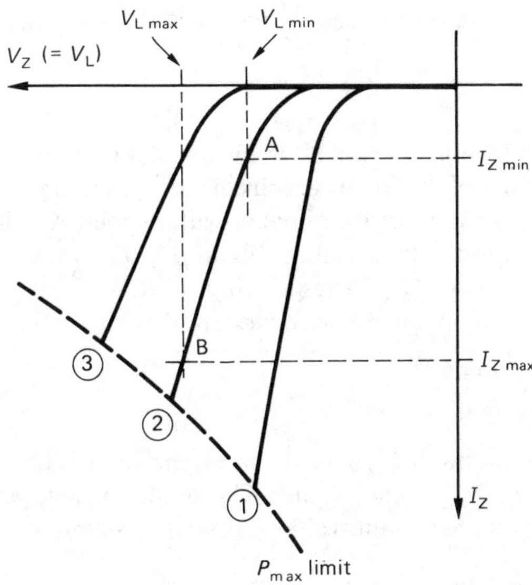

Figure 11.17 Diode selection for a shunt diode regulator

Design of a shunt diode regulator

The regulator specification normally states the ranges of average input voltage $V_I$min to $V_I$max and average load current $I_L$min to $I_L$max with which the circuit must cope while maintaining the average load voltage within certain limits, $V_L$min to $V_L$max. The design exercise requires selection of an appropriate diode and resistor R_1 to meet the specification noting that in terms of average values, from figure 11.16a,

$$R_1 = \frac{V_I - V_L}{I_Z + I_L} \tag{11.77}$$

Diode selection

In order for the see-saw action between I_Z and I_L to be effective in minimising the fluctuation of current drawn from the smoothing circuit, so improving the regulation as much as possible, the diode must be capable of handling a *change* in current equal to or greater than the *change* of load current ($I_L$max $-$ $I_L$min) that the circuit is required to provide. Using the set of $I_Z - V_Z$ diode characteristics provided by the manufacturer, a diode is selected that allows an adequate change of I_Z, while V_Z ($= V_L$) remains within the $V_L$min to $V_L$max allowable range as represented in figure 11.17; in this case diode ② would be selected. Note that in some situations the $I_Z$max limit may be set by the P_{max} limit of the diode rather than $V_L$max. If the range $I_Z$max$-$$I_Z$min provided by a certain diode type is too restricted, it is necessary to change to a diode type that has a higher P_{max} rating. Diodes can be combined in series if necessary but as the slope resistances of the diode are then added, the slope of the combined characteristic is lower, resulting in poorer regulation. An important property of reference diodes is that the temperature coefficient S_Z (variation of breakdown voltage V_B with temperature) is negative for diodes having $V_B < 5.6$ V and positive for those with $V_B > 5.6$ V. This change of sign of S_Z provides a method of improving the stability of the voltage reference for change of temperature, for example, a series combination of 3.3 V (S_Z negative) and 6.8 V

(S_Z positive) diodes provides a more stable reference than a single 10 V diode for varying temperature.

Selection of R_1

The value of R_1 (figure 11.16a) is selected within the allowable range R_1min to R_1max set by the operational extremes of the circuit which corresponds to points A and B in figure 11.17.

From see-saw action, I_Z will be at its minimum value (point A) when I_L is at its maximum which corresponds to minimum load voltage (figure 11.17). $I_Z\text{min} + I_L\text{max}$ is supplied from V_I through R_1 and the worst-case, corresponding to R_1max, is that this current must be supplied when V_I is at its minimum value. Including these limits in equation 11.77 gives

$$R_1\text{max} = \frac{V_I\text{min} - V_L\text{min}}{I_Z\text{min} + I_L\text{max}} \tag{11.78}$$

At the other extreme, point B ($I_Z$max, $V_L$max), the diode current is a maximum when minimum current is drawn by the load, $I_L$min. This diode current must not be exceeded when the input voltage V_I is at its maximum value and so the minimum value of R_1 is given by

$$R_1\text{min} = \frac{V_I\text{max} - V_L\text{max}}{I_Z\text{max} + I_L\text{min}} \tag{11.79}$$

For a particular design, a resistor of adequate power rating $(I_I\text{max})^2 R_1$ is chosen having an *actual* value, that is, allowing for the selection tolerance (see example 11.4), within the range R_1min to R_1max. Note that if the allowed I_Z range is too restricted relative to the ranges of V_I, I_L and V_L, calculation of R_1min and R_1max using equations 11.78 and 11.79 results in $R_1\text{min} > R_1\text{max}$, an impossible situation, which indicates that the specification cannot be met using the diode that has been selected. In such a case either a higher power, lower resistance diode must be selected, allowing the I_Z range to be increased, or a more sophisticated regulator circuit must be used.

Example 11.4: Shunt diode regulator design

A basic shunt diode regulator is required to provide an output voltage of 5 V ± 5 per cent for a resistive load which draws up to 100 mA. The unregulated dc input may vary between 10 V and 15 V. Select a suitable diode from available ranges together with resistor R_1 (figure 11.16a) to meet the specification. Estimate the ripple reduction provided by the regulator.

With reference to the circuit of figure 11.16a, $V_{I(AV)}$ can vary from 10 V to 15 V, thus $V_I\text{max} = 15$ V and $V_I\text{min} = 10$ V. $V_{L(AV)}$ must remain within the range 5 V ± 5 per cent while $I_{L(AV)}$ varies from zero to 100 mA, thus $V_L\text{max} = 5$ V + 5 per cent = 5.25 V (at $I_L\text{min} = 0$) and $V_L\text{min} = 5$ V − 5 per cent = 4.75 V (at $I_L\text{max} = 100$ mA).

Diode selection. From see-saw action, the selected diode should be able to accommodate a 100 mA change of current while maintaining the diode voltage (= load voltage) within the 4.75 V to 5.25 V specified range.

Examination of the static characteristics of the 500 mW BZX 79 range of typical low-power diodes (appendix E, section E.2) shows that, for the 4.75 V to 5.25 V range, only the C4V7 diode is applicable. The corresponding I_Z range, using the construction of figure 11.17, is approximately 10 mA to 97 mA (limited by Pmax) which does not accommodate a 100 mA change.

The 1.3 W BZV 85 C4V7 (appendix E, section E.3) has a corresponding current range of 50 mA to 180 mA which seems suitable. The slope resistance r_z in this range is approximately $\Delta V_Z/\Delta I_Z = (5.25\text{ V} - 4.75\text{ V})/(180\text{ mA} - 50\text{ mA}) = 500\text{ mV}/130\text{ mA} \simeq 3.8\ \Omega$. The diode data sheet quotes a value of differential (slope) resistance of $\leqslant 13\ \Omega$ at 45 mA.

R_1 selection. Using the maximum and minimum values of V_I (15 V, 10 V), V_L (5.25 V, 4.75 V), I_L (100 mA, 0) and I_Z (180 mA, 50 mA from above), the allowable range of R_1, from equations 11.78 and 11.79, is found to be 35.0 Ω to 54.1 Ω.

The mean of this range is approximately 44.6 Ω, allowing an E24 value of 43 Ω to be selected. Note that the range of the selected value corresponding to the selection tolerance must be checked to ensure that the *actual* value is always within the allowable range. In this instance, if a ±2 per cent resistor is selected, the actual resistance will be in the range 43 Ω ±2 per cent which is well within the allowed limits.

Maximum power dissipation occurs in R_1 when $I_I\ (= I_Z + I_L)$ is a maximum. Projecting the breakdown characteristic of the BZV 85 C4V7 diode back to the V_Z-axis gives the hypothetical breakdown voltage (figure 11.15b) as about 4.6 V (appendix E, section E.3). Using the model of figure 11.16d with $R_1 = 43\ \Omega$, $V_B = 4.6$ V and $r_z = 3.8\ \Omega$, $I_I\text{max}$ is found to be 213.04 mA, corresponding to $V_I\text{max} = 15$ V and $I_L\text{max} = 100$ mA. The maximum dissipation in R_1 is therefore $(213.04\text{ mA})^2\ (43\ \Omega) = 1.95$ W, allowing selection of a 2 W component.

Ripple reduction. The relationship between input and output ripple is given by the model of figure 11.16e and correspondingly, equation 11.76. Here $R_1 \simeq 43\ \Omega$, $r_z \simeq 3.8\ \Omega$ and $R_L \simeq 50\ \Omega - \infty$, corresponding to $I_L = 100$ mA–0 at $V_L \simeq 5$ V. Since r_z is always $\ll R_L$:

$$\frac{\Delta v_L}{\Delta v_I} \simeq \frac{r_z}{R_1 + r_z} = \frac{3.8\ \Omega}{43\ \Omega + 3.8\ \Omega} \simeq 0.081$$

showing that the ripple at the output is only about 8 per cent of that at the input to the regulator, a significant improvement.

Power supply regulation

The output voltage provided by a power supply falls as the current drawn increases, as shown in figure 11.18a. This aspect of performance is described quantitatively by the *voltage regulation*

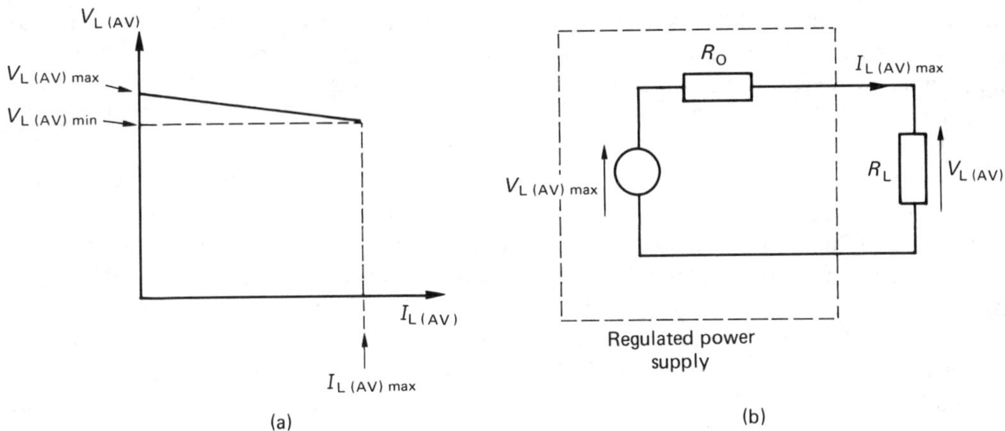

Figure 11.18 Regulation of a power supply

of the supply which is given by

$$\text{Voltage regulation} = \frac{V_{L(AV)}\max - V_{L(AV)}\min}{V_{L(AV)}\max} \tag{11.80}$$

where $[V_{L(AV)}\max - V_{L(AV)}\min]$ is the fall in output (load) voltage as the load current increases from zero to the specified maximum value $I_{L(AV)}\max$. Note that this definition of voltage regulation, which is usually expressed as a percentage, compares directly with that of equation 11.11 describing voltage regulation of a transformer.

This property can be represented by the model of figure 11.18b where R_O is the output resistance of the regulated supply. From the model, at maximum load current $I_{L(AV)}\max$:

$$V_{L(AV)}\min = V_{L(AV)}\max - R_O I_{L(AV)}\max \tag{11.81}$$

Combining equations 11.80 and 11.81:

$$\text{Voltage regulation} = \frac{R_O I_{L(AV)}\max}{V_{L(AV)}\max} \simeq \frac{R_O I_{L(AV)}\max}{V_{L(AV)}\min} = \frac{R_O}{R_L\min} \tag{11.82}$$

since for good regulation the fall in output voltage is small and the ratio $V_{L(AV)}\min / I_{L(AV)}\max$ is the load resistance at full load $R_L\min$. Equation 11.82 shows that for good regulation, that is, load voltage varying only marginally with load current, the output resistance of the regulator stage must be small compared with the minimum load resistance that is to be driven. A typical integrated regulator has an output resistance of $< 50\ \text{m}\Omega$.

Series voltage regulator

The basic shunt diode regulator previously considered is suitable only for low load current applications, otherwise the power dissipation capability of the reference diode is excessive relative to the load power. Note that in example 11.4, a 1.3 W diode is used for an application where the maximum load power is only 0.5 W (100 mA at 5 V). Performance and/or output current capability can be improved by introducing a transistor as in the series voltage regulator of figure 11.19a, so named because the output (C–E) terminals of the BJT are in *series* with the load.

The circuit is essentially an emitter-follower (common-collector amplifier, figure 3.15c) with a 'fixed' bias provided by the reference diode and an unregulated collector supply v_I as shown in figure 11.19b; the load forms the emitter resistor. With the base–emitter voltage of the BJT being only slightly dependent on current flow for active region operation (figure 11.19c), the load voltage is fixed by the reference voltage v_z at

$$v_L = v_Z - v_{BE} \tag{11.83}$$

An important property of the emitter-follower is its low output resistance ($\simeq 1/g_{fe}$, equation 3.117) indicating good regulation in this context (equation 11.82).

The circuit maintains the load voltage approximately constant as the load resistance (load current demanded) changes by controlling the degree of conduction of the BJT, which, in its role as a control element is often referred to as the *pass* transistor. Provided the range of operation of the BJT, as determined by the ranges of v_I and i_L, is such that it remains in its active region of operation (section 2.3.3), the degree of conduction of the BJT is sensitive to small changes of v_{BE}. With v_Z approximately fixed, if R_L reduces, instantaneously v_L starts to fall causing v_{BE} to rise. The increasing v_{BE} causes the degree of conduction of the BJT to increase so increasing i_L and restoring v_L to approximately its original value. The speed of

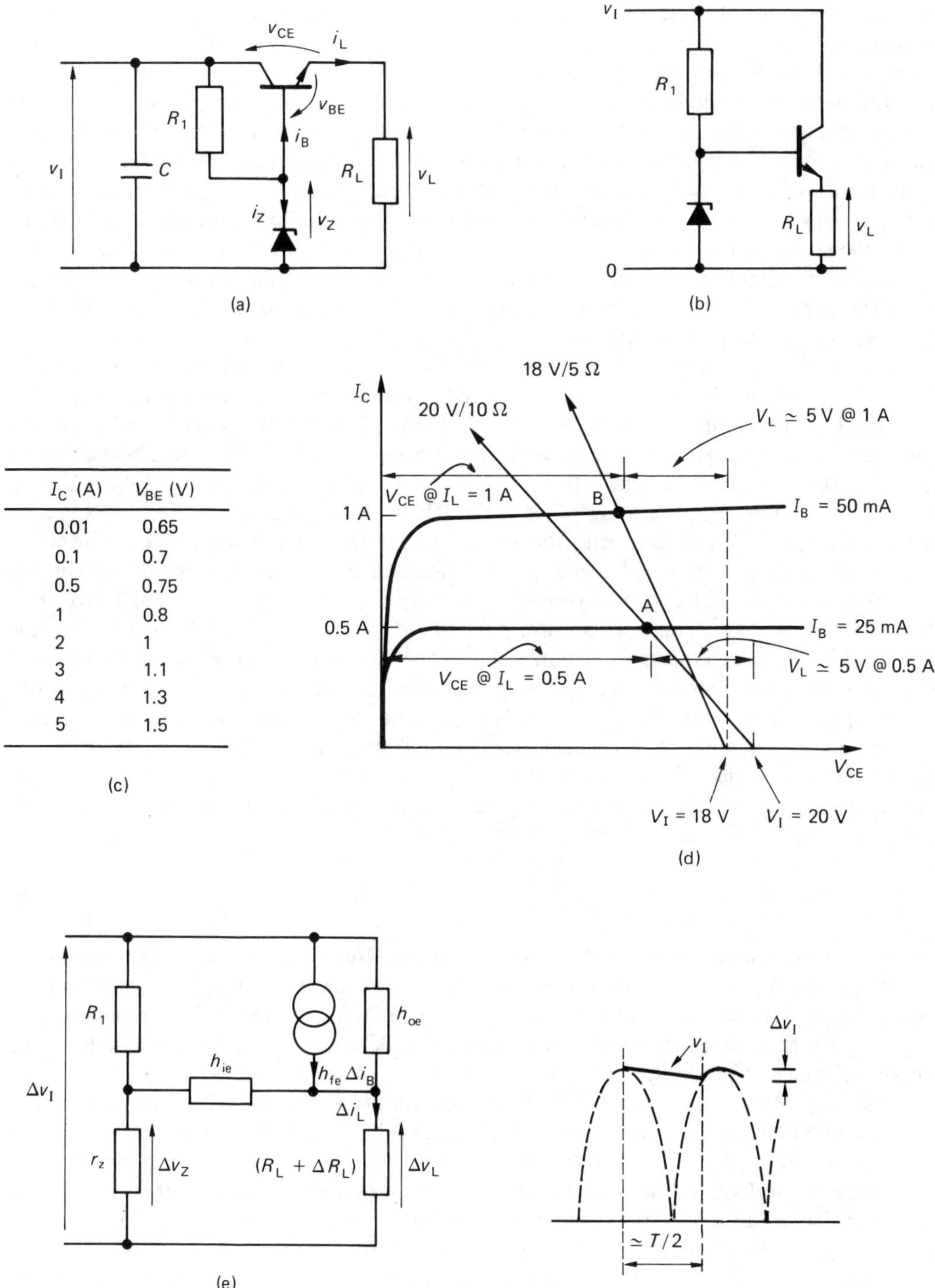

I_C (A)	V_{BE} (V)
0.01	0.65
0.1	0.7
0.5	0.75
1	0.8
2	1
3	1.1
4	1.3
5	1.5

Figure 11.19 Series voltage regulator

the correction, which features in the regulation provided, depends on the gain of the BJT for changing voltage and current, namely g_{fe} ($=\Delta I_C/\Delta V_{BE}$) or h_{fe} ($=\Delta I_C/\Delta I_B$), see figure 3.9a.

The improvement in performance provided by the series regulator (figure 11.19a) compared with the basic shunt diode circuit of figure 11.16a can be appreciated by considering the see-saw action between the load and diode currents. In the shunt diode circuit, change in i_L results in a similar change (of opposite sign) in i_Z. Depending on r_z of the diode, this causes a change in v_Z and v_L as previously discussed. In the series regulator, however, the see-saw action is not between i_Z and i_L directly but between i_Z and the base current of the BJT, i_B, and as the static gain of the BJT h_{FE} is $\gg 1$ the change of i_L results in a smaller change of i_B with a correspondingly smaller change of i_Z, hence providing improved regulation. Conversely, for the same regulation, the series regulator can cope with a range of load current approximately h_{FE} times that of the shunt diode circuit.

Circuit performance can be represented graphically using the load line construction of figure 11.19d. For a 5 V, 0.5 A output using a BJT with $h_{FE} = 19$ and an input voltage V_I of 20 V, the load line is drawn from 20 V, 0 mA to 0 V, (20 V/10 Ω) A (section 1.2.2) on the output characteristics of the BJT, the load resistance being 5 V/0.5 A = 10 Ω. At a load (emitter) current of 0.5 A, the base current, which is $I_L/(h_{FE}+1)$ as $I_B = I_C/h_{FE}$ and $I_L = I_E = I_C + I_B$, is 0.5 A/20 = 25 mA. The operating point of the BJT is therefore at the intercept of the load line with the $I_B = 25$ mA characteristic (point A). If the load resistance is reduced to 5 Ω, so demanding 1 A at 5 V, and as a consequence, because the regulation of the transformer–rectifier–filter circuit providing the input to the regulator, V_I falls to 18 V, the load line would change as shown, the BJT Q-point moving to point B on the $I_B = 1$ A/20 = 50 mA characteristic. Notice that while V_L remains approximately constant at 5 V, the reduction in input voltage V_I is accommodated by a fall in V_{CE} across the transistor.

Corresponding to figure 11.16e for the shunt diode circuit, the series regulator can be analysed for variation of input voltage using the small-signal model of figure 11.19e in which the performance of the BJT for small changes of current and voltage is represented by the h-parameter model of figure 3.9d (h_{re} being neglected). The change in load voltage Δv_L due to the combined variation of v_I and i_L can be written

$$\Delta v_L = \Delta v_I \left[\frac{\partial v_L}{\partial v_I}\right]_{R_L\ \text{constant}} + \Delta i_L \left[\frac{\partial v_L}{\partial i_L}\right]_{v_I\ \text{constant}} \tag{11.84}$$

where the two bracketed terms are the input stabilisation factor (S_V) and the output regulation factor (S_I); note that S_I is the output resistance of the regulator. Analysis shows that for typical values, $S_V \simeq r_z/(R_1 + r_z)$ corresponding to equation 11.76 for the basic shunt regulator and $S_I \simeq 1/g_{fe}$ where g_{fe} is the forward transconductance of the BJT which corresponds to the output resistance of the emitter-follower (equation 3.117).

In this application in an ac–dc supply the regulator input v_I is supplied from rectified mains, initial smoothing being provided by capacitor C (figure 11.19a). As the action of the regulator in stabilising the output for a changing input provides a degree of smoothing, usually basic capacitance smoothing at the input is sufficient. By including initial smoothing, the input ripple is reduced and so the specification of the regulator can be relaxed. Assuming full-wave rectification, the discharge interval for the capacitor is approximately half the period of the sinusoidal mains input as shown in figure 11.19f which corresponds to the basic capacitance smoothing case of figure 11.11b. The discharge is greatest, and hence the ripple the largest, when the current drawn by the regulator is at a maximum which is approximately $I_{L(AV)}$max, ignoring the diode and base current components. During the discharge interval the reduction in capacitor charge Δq, corresponding to voltage reduction Δv_I, is the current × time product

$I_{L(AV)}\max(T/2)$. For a maximum input ripple $(\Delta v_I)\max$, chosen typically to be 10–20 per cent of $V_{I(AV)}$, the minimum required capacitance value is given, using equation 2.23, by

$$C_{\min} = \frac{\Delta q}{(\Delta v_I)\max} = \frac{I_{L(AV)}\max(T/2)}{(\Delta v_I)\max} \qquad (11.85)$$

Design of a series voltage regulator

(1) The BJT is selected according to the required current capability $I_C\max$ and power dissipation $P_{tot}\max$.

$$I_C\max = \left(\frac{h_{FE}}{h_{FE}+1}\right) I_{L(AV)}\max \qquad (11.86)$$

since $I_L = I_E = I_C + I_B$ and $I_B = I_C/h_{FE}$. If h_{FE} is not too low, $I_C\max$ may be taken as approximately equal to $I_{L(AV)}\max$, but note that h_{FE} may be as low as 10 for a moderate-to-high power BJT.

From equation 2.16

$$P_{tot}\max \simeq (V_{CE} I_C)\max \qquad (11.87)$$

for static operation. Here, $v_{CE} = v_I - v_L$ (figure 11.19a) where v_L is approximately constant at the nominal output value $V_{L(AV)}$ and $v_{CE}\max$ therefore occurs when v_I is at its maximum value. Although $V_I\max$ does not occur at the same time as $I_C\max$, because of the regulation performance of the transformer–rectifier–smoothing circuit, selection of the BJT on the basis of

$$(P_{tot}\max)\min = (V_I\max - V_{L(AV)}) I_C\max \qquad (11.88)$$

is safe.

(2) The max–min range of h_{FE} for the selected type of BJT is then estimated using manufacturers data taking account of
   (i) current range, and
   (ii) spread of h_{FE} for that type of BJT.

(3) The range of base current can then be determined from

$$I_B\max = \frac{I_{L(AV)}\max}{h_{FE}\min + 1} \qquad (11.89)$$

and

$$I_B\min = \frac{I_{L(AV)}\min}{h_{FE}\max + 1} \qquad (11.90)$$

since $I_L = I_E = I_C + I_B$ and $I_B = I_C/h_{FE}$.

(4) A suitable reference diode is then selected in a similar way to that adopted for the basic shunt diode circuit previously considered, but noting that v_Z must be higher than the required v_L due to v_{BE} (equation 11.83). Note that the value of base–emitter voltage increases with collector current (figure 11.19c).

(5) Resistor R_1 must be able to supply $(i_B + i_Z)$ from the v_I supply. Its value can be selected using

$$R_1 = \frac{V_I - V_Z}{I_B + I_Z} \qquad (11.91)$$

where V_I, V_Z, I_B and I_Z are the mid-range dc components, for example $V_I = (V_I\max + V_I\min)/2$. Having selected the value of R_1 it is then necessary to check that I_Z does not fall below $I_Z\min$ (corresponding to $V_Z\min$, figure 11.17) when I_B is at its maximum value and V_I a minimum; also that $I_Z\max$ is not exceeded at $I_B\min$, $V_I\max$. If I_Z does vary outside the permissible range it is necessary to change the diode for a higher power, lower r_z, type that allows a greater current variation.

(6) Depending on the permitted ripple voltage at the load Δv_L, the maximum allowable input ripple $(\Delta v_I)\max$ can be estimated using the input stabilisation factor S_V for the circuit as obtained from the small-signal model of figure 11.19e. This approximates to $r_z/(R_1 + r_z)$ as for the basic shunt regulator (equation 11.76). Having estimated $(\Delta v_I)\max$, a suitable value of smoothing capacitor can be calculated using equation 11.85.

Example 11.5: Series voltage regulator design

A nominal 20 V dc, 0–0.5 A supply is to be provided from 50 Hz mains. The average output voltage must remain within ± 10 per cent of the nominal value and the output ripple factor must not exceed 1 per cent. Regulation of the full-wave rectified sinusoidal input over the specified current range is 15 per cent, the peak input voltage being 45 V at no load. Select suitable components for a basic emitter-follower regulator (figure 11.19a) to meet the specification.

At no load ($I_L = 0$), $V_{IM} = 45$ V and so $V_{I(AV)}\max = \dfrac{2}{\pi}(45\text{ V}) \simeq 28.65$ V using equation 11.21 for a full-wave rectified sinewave.

Using the definition of regulation (equation 11.80), the range of $V_{I(AV)}$ is 15 per cent of 28.65 V, that is, approximately 4.3 V, so that $V_{I(AV)}\min$ is 28.65 V − 4.3 V = 24.35 V. Thus as the load current increases from zero to 0.5 A, the average input voltage $V_{I(AV)}$ falls from 28.65 V to 24.35 V.

Over this range $V_{L(AV)}$ must remain between 20 V $\pm$ 10 per cent, that is, 22 V to 18 V, and the output ripple voltage Δv_L must not exceed 1 per cent of 20 V = 200 mV (using $\Delta v_L = F_r V_{L(AV)}$, equation 11.26).

BJT selection. Assuming $h_{FE}\min$ is not very low, the required minimum BJT ratings are

$$(I_C\max)\min \simeq I_{L(AV)}\max = 0.5\text{ A}$$

and

$$(P_{tot}\max)\min = (28.65\text{ V} - 20\text{ V})0.5\text{ A} \simeq 4.33\text{ W}$$

using equation 11.88.

On the basis of availability and cost, a type TIP 31 BJT (appendix E, section E.6) which has P_{tot}, I_C and V_{CE} ratings of 40 W (at $T_{mb} \leqslant 25\,^\circ$C), 3 A and 40 V is selected. Note that although the power rating seems unnecessarily high, this is for a mounting base (mb) temperature not exceeding 25 °C which implies the use of a heatsink; refer to example 11.6 for details of heatsink selection. The data sheet gives the free-air rating, that is, without a heatsink, as only 2 W.

From the characteristic showing variation of h_{FE} with I_C for a *typical* TIP 31, it can be seen that h_{FE}(typ) varies from about 20 at low I_C to about 78 at $I_C = 0.5$ A. The spread of h_{FE} is given as typically 10 to 50 at $I_C = 3$ A at which h_{FE}(typ) is approximately 22. Combining these two sets of information, the maximum gain at low I_C (which corresponds to minimum base current and hence maximum diode current) is of the order of $20 \times \frac{50}{22} \simeq 45$ and the minimum gain at $I_C \simeq I_{L(AV)}\max = 0.5$ A, which corresponds to $I_B\max$ and hence $I_Z\min$, is approximately $78 \times \frac{10}{22} \simeq 35$. The regulator circuit must therefore function with an estimated range of BJT h_{FE} from about 45 at low load currents to about 35 at the maximum load current of 0.5 A. In fact the gain at low load currents is not important in this particular case because I_L varies down to zero so that $I_B\min$ is also zero and is not dependent on h_{FE}.

$I_B\max$, which occurs at $I_{L(AV)}\max$ of 0.5 A, at which $h_{FE}\min$ has been estimated as 35, is approximately $0.5\text{ A}/(35 + 1) \simeq 14$ mA using equation 11.89.

Diode selection. V_{BE} for the BJT varies from typically 0.65 V at low I_C to about 0.75 V at $I_C = 0.5$ A (figure 11.19c), the mid-range value being about 0.7 V.

The mid-range value of V_Z, from equation 11.83, is thus required to be 20 V + 0.7 V = 20.7 V, and diode characteristics are investigated to enable selection of a suitable device. This mid-range value of 20.7 V must be achieved at a value of I_Z that is sufficiently large to accommodate the see-saw effect as I_B varies over the range 0 to 14 mA, that is, ± 7 mA about the mid-range value, while maintaining V_Z between $V_{L(AV)}\min + V_{BE}\max$ = 18 V + 0.75 V = 18.75 V and $V_{L(AV)}\max + V_{BE}\min$ = 22 V + 0.65 V = 22.65 V. Note that minimum load voltage corresponds to maximum collector current at which V_{BE} is also a maximum, and vice versa.

A 1.3 W BZV 85 C20 reference diode is selected (appendix E, section E.3) for which $V_Z = 20.7$ V corresponds to $I_Z \simeq 20$ mA, and I_Z variation from 0 to 57 mA (the maximum range from breakdown to $P_{tot}\max = 1.3$ W) corresponds to variation of V_Z from 20 V to 22.2 V which is within the allowable 18.75 V to 22.65 V range. The slope resistance r_z of the diode is of the order of 40 Ω.

R_1 selection. Using mid-range average values of V_I, V_Z, I_B and I_Z, namely (28.65 V + 24.35 V)/2 = 26.5 V, 20.7 V, 14 mA/2 = 7 mA and 20 mA respectively, R_1 is calculated using equation 11.91 as (26.5 V − 20.7 V)/(7 mA + 20 mA) ≃ 215 Ω, allowing an E24 value of 220 Ω to be selected.

It is now necessary to check that this value of R_1 allows satisfactory operation under worst-case conditions.

(1) At $I_{L(AV)}\min$ (= 0) and $V_I\max = 28.65$ V; since $I_B = 0$ under these conditions, the values of I_Z and V_Z can be found by constructing the load line on the I_Z–V_Z diode characteristic from (28.65 V, 0 mA) to (0 V, 28.65 V/220 Ω = 130 mA) using the construction technique explained in section 1.2.2. This gives $V_Z = 21.9$ V and $I_Z = 47$ mA; the corresponding value of $V_{L(AV)}$ is about 21.9 V − 0.65 V = 21.25 V. This is the maximum value of $V_{L(AV)}$ and is within specification, being below the upper limit of 22 V.

(2) At the other operational limit, $I_{L(AV)}\max$ and $V_I\min = 24.35$ V, analysis using a 40 Ω, 20 V PWL model (figure 11.15c), allowing for the 14 mA base current under these conditions, gives $I_Z = 4.88$ mA and $V_Z = 20.20$ V which provides $V_{L(AV)}$ of 20.20 V − 0.75 V = 19.45 V, well within the 18 V lower limit.

Using the 40 Ω, 20 V PWL model of the diode once again, the maximum current through R_1, corresponding to $V_{I(AV)}\max$ and $I_B\max$, is 35.42 mA which gives a maximum power dissipation of $(35.42\text{ mA})^2(220\ \Omega) = 0.28$ W, indicating requirement of a 0.5 W resistor.

Input smoothing. Maximum ripple occurs when the load current is at its maximum value, $I_{L(AV)}\max = 0.5$ A, as under these conditions the discharge of the input smoothing capacitor is greatest. Under these conditions R_L is at its minimum value of $V_{L(AV)}/I_{L(AV)}\max$ =

20 V/0.5 A = 40 Ω. With r_z of the diode also 40 Ω (from above), this means that $S_V\max = (\Delta v_L)\max/\Delta v_I \simeq 20\,\Omega/(220\,\Omega + 20\,\Omega) \simeq 0.083$ corresponding to the small-signal model of figure 11.16e which applies here if the small variation of the base–emitter voltage of the BJT is ignored.

To restrict Δv_L to 200 mV as specified, $(\Delta v_I)\max = 200\text{ mV}/0.083 \simeq 2.4$ V and using equation 11.85 with $T = 1/(50\text{ Hz}) = 20$ ms, $C_{min} = (0.5\text{ A})(10\text{ ms})/2.4\text{ V} = 2083\,\mu$F, enabling choice of the E6 value 3300 μF allowing for a typical lower tolerance of −20 per cent. The working voltage of the capacitor must be in excess of V_{IM} (45 V).

Heatsink selection

Use of transistors at moderate-to-high power levels often requires the use of a heatsink to act as a thermal shunt from the transistor package, called the *case* or *mounting base*, to ambient. The shunt provides a low thermal resistance path for the heat flow, so limiting the temperature rise of the transistor.

Power is dissipated in a BJT, and hence heat generated, at the junctions where the main voltage drops occur. For active region operation this is mainly at the C–B junction which is reverse-biased and therefore has a substantial voltage across it. Heat flows from the *junction* J to the transistor *case* C and then is conducted away to the surrounding air called the *ambient*. This situation can be represented by the thermal model of figure 11.20 in which $R_{th(j-c)}$ and $R_{th(c-amb)}$ are the thermal resistances between the junction and case, and between the case and ambient respectively. From the thermal equivalent of Ohm's law:

$$\Delta T = R_{th} P \tag{11.92}$$

the larger R_{th}, the greater the temperature rise ΔT above ambient temperature T_{amb} for a certain heat (power) flow P.

The maximum junction temperature of a transistor, $T_j\max$, for safe operation is usually quoted on the data sheet and the values of thermal resistance are also given. Knowing $T_j\max$ and $T_{amb}\max$ in which the BJT is required to function, the maximum allowable thermal resistance from junction to ambient can be calculated for a certain maximum power level

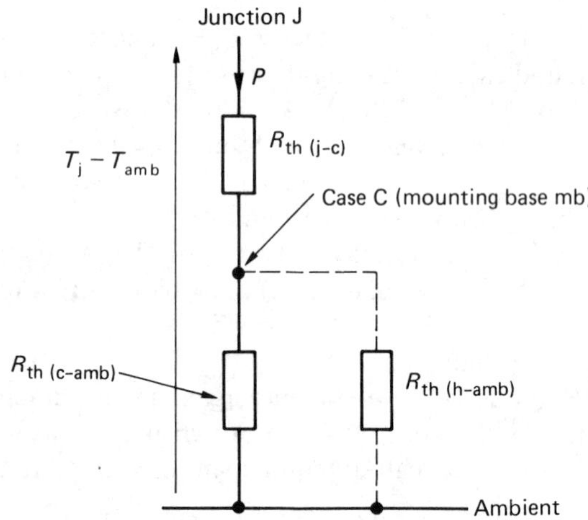

Figure 11.20 Thermal model of a transistor

Pmax using

$$R_{th(j-amb)}\max = \frac{T_m\max - T_{amb}\max}{P\max} \tag{11.93}$$

Correspondingly the maximum thermal resistance of the heatsink to ambient $R_{th(h-amb)}$max can be calculated and a suitable size of heatsink then selected using the chart of figure 11.21.

Example 11.6: Heatsink selection

The TIP 31 BJT in the regulator of example 11.5 is required to dissipate up to 4.33 W. If the regulator must function satisfactorily for ambient temperatures up to 50°C, select a suitable heatsink.

From the TIP 31 data sheet (appendix E, section E.6), $T_j$max = 150°C, $R_{th(j-c)} = 3.125$°C/W and $R_{th(j-amb)} = 62.5$°C/W.

Without a heatsink, at $T_{amb} = 25$°C, from equation 11.93, the maximum allowable power dissipation is

$$P_{max} = \frac{150°\text{C} - 25°\text{C}}{62.5°\text{C/W}} = 2\ \text{W}$$

which is the quoted 'free air' value and clearly indicates that a heatsink is required in this application.

To safely dissipate 4.33 W in an ambient having a maximum temperature of 50°C, the maximum thermal resistance from junction to ambient is

$$R_{th(j-amb)}\max = \frac{150°\text{C} - 50°\text{C}}{4.33\ \text{W}} = 23.095°\text{C/W}$$

using equation 11.93. But $R_{th(j-case)}$ is 3.125°C/W for the BJT and so the maximum allowable case to ambient value is

$$R_{th(c-amb)}\max = 23.095°\text{C/W} - 3.125°\text{C/W} = 19.97°\text{C/W}$$

Since the effective value two thermal resistances in parallel is lower than the individual values, a safety margin is included if the heatsink is assumed to provide all the thermal resistance from case to ambient; thus select the heatsink to have a thermal resistance of 20°C/W. Note that the effect of the heat sink being shunted by $R_{th(c-amb)}$ of the BJT (= 62.5°C/W − 3.125°C/W = 59.375°C/W) will in fact reduce the combined case–ambient value to 20°C/W // 59.375°C/W ≃ 15°C/W, providing a safety margin.

For a bright, vertically positioned, flat aluminium sheet heatsink of thickness 1 mm, the chart of figure 11.21 shows that the TIP 31 in a TO 220 style package requires a heatsink area of only about 16 cm^2 to allow safe operation at the power level of 4.33 W.

Improvements to the basic series voltage regulator

Performance can be improved by replacing the single pass transistor by a Darlington pair such as the T_1, T_2 combinations of figures 6.7a, c. The high current gain of the Darlington combination (equation 6.37) means that the base current requirement is substantially reduced, as is the variation of base current with load current. Thus the reference diode current variation is reduced and the 'speed of correction' when the load changes is increased, improving output

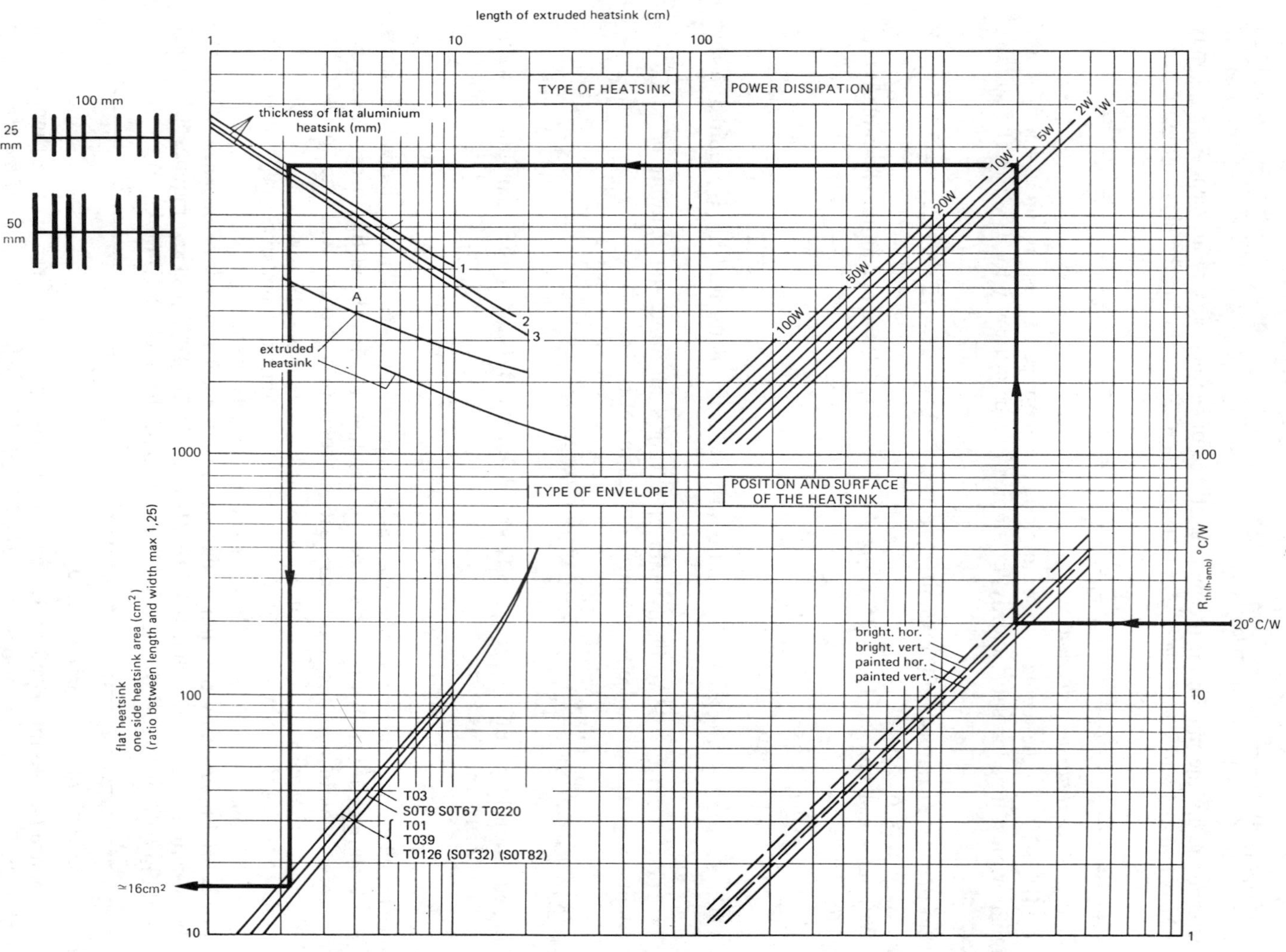

Figure 11.21 Heatsink selection (*courtesy of Philips, formerly Mullard, Limited*)

regulation. Typical of available Darlington devices are the 40 W, 6 A BD 679 having $h_{FE} > 2200$ and the 125 W, 12 A BDV 65 having $h_{FE} > 1000$. In circuit design using npn–npn Darlingtons (figure 6.7a) allowance must be made for the double V_{BE} voltage drop between 'base' and 'emitter'. This increased voltage drop compared with a single pass transistor does not occur with the complementary npn–pnp Darlington of figure 6.7c.

Ripple performance can be improved by shunting the reference diode by a capacitor C'. For the small-signal model of figure 11.16e, which applies to the series regulator if the base–emitter voltage is assumed constant, with C' across r_z equation 11.76 becomes

$$\Delta v_L = \left[\frac{r_z /\!/ R_L /\!/ X_{C'}}{R_1 + (r_z /\!/ R_L /\!/ X_{C'})}\right] \Delta v_I \qquad (11.94)$$

where $X_{C'}$ is the reactance of C' at the frequency of the dominant ripple component which is twice the mains input frequency for full-wave rectification (figure 11.11b). If C' is selected so that $X_{C'} \ll r_z$ and R_1, equation 11.94 reduces to

$$\frac{\Delta v_L}{\Delta v_I} \simeq \left|\frac{X_{C'}}{R_1}\right| = \frac{1}{2\pi(2f)C'R_1} \qquad (11.95)$$

where f is the mains frequency.

Considerable improvement is provided by the introduction of negative feedback as in the arrangement of figure 11.22 in which T_2 acts as a feedback amplifier. Circuit operation is similar to that of the basic single transistor series regulator of figure 11.19a but here a change of R_L causes both the emitter *and* base potentials of the pass transistor (T_1) to change, so magnifying the change of base–emitter voltage compared with that for the basic circuit in which the base potential is 'fixed'. If R_L reduces, for example, v_L instantaneously falls and with it the emitter potential of T_1. With v_L falling, the base–emitter voltage of T_2 also falls via the R', R'' potential divider so that the level of conduction of T_2 is reduced and its collector potential, which is the base potential of T_1, rises. This 'double action' of the emitter potential of T_1 falling and its base potential rising means that v_{BE_1} rises more rapidly than in the basic circuit, providing a more rapid response to load variation and thereby improving regulation.

An alternative way to appreciate this improvement is to consider the two-transistor regulator as a feedback amplifier with T_1, R_1, R_L forming the forward amplifier, using the terminology of chapter 5, and the remainder of the circuit (T_2, R', R'', R_2 and the reference diode) providing *voltage* negative feedback. Equation 5.30 shows that shunt (voltage) sampling reduces the circuit output resistance; the reduction in R_O provides an improvement in regulation (equation 11.82).

Circuit design follows a similar process to that for the basic series regulator (example 11.5) except the base potential of the pass transistor ($v_L + v_{BE_1}$) is shared between v_Z and v_{CE_2}, the base potential of T_2 ($= v_L R''/(R' + R'')$ by potential division) being designed to be $v_Z + v_{BE_2}$. Knowing the nominal value of $V_{L(AV)}$, a diode is selected providing $V_Z \simeq V_{L(AV)}/2$ so that $V_{L(AV)} + V_{BE_1}$ is split approximately equally between T_2 and the diode. Sense current i' must be $\gg i_{B_2}$ for the R', R'' chain to act as a basic divider, corresponding to point (4) preceding equation 3.19 concerning BJT biasing. However i' should be $\ll I_{L(AV)}$max otherwise overall power efficiency will be poor. Resistor R_1 provides $i_{B_1} + i_{C_2}$, see-saw action occurring between i_{B_1} and i_{C_2} as v_I and i_L fluctuate corresponding to the action of R_1 in the basic circuit providing $i_B + i_Z$. Resistor R_2 provides a bias current for the diode which helps stabilise the diode operating point. As i_{C_2} rises, for example, i_Z and hence v_Z rise, but v_Z rising causes i_2 to fall so reducing the change in i_Z ($= i_{C_2} + i_2$).

Because of the degree of uncertainty as to the nominal value of v_{CE_2}, caused by the choice of preferred values for R', R'' and the parameter spread of T_2, it is not usually possible to provide the required output voltage to within a narrow tolerance. It is therefore common to provide a degree of adjustment, called *trimming*, by including a potentiometer in the feedback loop, as VR_1 in figure 11.22. The maximum resistance of the potentiometer is chosen typically as about 5 per cent of $(R' + R'')$.

If a variable output supply is required, the sense branch can be completely replaced by a potentiometer as in the circuit of figure 11.23. Notice that if it is required that the output is variable down to zero, a negative supply is required since, for the regulator to function, the output potential relative to the diode anode has to be $> v_Z$. In the circuit shown, electrolytic capacitors C_1 provide the main (low frequency) smoothing at the regulator input. The series resistance of high-value electrolytic capacitors renders them ineffective at high frequency and so low-loss capacitors C_2 are included to remove any superimposed high-frequency noise. These low-loss capacitors are commonly polycarbonate type (section 2.4.2) of value less than 1 μF; note that at *high* frequency, only a low value of capacitance is required to provide a low impedance path.

The series regulator circuits considered above have assumed the common supply line between input and output to be the negative line and correspondingly the emitter-follower employs an npn BJT. If it is necessary to make the positive line common, making v_I and v_L numerically negative, the same circuits can be used if the BJTs are replaced by pnp types.

It has been explained above that the performance of the series voltage regulator is improved by the introduction of a feedback amplifier. Performance is further improved if the gain of the feedback amplifier is increased so making the circuit more sensitive to change of output voltage, increasing the speed of correction. Compared with the circuit of figure 11.22, the feedback gain can be increased by replacing T_2 by a high-gain differential stage corresponding to figure 6.6a in which the inputs to the two bases are provided, respectively, by the voltage reference and the output sensing network, while the loaded collector provides control of the base drive to the pass transistor. Commercial integrated regulators use this configuration,

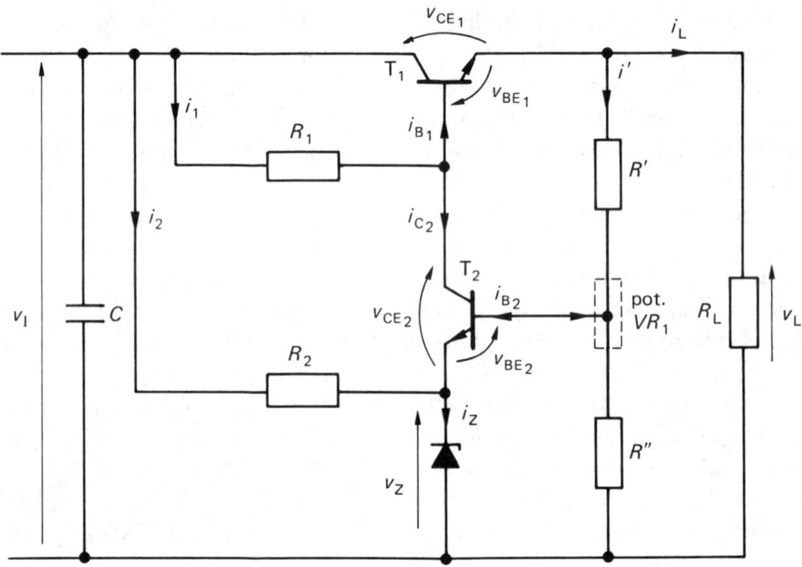

Figure 11.22 Series voltage regulator with a negative feedback

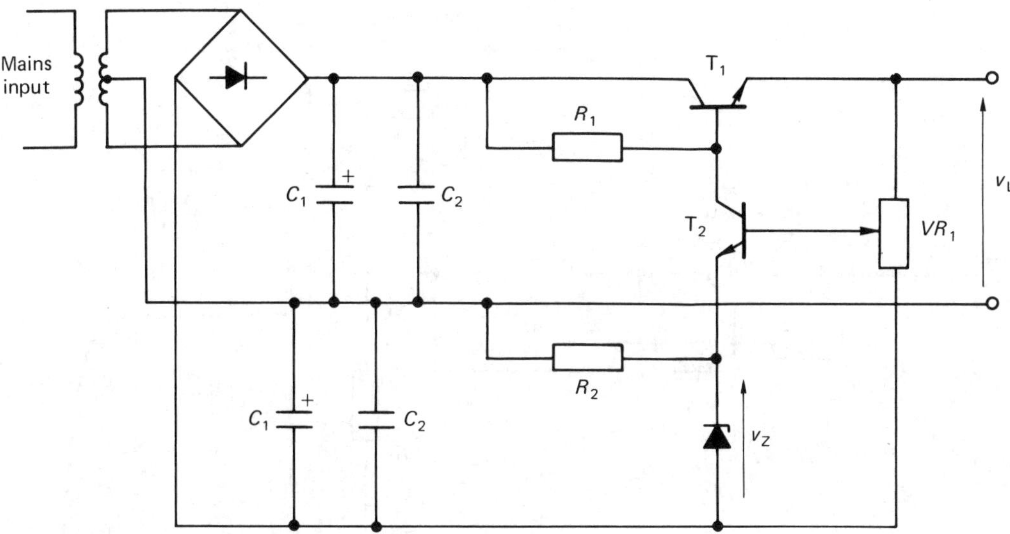

Figure 11.23 Stabilised ac–dc supply with variable output

often with the differential transistors both being Darlington arrangements. Even higher feedback gain can be achieved using an op-amp in place of the differential stage, either driving the control transistor T_2 (figure 11.22) or to drive the pass transistor T_1 directly. Integrated regulators are readily available with output current ratings in the range 100 mA to 10 A, the higher current types usually requiring the connection of some external components. Most cope with a wide input voltage range and provide load regulation better than 1 per cent with ripple rejection better than 50 dB.

The transistorised regulators discussed in this section are termed *linear* regulators because the BJTs are operating in their linear (active) mode, allowing the conduction of the pass transistor to be continuously adjusted to cope with the demand of the load. This continuous conduction mode is the major disadvantage of this type of regulator in that considerable power is dissipated in the pass transistor, reducing overall efficiency. It is this disadvantage that has encouraged the development of switched-mode techniques as discussed in section 11.2.6.

11.2.5 *Current limiting and protection*

To protect the pass transistor in the regulator and/or the load being driven, it is necessary to sense the load current and take effective action when the limiting value is reached. Fuses and resetable thermal switches are inconvenient, imprecise and do not operate sufficiently rapidly to protect semiconductor equipment.

Figure 11.24a shows the essential features of an automatic limit incorporated in a linear regulator. The limit circuit comprises a low-value resistor *R*, which may be variable, through which the load current passes and the voltage developed across R $(= i_L R)$ controls the conduction of T_3. The value of R is such that at the maximum allowed value of load current $I_L$max, v_R is equal to the threshold voltage V_γ (figure 2.3c) of T_3. As the current reaches its upper limit, therefore, T_3 begins to conduct, shunting base drive away from the pass transistor

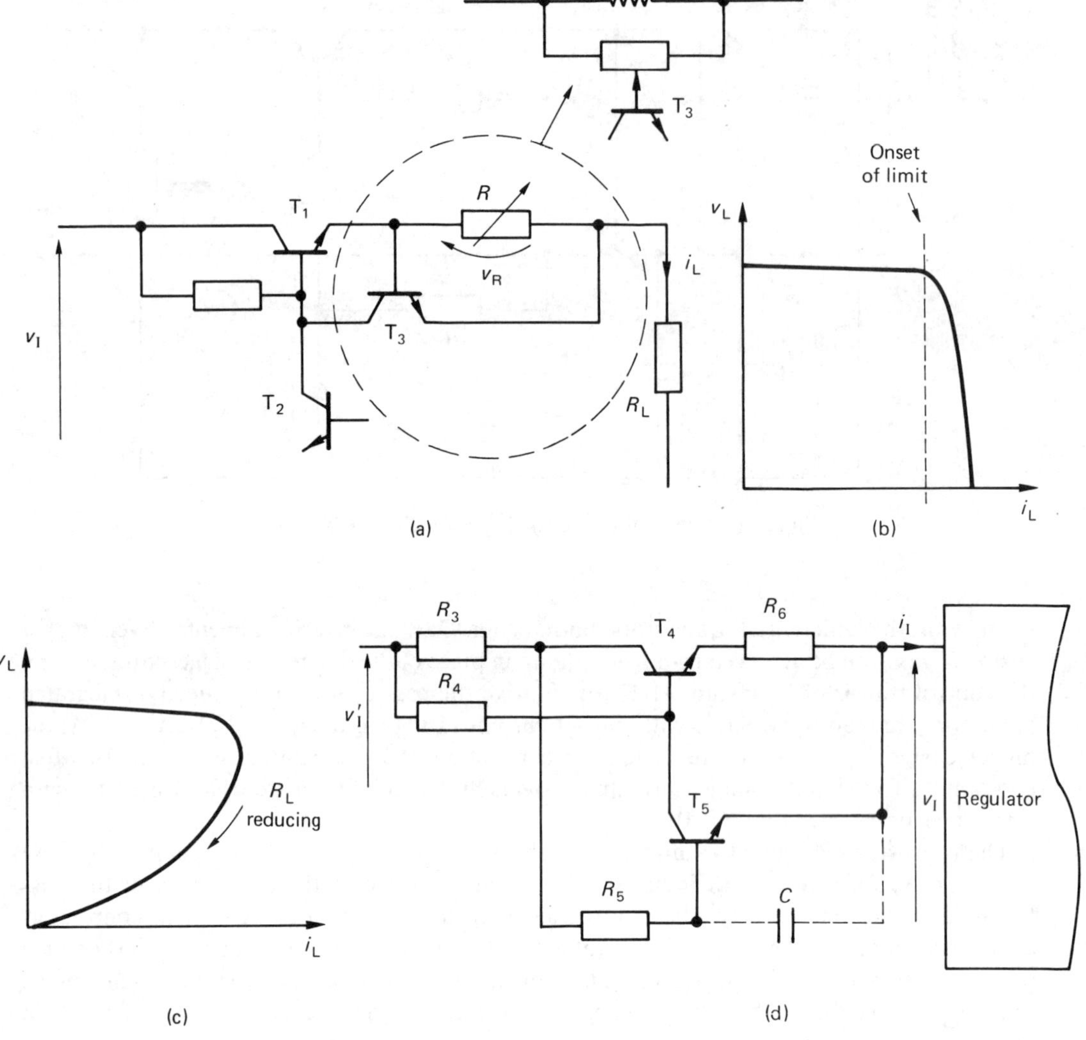

Figure 11.24 Current limiting and protection

T_1 and so limiting its level of conduction. This results in the output characteristic of figure 11.24b. Note that, in practice, because of the difficulty of obtaining a low-value, high-current potentiometer, the R, T_3 arrangement is usually implemented using a current shunt as shown in the insert in figure 11.24a.

This basic protection arrangement has the disadvantage that during the limiting process, as v_L falls, the voltage v_{CE_1} across the pass transistor rises and if the output is shorted the full input voltage v_I falls across T_1. As the current flow remains approximately constant at the limited value, the power dissipation in T_1 increases substantially which may cause damage. To protect the pass transistor it is necessary to provide a 'foldback' limit in which the load current falls with the load voltage (figure 11.24c). This performance characteristic can be implemented by the circuit of figure 11.24d connected in series with the regulator. For i_I less than the limited value, circuit values are selected to ensure T_4 is saturated and the voltage $(V_{CE_4(sat)} + v_{R_6})$ is not high enough to cause T_5 to conduct. The voltage 'loss' across this circuit is then $V_{CE_4(sat)} + i_I(R_3 + R_6)$ which must be compensated by a higher output from the transformer–rectifier–smoothing stage. At the onset of limiting, v_{R_6} is sufficient to cause T_5 to begin to switch ON, diverting base drive from T_4 which comes out of saturation, and v_{CE_4} rises so turning T_5 ON harder. Current flow progressively transfers from C→E of T_4 to C→E and B→E of T_5, the flow through T_5 being made small by careful component selection, resulting in a foldback characteristic. Capacitor C can be included to provide discrimination between short- and long-term overloads.

11.2.6 *Switched-mode techniques*

At cut-off the current I_C through a BJT is approximately zero while at saturation the voltage V_{CE} across the transistor is very low (section 2.3.3), and so in either state the power dissipated in the BJT ($\simeq V_{CE}I_C$, equation 2.16) is very low. Therefore, by operating the pass transistor in a regulator as a switch instead of as a linear amplifier, power dissipation within the regulator can be reduced and overall power efficiency greatly increased.

Figure 11.25 shows the essential features of a switching regulator. The op-amp acts as a comparator (section 7.3.2) giving a high or low output depending on whether $(V_Z - v_L)$ is positive or negative. If $v_L < V_Z$, the control voltage v_C is positive, the pass transistor T_1 is switched ON, voltage v_I is applied to the LC filter causing C to charge and v_L rises. As soon as v_L exceeds V_Z, T_1 switches OFF, the energy stored in the inductor decays via the 'free-wheel' diode D_1, C starts to discharge through R_L and v_L falls, and then the cycle repeats. The load voltage therefore fluctuates slightly, the degree of ripple depending on the switching performance of the op-amp and pass transistor. The LC smoothing circuit functions as

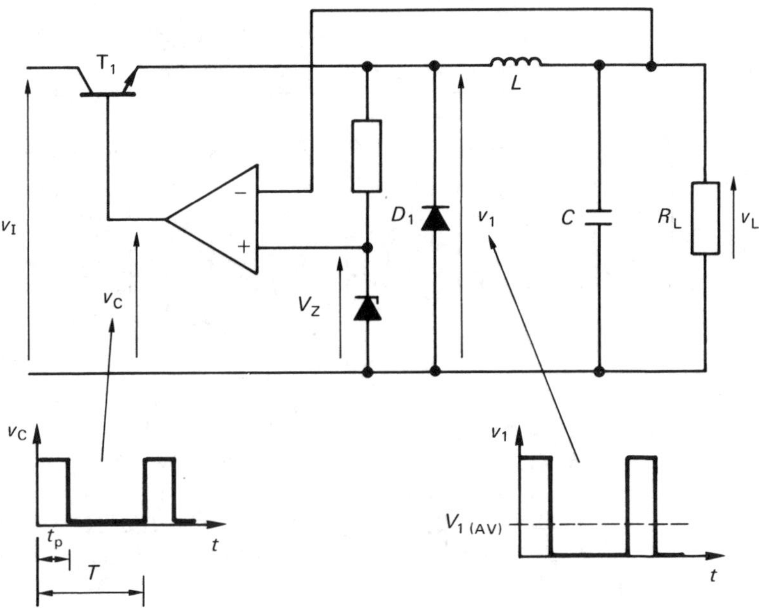

Figure 11.25 Switching regulator

described in section 11.2.3 although here the input v_1 is a pulse waveform in place of the rectified sinewave in a linear power supply. Another important difference is that the switching frequency is typically in the range 10–100 kHz; this high operating frequency means that only relatively small values of L and C are required, typically 1 mH and 10 μF. The duty cycle ($d = t_p/T$) of the switching waveform depends on the value of v_I relative to the reference voltage V_Z; the LC filter makes $V_{L(AV)} \simeq V_{1(AV)}$, assuming the choke resistance is small.

The switched-mode principle has been extended to provide smaller, cheaper, lighter, more efficient ac–dc supplies than the traditional mains transformer–rectifier–filter–regulator supplies considered above. A major disadvantage of the traditional power supply is the relatively heavy, costly input transformer which, operating at mains (low) frequency, has a substantial power loss. Figure 11.26 gives a block diagram representation of a switched-mode ac–dc power supply (SMPS) showing that the mains input is rectified, without prior transformation, and the output is then smoothed to provide an approximately constant, high-value voltage at XX. Using a transistor switching circuit operating typically at 100 kHz, this constant input is *chopped* to produce a high-amplitude pulse waveform. A transformer then provides amplitude changing as required but because it is operating at high frequency, a small, light, ferrite-cored transformer can be used which has a low power loss. The transformer output is then rectified and smoothed, typically using an LC filter, to provide v_L. As for the switching regulator described above, only modest values of L and C are required because of the high operating frequency. Feedback to control the duty cycle of the switching circuit provides both output voltage control and regulation for change of load, so that a separate regulator stage is not required. This type of supply is now widely used, particularly in mains-powered portable equipment for which power supply size and weight are of major importance. The main disadvantage of switched-mode techniques is that the rapidly changing currents in the switching stage cause significantly more electromagnetic interference than the mains 'hum' associated with traditional supplies, and so effective screening is very important.

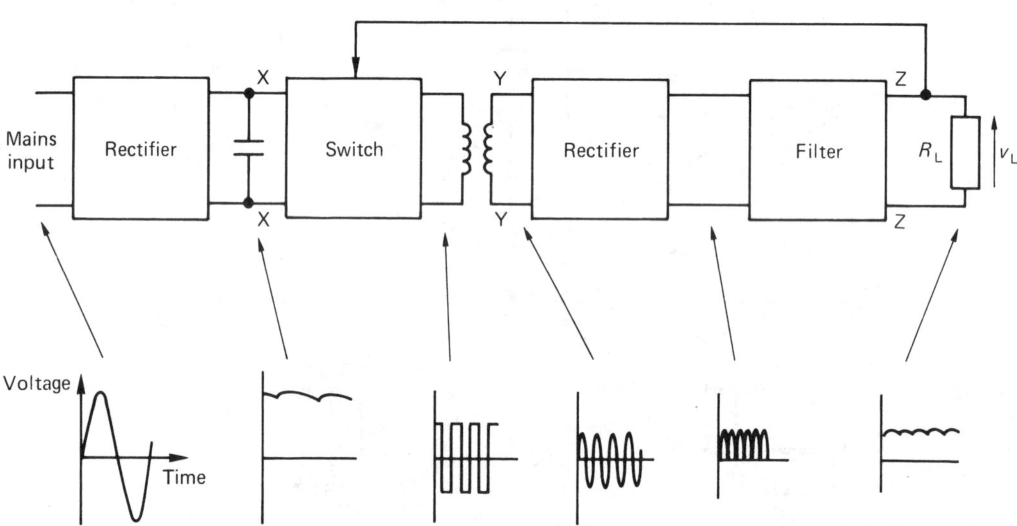

Figure 11.26 Block diagram representation of a switched-mode ac–dc power supply

11.3 DC–AC supplies

A power supply that generates an alternating output from a dc source is called an *inverter*. Applications range from those having a low-power requirement such as powering fluorescent lighting from a vehicle battery to high-power standby systems required to provide a replacement ac supply, in the event of a mains failure, for essential services such as hospitals and vital computer installations.

Inverters consist basically of a switching circuit to generate a pulse waveform from the dc source and, depending on the quality of output required, a low-pass filter may be incorporated to provide a sinusoidal output having low harmonic distortion. This arrangement is represented in figure 11.27a in which the switch may be a BJT with the drive waveform provided by a free-running oscillator; the transformer provides either voltage step-up or step-down depending on the relative values of V_{DC} and V_{ac}. In some applications such as powering fluorescent lighting from a 12 V vehicle battery, the frequency of the ac output is not critical and therefore a high-frequency output in the range 20–100 kHz is provided, permitting the use of a small, low-loss ferrite core transformer. Additionally, the purity of the output waveshape is of little significance and therefore it is unlikely that any filtering would be included. Note that this inverter forms the section XX–YY of the switched-mode supply of figure 11.26.

At high power levels, switching is usually performed using thyristors [1c]; available devices have ratings of ON state current and OFF state voltage in the range 1 A, 400 V to 1.5 kA, 4 kV. Figure 11.27b shows a basic biphase thyristor inverter, the thyristors being switched

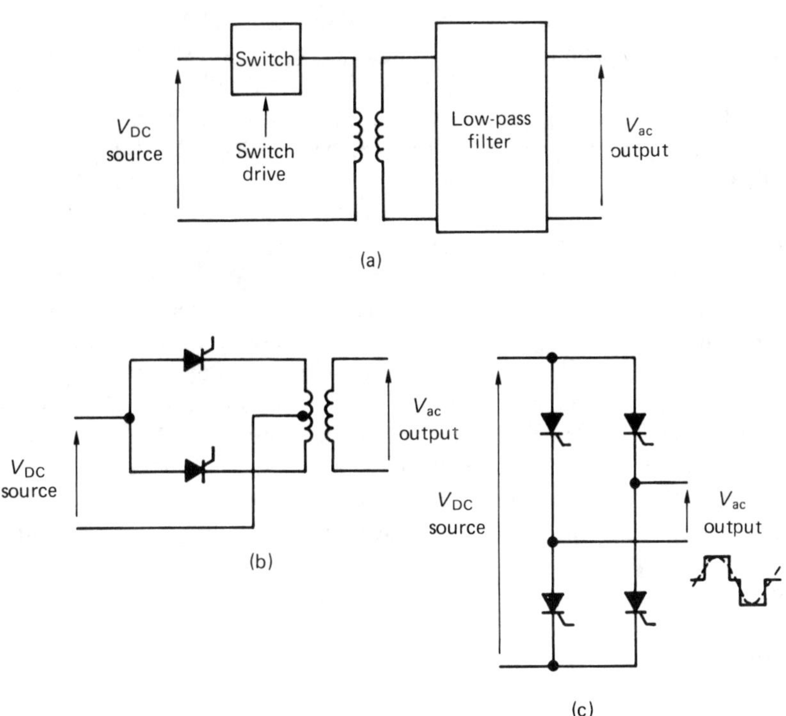

Figure 11.27 Basics of inverter power supplies

ON and OFF in antiphase at the required frequency by externally-generated drive waveforms applied to the gates. In the popular bridge arrangement of figure 11.27c diagonal thyristors are switched together, the two diagonals being switched in antiphase. To ensure that the thyristors are never all switched ON at the same time, the gate drive signals are such that all thyristors are OFF for a short interval between the positive and negative pulses; the sinusoidal fundamental of the output waveform is shown dashed.

Design of practical power inverters is highly specialised, particularly at high power levels where device protection is also of fundamental importance. Some loads require an *uninterruptible* power supply (UPS) in which the standby inverter supply must take over from the mains supply instantaneously at a mains failure, matching amplitude, frequency and phase to within close tolerances; such requirements place a considerable demand on the expertise of the designer. This type of supply is usually specified for vital computer installations in which loss of the supply voltage even for only a very short period may cause major data corruption. In addition to these severe constraints on inverter performance, most practical loads are reactive which creates further design problems. Detailed consideration of inverter design and performance can be found in references [2], [3a] and [4].

11.4 DC–DC supplies

Power supplies that provide a dc output from a dc source of different voltage are termed dc *converters*; they are further described as step-up or step-down depending on whether the output voltage is higher or lower, respectively, than the source voltage. The linear regulators of section 11.2.4 are step-down converters providing a dc output from a higher dc input. Design follows the same procedure as that outlined in section 11.2.4, the range of input voltage $V_I\text{max}$ to $V_I\text{min}$ being determined by the regulation of the source; for a battery source this range would be given by the start-of-life no-load and end-of-life full-load terminal voltages of the battery. The switching regulator of section 11.2.6 is also a step-down converter in which the pass transistor can be replaced by a thyristor with its associated gate drive circuit.

Figure 11.28 gives two further examples of switching dc converters. In the 'ringing choke' version of figure 11.28a, when the switch is ON, the source voltage is applied across L and the current through it increases linearly (equation 2.33). When the switch is OFF, current continues to flow through the choke–diode–load circuit but it reduces as the choke energy falls. Thus the capacitor provides the load current while the switch is ON, and while the switch is OFF the choke energy is restored, the capacitor recharged and the load current provided from the source. The ratio of output to source voltage is equal to the ratio of the period of the switching waveform to the OFF time of the switch [3b]; the switch is either a BJT or a thyristor. The transformer-coupled converter of figure 11.28b provides either step-up or step-down operation depending on the transformer turns ratio n being less than or greater than unity. Notice this arrangement forms the section XX–ZZ of the switched-mode ac–dc supply of figure 11.26. Detailed treatment of switching dc power converters can be found in reference [3b].

11.5 Voltage multiplication

High-voltage, low-current dc supplies can be provided economically from an ac source using diode–capacitor multiplier arrangements. The basic voltage *doubler* is represented by the

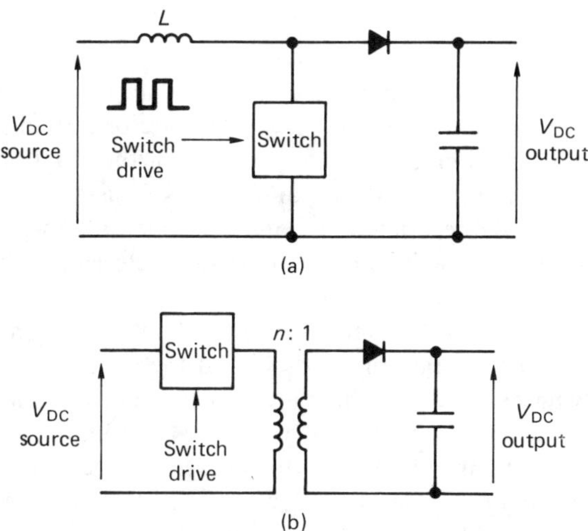

Figure 11.28 Switching dc power converters

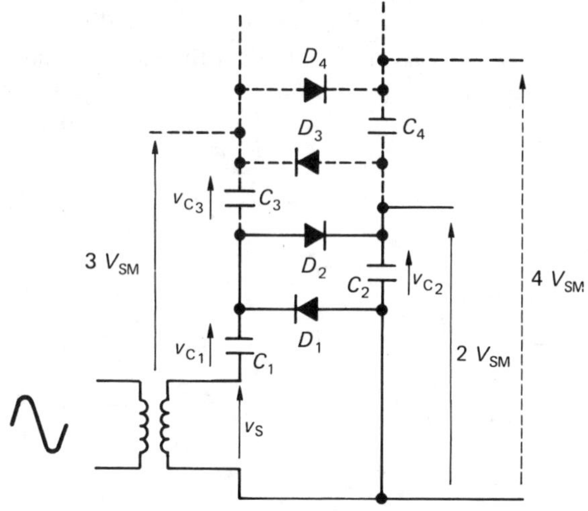

Figure 11.29 Voltage multiplication

full-line circuit of figure 11.29. During the first negative half-cycle of the ac source voltage v_S, capacitor C_1 charges to $v_{C_1} = V_{SM}$ via diode D_1, where V_{SM} is the amplitude of v_S. During the next (positive) half-cycle, C_2 charges to $v_{C_1} + V_{SM}$ via D_2 so that v_{C_2} becomes $2V_{SM}$, providing a dc output that is twice the amplitude of the ac input. By extending the diode–capacitor ladder as shown dashed in figure 11.29, voltage *tripler* and *quadrupler* circuits are formed. Having established $2V_{SM}$ across C_2, D_3 conducts on the next negative half-cycle of v_S and $v_{C_1} + v_{C_3}$ becomes $v_{C_2} + V_{SM}$ which is $3V_{SM}$; correspondingly, with D_4 and C_4 added, a $4V_{SM}$ output is provided on the next positive half-cycle of v_S. Note that with the exception of C_1, each capacitor acquires a voltage $2V_{SM}$ and the voltage rating of the capacitors must be chosen accordingly. This technique can be extended to provide a very high voltage output from an ac source of only modest amplitude.

11.6 Batteries

Batteries store electricity chemically and are convenient dc power sources, particularly for portable equipment. They rely on the *electrochemical* nature of certain reactions whereby the net steady-state electronic requirements of the products of the reaction differ from those of the reactants, resulting in an excess or deficit of electrons. This causes a potential difference across the interface between the reacting materials, the value of the voltage depending on the extent of the electronic excess or deficit and is therefore characteristic of the particular materials involved.

The reaction between materials M_1 and M_2 (figure 11.30a) is such that M_1 acquires an excess of electrons (e^-) as the reaction proceeds so that the voltage V_{12} is negative. Similarly, another reaction involving M_2 in which there is a shortage of electrons, as with material M_3 (figure 11.30b), results in a positive voltage V_{32}. With M_2 common to both these reactions, they can be combined as in figure 11.30c and the voltage between the *electrodes* (plates) V_{31} is $(V_{32} - V_{12})$. M_2 is a conducting solution, termed the *electrolyte*, which decomposes by electrolysis into ions M_2^+ and M_2^-.

If a load R_L is connected between the terminals as in figure 11.30d, the excess electrons on M_1 are forced to flow through the load by the voltage V_{12}. The flow, which tends to offset the deficit of electrons on M_3, develops an electrical power IV_{31} in R_L; note that conventional current flow I from higher to lower potential is in the opposite direction to electron flow. The positive terminal *out of which current flows* is termed the *cathode* and the negative terminal *into which current flows* is the *anode*. This basic M_1, M_2, M_3 arrangement is termed a *cell*;

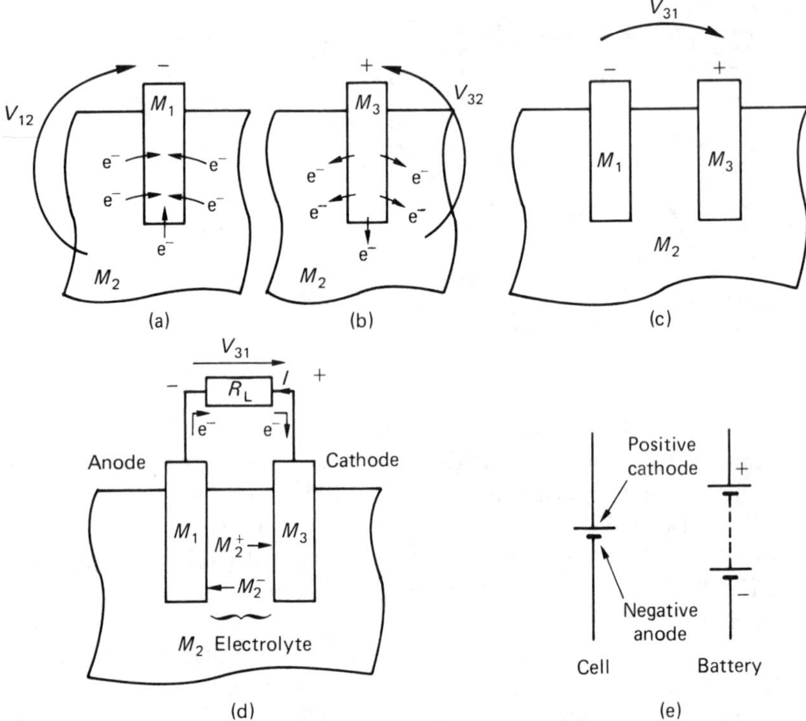

Figure 11.30 Battery reactions and circuit symbols

a *battery* is a series and/or parallel combination of basic cells providing increased terminal voltage and/or current capability. Circuit symbols are shown in figure 11.30e.

Under load, the removal of electrons from M_1 and their addition to M_2 upsets the initial (no load) equilibrium, causing the chemical reactions to continue and thus maintaining the current flow. The circuit is completed within the electrolyte by the transfer of charge via the ions M_2^+ and M_2^-. M_2^- ions move to the anode and react with M_1 according to the *anode reaction*

$$M_1 + M_2^- \rightarrow P_{12} + \bar{e}s \tag{11.96}$$

where P_{12} represents the reaction products and $\bar{e}s$ the excess electrons. M_2^+ ions move to the *cathode* and react with M_3 creating products P_{23}. These products require additional electrons which are drawn in from the external circuit maintaining the flow; the *cathode* reaction is thus

$$M_3 + M_2^+ + \bar{e}s \rightarrow P_{23} \tag{11.97}$$

The role of the electrolyte is thus to provide the ions that take part in the anode and cathode reactions, and for good performance the electrolyte must have a high ionic conductivity. During operation, the active electrode materials M_1 and M_3 are progressively converted to the products P_{12} and P_{23}, a process termed *discharge*.

Anodes are usually metallic, lead, zinc, cadmium, lithium and iron being the most common, while cathodes are commonly metal oxides, notably oxides of lead, manganese, mercury and silver, but also including nickel hydroxide. Electrolytes are commonly aqueous solutions of acids or alkalis such as sulphuric acid, potassium hydroxide and sodium hydroxide, of concentration typically in the range 20–45 per cent. Ammonium and zinc chlorides are also widely used.

Battery types

There are two basic types of battery: *disposable* types which are useless once the electrode materials are exhausted, and *rechargeable* types for which the anode and cathode reactions are reversible, the materials M_1 and M_3 being reformed if a reverse (charging) current is passed through the battery. Disposable types are also called *primary* batteries as the generated current is a direct effect of the chemical reaction between the original plate and electrolyte materials. Rechargeable types are termed *secondary* as the reactions can only take place after an initial 'forming' process which creates a layer of active material on the 'carrier' plate. This process involves one or more charge–discharge cycles.

Batteries are also classified as *wet* or *dry* and as *vented* or *sealed*. In wet types the electrolyte is in liquid form as in the lead–acid type widely used in traction and standby storage applications. So-called dry construction immobilises the electrolyte in the form of a paste or gel in a separator material. The reactions in rechargeable cells liberate hydrogen and/or oxygen, a process termed *gassing*. In vented types the gas is released to the atmosphere, while in sealed construction the battery case is designed to withstand the pressure, care being taken in battery design to minimise the degree of gassing.

Battery performance

The main performance parameters are:

Energy W, which is the available electrical energy in joules (J) or watt-hours (Wh) from a battery and depends on the particular materials involved and their contact area.

Power P is the available rate of supply of electrical energy in watts (W) under load.,

Energy density ρ. This is a figure-of-merit for a battery, describing the available energy per unit weight or volume in W h/kg or W h/m^3. Power density in W/kg or W/m^3 is also used. Values are quoted at a specific rate of discharge.

Capacity C. The available charge in the fully-charged state is expressed as the current × time product in *ampere-hours* (A h). A 1 A h battery can theoretically supply 1 A at the particular terminal voltage of the battery for 1 h, or 500 mA for 2 h, or 2 A for 0.5 h, and so on. In practice, battery voltage falls during discharge (figure 11.31a) and an end-of-life (primary) or end-of-charge (secondary) point is quoted, usually at a certain ambient temperature.

Rate of charge/discharge. Charge/discharge currents are normally specified in terms of capacity. For example, a *drain* of 200 mA from a 5 A h battery is described as a discharge at the 25 h or 0.04C rate; a 5 A h battery can theoretically supply 200 mA for 25 h. The capacity $C(=5$ A h) provides a theoretical discharge capability of 5 A for 1 h so that a 5 A discharge is described as the 1C rate for a 5 A h battery; a discharge of 200 mA is 1/25th of this rate and is therefore referred to as the 0.04C rate. Correspondingly, 100 h, 50 h, 20 h, 10 h, 5 h, 2 h, 1 h, 0.5 h charge/discharge rates correspond to rates of 0.01C, 0.02C, 0.05C, 0.1C, 0.2C, 0.5C, 1C, 2C respectively; note that in each case the product of the rates in terms of hours and capacity is unity.

Internal resistance. Battery resistance is important because it reduces the terminal voltage under load and causes wasteful power loss, resulting in higher internal temperature. Resistance depends on cell materials, construction, size, state of charge, temperature and type of load (steady or pulsed). Typical values range from about 1 mΩ for a high-capacity fully-charged liquid electrolyte battery to 5 Ω or more for a miniature dry 'button' cell.

Shelf life. A charged battery slowly discharges even on no load because of internal reactions; the rate of this *self discharge* determines the charge (capacity) retention or shelf life of the battery. Shelf life, which is dependent on storage temperature, may be defined as the time for the battery capacity to fall to 90 per cent of its original value.

Figure 11.31 provides an overall comparison of battery performance. The discharge characteristic of most types follows the pattern of figure 11.31a; after an initial fall from the no-load value, a 'plateau' region is reached which is the working range of the battery. If the discharge rate (drain) is increased, the working life is shortened and the voltage droop over the working range increases. As the cell becomes exhausted, the internal resistance increases and the terminal voltage falls sharply.

Shelf life is represented in figure 11.31b which shows that the capacity of an open-circuit battery decreases with time from the newly-produced/freshly-charged (100 per cent) value; the rate of decline increases with temperature. Note that for rechargeable types, the freshly-charged capacity progressively decreases with number of charge–discharge cycles.

For rechargeable batteries, the terminal voltage rises during charging as represented in figure 11.31c; charging beyond the rated capacity is termed *overcharging* during which the internal temperature of the battery rises sharply in a sealed cell while in a vented type water decomposes and the cell gasses.

Figure 11.31d compares the discharge characteristics of popular primary cells for medium loading. The general-purpose market is catered for by the standard-power (SP) range of zinc–manganese/carbon Leclanché cells for low-to-medium drain applications and the high-power (HP) range of zinc chloride–manganese/carbon Leclanché cells for higher drain uses; a *medium* drain is taken typically as the 0.01C rate for 1 h/day. The shelf life of these types is quoted as up to 18 months at 20°C. The use of the zinc chloride electrolyte in the HP cell in place of the ammonium chloride/zinc chloride combination in the SP cell reduces 'electrode blocking' by reaction products at higher current densities but introduces greater demands on the cell seal. Alkaline–manganese batteries are a better quality general-purpose product.

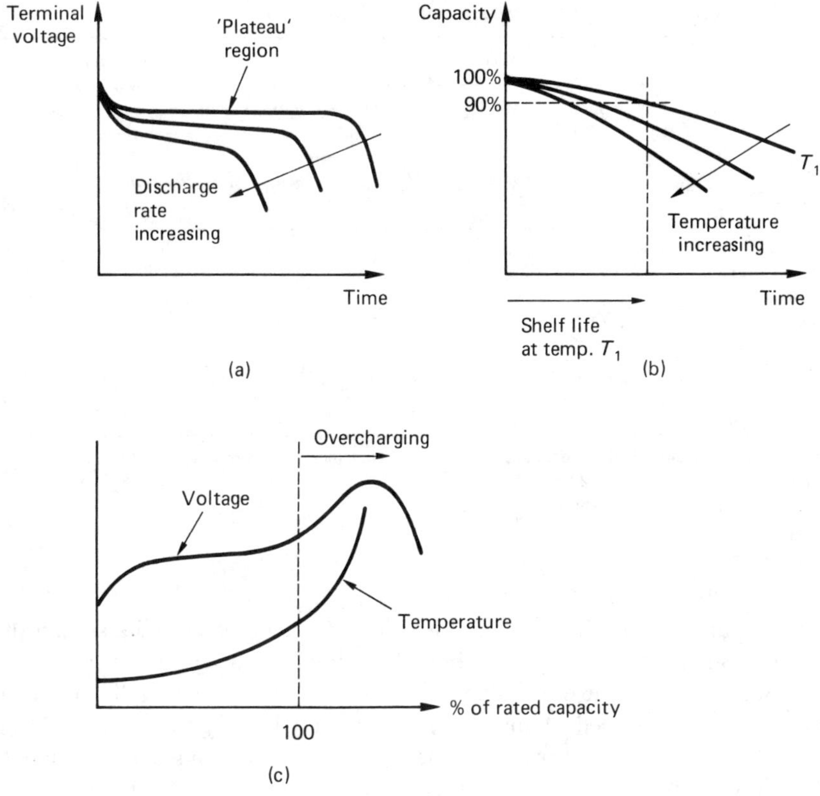

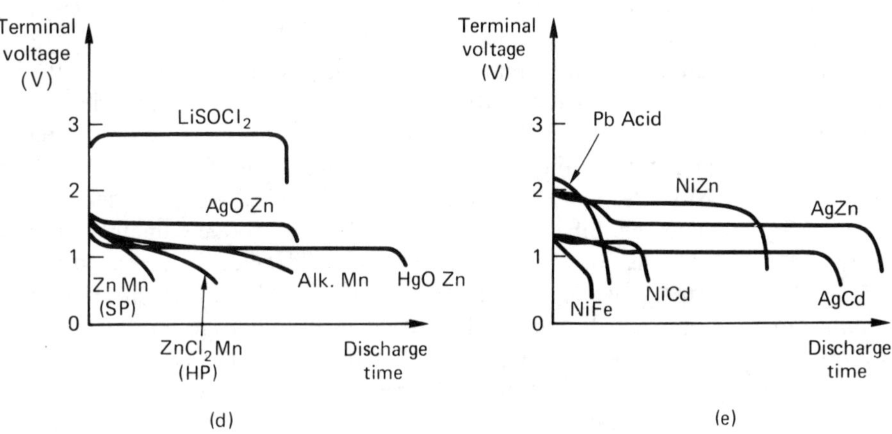

Figure 11.31 Battery performance

For the same physical size battery, the capacity of the alkaline type is approximately twice that of the Leclanché version but the cost is also approximately double, so that the capacity/cost ratio is about the same for the two types. However the alkaline battery has the advantages of a longer shelf life, typically 36 months at 20°C, and lower voltage droop over the working range.

Table 11.2 Designation and capacities of some popular battery sizes

Size Name/code	Primary batteries: Leclanché ZnMn (1.5 V) IEC‡ code	Capacity* (A h)	Primary batteries: Alkaline-Manganese (1.5 V) IEC‡ code	Capacity* (A h)	Secondary batteries Nickel–Cadmium (1.2 V) Capacity* (A h)	Charge rate (mA) for 14 h (non-continuous)
Slim penlight/AAA (ANSI†)	R03	0.4	LR03	0.8	0.18	17
Penlight/AA (ANSI†)	R6	1	LR6	2.2	0.5	50
Baby/C (ANSI†)	R14	2.5	LR14	7	2.2	200
Mono/D (ANSI†)	R20	5.5	LR20	15	4	400
Power Packs (9 V) PP3	6F22	0.3	6LF22	0.5	8.4 V 0.11	11
Power Packs (9 V) PP9	6F100	4	6LF100	6	8.4 V 1.2	120

* Capacities are a function of drain and temperature, also quoted capacities vary from one manufacturer to another. Figures shown are typical for a moderate drain at 20 °C.
† ANSI: American National Standards Institute.
‡ IEC: International Electrotechnical Commission.

The International Electrotechnical Commission (IEC) have produced a standard designation system for primary batteries [5] describing the voltage, capacity, dimensions and terminal arrangement. Sole code letter R indicates a cylindrical Leclanché 1.5 V cell while a numerical prefix shows the number of cells connected in series in a battery; thus code 3R refers to a $3 \times 1.5\text{ V} = 4.5\text{ V}$ battery. Cylindrical alkaline–manganese cells have the designation LR. The number following the letter code relates to the cell/battery capacity, the larger the number the larger the drain capability. Code F refers to flat cells which result in a rectangular shape battery such as the 6F22 and 6LF22 PP3 types of $6 \times 1.5\text{ V} = 9\text{ V}$. Table 11.2 gives the IEC codes and typical capacities for some popular sizes of Leclanché and alkaline batteries.

Lithium, silver and mercury-based primary cells are characterised by a wide, flat plateau and good shelf life, but the cost/capacity ratio is high. Lithium thionyl chloride ($LiSOCl_2$) cells are exceptional, having a high working terminal voltage (2.8 V), high power/weight and power/volume ratios typically three times the corresponding ratios of Leclanché types and a long shelf life of up to 10 years; however, the cost is high, typically eight times that of the equivalent capacity alkaline cell. Silver and mercury cells are produced mainly in 'button' cell form, the IEC codes being SR and MR respectively. Silver cells are produced in the capacity range 30 to 200 mA h, while mercury types are available from as little as 15 mA h, for such applications as hearing-aids and watches, to 1 A h, although special-purpose mercury batteries are produced up to about 30 A h. Note that the cost/capacity ratio of silver and mercury cells is high, typically 25 and 10 times, respectively, compared with alkaline cells.

Figure 11.31e gives a performance comparison for rechargeable cells. Silver-based cells give superior performance but at a relatively high cost. Nickel–zinc and nickel–cadmium cells give good overall performance while nickel–iron cells are noted for their low cost and robustness, both mechanically and electrically. The capacities of some popular sizes of nickel–cadmium batteries are compared with those of corresponding primary batteries in table 11.2. Nickel–cadmium batteries offer a good cycle life in excess of 2000 charge–discharge cycles in vented form, 500 cycles in sealed form. A wide range of lead–acid batteries is available, ranging from 2 V to 24 V with capacities from 1 A h to 110 A h; the largest sector is the 12 V and 24 V, 24 A h to 110 A h range for vehicle applications. Lead–acid batteries offer the advantages of good performance over a wide temperature range, good shelf life particularly when stored in the dry charged state (typically 3 per cent of rated capacity/month at 20°C), good cycle life (> 500 charge–discharge cycles), relatively high cell voltage and relatively low cost, but they have the disadvantage of a high weight/capacity ratio. This application accounts for about 80 per cent of the total world consumption of lead.

Battery choice

Selection is basically between disposable and rechargeable types, the main performance criterion in most cases being that the capacity must be sufficient, taking account of drain and duty cycle, to allow a reasonable interval between battery replacement/recharging. Other factors such as cost, size and weight may be particularly important in some applications. For a rechargeable system, the initial battery cost is typically 5–7 times the corresponding cost of disposable batteries and, in addition, a charger is required. This cost must be balanced against the total cost of replacement disposable batteries throughout the life of the equipment. In general, heavy use in terms of both drain and duty cycle favours a rechargeable system while disposable batteries are suited to light drain, intermittent use.

Data sheets provided by battery manufacturers give terminal voltage–discharge time characteristics for various discharge rates, corresponding to figure 11.31a. Knowing the typical drain for the application in question and the minimum allowable supply voltage for the equipment, a suitable battery capacity can be selected that will give a reasonable service life between replacements/recharging. If an end-of-life/charge voltage cannot be defined, it is common to allow a 25 per cent safety margin in capacity; thus if the drain is 50 mA and it is estimated that 20 h use must be provided between replacements/recharging, the required capacity is $50\text{ mA} \times 20\text{ h} = 1\text{ A h}$. Allowing a 25 per cent margin, the required battery capacity is 1.25 A h.

Comprehensive coverage of the popular battery types can be found in references [6], [7] and [8].

References and further reading

1. M.E. Goodge, *Semiconductor Device Technology* (Macmillan, 1985)
   (a) section 2.4.1,
   (b) sections 1.7 and 2.1.3,
   (c) section 2.4.3
2. B.M. Bird and K.G. King, *An Introduction to Power Electronics*, chapter 5 (Wiley, 1983)
3. K. Thorborg, *Power Electronics* (Prentice-Hall, 1988)
   (a) sections 4.1.6, 5.3 and 6.3,
   (b) chapter 7
4. B.W. Williams, *Power Electronics: Devices, Drivers and Applications*, chapter 14 (Macmillan, 1987)
5. *IEC Publication 86: System of Designation for Primary Cells and Batteries*, 1975.
6. T.R. Crompton, *Small Batteries, Vol. 1 Secondary Cells* (Macmillan, 1982)
7. T.R. Crompton, *Small Batteries, Vol. 2 Primary Cells* (Macmillan, 1983)
8. M. Barak (Ed.), *Electrochemical Power Sources: Primary and Secondary Batteries* (Peregrinus, 1980)
9. T.L. Floyd, *Electronic Devices*, 2nd edition, chapters 3 and 17 (Merrill, 1988)
10. J. Millman and A. Grabel, *Microelectronics*, 2nd edition, chapter 17 (McGraw-Hill, 1988)

11. R.J. Maddock and D.M. Calcutt, *Electronics: A Course for Engineers*, chapter 8 (Longman, 1988)
12. F.H. Mitchell, *Introduction to Electronics Design*, sections 5–4 to 5–8 (Prentice-Hall, 1988)
13. P.M. Chirlian, *Analysis and Design of Integrated Electronic Circuits*, 2nd edition, chapter 19 (Harper and Row/Wiley, 1987)
14. C.J. Savant, M.S. Roden and G.L. Carpenter, *Electronic Circuit Design*, sections 1.4, 1.6, 1.7, 6.6 and 6.7 (Benjamin/Cummings, 1987)
15. C.L. Alley and K.W. Atwood, *Microelectronics*, sections 3.8, 3.9 and chapter 16 (Prentice-Hall, 1986)
16. T.F. Bogart, *Electronic Devices and Circuits*, chapter 16 (Merrill, 1986)
17. R.A. Colclaser, D.A. Neamen and C.F. Hawkins, *Electronic Circuit Analysis*, chapter 16 (Wiley, 1984)
18. P. Horowitz and W. Hill, *The Art of Electronics*, chapter 5 (Cambridge, 1982)
19. T. Young, *Linear Integrated Circuits*, chapters 3 and 4 (Wiley, 1981)
20. E.N. Lurch, *Fundamentals of Electronics*, 3rd edition, chapters 3 and 20 (Wiley, 1981)
21. M. Cirovic, *Basic Electronics*, 2nd edition, chapters 8 and 19 (Prentice-Hall, 1979)
22. C.A. Holt, *Electronic Circuits*, chapter 24 (Wiley, 1978)

Tutorial questions

Note: Preferred (E-series) component values are given in appendix D. Answers correspond to rounding to 2 decimal places during calculation.

Rectification

11.1 A 10 V, 50 Hz sinewave is rectified using an *ideal* rectifier. Show from *first principles* that the average output voltage of the rectifier is 4.5 V for a half-wave rectifier and 9 V for a full-wave rectifier. If the output waveform is applied to a 1 kΩ load, show from first principles that the power developed in the load is 50 mW and 100 mW, respectively, for the two cases.

Note: Remember that when an alternating voltage is specified simply as so many volts with no other reference, such as peak, the quoted value refers to the rms value of the alternating voltage.

11.2 If the diodes used in the rectifier of question 11.1 have an effective forward resistance of 100 Ω, show that the answers to question 11.1 become 4.09 V and 41.34 mW for the half-wave case, 8.18 V and 82.63 mW for a two-diode full-wave rectifier, and 7.50 V and 69.39 mW for a bridge rectifier. For each of the three cases calculate the rectification efficiency achieved.

[Answers: 36.84 per cent, 73.69 per cent, 67.55 per cent]

Basic capacitance smoothing

11.3 In the circuit of figure 11.11a, $V_{S(RMS)} = 40$ V, $C = 100\ \mu$F and $R_L = 22$ kΩ. Assuming a 50 Hz input, ideal bridge diodes and a linear capacitor discharge, estimate the maximum value of load voltage, the ripple voltage, the average load voltage, the ripple factor and the peak inverse voltage across the bridge.

[Answers: 56.57 V, 0.26 V, 56.44 V, 0.46 per cent, 113.14 V]

11.4 Recalculate V_{LM}, Δv_L and F_r in question 11.3 if each bridge diode introduces a voltage drop of 0.7 V when conducting.

[Answers: 55.17 V, 0.25 V, 0.45 per cent]

11.5 If the ripple factor in question 11.3 is to be improved to better than 0.2 per cent, choose the minimum E6 capacitance value (appendix D). Select the lowest allowable voltage rating for the capacitor from the available ratings of 10 V, 25 V, 63 V and 100 V.

[Answers: 330 μF, 63 V]

11.6 Estimate the ripple voltage in question 11.3 if the capacitor discharge is taken as the true exponential variation instead of making the linear discharge approximation. Compare the result with that obtained in question 11.3 and hence observe the validity of the linear approximation for the case of low ripple.

[Answer: 0.26 V]

11.7 Repeat question 11.3 with the bridge rectifier replaced by a half-wave arrangement. Note that for calculation of the peak inverse voltage in the half-wave case, when v_S is at its negative peak, v_L is equal to $V_{L(AV)}$ since the capacitor is approximately halfway through its discharge interval.

[Answers: 56.57 V, 0.51 V, 56.32 V, 0.91 per cent, 112.89 V]

11.8 The circuit of figure 11.11a is required to provide a nominal load voltage of 15 V for a load that draws up to 120 mA, the transformer primary being driven from 240 V, 50 Hz mains. Select the minimum allowable E6 value of capacitance (appendix D) if the ripple factor must not exceed 2 per cent, noting that the tolerance range of available capacitors is $\pm$ 20 per cent. What are the minimum permissible continuous and surge current ratings for the bridge rectifier? What is the required turns ratio of the transformer allowing for a 1.5 V drop across the bridge?

[Answers: 6800 μF, 120 mA, 5.39 A, 20.46:1]

Basic inductance smoothing

11.9 The circuit of figure 11.12a is used to supply dc power to a 100 Ω load from 240 V, 50 Hz mains. If the transformer ratio is 1:1 and the choke inductance is 5 H, what is the average load voltage and the second harmonic ripple voltage at the load assuming the voltage drop across the bridge rectifier and the choke resistance can be neglected? Hence determine the ripple factor at the load. Calculate the peak-to-peak fourth harmonic voltage at the load; what percentage is this of the peak-to-peak second harmonic load voltage?

[Answers 216.08 V, 9.17 V, 4.24 per cent, 0.92 V, 10 per cent]

11.10 A bridge rectifier and basic inductance smoothing are used to provide a nominal 10 V dc supply to a purely resistive 200 W load from 240 V, 50 Hz mains. If the load voltage must not vary by more than $\pm$ 1 per cent, calculate the minimum choke inductance required. If the forward voltage drop across each diode in the bridge is 0.7 V, calculate the required turns ratio of the transformer assuming the choke has negligible resistance.

[Answers: 53.05 mH, 19.83:1]

11.11 Recalculate the transformer turns ratio in question 11.10 to maintain the nominal 10 V dc load voltage if the choke coil has a resistance of 0.08 Ω.

[Answer: 17.30:1]

11.12 A full-wave rectifier and basic inductance filter are used to provide a nominal 20 V dc supply to a purely resistive load from 240 V, 50 Hz mains. If the average current drawn by the load may fall to 200 mA and the ripple factor must not exceed 1 per cent, calculate the minimum value of inductance required.
If the supply frequency was 20 kHz instead of 50 Hz, what would be the minimum value of required inductance? Note the reduced value compared with the 50 Hz case and hence what do you conclude regarding the practical use of basic inductance filters?

[Answers: 21.22 H; 53.05 mH, showing that basic inductance smoothing becomes more practical at a higher supply frequency]

Inductance-input smoothing

11.13 To meet the same specification as in question 11.12, with a 240 V, 50 Hz input, choose suitable parameter values for an *LC* filter and compare the practicality of the inductance required with that for the corresponding basic inductance filter case. Note that the choice of *L* and *C* should be such that neither is excessive and take account of the fact that capacitance values are usually only available in the E6 series (appendix D). The inductance value should be rounded to the next 10 mH for simplicity.

[Answers: Critical inductance is 106.10 mH and the minimum *LC* product 337.74 μs. The lowest allowable value of inductance, rounded to 10 mH, is therefore 110 mH but this corresponds to a relatively large value of capacitance, 3070.36 μF. Increasing *L* to 500 mH allows *C* to be reduced to 675.48 μF from which the E6 value 680 μF can be chosen. Alternatively, choice of the moderate capacitance value of 1000 μF enables the inductance to be reduced to 337.74 mH which may be rounded to 340 mH for convenience. Thus suitable component combinations are 500 mH, 680 μF and 1000 μF, 340 mH. Note that the required inductance is less than 2.5 per cent of the value required in question 11.12 to meet the same specification using basic inductance smoothing, indicating the practicality of the *LC* filter for moderate-to-high current unregulated supplies]

11.14 An unregulated power supply consists of a 10:1 transformer, a silicon bridge rectifier and a smoothing circuit consisting of a 500 mH choke having a 2 Ω winding resistance and a 1500 μF capacitor. If the supply is used to provide power for a 20 Ω resistive load from 240 V, 50 Hz mains, calculate the average load voltage and the ripple factor obtained. What is the minimum allowable rms ripple current rating of the capacitor?
Note: As the choke resistance must be taken into account, ripple factor cannot be calculated using equation 11.69 which assumes negligible choke resistance. Calculate the ripple voltage at the load taking account of the choke resistance and then find the ripple factor using the ratio $\Delta v_L / V_{L(AV)}$.

[Answers: 18.77 V, 0.49 per cent, allowing for a 1.5 V drop across the bridge; 28.16 mA]

Basic shunt diode regulator

11.15 In the basic shunt diode regulator of figure 11.16a, the reference diode has a nominal breakdown voltage of 8.2 V and a slope resistance of 20 Ω in the breakdown region.

If $V_I = 12$ V, $R_1 = 50\,\Omega$ and $R_L = 1$ kΩ, determine the output voltage V_L and the diode current I_Z using (a) analytical and (b) graphical techniques. What is the minimum power rating required for resistor R_1?

[Answers: 9.16 V, 47.77 mA, 162.05 mW]

11.16 If the diode in the circuit of question 11.15 has a maximum power dissipation limit of 400 mW, what is the maximum value of V_I for safe operation of the circuit? What is the value of V_L for this condition?
Note: Derive equations linking I_Z and V_Z for the breakdown characteristic of the diode and the maximum power condition of the diode, then solve the equations simultaneously to find $I_Z$max, $V_Z$max; hence $V_I$max.

[Answers: 11.74 V, 9.08 V]

11.17 The circuit of figure 11.16a is used to maintain a voltage of 7 V across a 280 Ω load, using a Philips BZX 79 C6V8 diode, from a 12 V dc supply. Using the static characteristic of the diode provided in appendix E, section E.2, determine a suitable E24 value (appendix D) for R_1. Calculate the power dissipation in R_1.

[Answers: For $V_L = V_Z = 7$ V, the diode current is estimated as 17 mA from the static I_Z–V_Z characteristic. Correspondingly, R_1 is calculated as 119.05 Ω, allowing a 120 Ω resistor to be selected; the power dissipated in R_1 is 211.68 mW]

11.18 A basic shunt diode regulator (figure 11.16a) is required to provide 8.5 V $\pm$ 300 mV from a dc supply that may vary between 15 V and 18 V; the resistive load draws a current of up to 50 mA. Select a suitable diode from the BZV 85 range (appendix E, section E.3) and associated E24 resistor (appendix D) to meet the specification. If resistors are available with power ratings of 0.125, 0.25, 0.5, 1 and 2 W, select the lowest adequate rating. Estimate the ripple rejection provided by the regulator.

[Answers: Select a 8V2 diode. Estimated allowable diode current range from the static characteristic is 5 mA to 104 mA; the slope resistance is approximately 6.5 Ω. Maximum and minimum values of R_1 are 123.63 Ω and 88.46 Ω, from which an E24 value of 110 Ω is selected as being nearest to the mean of the allowable range. The resistor tolerance must be $\leqslant \pm 12.3$ per cent; ± 5 per cent or ± 2 per cent would be typical choices. Using the PWL model of the diode performance, analysis shows that the current through R_1 peaks at 87.07 mA under conditions of maximum input voltage (18 V) and maximum load current (50 mA). The maximum power dissipated in R_1 is therefore 0.83 W, allowing a 1 W resistor to be used. For a diode slope resistance of 6.5 Ω, $R_1 = 110\,\Omega$ gives a ripple rejection of 25.07 dB from equation 11.76]

11.19 A power supply consists of a 20:1 transformer, silicon bridge rectifier and 4700 μF smoothing capacitor cascaded with a basic shunt diode regulator comprising a 4 Ω resistor and a nominal 9.1 V reference diode having a slope resistance of 2 Ω. If the resistive load varies in the range 20 Ω to 100 Ω, what will be the range of output voltage when the transformer primary is driven from 240 V, 50 Hz mains? Estimate the maximum power dissipation in the diode and the 4 Ω resistor.
Note: Using a piecewise-linear (PWL) model of the diode, calculate the effective input resistance R_I of the regulator for the cases of $R_L = 20\,\Omega$ and 100 Ω. Then, treating the circuit as a basic capacitance smoothing arrangement, find the range of average input voltage to the regulator using $\tau = CR_I$ and $F_r = T/2\tau$. Using the

PWL model again, calculate $V_{L(AV)}$max and $V_{L(AV)}$min corresponding to the input voltage range $V_{I(AV)}$max to $V_{I(AV)}$min.

[Answers: Allowing for a 1.5 V drop across the bridge rectifier, $V_{I(AV)}$ ranges from 14.25 V to 14.38 V and the corresponding range of $V_{L(AV)}$ is 10.14 V to 10.72 V. Maximum power dissipation in the diode is 8.68 W when R_L is at its maximum value while power dissipation in the 4 Ω resistor peaks at 4.24 W when R_L is a minimum]

Series voltage regulators

11.20 The basic series voltage regulator of figure 11.19a has a nominal 4.3 V reference diode and R_1 is 100 Ω. The circuit drives a resistive load that draws up to 1 A and is powered from a dc source that may vary from 10 V to 20 V. If the diode has a slope resistance of 4 Ω, the base–emitter voltage of the BJT increases from 0.65 V to 0.8 V as the load current increases from zero to 1 A and the static gain of the BJT is 20 at full load, what is the range of output voltage supplied? Calculate the maximum power dissipation in the BJT, the diode and R_1.

[Answers: 3.54 V to 4.25 V; 15.31 W, 739.70 mW, 2.33 W]

11.21 A single transistor emitter-follower regulator is used to provide a nominal 6 V output from a 9 V battery. The load current may vary in the range 0.5–1 A and the output must remain within 400 mV of the nominal value. The freshly-charged and end-of-charge output voltages of the battery are 9 V and 7.5 V respectively. A range of breakdown diodes is available having nominal breakdown voltages in the E24 range, each having a slope resistance of 20 Ω. Taking BJT static gain as 50 and base–emitter voltage as 0.7 V, select a suitable diode and E24 resistor for the circuit. For the chosen components, what are the maximum and minimum values of load voltage over the working range of the circuit neglecting component tolerances? State the conditions relating to these limiting values. Calculate the maximum power dissipation in the BJT, the diode and R_1, and in each case state the conditions under which maximum power occurs.

[Answers: Select a 6V2 diode and a 43 Ω ±2 per cent resistor. $V_L$max is 6.26 V which occurs at maximum battery voltage (9 V) and minimum load current (0.5 A). $V_L$min is 5.65 V when the battery voltage is a minimum (7.5 V) and the load current at its maximum (1 A).
Power ratings: BJT 2.82 W (for 9 V input and 1 A load)
Diode 262.62 mW (for 9 V input and 0.5 A load)
R_1 110.40 mW (for 9 V input and 1 A load)]

11.22 A two-transistor regulator based on the circuit of figure 11.22 is required to provide a nominal 20 V, 0–1 A output to a resistive load from an unregulated 25–30 V dc source. Using a TIP 31 (appendix E, section E.6) as the pass transistor, a BFY 51 as the feedback transistor and a reference diode from the E24 range (appendix D), select suitable components for the circuit. Check the thermal operating conditions of the selected components assuming the ambient temperature may rise to 50°C and use the chart of figure 11.21 to make suitable recommendations where necessary. Assuming that the regulator is driven from a full-wave rectified, 50 Hz sinusoidal source and the circuit provides ripple rejection of 40 dB, specify a suitable E6 (±20 per cent) value for the smoothing capacitor if the ripple voltage at the load must not exceed 20 mV.

Note: Relevant data for a BFY 51 BJT: $I_C$max = 1 A, V_{CE}max = 30 V, h_{FE}min at 100 mA ≃ 40, P_{tot}max = 5 W at T_{case} = 25°C and 800 mW at T_{amb} ⩽ 25°C, $T_j$max = 200°C, TO 39 style package.
The reference diode has a maximum dissipation of 2.5 W at T_{amb} ⩽ 25°C with $T_j$max = 200°C. Available ranges of resistors have power ratings of 0.125, 0.25, 0.5, 1 and 2 W at T_{amb} ⩽ 70°C.

[Specimen design: Minimum h_{FE} of a TIP 31 at 1 A is estimated as 25 from the data sheet so that the base current of the pass BJT varies from zero to about 38 mA. P_{tot}max for T_1, which occurs at $V_I$max, is approximately 10 W and for T_{amb}max = 50°C, $R_{th(j-amb)}$ must therefore not exceed 10°C/W. $R_{th(j-case)}$ for a TIP 31 is quoted as 3.125°C/W, showing that the thermal resistance of the heatsink needs to be about 7°C/W. The chart shows that 90 cm^2 of bright, vertically-mounted, 2 mm thick aluminium sheet would provide adequate heatsinking. Choosing a nominal low value of 10 mA for I_{C_2}min, which corresponds to I_{B_1}max, allows a 91 Ω resistor to be selected for R_1 which dissipates approximately 947 mW under worst-case ($V_I$max) conditions; a 1 W component is selected.
($V_Z + V_{CE_2}$) is approximately 20.7 V and a 10 V reference diode is selected to divide this voltage approximately equally between the diode and T_2.
I_{C_2}max is approximately 102 mA, at I_{B_1}min = 0 and $V_I$max, and with V_{CE_2} ≃ 10.7 V the maximum power dissipation in T_2 is 1.09 W. For T_{amb}max = 50°C, $R_{th(j-amb)}$max is therefore approximately 138°C/W, and with $R_{th(j-case)}$ for a BFY 51 being 35°C/W, the maximum thermal resistance of the heatsink is 103°C/W. The chart shows this to correspond to a very small size, and so it is proposed to specify a convenient clip-on type of heatsink.
With I_{C_2}max of 102 mA, the additional (10 per cent) diode bias provided via R_2 is about 10 mA making $I_Z$max approximately 112 mA with a corresponding maximum dissipation of 1.12 W. The diode range can dissipate up to 2.5 W at T_{amb} = 25°C giving $R_{th(j-amb)}$ of 70°C/W. Thus the maximum dissipation at T_{amb} = 50°C is 2.14 W, indicating safe operation here.
R_2 = 2 kΩ, 0.25 W provides the additional 10 mA diode bias at $V_I$max; at lower values of V_I this additional bias component will be reduced, but this is satisfactory as the original choice of value was arbitrary.
I_{B_2}max is approximately 2.4 mA and therefore bias I' for the R', R'' divider is set at about 25 mA, 10 × I_{B_2}max, $I_L$max/40. This allows R' = 390 Ω and R'' = 430 Ω, both 0.25 W components, to be selected. A trim potentiometer of about 5 per cent $(R' + R'') \simeq 40$ Ω, minimal wattage, can be included if desired.
For Δv_Lmax = 20 mV, ripple rejection of 40 dB allows Δv_Imax of 2 V to be tolerated. Correspondingly, using equation 11.85, C_{min} is 5000 μF allowing an E6 value of 6800 μF ± 20 per cent to be selected]

Appendix A: Fourier Representation

A.1 Fourier Series

Any *periodic* waveform $f(\omega t)$, of angular frequency ω, can be represented by the Fourier series

$$f(\omega t) = a_0 + \sum_{n=1}^{\infty} (a_n \cos n\omega t + b_n \sin n\omega t) \tag{A.1}$$

where the coefficients are given by

$$a_0 = \frac{1}{2\pi} \int_{-\pi}^{\pi} f(\omega t)\, d(\omega t) \tag{A.2}$$

$$a_n = \frac{1}{\pi} \int_{-\pi}^{\pi} f(\omega t) \cos n\omega t\, d(\omega t) \tag{A.3}$$

$$b_n = \frac{1}{\pi} \int_{-\pi}^{\pi} f(\omega t) \sin n\omega t\, d(\omega t) \tag{A.4}$$

a_0 is the average value of the variable over a complete period. Terms $a_n \cos n\omega t$ ($n = 1 \rightarrow \infty$) and $b_n \sin n\omega t$ ($n = 1 \rightarrow \infty$) are the *harmonic* components of $f(\omega t)$; the $n = 1$ term is the *fundamental* component which has the same frequency as $f(\omega t)$ while the $n = 2$ term is the *second harmonic*, the $n = 3$ term the *third harmonic* and so on.

Table A.1 gives the series for some common waveshapes, voltage being used as the variable for example. In each case the waveform has an amplitude V with the most negative part of the waveform taken as zero. Note that if the waveshape is shifted along the *voltage* axis, this only affects the first term (average value) in the series. Thus the Fourier series for a square wave that is symmetrical about the time axis varying from $+V/2$ to $-V/2$ has the same harmonic content as the wholly positive square wave of table A.1 (1), but the average value would then be zero instead of $V/2$ for the case shown.

If the waveshape is shifted along the *angle* (*time*) axis, the average value remains unaltered as do the frequencies of the harmonics, but the phase of some or all of the harmonics will be affected. For purposes of example, two representations of a half-wave rectified sinusoid are given in table A1 (4a) and (4b). It can be seen that the change of the $\omega t = 0$ reference alters the fundamental from sine to cosine and changes the sign of the $2\omega t$, $6\omega t$, $10\omega t \ldots$ terms, each representing a $\pi/2$ shift in phase.

A particularly important case is that of the pulse waveform of figure A.1a encountered in sampling applications. The line spectrum showing the amplitudes of the various frequency components corresponding to a pulse width t_p and waveform period T is as shown in figure A.1b; each vertical line represents a single frequency component. The envelope of the

Table A.1 Fourier series for some common waveshapes

	Waveshape	Fourier series
(1) Square	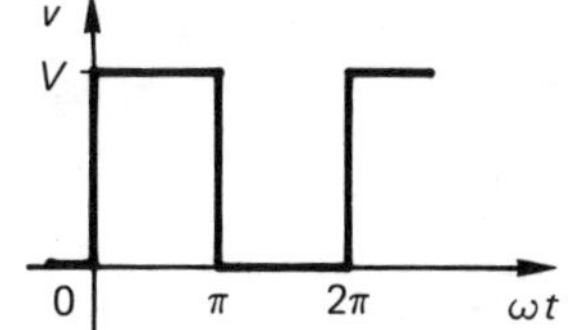	$v = V\left[\frac{1}{2} + \frac{2}{\pi}\sin\omega t + \frac{2}{3\pi}\sin 3\,\omega t \ldots + \frac{2}{n\pi}\sin n\,\omega t\right]$ n odd (1, 3, 5 . . . ∞), no even harmonics
(2) Triangular	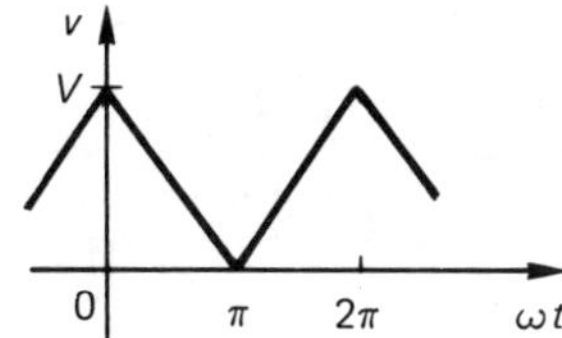	$v = V\left[\frac{1}{2} + \frac{4}{\pi^2}\cos\omega t + \frac{4}{9\pi^2}\cos 3\omega t \ldots + \frac{4}{n^2\pi^2}\cos n\omega t\right]$ n odd (1, 3, 5 . . . ∞), no even harmonics
(3) Sawtooth (ramp)	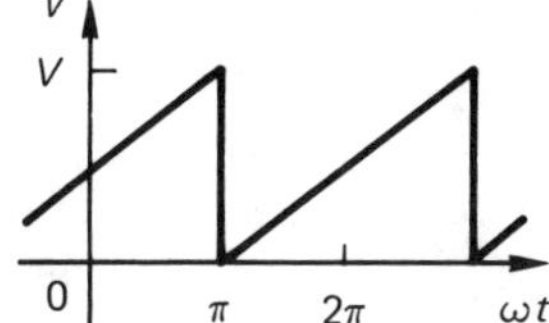	$v = V\left[\frac{1}{2} + \frac{1}{\pi}\sin\omega t - \frac{1}{2\pi}\sin 2\,\omega t \ldots - \frac{(-1)^n}{n\pi}\sin n\,\omega t\right]$ $n = 1, 2 \ldots \infty$
(4) Half-wave rectified sinusoid	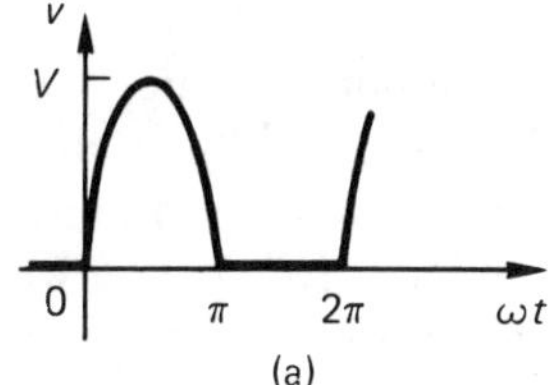 (a)	$v = V\left[\frac{1}{\pi} + \frac{1}{2}\sin\omega t - \frac{2}{3\pi}\cos 2\,\omega t \ldots - \frac{2}{(n^2-1)\pi}\cos n\omega t\right]$ n even (2, 4, 6 . . . ∞), no odd harmonics except the fundamental
	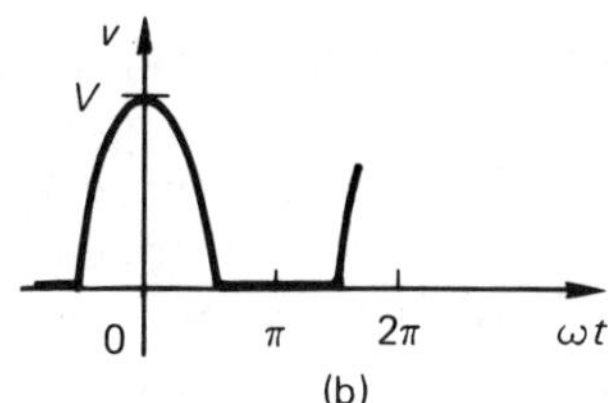 (b)	$v = V\left[\frac{1}{\pi} + \frac{1}{2}\cos\omega t + \frac{2}{3\pi}\cos 2\omega t \ldots -(-1)^{n/2}\frac{2}{(n^2-1)\pi}\cos n\omega t\right]$ n even (2, 4, 6 . . . ∞), no odd harmonics except the fundamental
(5) Full-wave rectified sinusoid	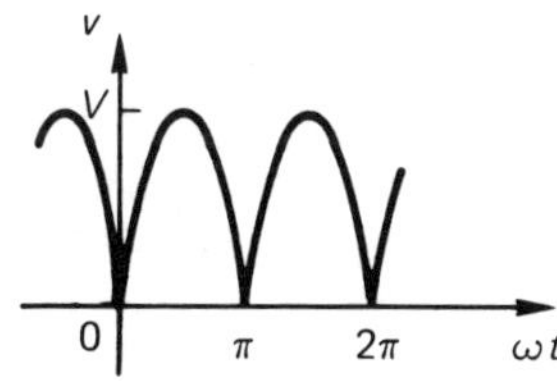	$v = V\left[\frac{2}{\pi} - \frac{4}{3\pi}\cos 2\omega t - \frac{4}{15\pi}\cos 4\omega t \ldots - \frac{4}{(n^2-1)\pi}\cos n\omega t\right]$ n even (2, 4, 6 . . . ∞), no odd harmonics

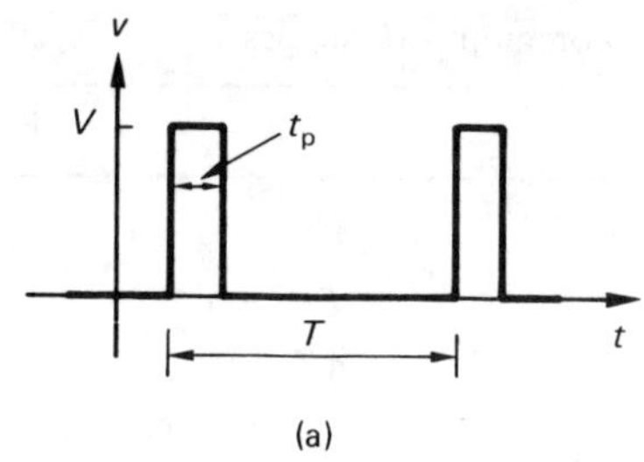

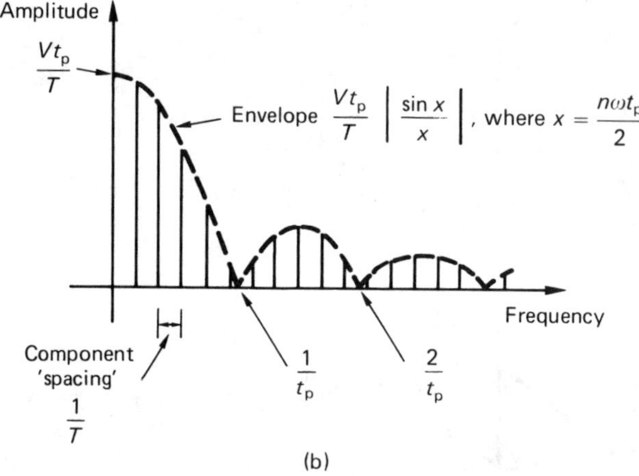

Figure A.1 Frequency spectrum of a pulse waveform

component amplitudes is proportional to the modulus of the sampling function $|\mathrm{Sa}(x)|$ which is equal to $|(\sin x)/x|$ where $x = n\omega t_p/2$. Notice that as the pulse width t_p decreases, the frequencies of the zeros of the envelope increase, and as the period of the sampling waveform increases the frequency separation between the components reduces. In the limit when $T \to \infty$ the waveform reduces to a single pulse and the separation reduces to zero, resulting in a *continuous* spectrum containing all frequency components in place of the *discrete* spectrum for periodic waveforms. The importance of this information regarding the frequency content of pulse waveforms is that it indicates the bandwidth required to transmit such a waveshape without severe distortion.

Further details of the mathematical basis of Fourier representation can be found in mathematics texts, such as K.A. Stroud, *Further Engineering Mathematics*, programme 17 (Macmillan, 1986) and texts concerned with signal analysis such as W.H. Hayt and J.E. Kemmerly, *Engineering Circuit Analysis*, 4th edition, chapters 17 and 18 (McGraw-Hill, 1987).

Appendix B: Tuned Circuits

B.1 Resonance

The operational impedance $\boldsymbol{Z}'$ of the theoretical* parallel R', L', C' circuit of figure B.1a is the parallel combination of R' and the operational reactances $j\omega L'$ and $1/j\omega C'$ (equations 2.27 and 2.39). Thus if $\boldsymbol{Y}'$ is the operational admittance of the circuit

$$\boldsymbol{Z}' = \frac{1}{\boldsymbol{Y}'} = \frac{1}{\dfrac{1}{R'} + \dfrac{1}{j\omega L'} + j\omega C'} = \frac{R'}{1 + jR'\left(\omega C' - \dfrac{1}{\omega L'}\right)} \tag{B.1}$$

where ω is the angular frequency $(=2\pi f)$ of the sinusoidal excitation.

As ω varies, $\boldsymbol{Z}'$ varies having a maximum value R' when the frequency is such that the quadrature component (often termed the *imaginary* Im component) of the denominator is zero which occurs at a frequency

ω_o $(=2\pi f_o)$ given by

$$\omega_o C' - \frac{1}{\omega_o L'} = 0 \tag{B.2}$$

from which

$$f_o = \frac{1}{2\pi\sqrt{(L'C')}} \tag{B.3}$$

This condition is termed *resonance*, f_o being the resonant frequency of the circuit. As $\boldsymbol{Z}'$ is entirely real at this frequency, v and i are in phase. At resonance, the inductive and capacitive reactances of the circuit are equal (equation B2) so that the alternating currents through L' and C' due to v are equal in amplitude but they have a phase difference of a half cycle, so that they cancel as far as the source v is concerned. At this frequency, therefore, the only current drawn from the source is that flowing through R'. Physically, this condition occurs because of the repetitive transfer of energy between the magnetic field associated with the inductor and the electric field within the capacitor at a natural frequency f_o. When the excitation v is at the same frequency, L' and C' draw no energy from the source.

In a practical parallel tuned circuit, a coil having inductance L *and* resistance R is shunted

---

* The parallel circuit of figure B.1a is theoretical because an ideal inductor (one having zero coil resistance) is not realisable.

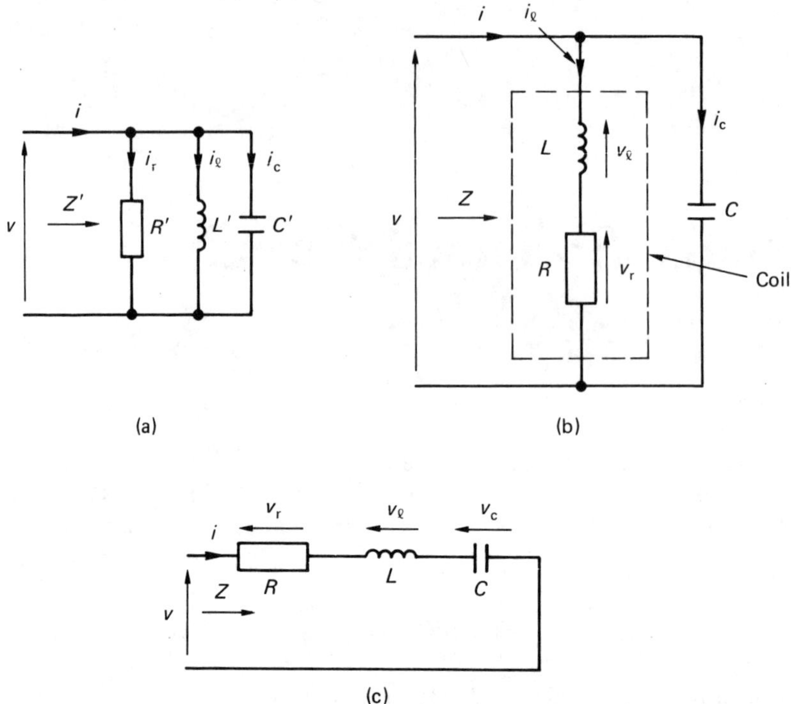

Figure B.1 Tuned circuits

by a capacitor C as in figure B1b. The corresponding operational impedance is therefore

$$\boldsymbol{Z}=(R+j\omega L)/\!/(1/j\omega C)$$

$$=\frac{(R+j\omega L)(1/j\omega C)}{(R+j\omega L)+(1/j\omega C)}$$

$$=\frac{(R+j\omega L)(1-\omega^2 LC-j\omega CR)}{(1-\omega^2 LC)^2+(\omega CR)^2} \tag{B.4}$$

The resonance condition occurs, as for the theoretical parallel R', L', C' case above, when the impedance is entirely real, v and i then being in phase. This occurs at a frequency ω_o at which the quadrature component of equation B.4 is zero; as the denominator is entirely real, this occurs when

$$\operatorname{Im}[(R+j\omega_o L)(1-\omega_o^2 LC-j\omega_o CR)]=0$$

from which

$$f_o=\frac{\omega_o}{2\pi}=\frac{1}{2\pi}\sqrt{\left(\frac{1}{LC}-\frac{R^2}{L^2}\right)} \tag{B.5}$$

Notice that the resonant frequency depends on circuit resistance which is in contrast to the case of the theoretical R', L', C' circuit (equation B.3). Substitution of $\omega=\omega_o$ from equation

B.5 into B.4 shows that the impedance of a practical parallel tuned circuit (figure B.1b) at resonance is L/CR; this is termed the *dynamic impedance* of the circuit.

If $R \ll \omega_o L$, the R^2/L^2 term in equation B.5 is negligible and the resonant frequency of the practical parallel tuned circuit is then the same as that for the theoretical parallel circuit of figure B.1a (equation B.3). The relative magnitudes of R and ωL are described in terms of the *quality* (Q-) *factor* of the coil (Q_L) which is defined as

$$Q_L = 2\pi\left(\frac{\text{Maximum energy stored in the coil}}{\text{Energy dissipated/cycle}}\right) \tag{B.6}$$

From equation 11.4, the energy w delivered to an electrical element in time t is

$$w = \int_0^t vi\,dt \tag{B.7}$$

For the inductive component of the coil, a time-varying current i causes an induced voltage $v = L\dfrac{di}{dt}$ (figure 2.5c). As i increases from zero to a peak value I_m, the energy stored in the magnetic field associated with the coil is, from equation B.7:

$$w_{L(stored)} = \int_0^{I_m} vi\,dt = \int_0^{I_m}\left(L\frac{di}{dt}\right)i\,dt = L\int_0^{I_m} i\,di = LI_m^2/2 \tag{B.8}$$

For sinusoidal excitation of frequency ω, $i = I_m \sin\omega t$, and the energy dissipated in the coil resistance R in one cycle (period $T = 1/f = 2\pi/\omega$) is, from equation B.7:

$$w_{diss/cycle} = \int_0^{2\pi/\omega} vi\,dt = \int_0^{2\pi/\omega} i^2R\,dt = \int_0^{2\pi/\omega} I_m^2 R\sin^2\omega t\,dt$$

$$= \tfrac{1}{2}I_m^2 R\int_0^{2\pi/\omega}(1-\cos 2\omega t)\,dt = \frac{\pi I_m^2 R}{\omega} \tag{B.9}$$

noting that $v = Ri$ for the resistive component of the coil, $\sin^2\omega t = \frac{1}{2}(1-\cos 2\omega t)$ and the time integral of a function that is symmetrical about the time axis, such as $\cos 2\omega t$, over a complete cycle is zero. Substituting expressions for $w_{L(stored)}$ and $w_{diss/cycle}$ from equations B.8 and B.9 into B.6 gives the Q-factor of the coil at frequency ω as

$$Q_L(\omega) = 2\pi\left(\frac{LI_m^2/2}{\pi I_m^2 R/\omega}\right) = \frac{\omega L}{R} \tag{B.10}$$

Note that the coil current i_l, having maximum value I_{lm}, flows through both L and R (figure B.1b) and the ratio of the maximum values V_{lm} and V_{rm} of the voltage components v_l and v_r is therefore

$$\frac{V_{lm}}{V_{rm}} = \frac{X_L I_{lm}}{RI_{lm}} = \frac{X_L}{R} = \frac{\omega L}{R} = Q_L(\omega) \tag{B.11}$$

Equation B.11 shows that $Q_L(\omega)$ is also a measure of the inductive voltage component V_{lm} relative to the resistive voltage component V_{rm}; hence the alternative name for Q, the *magnification factor*. Clearly, the higher ωL relative to R, the higher V_{lm} relative to V_{rm} and the 'better' the coil in the sense that it more closely approaches the theoretical ideal for which R, and hence V_{rm}, is zero.

From equation B.5:

$$f_o = \frac{1}{2\pi\sqrt{(LC)}}\sqrt{\left(1-\frac{CR^2}{L}\right)}$$

$$\simeq \frac{1}{2\pi\sqrt{(LC)}}\left(1-\frac{1}{Q_L^2(\omega_o)}\right)^{\frac{1}{2}} \tag{B.12}$$

since $Q_L(\omega_o)=\omega_o L/R$, the Q-factor of the coil at the resonant frequency ω_o of the circuit, and $\omega_o^2 \simeq 1/LC$ if R is small, that is for 'high Q' coils. Expansion of the $(\ )^{\frac{1}{2}}$ term in equation B.12 gives

$$f_o \simeq \frac{1}{2\pi\sqrt{(LC)}}\left(1-\frac{1}{2Q_L^2(\omega_o)}+\cdots\right) \tag{B.13}$$

indicating that the fractional error in the use of the theoretical expression for f_o (equation B.3) in place of the actual expression for the practical circuit (figure B.1b, equation B.5) is of the order of $+1/2Q_L^2(\omega_o)$ for high Q (low R) coils. Thus for the practical case of coils having $Q_L > 10$, the error is $< 1/2(10)^2$ or < 0.5 per cent. Coils having $Q_L > 10$ at the frequency of interest can therefore be described as 'high Q' in this context.

B.2 **Representation of a practical parallel tuned circuit by the theoretical parallel equivalent**

For purposes of analysis it is often convenient to represent the practical tuned circuit of figure B.1b in terms of its purely parallel equivalent (figure B.1a).

The capacitance appears directly across the input in both cases and so

$$C' = C \tag{B.14}$$

Determination of L' and R' in terms of L and R involves equating the real and quadrature components of the corresponding admittance expressions. For the practical case of L and R in series, the operational admittance $\mathbf{Y}_L$ of the coil is

$$\mathbf{Y}_L = \frac{1}{\mathbf{Z}_L} = \frac{1}{R+j\omega L} = \left(\frac{R}{R^2+\omega^2L^2}\right) - j\left(\frac{\omega L}{R^2+\omega^2L^2}\right) \tag{B.15}$$

while for the parallel combination of L' and R',

$$\mathbf{Y}'_L = \frac{1}{R'} + \frac{1}{j\omega L'} = \left(\frac{1}{R'}\right) - j\left(\frac{1}{\omega L'}\right) \tag{B.16}$$

For the parallel representation to be equivalent to the series case, $\mathbf{Y}'_L = \mathbf{Y}_L$, and equating the corresponding parts of equations B.15 and B.16 gives

$$R' = \frac{R^2+\omega^2L^2}{R} \tag{B.17}$$

and

$$L' = \frac{R^2+\omega^2L^2}{\omega^2 L} \tag{B.18}$$

It is convenient to express R' and L' in terms of the Q-factor of the coil at frequency ω (equation B.10), that is, from equations B.17 and B.18:

$$R' = R + \frac{\omega^2 L^2}{R} = R\left(1 + \frac{\omega^2 L^2}{R^2}\right) = R(1 + Q_L^2)$$

$$\simeq Q_L^2 R \tag{B.19}$$

and

$$L' = \frac{R^2}{\omega^2 L} + L = L\left(\frac{R^2}{\omega^2 L^2} + 1\right) = L\left(\frac{1}{Q_L^2} + 1\right)$$

$$\simeq L \tag{B.20}$$

for 'high Q' coils having $Q_L^2 \gg 1$.

B.3 Circuit *Q*-factor

The fundamental definition of Q-factor (equation B.6) used in section B.1 as a figure-of-merit parameter for a *coil* is also usefully applied to a complete tuned *circuit*.

Parallel R', L', C' circuit

Applying the basic energy relation (equation B.7), in turn, to L' and C' in figure B.1a, the instantaneous energy stored in each element is, respectively:

$$w_{L(\text{stored})} = \int v i_l \, dt = \int \left(L' \frac{di_l}{dt}\right) i_l \, dt = L' i_l^2 / 2 \tag{B.21}$$

and

$$w_{C(\text{stored})} = \int v i_c \, dt = \int v \left(C' \frac{dv}{dt}\right) dt = C' v^2 / 2 \tag{B.22}$$

since $v = L' \dfrac{di_l}{dt}$ and $i_c = C' \dfrac{dv}{dt}$ (figures 2.5b, c).

Summing expressions B.21 and B.22, the instantaneous total energy stored in the *circuit* w_{stored} is

$$w_{\text{stored}} = L' i_l^2 / 2 + C' v^2 / 2 \tag{B.23}$$

For sinusoidal excitation $v = V_m \sin \omega t$, $i_l = \dfrac{1}{L'} \int v dt = -\left(\dfrac{V_m}{\omega L'}\right) \cos \omega t$, (equation 2.37) and so

$$w_{\text{stored}} = \left(\frac{V_m^2}{2\omega^2 L'}\right) \cos^2 \omega t + \left(\frac{C' V_m^2}{2}\right) \sin^2 \omega t \tag{B.24}$$

At the resonant frequency of the circuit ω_o, $1/\omega_o L' = \omega_o C'$ (equation B.2), and therefore the instantaneous stored energy is

$$w_{\text{stored}} = \left(\frac{C' V_m^2}{2}\right) (\cos^2 \omega t + \sin^2 \omega t)$$

$$= C' V_m^2 / 2 \tag{B.25}$$

as $\cos^2 \omega t + \sin^2 \omega t = 1$. Note that the instantaneous total energy stored, w_{stored}, does not vary with time, however the portions stored in the inductor and capacitor do fluctuate with time as energy transfers back and forth.

Energy is dissipated only in the resistor R' and so, using the result of equation B.9, noting that $I_m = V_m/R'$ for the resistor, the energy dissipated/cycle in the circuit at resonance is

$$w_{\text{diss/cycle}}(\omega_o) = \frac{\pi V_m^2}{\omega_o R'} \tag{B.26}$$

The Q-factor of the parallel R', L', C' circuit is

$$Q = 2\pi\left(\frac{\text{Energy stored in the circuit}}{\text{Energy dissipated/cycle at resonance}}\right) \tag{B.27}$$

and substituting for w_{stored} and $w_{\text{diss/cycle}}(\omega_o)$ from equations B.25 and B.26

$$Q(/\!/ R', L', C' \text{ circuit}) = 2\pi\left(\frac{C'V_m^2/2}{\pi V_m^2/\omega_o R'}\right)$$

$$= \omega_o C'R' = \frac{R'}{\omega_o L'} \tag{B.28}$$

as $\omega_o C' = 1/\omega_o L'$ (equation B.2).

Note that by substituting for R' and L' in equation B.28 from equations B.19 and B.20, the Q-factor of a practical parallel tuned circuit (figure B.1b) is

$$Q(\text{pract.} /\!/ \text{tuned circuit}) \simeq \frac{Q_L^2 R}{\omega_o L} = \frac{\omega_o L}{R} = Q_L(\omega_o) \tag{B.29}$$

for the case of a 'high Q' coil; the circuit Q is thus approximately the same as the Q of the coil *at the resonant frequency of the circuit*. In application, however, a tuned circuit is usually shunted by an external resistance resulting in an effective Q-factor that is lower than the value given in equation B.28.

Series R, L, C circuit

For the series tuned circuit of figure B.1c, the instantaneous energies stored in L and C are $Li^2/2$ and $Cv_c^2/2$ respectively, corresponding to equations B.21 and B.22 for the parallel circuit. In the series case, therefore, for sinusoidal excitation $i = I_m \sin \omega t$:

$$v_c = \frac{1}{C}\int i \, dt = -\left(\frac{I_m}{\omega C}\right)\cos \omega t$$

The instantaneous total energy stored in the circuit is

$$w_{\text{stored}} = Li^2/2 + Cv_c^2/2$$

$$= \left(\frac{LI_m^2}{2}\right)\sin^2 \omega t + \left(\frac{I_m^2}{2\omega^2 C}\right)\cos^2 \omega t \tag{B.30}$$

The operational impedance of the series R, L, C circuit is

$$\boldsymbol{Z} = R + j\omega L + \frac{1}{j\omega C}$$

$$= R + j\left(\omega L - \frac{1}{\omega C}\right) \tag{B.31}$$

and at the resonant frequency ω_o

$$\omega_o L = \frac{1}{\omega_o C} \tag{B.32}$$

giving $Z(\omega_o) = R$. Thus ω_o and $Z(\omega_o)$ for the series circuit are the same as for the theoretical parallel circuit (section B.1) although the impedance of the series circuit is a *minimum* at ω_o in contrast to maximum for the parallel arrangement. Using equation B.32, the instantaneous stored energy at the resonant frequency ω_o, from equation B.30, is

$$w_{\text{stored}} = LI_m^2/2 \tag{B.33}$$

From equation B.9, the energy dissipated in the circuit/cycle at frequency ω_o is

$$w_{\text{diss/cycle}} = \pi I_m^2 R/\omega_o \tag{B.34}$$

Substituting these expressions into equation B.27 gives the Q-factor of the series R, L, C circuit as

$$Q(\text{series } R, L, C \text{ circuit}) = 2\pi\left(\frac{LI_m^2/2}{\pi I_m^2 R/\omega_o}\right)$$

$$= \frac{\omega_o L}{R} = \frac{1}{\omega_o CR} \tag{B.35}$$

as $\omega_o L = 1/\omega_o C$ (equation B.32). Notice that the expression for the Q-factor of the series circuit is the reciprocal of that for the theoretical parallel circuit (equation B.28).

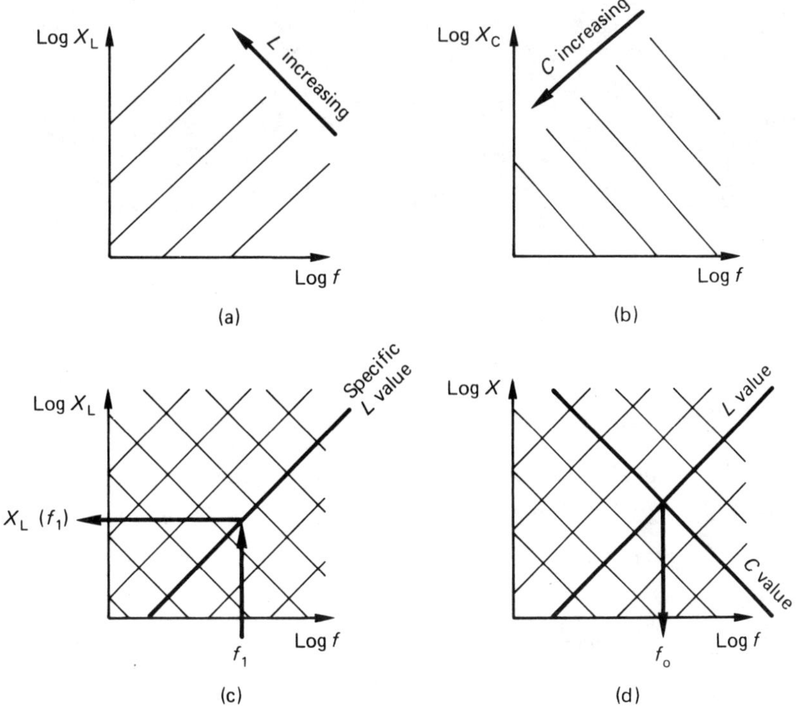

Figure B.2 Basis and use of the reactance chart

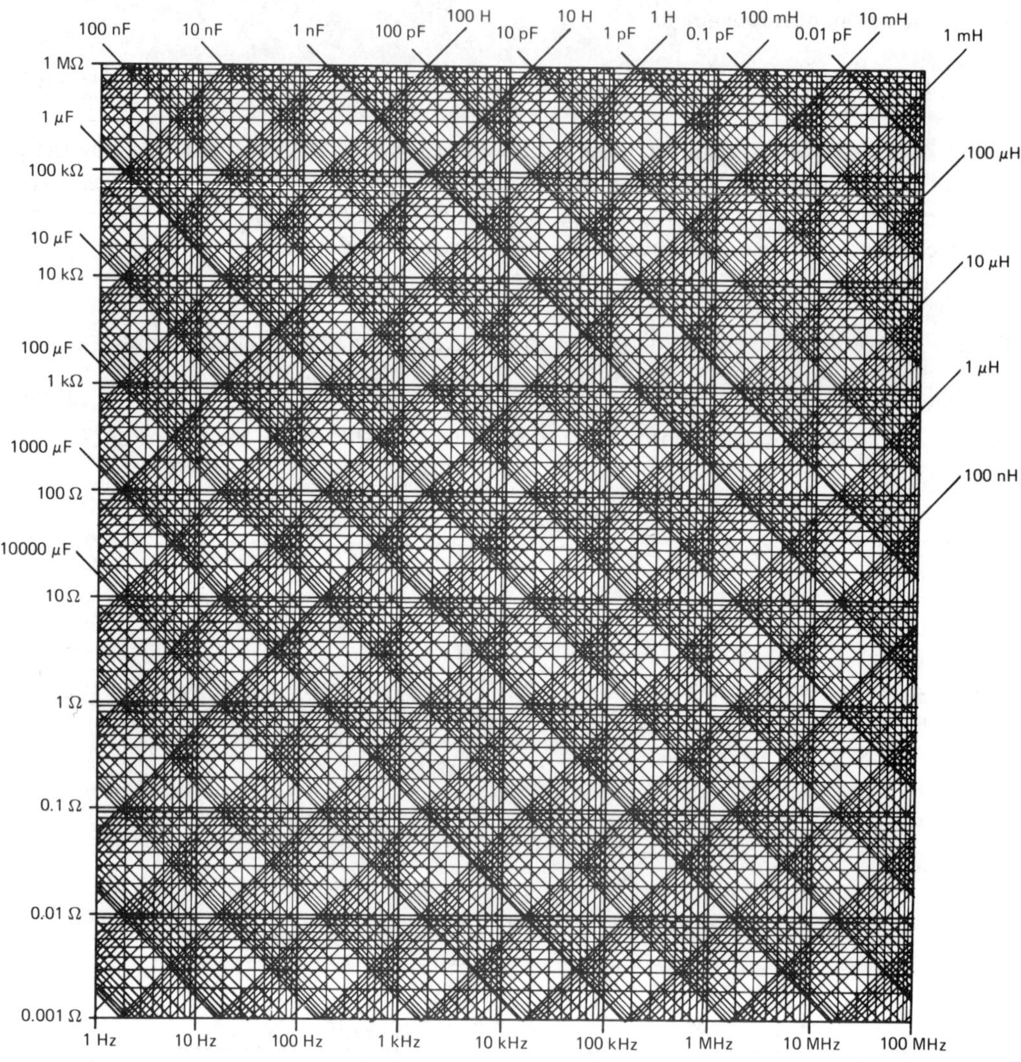

Figure B.3 Reactance chart

B.4 Reactance chart

From equations 2.38 and 2.26, inductive and capacitive reactances X_L and X_C are $2\pi fL$ and $1/2\pi fC$ respectively, noting that angular frequency ω is $2\pi f$, from which

$$\log X_L = \log f + \log(2\pi L) \qquad (B.36)$$

and

$$\log X_C = -\log f - \log(2\pi C) \qquad (B.37)$$

Plots of log X_L and log X_C against log f are therefore straight lines of slope +1 and −1 respectively, as shown in figures B.2a, b.

Combination of these two sets of plots using common reactance and frequency scales results in the reactance chart of figure B.3 which can be used to find the reactance of inductors and capacitors at any frequency in the range 1 Hz to 100 MHz. The appropriate diagonal L or C line is selected corresponding to the component value, and projecting from the frequency axis enables the reactance at a specific frequency f_1 to be determined as illustrated in figure B.2c. Also, because the X_L and X_C scales are common, the chart enables the resonant frequency f_o of an LC circuit to be read directly (figure B.2d) as at f_o, $X_L = X_C$ (equations B.2 and B.32).

Appendix C: Component Coding

Colour-coding is widely used to indicate the value and selection tolerance of resistors and some plastic-dielectric capacitors, the information being given by a series of coloured bands around the body of the component.

The colour code conforming to BS 1852:1967 and accepted by the International Electrotechnical Commission (IEC publication 62/1968) and the Electronics Industries Association (EIA) is given in table C.1.

Resistors

General-purpose resistors are produced mainly in the E12 and E24 ranges of *preferred* values (appendix D) and have a 4-band code (figure C.1a). Close-tolerance ($\leqslant \pm 1$ per cent) types are usually available in the E48 or E96 ranges and have a 5-band code (figure C.1a).

The code indicates the *nominal* value of resistance and the selection *tolerance* gives the range either side of the nominal value within which the *actual* resistance of an individual resistor is guaranteed to lie. Some precision types have an additional band, forming a 6-band code (figure C.1a), showing the temperature coefficient (TC) in parts/million (ppm)/degree Kelvin. For example, the resistance of a 1 kΩ resistor having a TC of 15 ppm/K will vary by no more than $1\ \text{k}\Omega \times \dfrac{15}{10^6} = 0.015\ \Omega$ per degree Kelvin change in temperature.

BS 1852 also recommends that in written resistor values, the Ω symbol and the position of the decimal point should be replaced by a letter:

R for the decimal point, giving the value in Ω

K for the decimal point and $\times\ 10^3\ \Omega$ (that is, kilohms, kΩ)

M for the decimal point and $\times\ 10^6\ \Omega$ (that is, megohms, MΩ)

Examples

R47 = 0.47 Ω   1K0 = 1 kΩ

4R7 = 4.7 Ω   47K = 47 kΩ

47R = 47 Ω   10M = 10 MΩ

In addition, IEC publication 62/1968 recommends the following tolerance codes

F ≡ ±1 per cent, G ≡ ±2 per cent, J ≡ ±5 per cent, K ≡ ±10 per cent,

M ≡ ±20 per cent

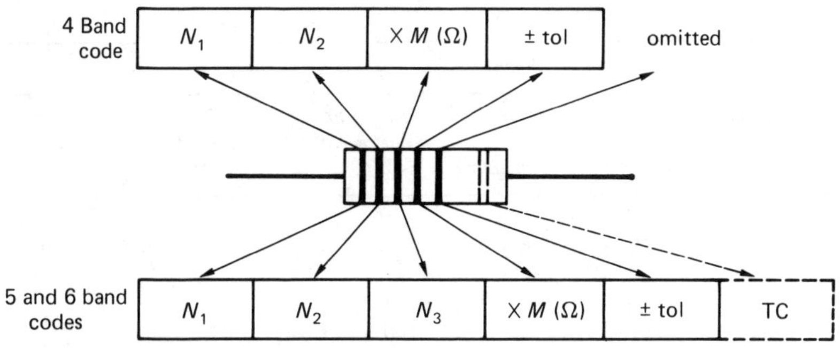

Examples:
4 band code: brown, black, red, red $\equiv 10 \times 10^2\,\Omega \pm 2\% = 1\,\text{k}\Omega \pm 2\%$
5 band code: brown, grey, red, orange, brown $\equiv 182 \times 10^3\,\Omega \pm 1\%$
$= 182\,\text{k}\Omega \pm 1\%$

(a) Resistor coding

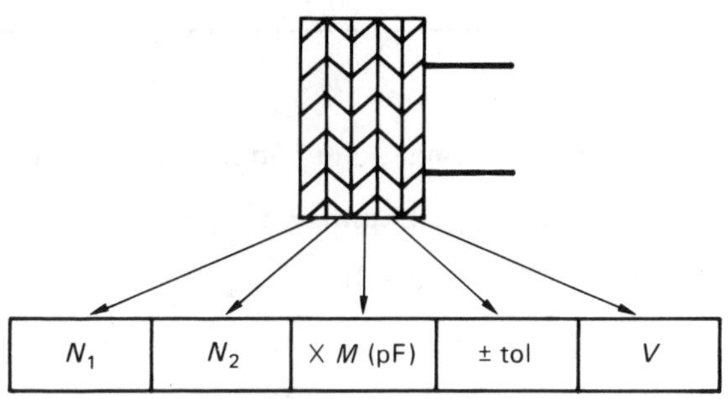

Example:
yellow, violet, yellow, white, red $\equiv 47 \times 10^4$ pF $\pm$ 10%, 250 V dc
= 0.47 μF $\pm$ 10%, 250 V dc

(b) Capacitor coding

Figure C.1 Resistor and capacitor colour-coding

Examples

A resistor coded: 390RJ is 390 Ω ± 5 per cent

68KF is 68 k$\Omega \pm 1$ per cent

4K7G is 4.7 kΩ ± 2 per cent

Capacitors

Some plastic-dielectric capacitors have the capacitance value, tolerance and dc working voltage colour coded on the capacitor body as represented in figure C.1b, the code being given in table C.1.

Capacitance values are given in μF ($\times 10^{-6}$ F), nF ($\times 10^{-9}$ F) or pF ($\times 10^{-12}$ F) as appropriate; the symbol μ can be replaced by U. As for resistance values, BS 1852 recommends

Table C.1 Component colour code

Colour	Significant figures N	Resistors: Multiplier M	Tolerance	Temperature coefficient TC*	Capacitors: Multiplier M	Tolerance T	dc working voltage V
Blank			±20%				
Silver		$\times 10^{-2}\,\Omega$	±10%				
Gold		$\times 10^{-1}\,\Omega$	±5%				
Black	0	$\times 1\,\Omega$			×1 pF	±20%	
Brown	1	$\times 10\,\Omega$	±1%	100 ppm/K	×10 pF		100 V
Red	2	$\times 10^{2}\,\Omega$	±2%	50 ppm/K	$\times 10^{2}$ pF		250 V
Orange	3	$\times 10^{3}\,\Omega$		15 ppm/K	$\times 10^{3}$ pF		
Yellow	4	$\times 10^{4}\,\Omega$		25 ppm/K	$\times 10^{4}$ pF		400 V
Green	5	$\times 10^{5}\,\Omega$	±0.5%		$\times 10^{5}$ pF	±5%	
Blue	6	$\times 10^{6}\,\Omega$	±0.25%		$\times 10^{6}$ pF		
Violet	7	$\times 10^{7}\,\Omega$	±0.1%				
Grey	8	$\times 10^{8}\,\Omega$			$\times 10^{-2}$ pF		
White	9	$\times 10^{9}\,\Omega$			$\times 10^{-1}$ pF	±10%	

* ppm = parts per million.

the use of a letter to represent the decimal point and multiplier in written capacitance values:

μ (micro-) or U for the decimal point and $\times 10^{-6}$ F

n (nano-) for the decimal point and $\times 10^{-9}$ F

p (pico-) for the decimal point and $\times 10^{-12}$ F

Examples

100μ or 100U = 100 μF

33n = 33 nF

2n2 = 2.2 nF (= 2200 pF)

n15 = 0.15 nF (= 150 pF)

68p = 68 pF

1p8 = 1.8 pF

Also the system of tolerance codes is extended for use with capacitors

C ≡ ±0.25 pF   J ≡ ±5 per cent

D ≡ ±0.5 pF   K ≡ ±10 per cent

F ≡ ±1 per cent   M ≡ ±20 per cent

G ≡ ±2 per cent   Z ≡ −20 per cent + 80 per cent

Examples

A capacitor coded: 6p8C is 6.8 pF ±0.25 pF

47nJ is 47 nF ±5 per cent

3300UZ is 3300 μF −20 per cent + 80 per cent

Ceramic capacitors are characterised according the value of the permittivity of the ceramic dielectric as high K, medium K or low K; the letter K referring to permittivity in place of ε (equation 2.30). High K types offer higher capacitance values but have relatively poor stability for change of temperature; low K types are usually only available in small capacitance values but offer good stability. The temperature coefficient of resin-dipped disc ceramic capacitors is often shown as a coloured band:

High K: green

Medium K: yellow

Low K:
- + 100 ppm/K: red/violet
- zero TC: black
- − 150 ppm/K: orange
- − 750 ppm/K: violet
- − 1500 ppm/K: double orange

Appendix D: Preferred (E-series) Component Values

A series of *preferred* or *standard* nominal values for components was devised originally so that all component values could be covered by the series of nominal values and the associated selection tolerance. The tolerances involved are ± 20 per cent, ± 10 per cent, ± 5 per cent, ± 2 per cent and ± 1 per cent, and the corresponding series of preferred values became known as the 20 per cent, 10 per cent, 5 per cent, 2 per cent and 1 per cent ranges. The five ranges comprise 6, 12, 24, 48 and 96 nominal values respectively and are now known (BS 2488:1966 and IEC publication 63) as the E6, E12, E24, E48 and E96 series respectively.

With reference to figure D.1, consider the establishment of the E6 or 20 per cent series. If the first nominal value in the decade is taken as 10, the range of values covered by this value with a selection tolerance of 20 per cent is 10 ± 20 per cent, that is, from 8 to 12. To avoid gaps in the range, the next nominal value (x) in the series must be such that $x - 20$ per cent $\leqslant 12$, from which $x = 15$ is chosen. The next nominal value (y) must be such that $y - 20$ per cent $\leqslant 15 + 20$ per cent, that is, $0.8y \leqslant 18$ or $y \leqslant 22.5$, and so the integer 22 is chosen as the next value. Figure D.1 shows that the ± 20 per cent range of the six values 10, 15, 22, 33, 47 and 68 covers the complete decade from 8 to 80. Similarly, the decades 0.8 to 8 and 80 to 800 are covered by the sub-multiple and multiple ranges 1.0, 1.5, 2.2, 3.3, 4.7, 6.8 and 100, 150, 220, 330, 470, 680 respectively. Note that the six base values in the E6 series are given *approximately* by the geometric (logarithmic) series $10^{n/6}$, $n = 0$–5 which gives values 1.0, 1.5, 2.2, 3.2, 4.6 and 6.8 each rounded to two significant figures.

For a lower selection tolerance, more values are required in the preferred range as provided in the E12, E24, E48 and E96 series shown below, as given approximately by the series $10^{n/12}$, $n = 0$–11; $10^{n/24}$, $n = 0$–23; $10^{n/48}$, $n = 0$–47 and $10^{n/96}$, $n = 0$–95 respectively.

The preferred ranges are

E6 (± 20 per cent) series 10, 15, 22, 33, 47, 68.

E12 (approximate ± 10 per cent) series 10, 12, 15, 18, 22, 27, 33, 39, 47, 56, 68, 82.

E24 (approximate ± 5 per cent) series 10, 11, 12, 13, 15, 16, 18, 20, 22, 24, 27, 30, 33, 36, 39, 43, 47, 51, 56, 62, 68, 75, 82, 91.

E48 (approximate ± 2 per cent) series 100, 105, 110, 115, 121, 127, 133, 140, 147, 154, 162, 169, 178, 187, 196, 205, 215, 226, 237, 249, 261, 274, 287, 301, 316, 332, 348, 365, 383, 402, 422, 442, 464, 487, 511, 536, 562, 590, 619, 649, 681, 715, 750, 787, 825, 866, 909, 953.

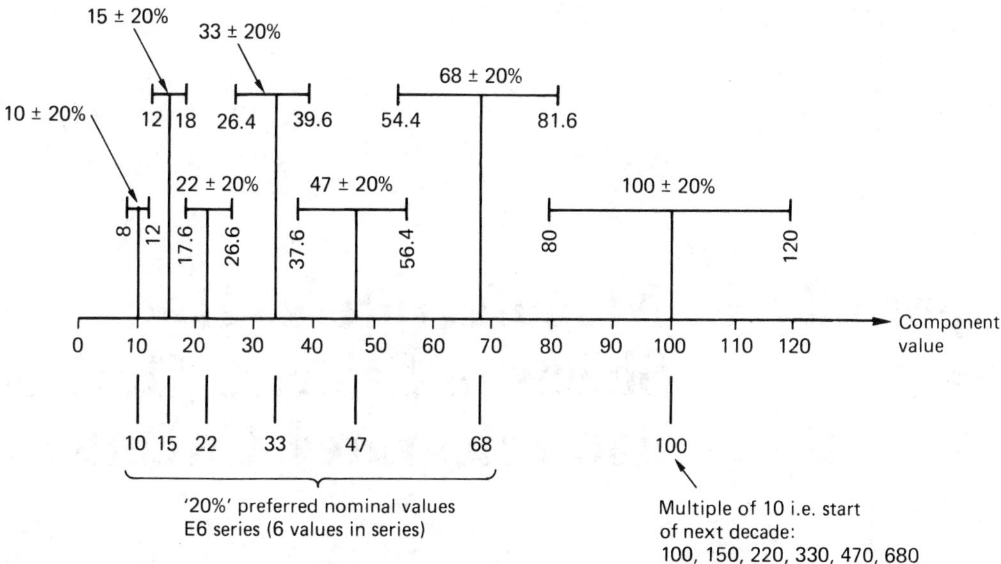

Figure D.1 E6 series of nominal component values

E96 (approximate ± 1 per cent) series 100, 102, 105, 107, 110, 113, 115, 118, 121, 124, 127, 130, 133, 137, 140, 143, 147, 150, 154, 158, 162, 165, 169, 174, 178, 182, 187, 191, 196, 200, 205, 210, 215, 221, 226, 232, 237, 243, 249, 255, 261, 267, 274, 280, 287, 294, 301, 309, 316, 324, 332, 340, 348, 357, 365, 374, 383, 392, 402, 412, 422, 432, 442, 453, 464, 475, 487, 499, 511, 523, 536, 549, 562, 576, 590, 604, 619, 634, 649, 665, 681, 698, 715, 732, 750, 768, 787, 806, 825, 845, 866, 887, 909, 931, 953, 976.

The E-number indicates the number of preferred values per decade.

General-purpose resistors are produced in the E12 and E24 series with some exceptions, capacitors are produced according to the E6 series. Although each series is associated with a certain selection tolerance, ranges of resistors having a certain selection tolerance may be produced in a lower E series, leaving gaps in the range. For example, Philips SFR 25 general-purpose metal-film resistors having a ± 2 per cent tolerance are produced in the E24 (± 5 per cent) series.

Appendix E: Manufacturers' Data Sheets of Selected Devices and Integrated Circuits

The data provided by a manufacturer for a particular type (number) of device includes typically:

(1) description of the device and a brief statement of intended applications;
(2) abridged data giving absolute maximum ratings;
(3) electrical performance for particular operating conditions;
(4) thermal properties;
(5) mechanical details: package style and dimensions;
(6) variation of electrical parameters/properties with operating conditions (for example, current, voltage, frequency, temperature); this information is usually presented graphically.

It must be emphasised that the data provided relates directly to the intended use of the device, thus for a low-power BJT intended for use as an amplifier at audio frequencies, *h*-parameter information would be supplied in considerable detail but there may be little information as to the switching performance. Alternatively, a large proportion of the data supplied for a high-power device is likely to be concerned with safe operating conditions (SOAR information) while devices intended for switching or high-frequency linear operation have detailed information on the device capacitance/or frequency response.

The information provided in this appendix illustrates the properties and performance of typical devices. The data for the BAX13 signal diode, BZX79 and BZV85 ranges of voltage-reference diodes, BY224 bridge rectifier, the BC 107–9 range of AF npn BJTs and the type 741 op-amp is reproduced by permission of Philips Components Limited. Information for the TIP 31 range of npn power BJTs is provided by courtesy of Texas Instruments Limited while details of the J 201 series of n-channel JFETs and the VN 46 AFD n-channel enhancement-type VMOS power FET is included with the permission of Siliconix Limited.

E.1 Philips signal diode type BAX13

BAX13

SILICON OXIDE PASSIVATED DIODE

Whiskerless diode in a glass subminiature envelope.
The BAX13 is primarily intended for general purpose applications.

QUICK REFERENCE DATA

Continuous reverse voltage	V_R	max.	50 V
Repetitive peak reverse voltage	V_{RRM}	max.	50 V
Repetitive peak forward current	I_{FRM}	max.	150 mA
Thermal resistance from junction to ambient	$R_{th\ j\text{-}a}$	=	0,60 °C/mW
Forward voltage at I_F = 20 mA	V_F	<	1,0 V
Reverse recovery time when switched from I_F = 10 mA to I_R = 60 mA; R_L = 100 Ω measured at I_R = 1 mA	t_{rr}	<	4 ns
Recovery charge when switched from I_F = 10 mA to V_R = 5 V; R_L = 500 Ω	Q_s	<	45 pC

MECHANICAL DATA Dimensions in mm

DO - 35

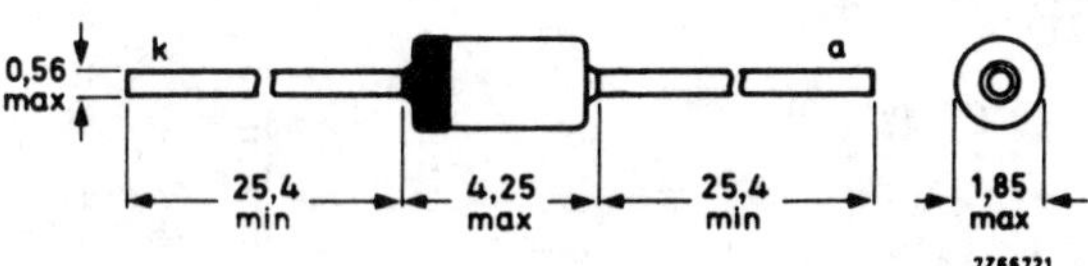

The coloured end indicates the cathode
The diodes may be type-branded or colour coded.

BAX13

RATINGS Limiting values in accordance with the Absolute Maximum System (IEC 134)

Voltages				
Continuous reverse voltage	V_R	max.	50	V
Repetitive peak reverse voltage	V_{RRM}	max.	50	V
Currents				
Average rectified forward current (averaged over any 20 ms period)	$I_{F(AV)}$	max.	75	mA
Forward current (d.c.)	I_F	max.	75	mA
Repetitive peak forward current	I_{FRM}	max.	150	mA
Non-repetitive peak forward current t = 1 µs	I_{FSM}	max.	2000	mA
t = 1 s	I_{FSM}	max.	500	mA
Temperatures				
Storage temperature	T_{stg}		−65 to +200	°C
Junction temperature	T_j	max.	200	°C

THERMAL RESISTANCE

From junction to ambient in free air	$R_{th\ j\text{-}a}$	=	0,60	°C/mW

CHARACTERISTICS T_j = 25 °C unless otherwise specified

Forward voltage					
I_F = 2 mA	V_F	<	0,7	V	
I_F = 10 mA; T_j = 100 °C	V_F	<	0,8	V	
I_F = 20 mA	V_F	<	1,0	V	[1]
I_F = 75 mA	V_F	<	1,53	V	[1]
Reverse current					
V_R = 10 V	I_R	<	25	nA	
V_R = 10 V; T_j = 150 °C	I_R	<	10	µA	
V_R = 25 V	I_R	<	50	nA	
V_R = 50 V	I_R	<	200	nA	
V_R = 50 V; T_j = 150 °C	I_R	<	25	µA	
Diode capacitance					
V_R = 0; f = 1 MHz	C_d	<	3	pF	

1) Measured under pulse conditions to avoid excessive dissipation.

Silicon oxide passivated diode

BAX13

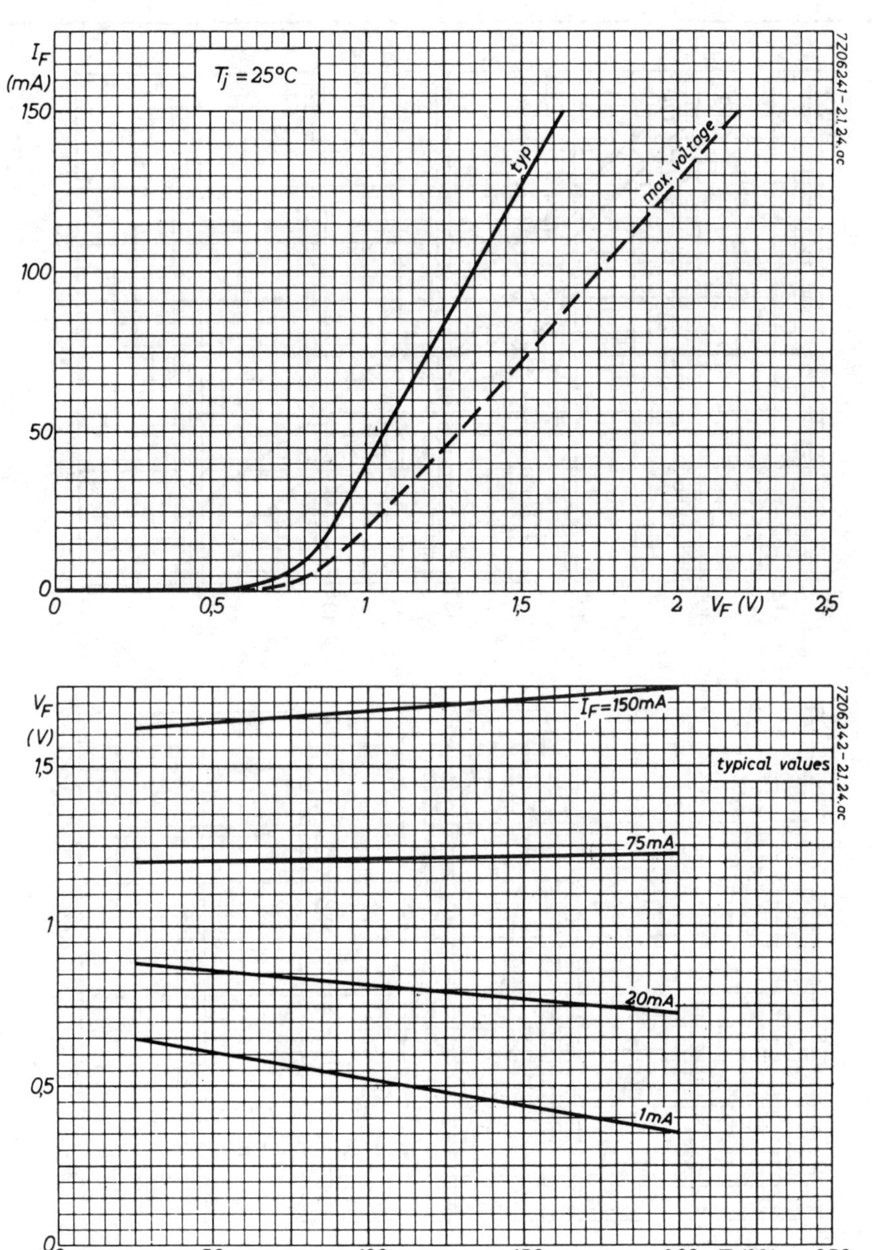

BAX13

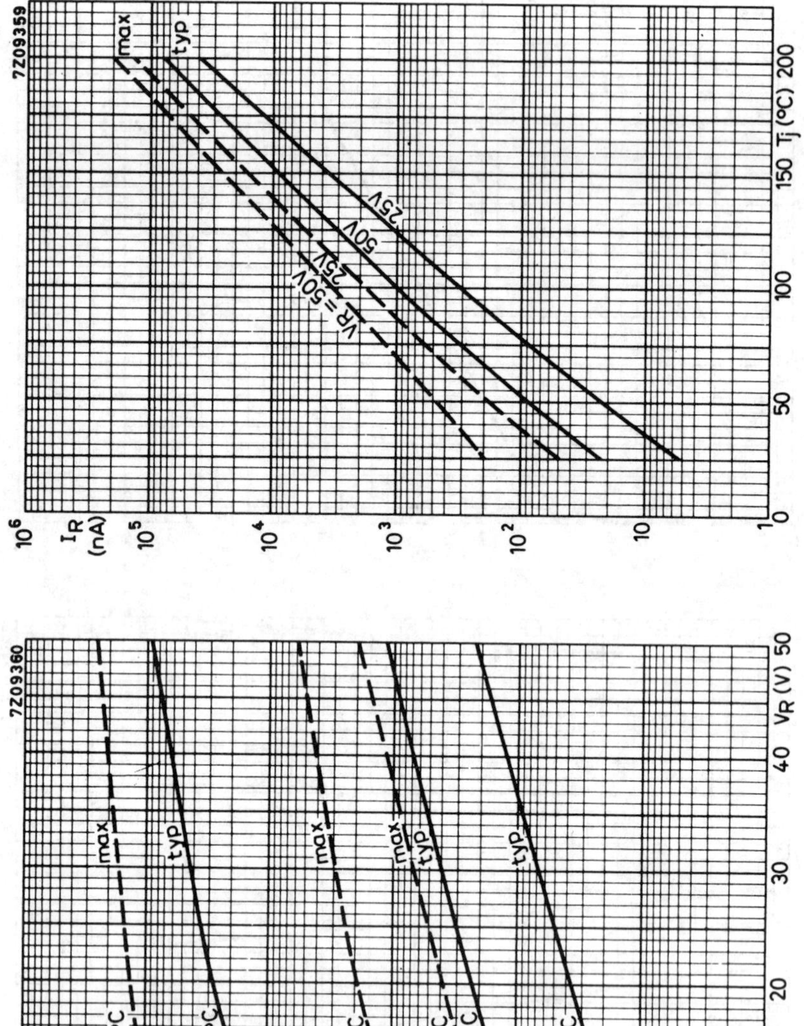

7Z09359
I_R (nA)
T_j (°C)
max
typ
V_R = 50V
25V
50V
25V
7Z09360
V_R (V)
T_j = 150°C
150°C
55°C
25°C
55°C
25°C

Silicon oxide passivated diode BAX13

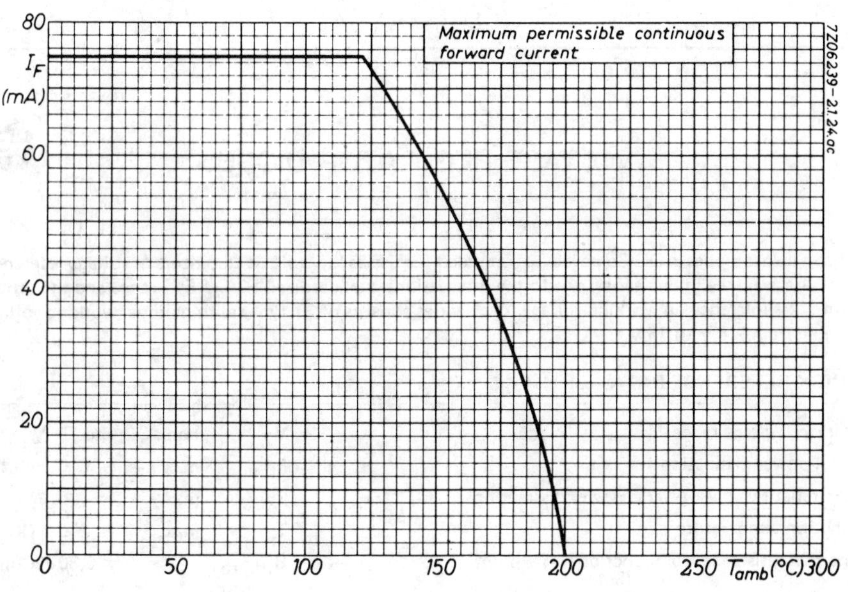

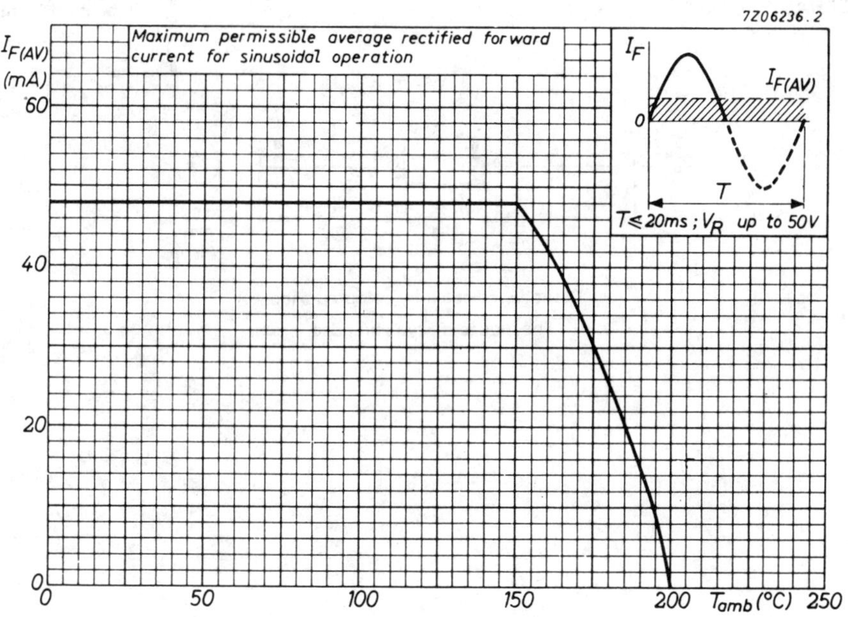

E.2 Philips voltage-reference diode type BZX79

BZX79 SERIES

VOLTAGE REGULATOR DIODES

Silicon planar diodes in DO-35 envelopes intended for use as low voltage stabilizers or voltage references. They are available in two series; one to the international standardized E24 (± 5%) range and the other with ± 2% tolerance on working voltage. Each series consists of 37 types with nominal working voltages ranging from 2,4 V to 75 V.

QUICK REFERENCE DATA

Working voltage range	V_Z	nom.	2,4 to 75 V
Total power dissipation	P_{tot}	max.	500 mW *
Non-repetitive peak reverse power dissipation	P_{ZSM}	max.	30 W
Junction temperature	T_j	max.	200 °C
Thermal resistance from junction to tie-point	$R_{th\ j\text{-}tp}$	=	0,30 °C/mW

* If leads are kept at T_{tp} = 50 °C at 8 mm from body.

MECHANICAL DATA

Dimensions in mm

Fig. 1 DO-35.

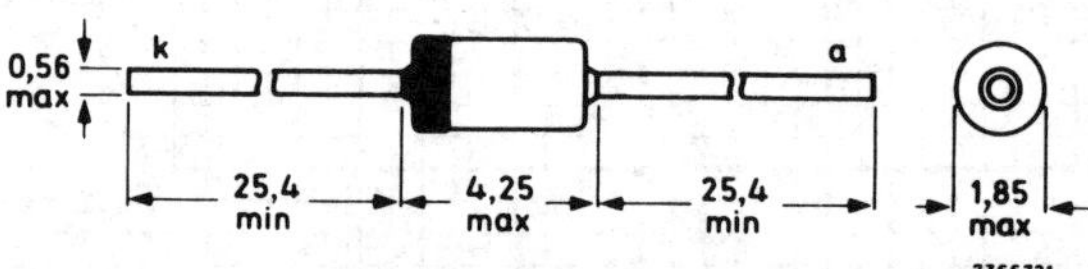

Cathode indicated by coloured band.

The diodes are type-branded

BZX79 SERIES

RATINGS

Limiting values in accordance with the Absolute Maximum System (IEC 134)

Average forward current (averaged over any 20 ms period)	$I_{F(AV)}$	max.	250 mA
Repetitive peak forward current	I_{FRM}	max.	250 mA
Total power dissipation	P_{tot}	max.	500 mW *
		max.	400 mW **
Non-repetitive peak reverse power dissipation $t = 100\ \mu s$; $T_j = 150\ ^oC$	P_{ZSM}	max.	30 W
Storage temperature	T_{stg}		−65 to + 200 °C
Junction temperature	T_j	max.	200 °C

THERMAL RESISTANCE

From junction to tie-point	$R_{th\ j\text{-}tp}$	=	0,30 °C/mW *
From junction to ambient	$R_{th\ j\text{-}a}$	=	0,38 °C/mW **

CHARACTERISTICS

$T_j = 25\ ^oC$

Forward voltage $I_F = 10$ mA		V_F	<	0,9 V
Reverse current				
BZX79-.2V4	$V_R = 1$ V	I_R	<	50 μA
.2V7	$V_R = 1$ V	I_R	<	20 μA
.3V0	$V_R = 1$ V	I_R	<	10 μA
.3V3	$V_R = 1$ V	I_R	<	5 μA
.3V6	$V_R = 1$ V	I_R	<	5 μA
.3V9	$V_R = 1$ V	I_R	<	3 μA
.4V3	$V_R = 1$ V	I_R	<	3 μA
.4V7	$V_R = 2$ V	I_R	<	3 μA
.5V1	$V_R = 2$ V	I_R	<	2 μA
.5V6	$V_R = 2$ V	I_R	<	1 μA
.6V2	$V_R = 4$ V	I_R	<	3 μA
.6V8	$V_R = 4$ V	I_R	<	2 μA
.7V5	$V_R = 5$ V	I_R	<	1 μA
.8V2	$V_R = 5$ V	I_R	<	700 nA
.9V1	$V_R = 6$ V	I_R	<	500 nA
.10	$V_R = 7$ V	I_R	<	200 nA
.11 to .13	$V_R = 8$ V	I_R	<	100 nA
.15 to .75	$V_R = 0{,}7\ V_{Znom}$	I_R	<	50 nA

. = B for 2% tolerance
. = C for E24 (± 5%) tolerance

* If leads are kept at $T_{tp} = 50\ ^oC$ at 8 mm from body. For the types 2V4 and 2V7 the power
* dissipation is limited by $T_{j\ max} = 150\ ^oC$.
** In still air at maximum lead length up to $T_{amb} = 50\ ^oC$.

Voltage regulator diodes

BZX79 SERIES

$T_j = 25\ ^oC$

E24 (± 5%) logarithmic range for ± 2% tolerance range

BZX79-...	working voltage V_Z (V)		differential resistance r_{diff} (Ω)		temperature coefficient S_Z (mV/^oC)			diode capacitance C_d(pF); f = 1 MHz $V_R = 0$	
	at I_{Ztest} = 5 mA		at I_{Ztest} = 5 mA		at I_{Ztest} = 5 mA				
	min.	max.	typ.	max.	min.	typ.	max.	typ.	max.
C2V4	2,2	2,6	70	100	−3,5	−1,6	0	375	450
C2V7	2,5	2,9	75	100	−3,5	−2,0	0	350	450
C3V0	2,8	3,2	80	95	−3,5	−2,1	0	350	450
C3V3	3,1	3,5	85	95	−3,5	−2,4	0	325	450
C3V6	3,4	3,8	85	90	−3,5	−2,4	0	300	450
C3V9	3,7	4,1	85	90	−3,5	−2,5	0	300	450
C4V3	4,0	4,6	80	90	−3,5	−2,5	0	275	450
C4V7	4,4	5,0	50	80	−3,5	−1,4	0,2	245	300
C5V1	4,8	5,4	40	60	−2,7	−0,8	1,2	235	300
C5V6	5,2	6,0	15	40	−2,0	1,2	2,5	225	300
C6V2	5,8	6,6	6	10	0,4	2,3	3,7	125	200
C6V8	6,4	7,2	6	15	1,2	3,0	4,5	105	200
C7V5	7,0	7,9	6	15	2,5	4,0	5,3	95	150
C8V2	7,7	8,7	6	15	3,2	4,6	6,2	90	150
C9V1	8,5	9,6	6	15	3,8	5,5	7,0	70	150
C10	9,4	10,6	8	20	4,5	6,4	8,0	70	90
C11	10,4	11,6	10	20	5,4	7,4	9,0	65	85
C12	11,4	12,7	10	25	6,0	8,4	10,0	65	85
C13	12,4	14,1	10	30	7,0	9,4	11,0	60	80
C15	13,8	15,6	10	30	9,2	11,4	13,0	55	75
C16	15,3	17,1	10	40	10,4	12,4	14,0	52	75
C18	16,8	19,1	10	45	12,4	14,4	16,0	47	70
C20	18,8	21,2	15	55	14,4	16,4	18,0	36	60
C22	20,8	23,3	20	55	16,4	18,4	20,0	34	60
C24	22,8	25,6	25	70	18,4	20,4	22,0	33	55
	at I_{Ztest} = 2 mA		at I_{Ztest} = 2 mA		at I_{Ztest} = 2 mA				
C27	25,1	28,9	25	80	21,4	23,4	25,3	30	50
C30	28,0	32,0	30	80	24,4	26,6	29,4	27	50
C33	31,0	35,0	35	80	27,4	29,7	33,4	25	45
C36	34,0	38,0	35	90	30,4	33,0	37,4	23	45
C39	37,0	41,0	40	130	33,4	36,4	41,2	21	45
C43	40,0	46,0	45	150	37,6	41,2	46,6	21	40
C47	44,0	50,0	50	170	42,0	46,1	51,8	19	40
C51	48,0	54,0	60	180	46,6	51,0	57,2	19	40
C56	52,0	60,0	70	200	52,2	57,0	63,8	18	40
C62	58,0	66,0	80	215	58,8	64,4	71,6	17	35
C68	64,0	72,0	90	240	65,6	71,7	79,8	17	35
C75	70,0	79,0	95	255	73,4	80,2	88,6	16,5	35

BZX79 SERIES

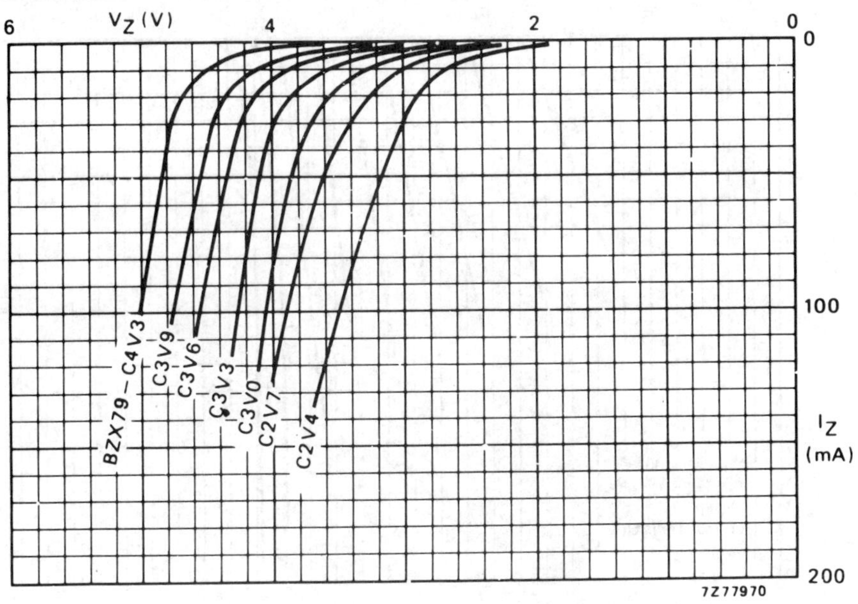

Static characteristics; typical values; T_{amb} = 25 °C.

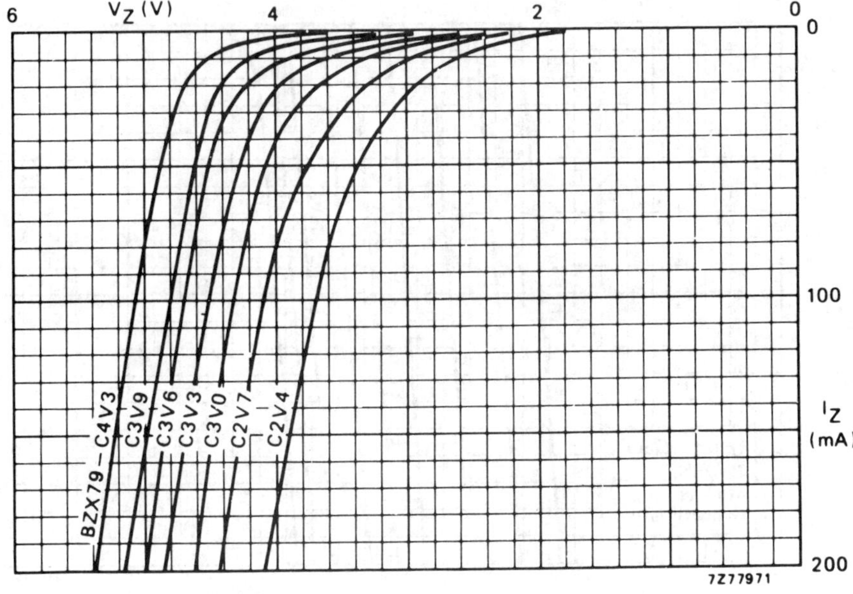

Dynamic characteristics; typical values; T_j = 25 °C.

Voltage regulator diodes

BZX79 SERIES

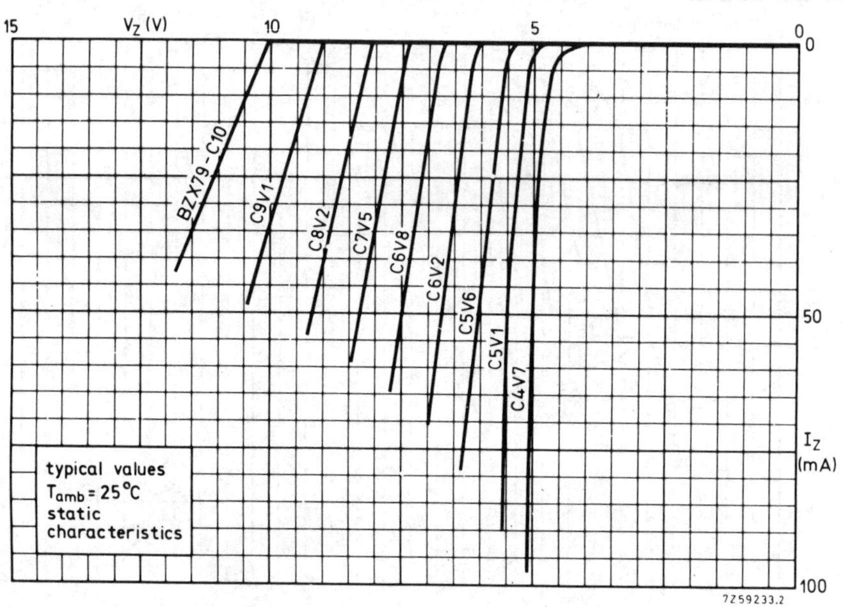

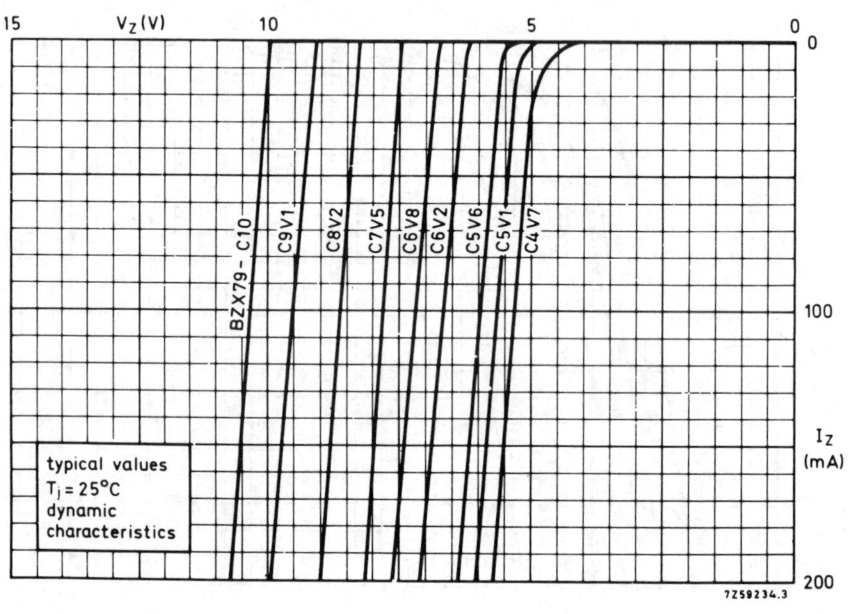

BZX79 SERIES

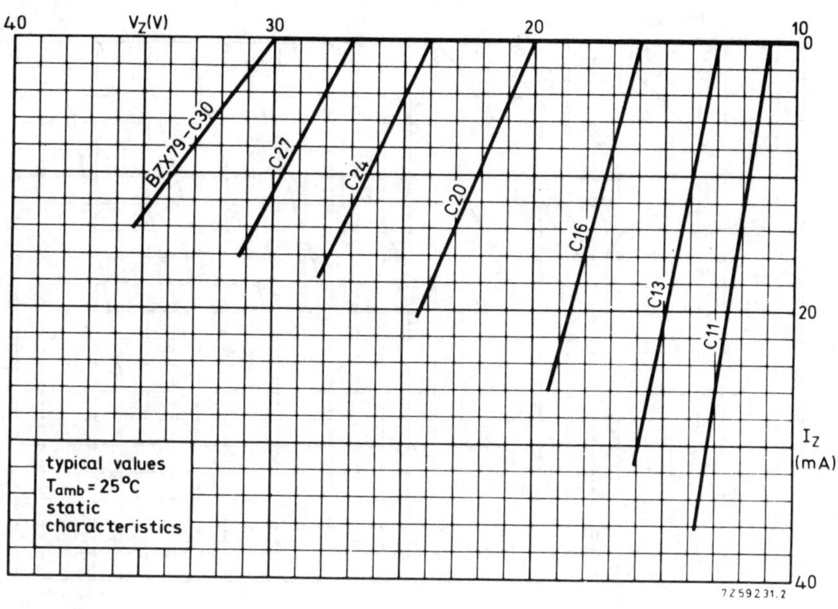

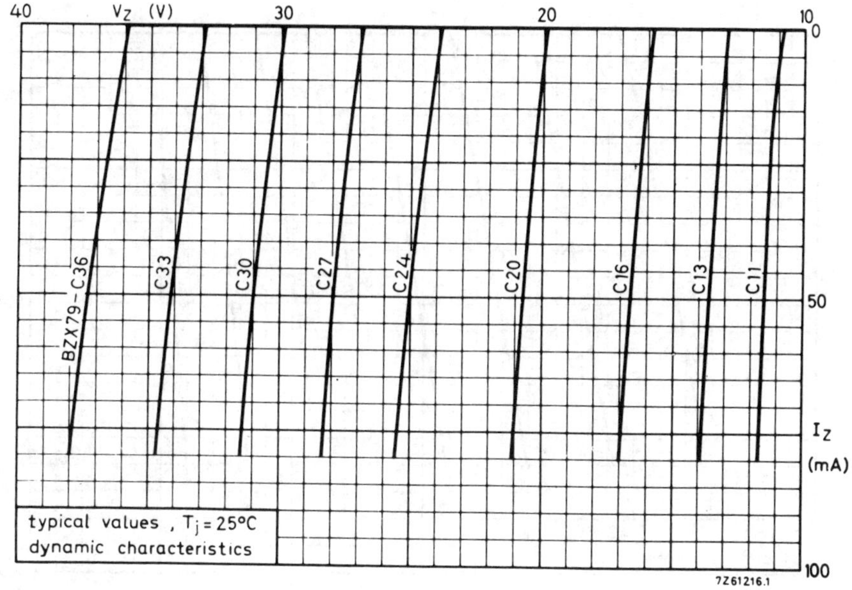

Voltage regulator diodes

BZX79 SERIES

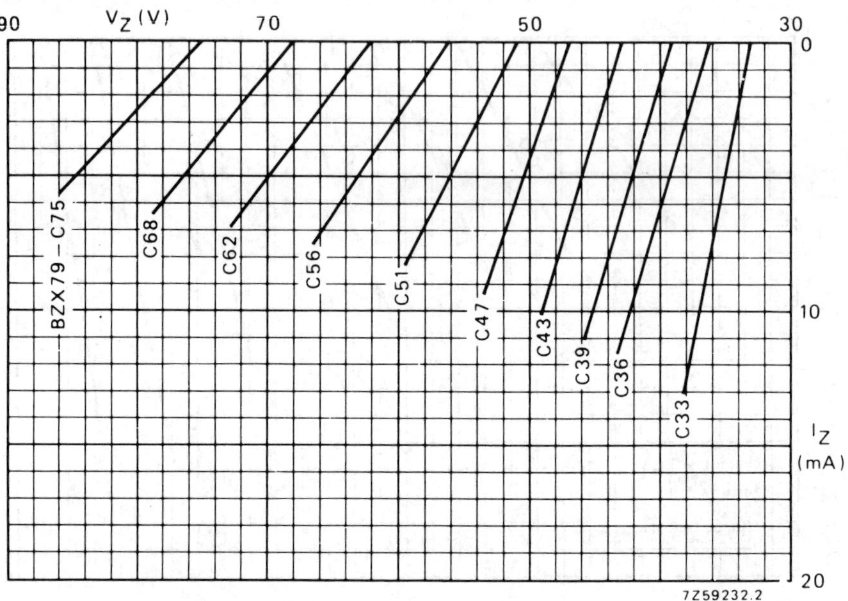

Static characteristics; typical values; T_{amb} = 25 °C.

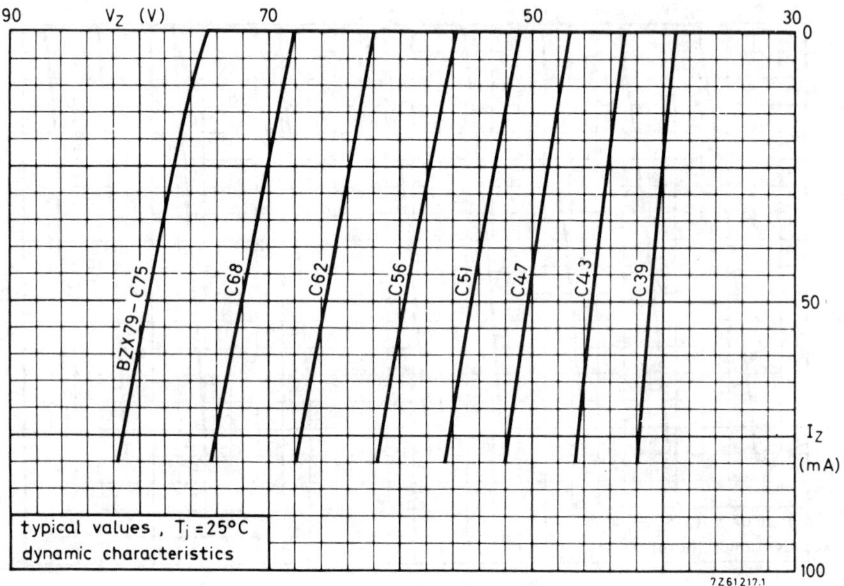

BZX79 SERIES

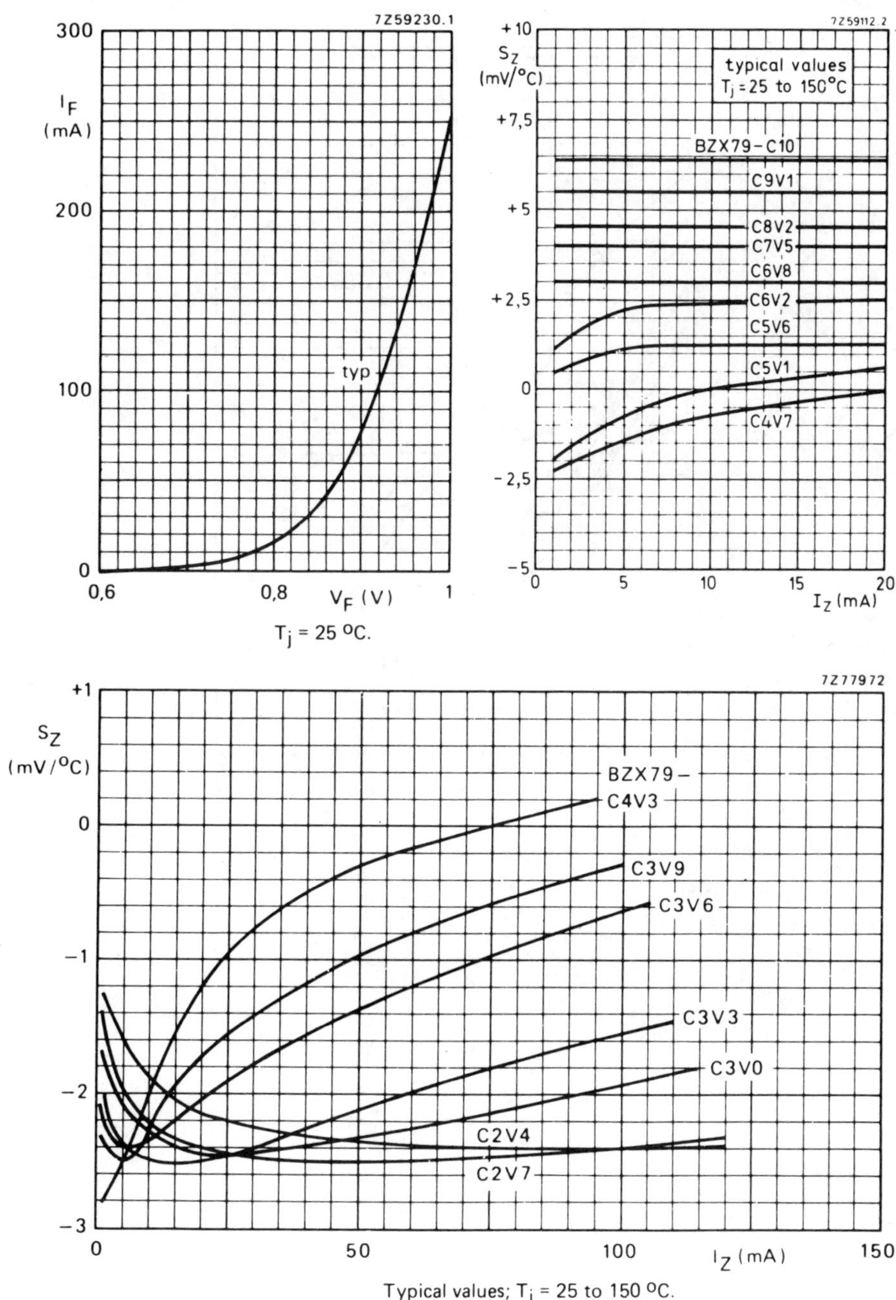

Typical values; T_j = 25 to 150 °C.

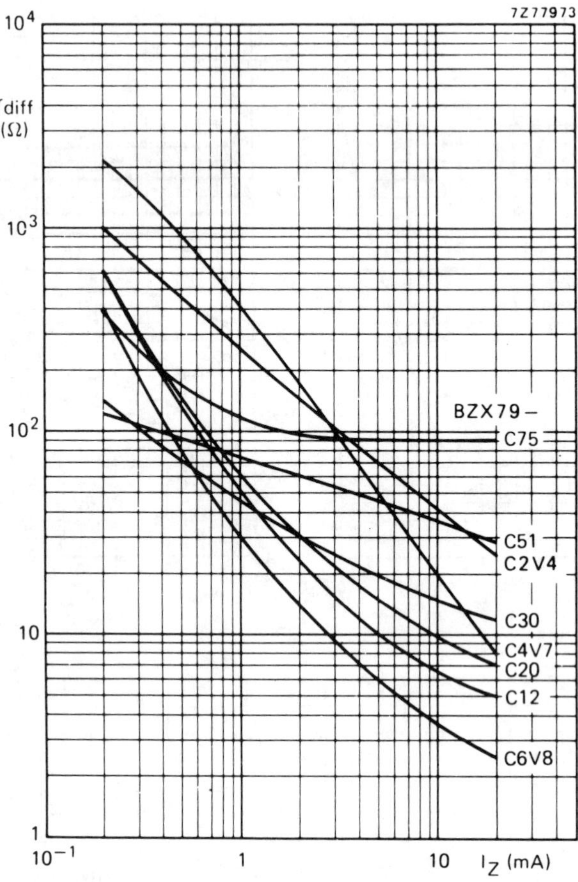

Typical values; T_j = 25 °C; f = 1 kHz.

E.3 Philips voltage-reference diode type BZV85

BZV85 SERIES

VOLTAGE REGULATOR DIODES

Silicon planar voltage regulator diodes in hermetically sealed DO-41 glass envelopes intended for stabilization purposes. The series covers the normalized E24 (± 5%) range of nominal working voltages ranging from 3,6 V to 75 V.

QUICK REFERENCE DATA

Working voltage range	V_Z	nom.	3,6 to 75 V
Total power dissipation	P_{tot}	max.	1,3 W*
Non-repetitive peak reverse power dissipation t_p = 100 μs; T_j = 25 °C	P_{ZSM}	max.	60 W
Junction temperature	T_j	max.	200 °C
Thermal resistance from junction to tie-point	$R_{th\ j\text{-}tp}$	=	110 K/W*

* If leads are kept at T_{tp} = 55 °C at 4 mm from body.

MECHANICAL DATA

Dimensions in mm

Fig. 1 DO-41 (SOD-66).

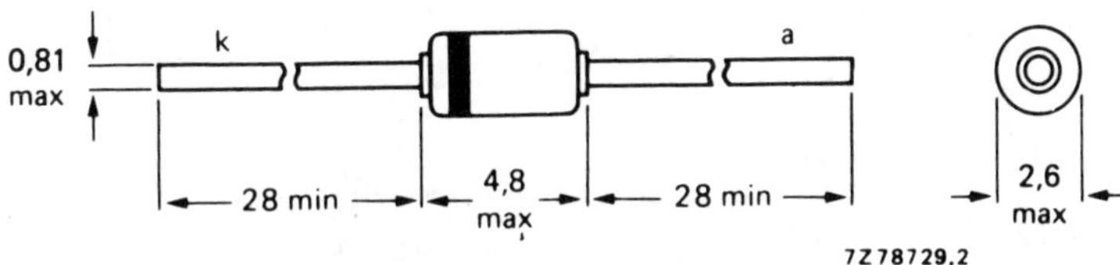

Cathode indicated by coloured band.

The diodes are type-branded.

BZV85 SERIES

RATINGS

Limiting values in accordance with the Absolute Maximum System (IEC 134)

Working current (d.c.)	I_Z	limited by $P_{tot\,max}$
Non-repetitive peak reverse current t_p = 10 ms; half sine-wave; T_{amb} = 25 °C	I_{ZSM}	see table below
Repetitive peak forward current	I_{FRM}	max. 250 mA
Total power dissipation (see also Fig. 2)	P_{tot}	max. 1,30 W* max. 1 W**
Non-repetitive peak reverse power dissipation t_p = 100 μs; T_j = 25 °C	P_{ZSM}	max. 60 W
Storage temperature	T_{stg}	−65 to + 200 °C
Junction temperature	T_j	max. 200 °C

THERMAL RESISTANCE

From junction to tie-point	$R_{th\,j\text{-}tp}$	= 110 K/W*
From junction to ambient mounted on a printed-circuit board	$R_{th\,j\text{-}a}$	= 175 K/W**

BZV85–....	Non-repetitive peak reverse current I_{ZSM} (mA) max.
C3V6	2000
C3V9	1950
C4V3	1850
C4V7	1800
C5V1	1750
C5V6	1700
C6V2	1620
C6V8	1550
C7V5	1500
C8V2	1400
C9V1	1340
C10	1200
C11	1100
C12	1000
C13	900
C15	760
C16	700

BZV85–...	Non-repetitive peak reverse current I_{ZSM} (mA) max.
C18	600
C20	540
C22	500
C24	450
C27	400
C30	380
C33	350
C36	320
C39	296
C43	270
C47	246
C51	226
C56	208
C62	186
C68	171
C75	161

* If the temperature of the leads at 4 mm from the body are kept up to T_{tp} = 55 °C.

** Measured in still air up to T_{amb} = 25 °C and mounted on printed-circuit board with lead length of 10 mm and print copper area of 1 cm^2 per lead.

Voltage regulator diodes

BZV85 SERIES

CHARACTERISTICS

$T_j = 25\ ^oC$

Forward voltage at $I_F = 50$ mA $V_F < 1,0$ V

	working voltage E24 (± 5%) V_Z (V) at I_{Ztest}			test current I_{Ztest} (mA)	differential resistance r_{diff} (Ω) at I_{Ztest}	temperature coefficient S_Z (mV/K) at I_{Ztest}		reverse current I_R (μA) at V_R	test voltage V_R (V)
BZV85–. . . .	min.	nom.	max.		max.	min.	max.	max.	
C3V6	3,4	3,6	3,8	60	15	–3,5	–1,0	50	1,0
C3V9	3,7	3,9	4,1	60	15	–3,5	–1,0	10	1,0
C4V3	4,0	4,3	4,6	50	13	–2,7	0	5	1,0
C4V7	4,4	4,7	5,0	45	13	–2,0	0,7	3	1,0
C5V1	4,8	5,1	5,4	45	10	–0,5	2,2	3	2,0
C5V6	5,2	5,6	6,0	45	7	0	2,7	2	2,0
C6V2	5,8	6,2	6,6	35	4	0,6	3,6	2	3,0
C6V8	6,4	6,8	7,2	35	3,5	1,3	4,3	2	4,0
C7V5	7,0	7,5	7,9	35	3	2,5	5,5	1	4,5
C8V2	7,7	8,2	8,7	25	5	3,1	6,1	0,7	5,0
C9V1	8,5	9,1	9,6	25	5	3,8	7,2	0,7	6,5
C10	9,4	10	10,6	25	8	4,7	8,5	0,2	7,0
C11	10,4	11	11,6	20	10	5,3	9,3	0,2	7,7
C12	11,4	12	12,7	20	10	6,3	10,8	0,2	8,4
C13	12,4	13	14,1	20	10	7,4	12,0	0,2	9,1
C15	13,8	15	15,6	15	15	8,9	13,6	0,05	10,5
C16	15,3	16	17,1	15	15	10,7	15,4	0,05	11,0
C18	16,8	18	19,1	15	20	11,8	17,1	0,05	12,5
C20	18,8	20	21,2	10	24	13,6	19,1	0,05	14,0
C22	20,8	22	23,3	10	25	16,6	22,1	0,05	15,5
C24	22,8	24	25,6	10	30	18,3	24,3	0,05	17
C27	25,1	27	28,9	8	40	20,1	27,5	0,05	19
C30	28	30	32	8	45	22,4	32,0	0,05	21
C33	31	33	35	8	45	24,8	35,0	0,05	23
C36	34	36	38	8	50	27,2	39,9	0,05	25
C39	37	39	41	6	60	29,6	43,0	0,05	27
C43	40	43	46	6	75	34,0	48,3	0,05	30
C47	44	47	50	4	100	37,4	52,5	0,05	33
C51	48	51	54	4	125	40,8	56,5	0,05	36
C58	52	56	60	4	150	46,8	63,0	0,05	39
C62	58	62	66	4	175	52,2	72,5	0,05	43
C68	64	68	72	4	200	60,5	81,0	0,05	48
C75	70	75	80	4	225	66,5	88,0	0,05	53

BZV85 SERIES

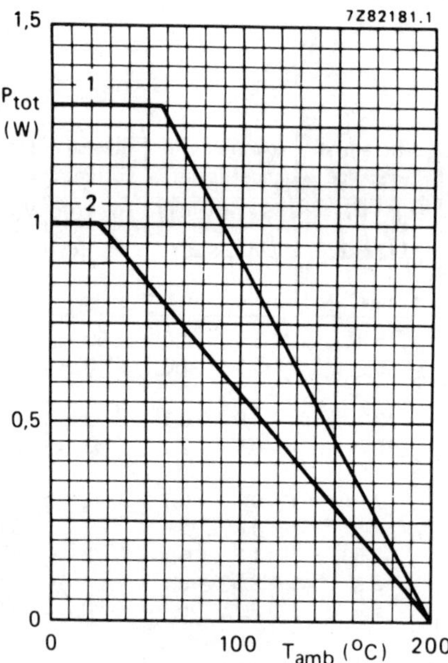

Fig. 2 Maximum permissible power dissipation versus ambient temperature.

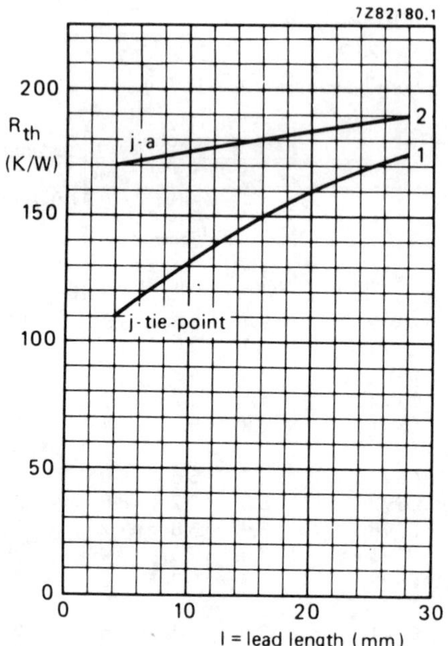

Fig. 3 Thermal resistance versus lead length.

Mounting methods (see Figs 2 and 3)

1. To tie-points (lead length = 4 mm in Fig. 2).
2. Mounted on a printed-circuit board (with lead length of 10 mm in Fig. 2) and print copper area of 1 cm^2 per lead.

BZV85 SERIES

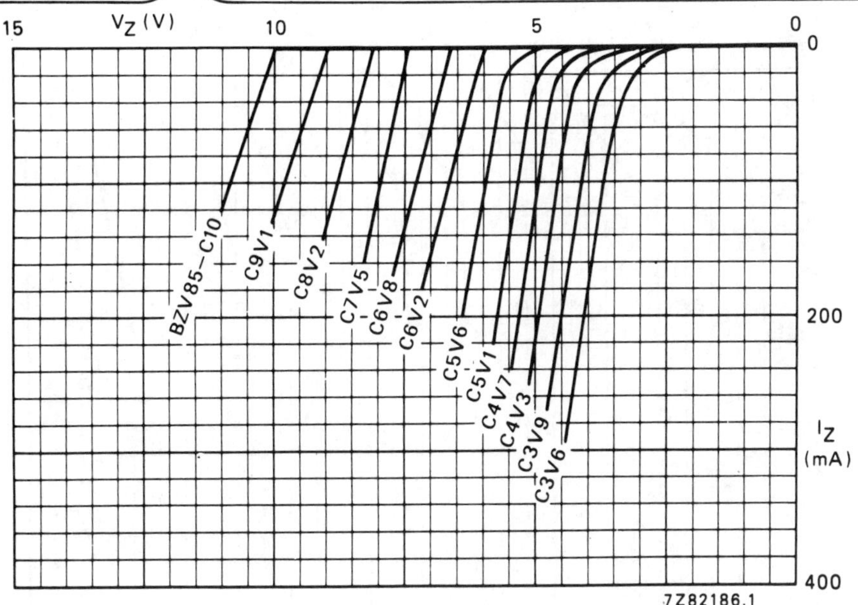

Static characteristics; typical values; T_{amb} = 25 °C.

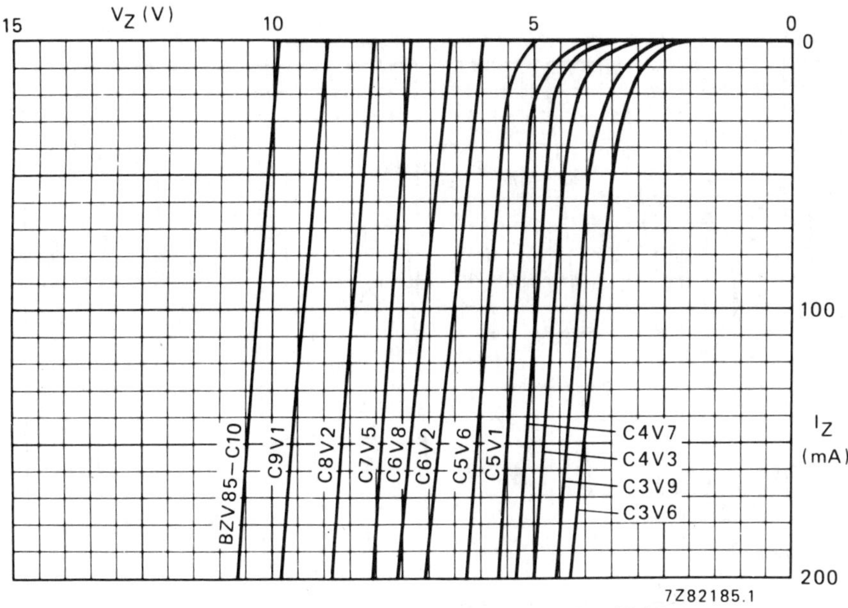

Dynamic characteristics; typical values; T_j = 25 °C.

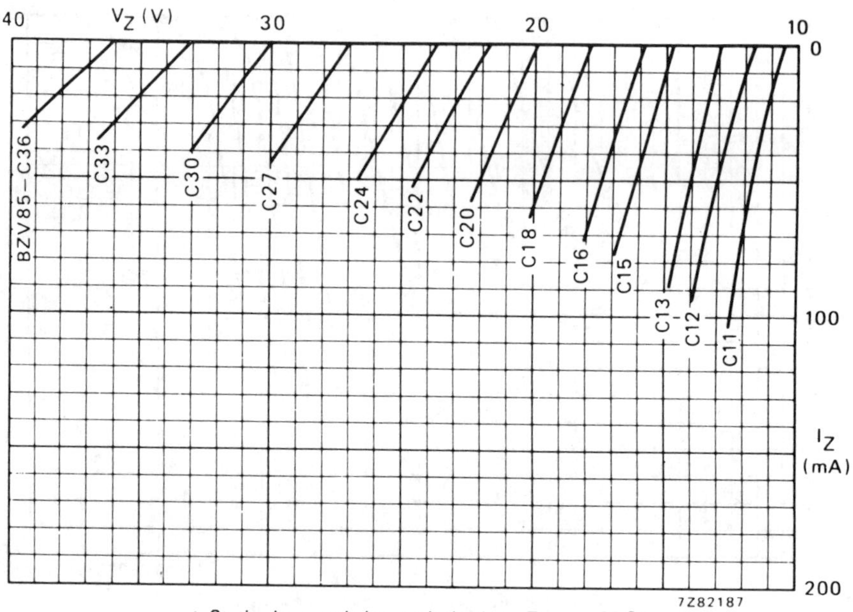

Static characteristics; typical values; T_{amb} = 25 °C.

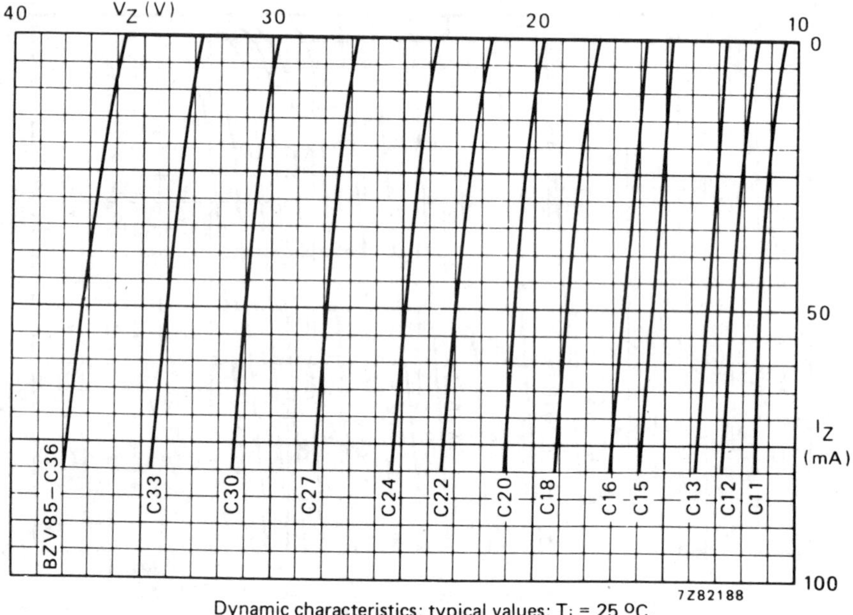

Dynamic characteristics; typical values; T_j = 25 °C.

BZV85 SERIES

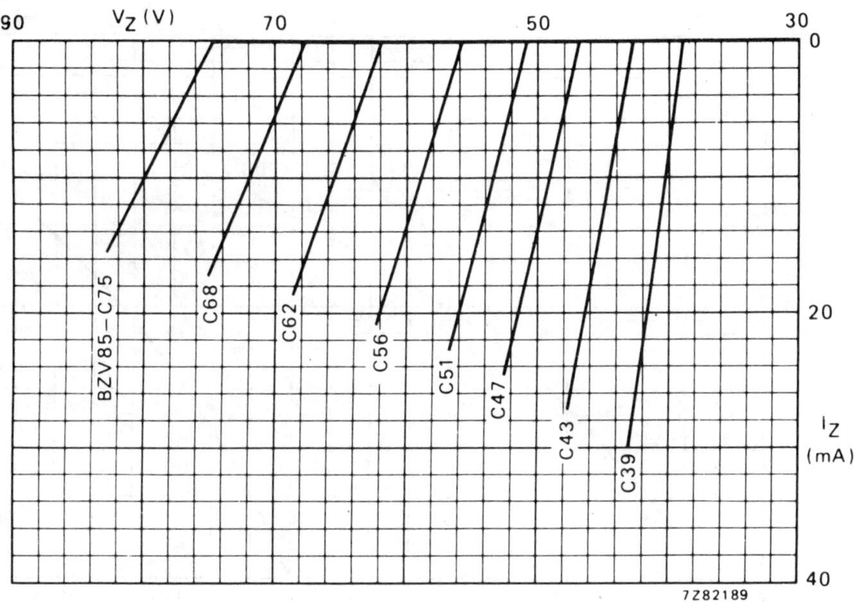

Static characteristics; typical values; T_{amb} = 25 °C.

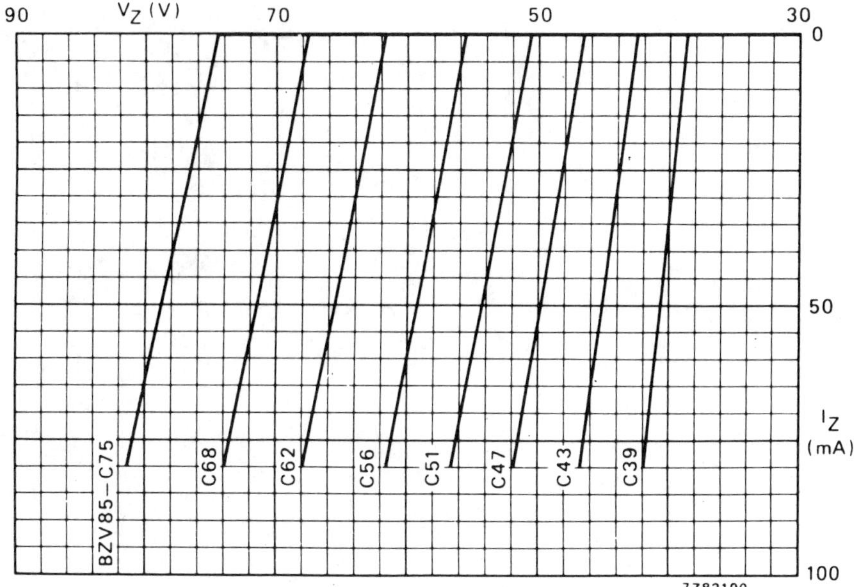

Dynamic characteristics; typical values; T_j = 25 °C.

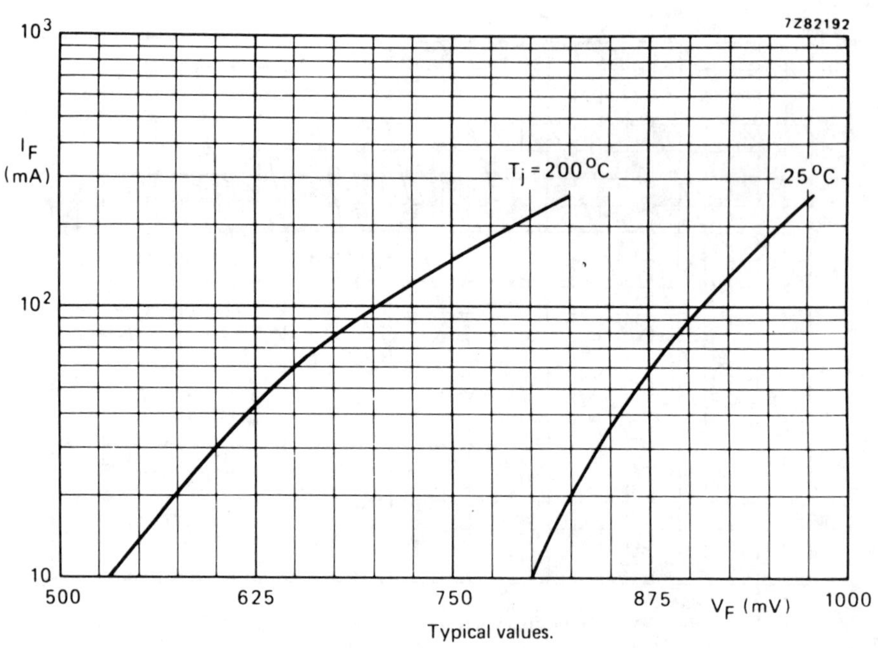

Typical values.

BZV85 SERIES

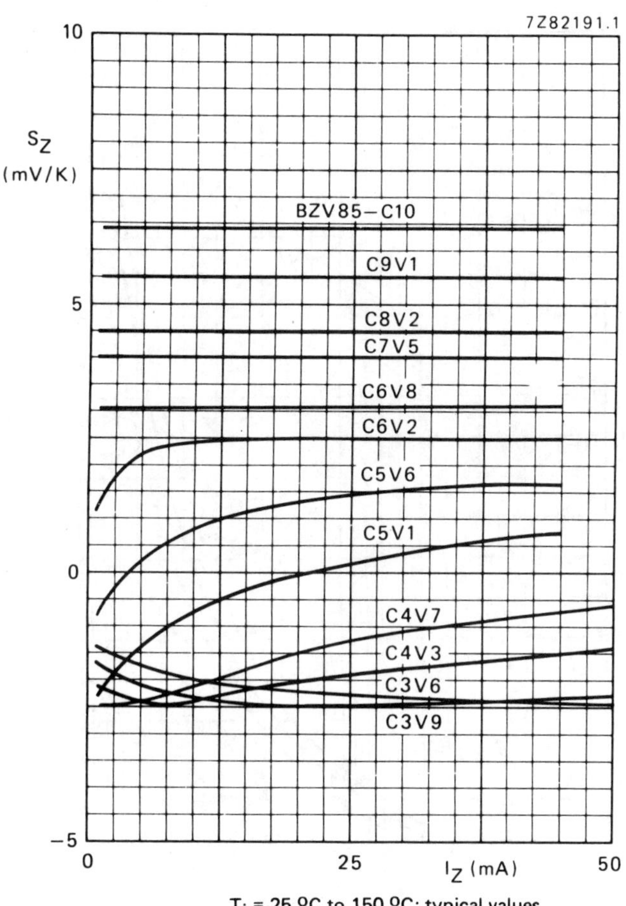

T_j = 25 °C to 150 °C; typical values.

For types above 7,5 V the temperature coefficient is independent of current and can be read from the table („CHARACTERISTICS")

Voltage regulator diodes

BZV85 SERIES

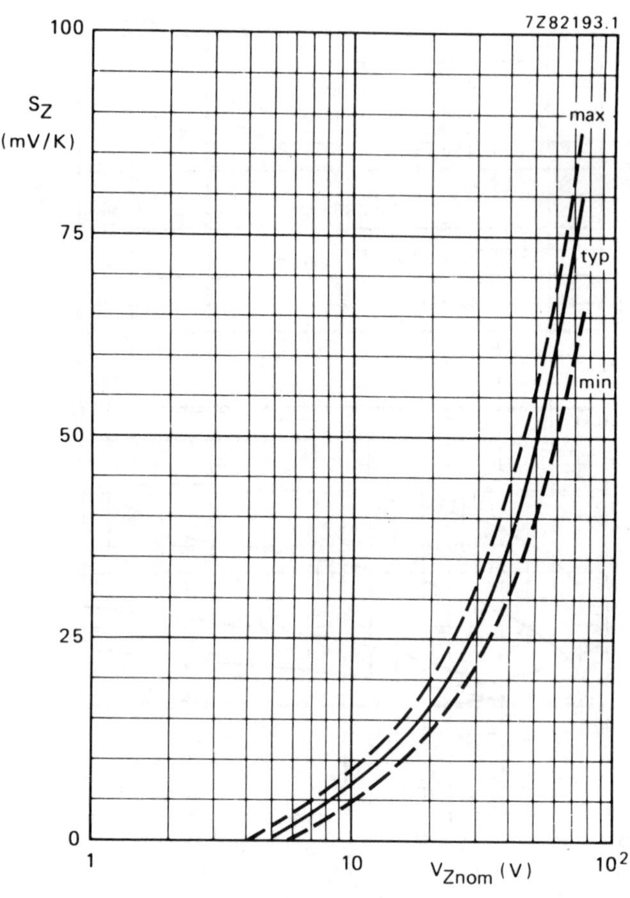

$I_Z = I_{Ztest}$; T_j = 25 °C to 150 °C.

BZV85 SERIES

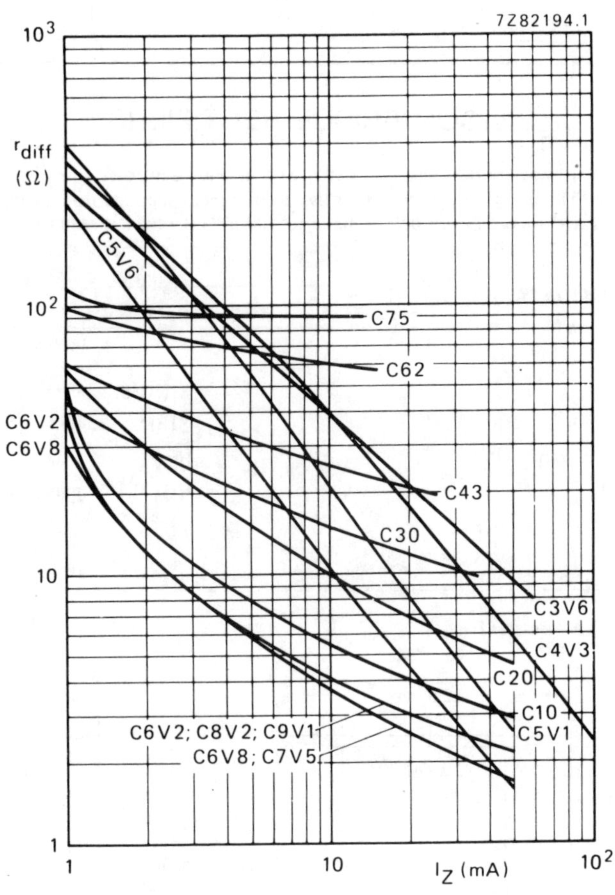

f = 1 kHz; T_j = 25 °C; typical values.

E.4 **Philips bridge rectifier type BY224**

BY224 SERIES

SILICON BRIDGE RECTIFIERS

Ready-for-use mains full-wave bridges, each consisting of four double-diffused silicon diodes, in a plastic encapsulation. The bridges are intended for use in equipment supplied from mains with r.m.s. voltages up to 280 V and are capable of delivering up to 1000 W into capacitive loads. They may be used in free air or clipped to a heatsink.

QUICK REFERENCE DATA

Input			BY224–400	600	V
R.M.S. voltage	$V_{I(RMS)}$	max.	220	280	V
Repetitive peak voltage	V_{IRM}	max.	400	600	V
Non-repetitive peak current	I_{ISM}	max.		100	A
Peak inrush current	I_{IIM}	max.		200	A
Output					
Average current	$I_{O(AV)}$	max.		4,8	A

MECHANICAL DATA (see also Fig. 1a) Dimensions in mm

Fig. 1 SOT-112.

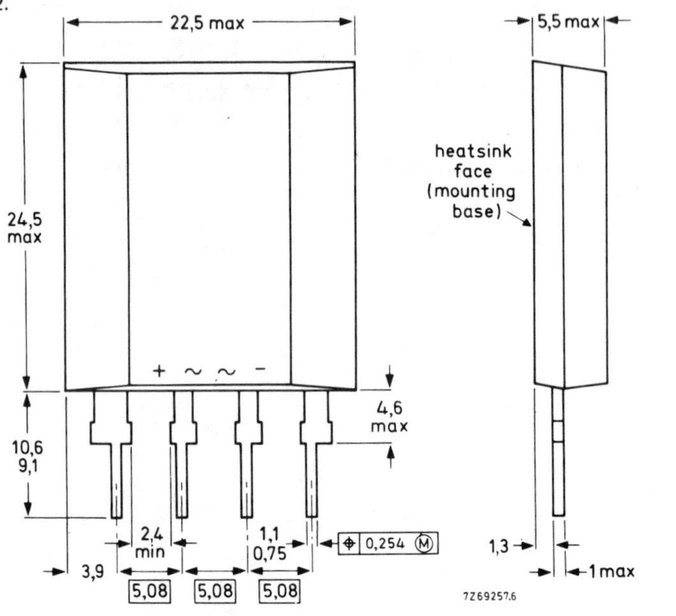

Net mass: 6,8 g

BY224 SERIES

MECHANICAL DATA (continued)

→ Fig. 1a

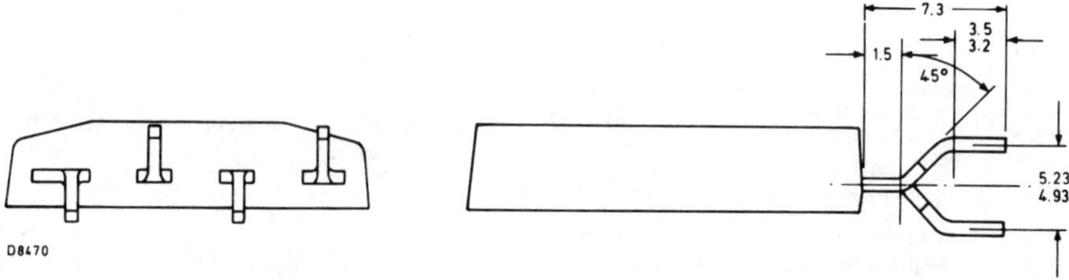

A version with cranked pins (as shown in figure 1a) is available on request.

RATINGS

Limiting values in accordance with the Absolute Maximum System (IEC 134)

Input			BY224-400	600	
Non-repetitive peak voltage ($t \leq 10$ ms)	V_{ISM}	max.	400	600	V
Repetitive peak voltage	V_{IRM}	max.	400	600	V
Crest working voltage	V_{IWM}	max.	350	400	V
R.M.S. voltage (sine-wave)	$V_{I(RMS)}$	max.	220	280	V
Non-repetitive peak current half sine-wave; t = 20 ms; with reapplied V_{IWMmax}					
T_j = 25 °C prior to surge	I_{ISM}	max.		100	A
→ T_j = 150 °C prior to surge	I_{ISM}	max.		85	A
Peak inrush current (see Fig. 6)	I_{IIM}	max.		200	A
Output					
Average current (averaged over any 20 ms period; see Figs 2 and 3)					
heatsink operation up to T_{mb} = 90 °C	$I_{O(AV)}$	max.		4,8	A
free-air operation at T_{amb} = 45 °C; (mounting method 1a)	$I_{O(AV)}$	max.		2,5	A
Repetitive peak current	I_{ORM}	max.		50	A
→ **Temperatures**					
Storage temperature	T_{stg}			−40 to +150	°C
Junction temperature	T_j	max.		150	°C

Silicon bridge rectifiers

BY224 SERIES

THERMAL RESISTANCE

From junction to mounting base $R_{th\ j\text{-}mb}$ = 4,0 °C/W

Influence of mounting method

1. Free-air operation

The quoted values of $R_{th\ j\text{-}a}$ should be used only when no loads of other dissipating components run to the same tie-point (see Fig. 3).

Thermal resistance from junction to ambient in free air

a. Mounted on a printed-circuit board with 4 cm^2 of copper laminate to + and – leads $R_{th\ j\text{-}a}$ = 19,5 °C/W

b. Mounted on a printed-circuit board with minimal copper laminate $R_{th\ j\text{-}a}$ = 25 °C/W

2. Heatsink mounted with clip (see mounting instructions)

Thermal resistance from mounting base to heatsink

a. With zinc-oxide heatsink compound $R_{th\ mb\text{-}h}$ = 1,0 °C/W

b. Without heatsink compound $R_{th\ mb\text{-}h}$ = 2,0 °C/W

MOUNTING INSTRUCTIONS

1. Soldered joints must be at least 4 mm from the seal.
2. The maximum permissible temperature of the soldering iron or bath is 270 °C; contact with the joint must not exceed 3 seconds.
3. Avoid hot spots due to handling or mounting; the body of the device must not come into contact with or be exposed to a temperature higher than 150 °C. ←
4. Leads should not be bent less than 4 mm from the seal. Exert no axial pull when bending.
5. Recommended force of clip on device is 120 N (12 kgf).
6. The heatsink should be in contact with the entire mounting base of the device and heatsink compound should be used.

CHARACTERISTICS

Forward voltage (2 diodes in series)
I_F = 10 A; T_j = 25 °C V_F < 2,3 V*

Reverse current (2 diodes in parallel)
$V_R = V_{IWMmax}$; T_j = 25 °C I_R < 200 μA

* Measured under pulse conditions to avoid excessive dissipation.

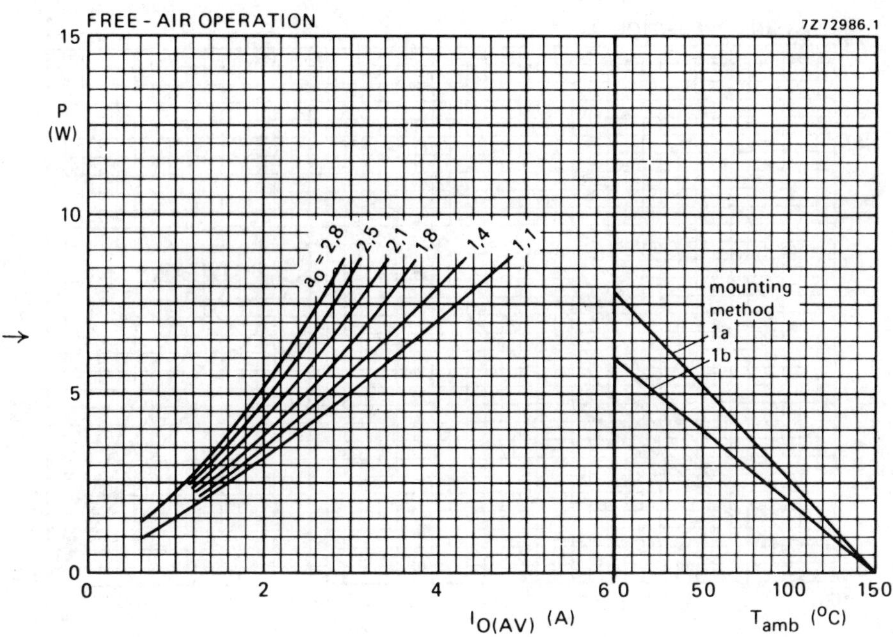

Fig. 2 The right-hand part shows the interrelationship between the power (derived from the left-hand graph) and the maximum permissible ambient temperature.

Output form factor $a_o = I_{O(RMS)}/I_{O(AV)} = 0{,}707 \times I_{F(RMS)}/I_{F(AV)}$ per diode.

Silicon bridge rectifiers

BY224 SERIES

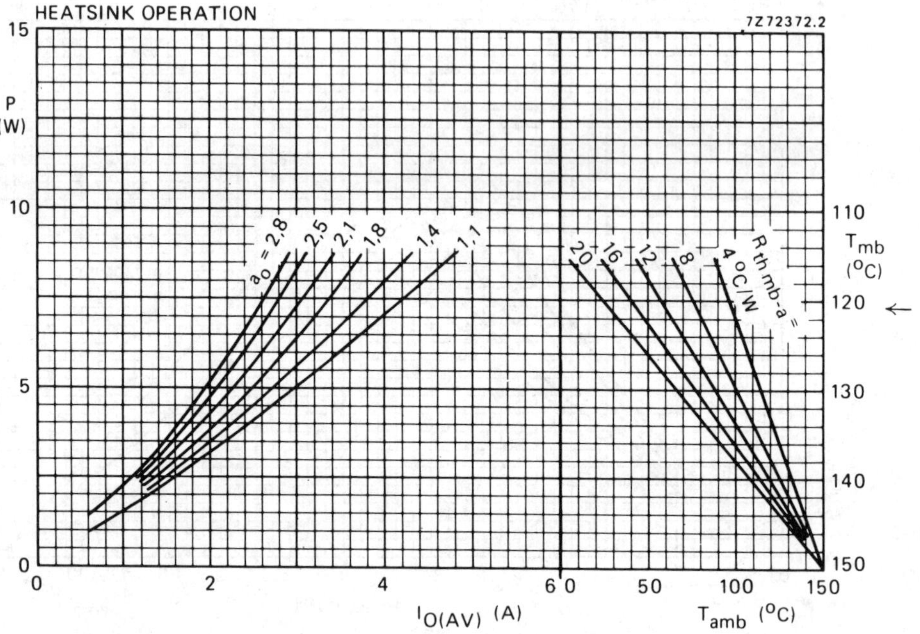

Fig. 3 The right-hand part shows the interrelationship between the power (derived from the left-hand graph) and the maximum permissible temperatures.

Output form factor $a_o = I_{O(RMS)}/I_{O(AV)} = 0{,}707 \times I_{F(RMS)}/I_{F(AV)}$ per diode.

BY224 SERIES

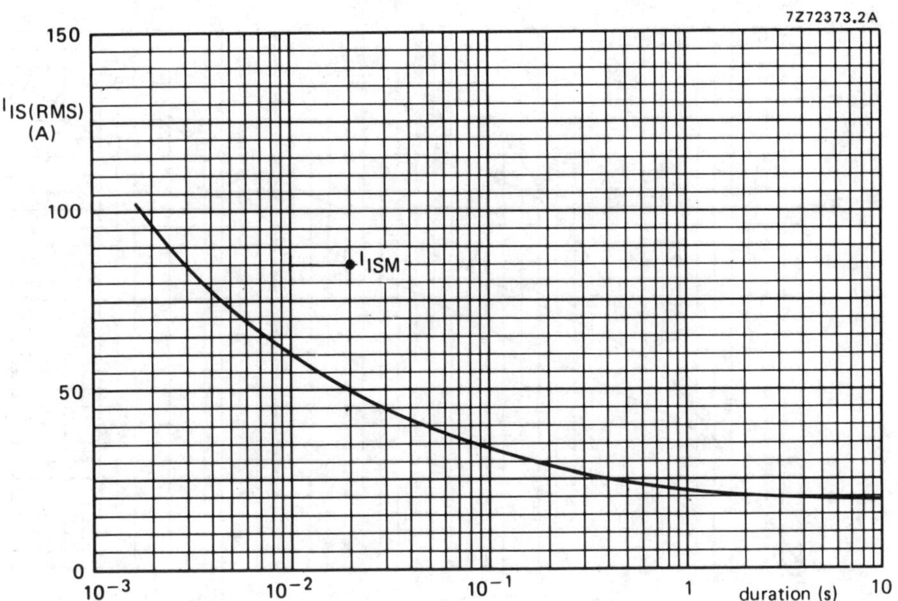

Fig.4 Maximum permissible non-repetitive r.m.s. input current based on sinusoidal currents (f = 50 Hz);
→ T_j = 150 °C prior to surge; with reapplied V_{IWMmax}.

I_{IS} $I_{IS(RMS)}$ time

→

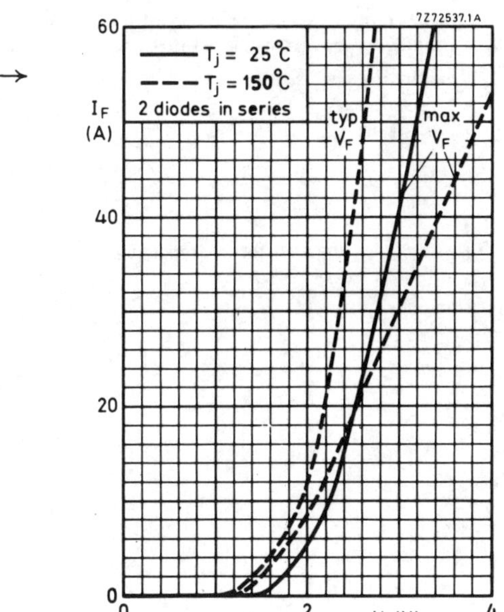

Fig.5

Silicon bridge rectifiers | **BY224 SERIES**

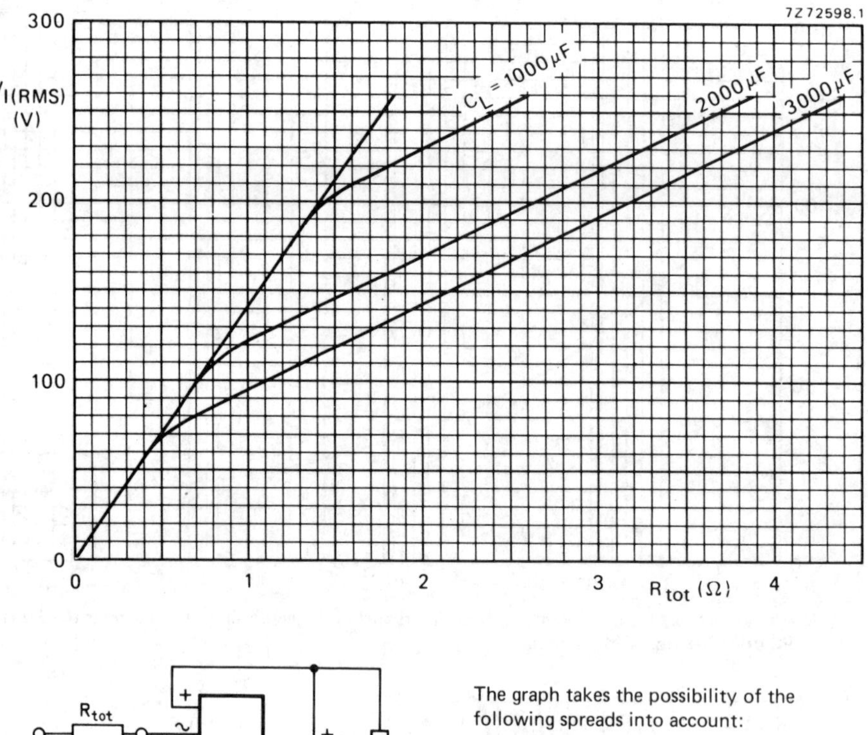

R_{tot} ~ V_I + ~ ~ − + C_L R_L

7Z72367.1

The graph takes the possibility of the following spreads into account:

mains voltage	+10%
capacitance	+50%
resistance	−10%

Fig. 6 Minimum value of the total series resistance R_{tot} (including the transformer resistance) required to limit the peak inrush current.

APPLICATION INFORMATION

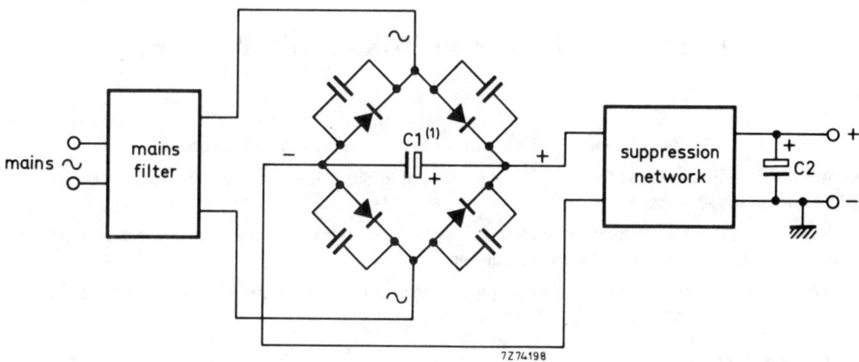

(1) External capacitor.

Fig. 7 Because smoothing capacitor C2 is not always connected directly across the bridge (a suppression network may be sited between capacitor and bridge as shown), it is necessary to connect a capacitor of about 1 μF, C1, between the + and – terminals of the bridge. This capacitor should be as close to the bridge as possible, to give optimum suppression of mains transients.

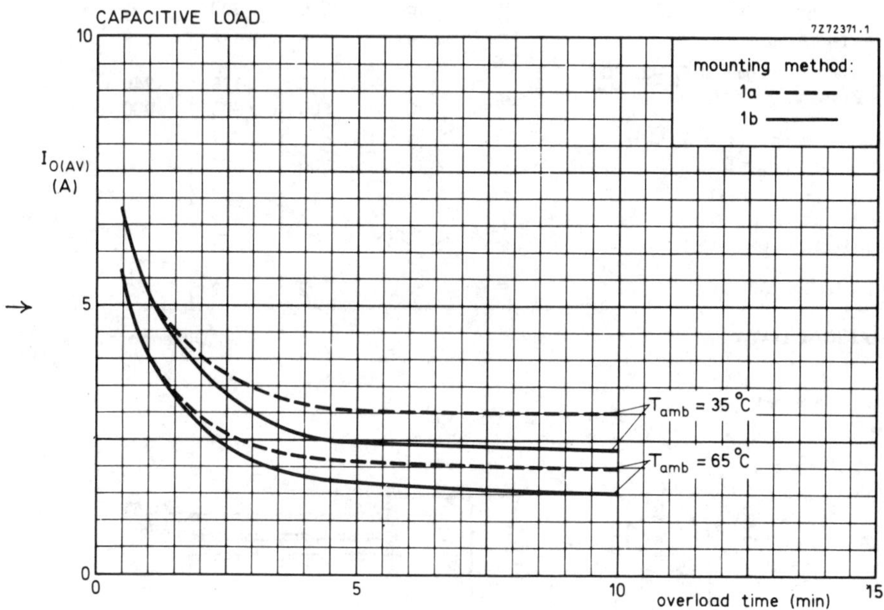

Fig.8

E.5 Philips low-power npn BJT type BC107–9

BC107 to 109

A.F. SILICON PLANAR EPITAXIAL TRANSISTORS

N-P-N transistors in TO-18 metal envelopes with the collector connected to the case.

The **BC107** is primarily intended for use in driver stages of audio amplifiers and in signal processing circuits of television receivers.

The **BC108** is suitable for multitude of low-voltage applications e.g. driver stages or audio preamplifiers and in signal processing circuits of television receivers.

The **BC109** is primarily intended for low-noise input stages in tape recorders, hi-fi amplifiers and other audio-frequency equipment.

QUICK REFERENCE DATA

			BC107	BC108	BC109	
Collector-emitter voltage (V_{BE} = 0)	V_{CES}	max.	50	30	30	V
Collector-emitter voltage (open base)	V_{CEO}	max.	45	20	20	V
Collector current (peak value)	I_{CM}	max.	200	200	200	mA
Total power dissipation up to T_{amb} = 25 °C	P_{tot}	max.	300	300	300	mW
Junction temperature	T_j	max.	175	175	175	°C
Small-signal current gain at T_j = 25 °C; I_C = 2 mA; V_{CE} = 5 V; f = 1 kHz	h_{fe}	$>$	125	125	240	
		$<$	500	900	900	
Transition frequency at f = 35 MHz; I_C = 10 mA; V_{CE} = 5 V	f_T	typ.	300	300	300	MHz
Noise figure at R_S = 2 kΩ; I_C = 200 μA; V_{CE} = 5 V; f = 30 Hz to 15 kHz	F	typ.	–	–	1,4	dB
		$<$	–	–	4,0	dB
f = 1 kHz; B = 200 Hz	F	typ.	2	2	1,2	dB

MECHANICAL DATA

Dimensions in mm

Fig. 1 TO-18.

Collector connected to case

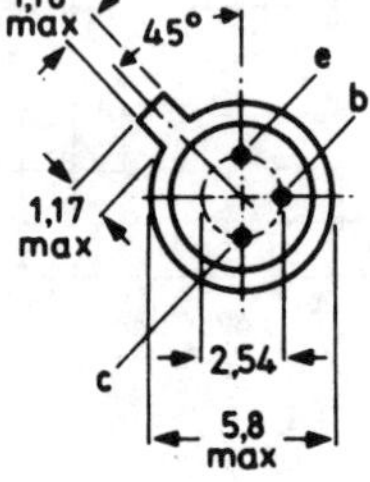

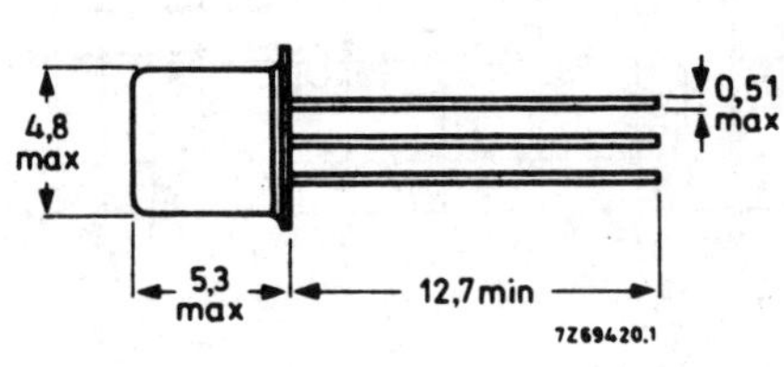

BC107 to 109

RATINGS Limiting values in accordance with the Absolute Maximum System (IEC 134)

Voltages			BC107	BC108	BC109	
Collector-base voltage (open emitter)	V_{CBO}	max.	50	30	30	V
Collector-emitter voltage (V_{BE} = 0)	V_{CES}	max.	50	30	30	V
Collector-emitter voltage (open base)	V_{CEO}	max.	45	20	20	V
Emitter-base voltage (open collector)	V_{EBO}	max.	6	5	5	V

Currents				
Collector current (d.c.)	I_C	max.	100	mA
Collector current (peak value)	I_{CM}	max.	200	mA
Emitter current (peak value)	$-I_{EM}$	max.	200	mA
Base current (peak value)	I_{BM}	max.	200	mA
Power dissipation				
Total power dissipation up to T_{amb} = 25 °C	P_{tot}	max.	300	mW
Temperatures				
Storage temperature	T_{stg}	−65 to +175		°C
Junction temperature	T_j	max.	175	°C

THERMAL RESISTANCE

From junction to ambient in free air	$R_{th\ j\text{-}a}$	=	0.5	°C/mW
From junction to case	$R_{th\ j\text{-}c}$	=	0.2	°C/mW

CHARACTERISTICS T_j = 25 °C unless otherwise specified

Collector cut-off current				
$I_E = 0$; $V_{CB} = 20$ V; $T_j = 150$ °C	I_{CBO}	<	15	μA
Base-emitter voltage [1]				
I_C = 2 mA; V_{CE} = 5 V	V_{BE}	typ.	620	mV
		550 to	700	mV
I_C = 10 mA; V_{CE} = 5 V	V_{BE}	<	770	mV

1) V_{BE} decreases by about 2 mV/°C with increasing temperature.

BC107 to 109

CHARACTERISTICS (continued) T_j = 25 °C unless otherwise specified

Saturation voltages [1]

I_C = 10 mA; I_B = 0.5 mA	V_{CEsat}	typ.	90	mV
		<	250	mV
	V_{BEsat}	typ.	700	mV
I_C = 100 mA; I_B = 5 mA	V_{CEsat}	typ.	200	mV
		<	600	mV
	V_{BEsat}	typ.	900	mV

Knee voltage

I_C = 10 mA; I_B = value for which I_C = 11 mA at V_{CE} = 1 V	V_{CEK}	typ.	300	mV
		<	600	mV

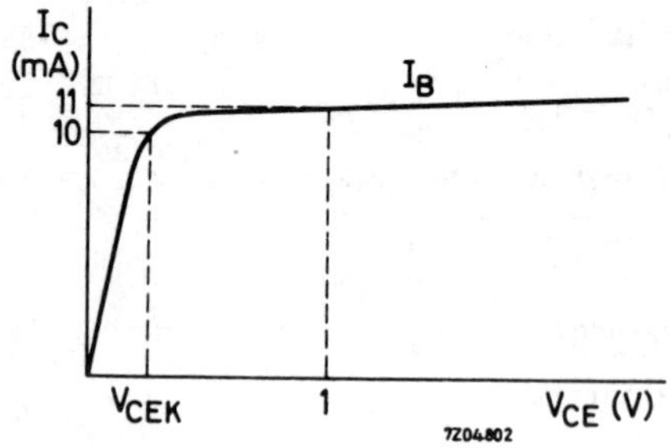

Collector capacitance at f = 1 MHz

$I_E = I_e = 0$; V_{CB} = 10 V	C_c	typ.	2.5	pF
		<	4.5	pF

Emitter capacitance at f = 1 MHz

$I_C = I_c = 0$; V_{EB} = 0.5 V	C_e	typ.	9	pF

Transition frequency at f = 35 MHz

I_C = 10 mA; V_{CE} = 5 V	f_T	typ.	300	MHz

Small signal current gain at f = 1 kHz

			BC107	BC108	BC109	
I_C = 2 mA; V_{CE} = 5 V	h_{fe}	>	125	125	240	
		<	500	900	900	

Noise figure at R_S = 2 kΩ
I_C = 200 μA; V_{CE} = 5 V

			BC107	BC108	BC109	
f = 30 Hz to 15 kHz	F	typ.			1.4	dB
		<			4	dB
f = 1 kHz; B = 200 Hz	F	typ.	2	2	1.2	dB
		<	10	10	4	dB

[1] V_{BEsat} decreases by about 1.7 mV/°C with increasing temperature.

BC107 to 109

CHARACTERISTICS (continued) T_j = 25 °C unless otherwise specified

			BC107A BC108A	BC107B BC108B BC109B	BC108C BC109C	
D.C. current gain						
I_C = 10 μA; V_{CE} = 5 V	h_{FE}	>		40	100	
		typ.	90	150	270	
I_C = 2 mA; V_{CE} = 5 V	h_{FE}	>	110	200	420	
		typ.	180	290	520	
		<	220	450	800	
h parameters at f = 1 kHz (common emitter)						
I_C = 2 mA; V_{CE} = 5 V						
Input impedance	h_{ie}	>	1.6	3.2	6	kΩ
		typ.	2.7	4.5	8.7	kΩ
		<	4.5	8.5	15	kΩ
Reverse voltage transfer ratio	h_{re}	typ.	1.5	2	3	10^{-4}
Small signal current gain	h_{fe}	>	125	240	450	
		typ.	220	330	600	
		<	260	500	900	
Output admittance	h_{oe}	typ.	18	30	60	$\mu\Omega^{-1}$
		<	30	60	110	$\mu\Omega^{-1}$

BC107 to 109

Typical behaviour of collector current versus collector-emitter voltage

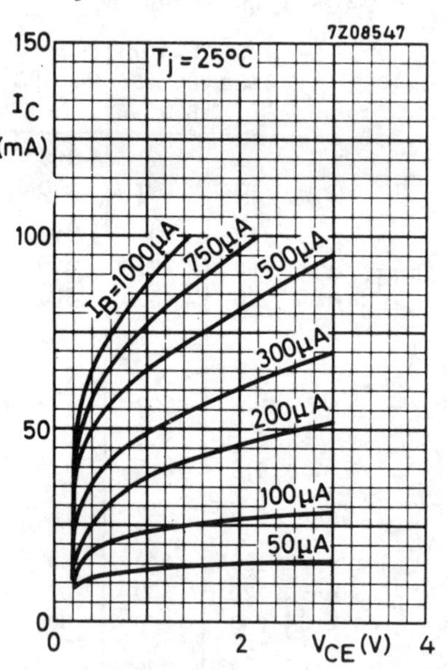

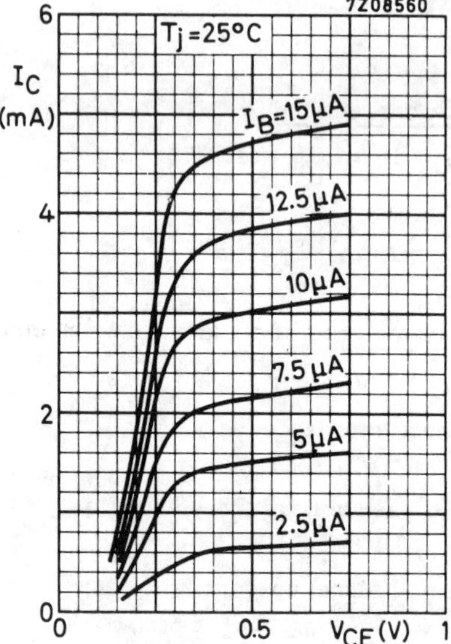

Typical behaviour of collector current versus collector-emitter voltage

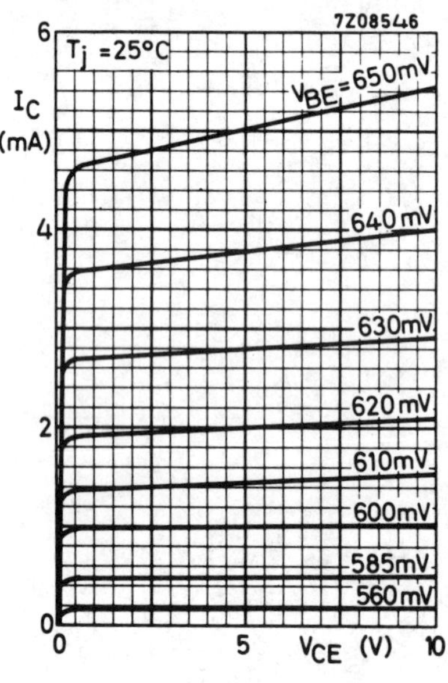

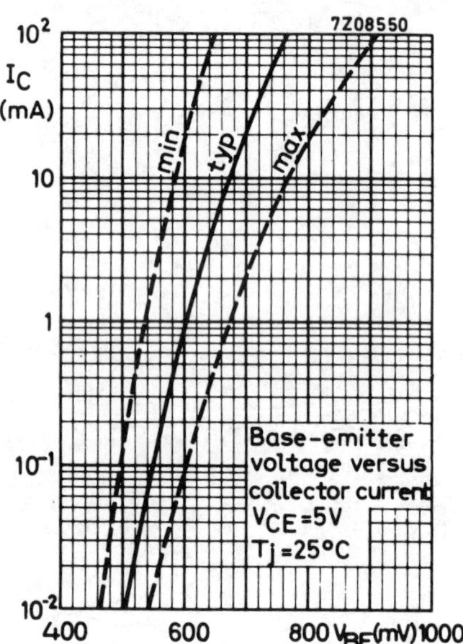

BC107 to 109

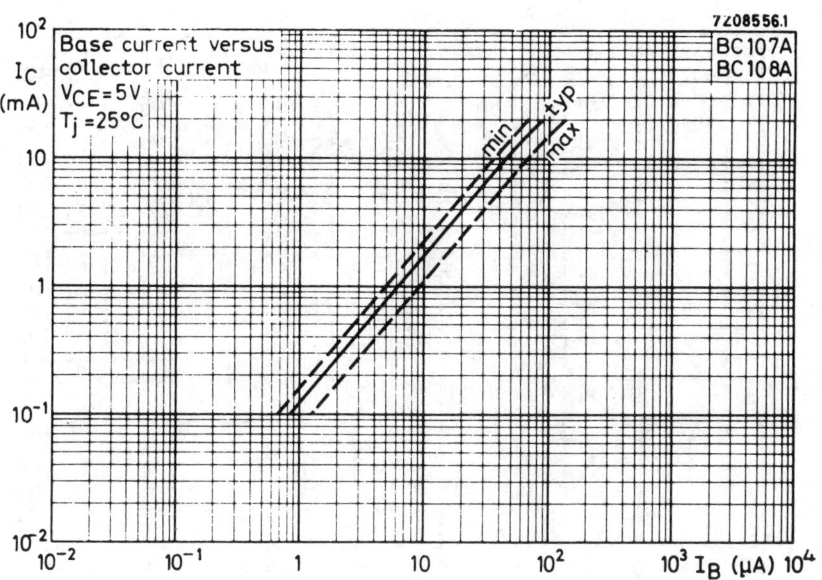
7Z08556.1
BC107A
BC108A
Base current versus
collector current
V_{CE}=5V
T_j =25°C
I_C (mA)
I_B (μA)
min
typ
max
10^2
10
1
10^{-1}
10^{-2}
10^{-2}
10^{-1}
1
10
10^2
10^3
10^4

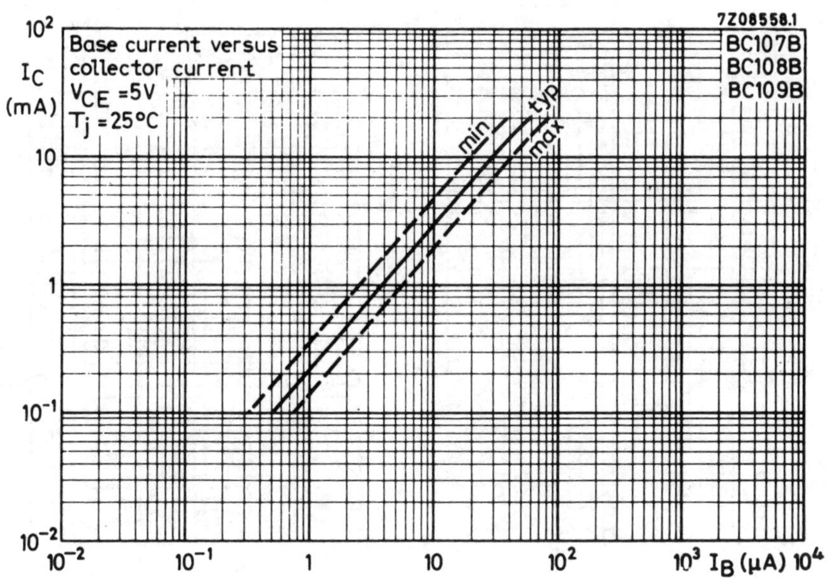
7Z08558.1
BC107B
BC108B
BC109B
Base current versus
collector current
V_{CE} =5V
T_j =25°C
I_C (mA)
I_B (μA)
min
typ
max
10^2
10
1
10^{-1}
10^{-2}
10^{-2}
10^{-1}
1
10
10^2
10^3
10^4

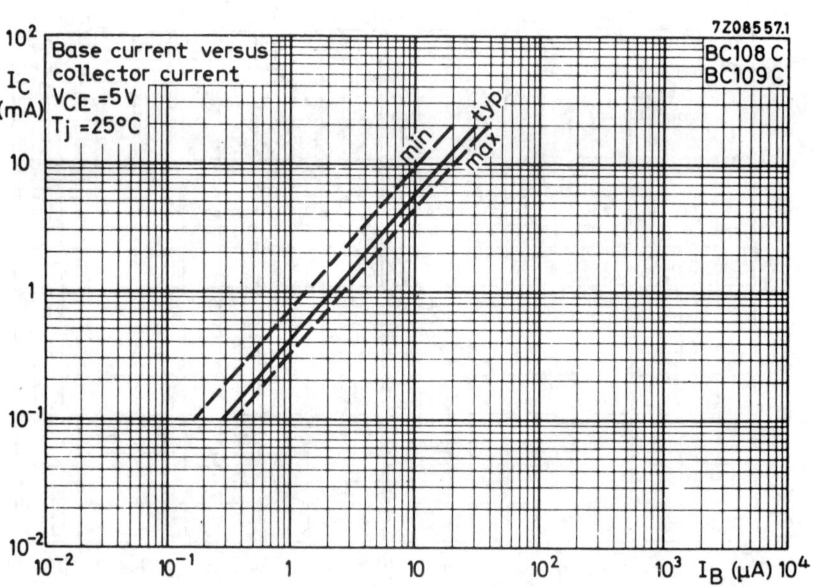
7Z08557.1
Base current versus
collector current
VCE =5V
Tj =25°C
BC108 C
BC109 C
IC
(mA)
min
typ
max
IB (μA)

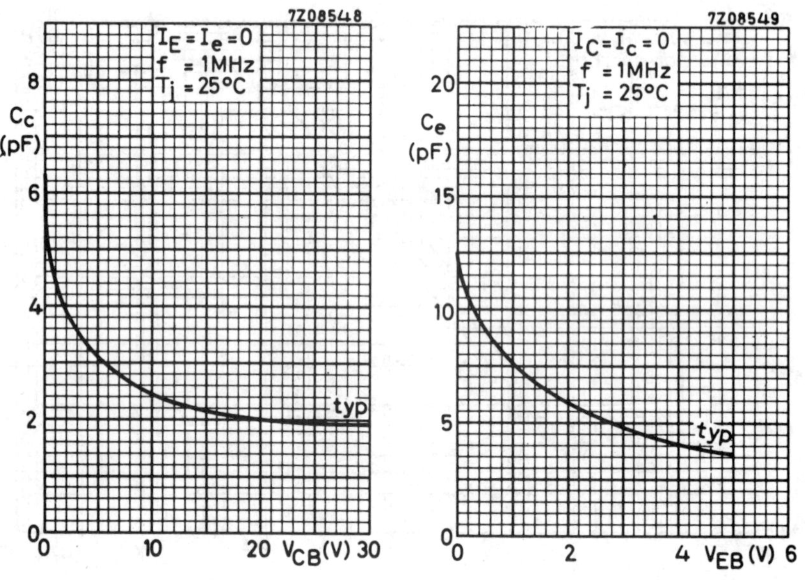
7Z08548
IE = Ie = 0
f = 1MHz
Tj = 25°C
Cc
(pF)
typ
VCB(V)
7Z08549
IC = Ic = 0
f = 1MHz
Tj = 25°C
Ce
(pF)
typ
VEB (V)

BC107 to 109

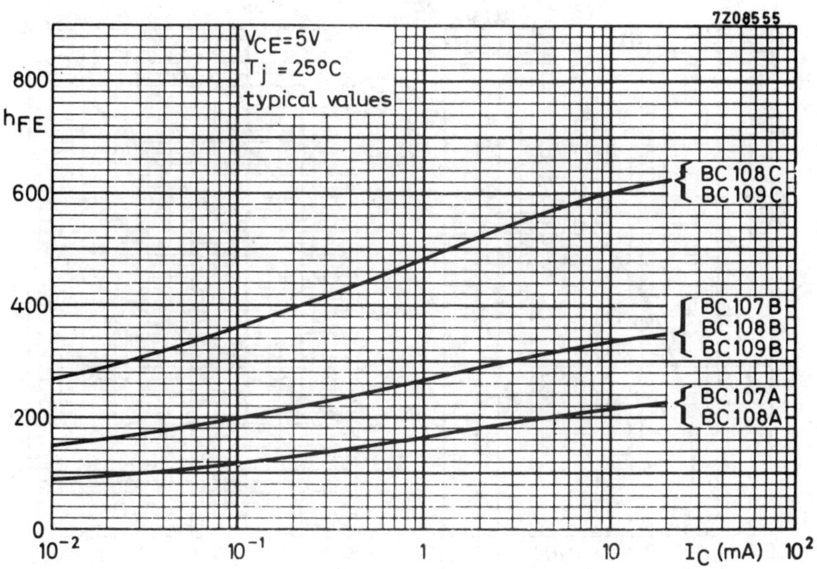

7Z08555
V_{CE}=5V
T_j = 25°C
typical values
h_{FE}
800
600
400
200
0
10^{-2}
10^{-1}
1
10
I_C (mA)
10^2
BC 108 C
BC 109 C
BC 107 B
BC 108 B
BC 109 B
BC 107A
BC 108A

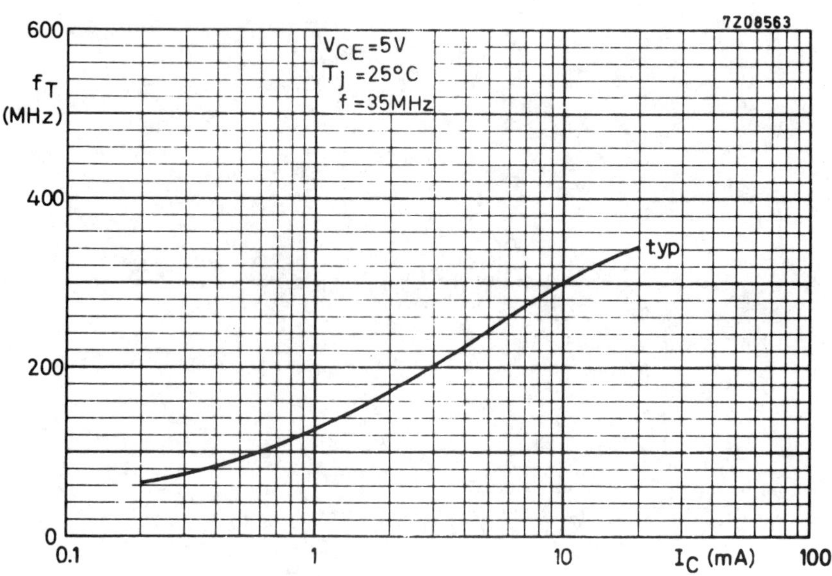

7Z08563
V_{CE}=5V
T_j =25°C
f =35MHz
f_T
(MHz)
600
400
200
0
0.1
1
10
I_C (mA)
100
typ

BC107 to 109

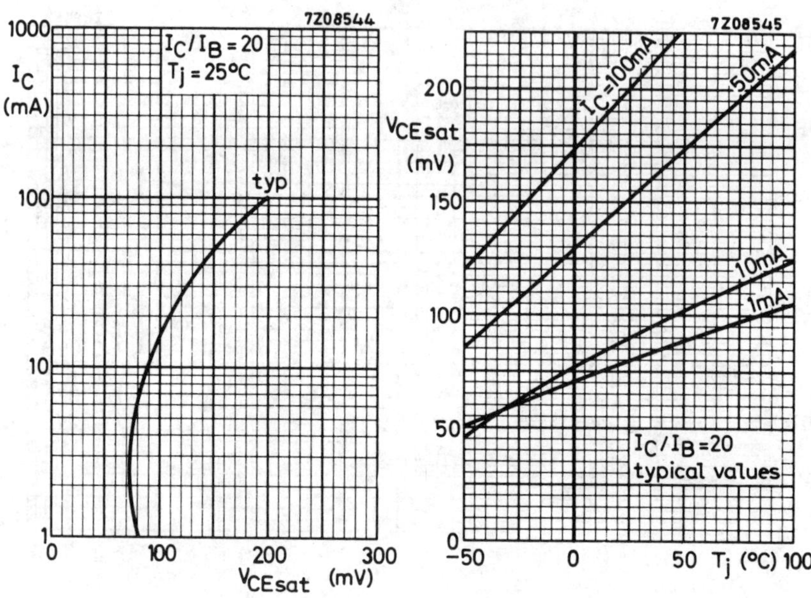
7Z08544
1000
I_C
(mA)
$I_C/I_B = 20$
$T_j = 25°C$
typ
100
10
1
0
100
200
300
V_{CEsat} (mV)
7Z08545
200
V_{CEsat}
(mV)
150
100
50
0
I_C=100mA
50mA
10mA
1mA
I_C/I_B=20
typical values
−50
0
50
T_j (°C)
100

BC107 to 109

Curves of constant noise figure

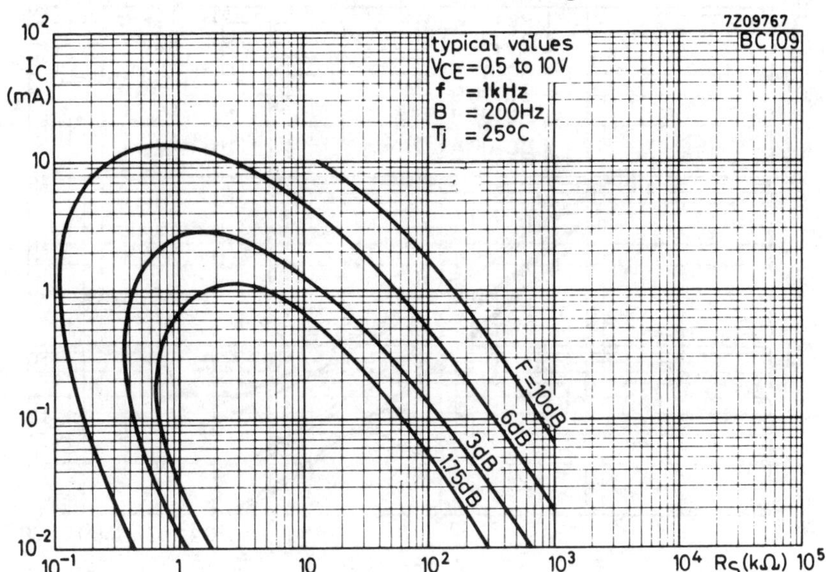

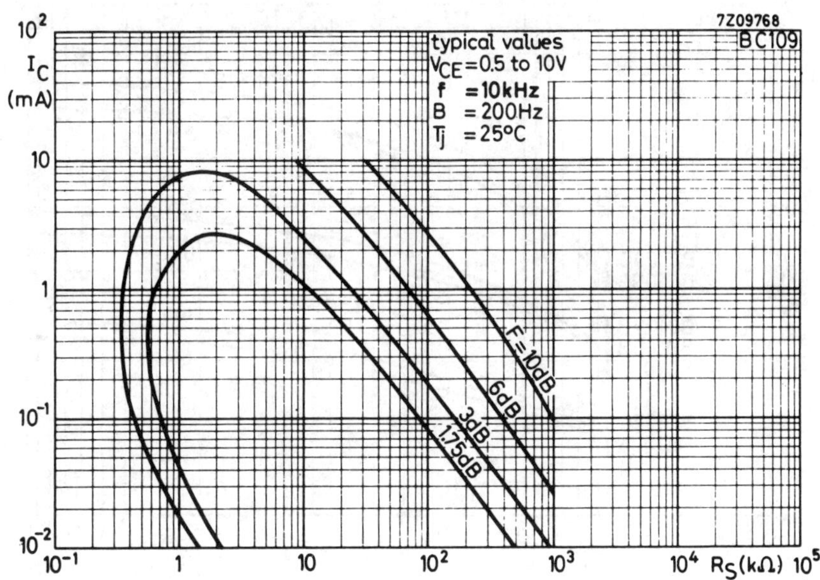

BC107 to 109

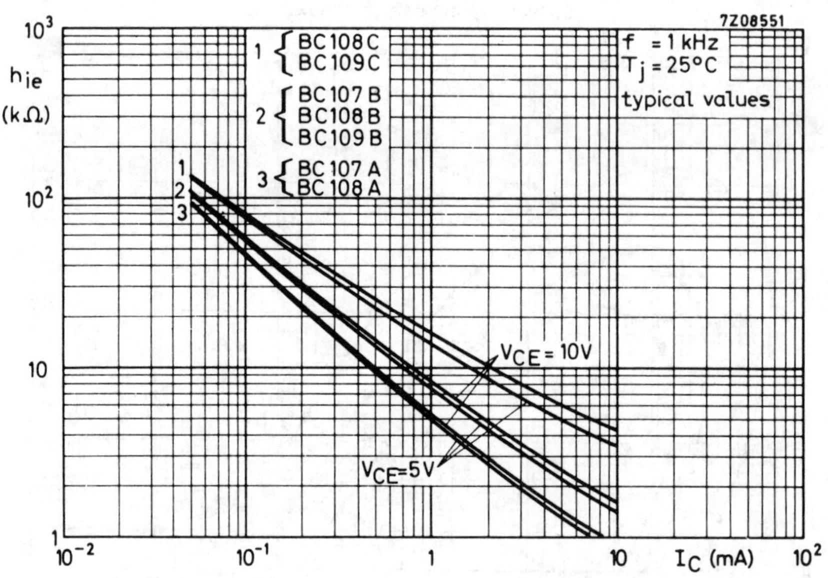
7Z08551
h_{ie}
(kΩ)
1 { BC108C BC109C
2 { BC107B BC108B BC109B
3 { BC107A BC108A
f = 1 kHz
T_j = 25°C
typical values
V_{CE} = 10V
V_{CE}=5V
I_C (mA)

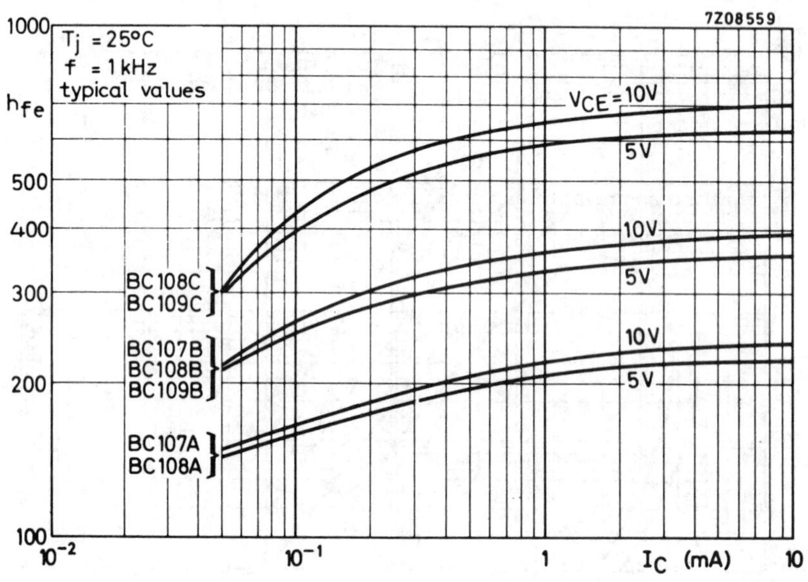
7Z08559
T_j = 25°C
f = 1 kHz
typical values
h_{fe}
V_{CE} = 10V
5V
10V
5V
10V
5V
BC108C BC109C
BC107B BC108B BC109B
BC107A BC108A
I_C (mA)

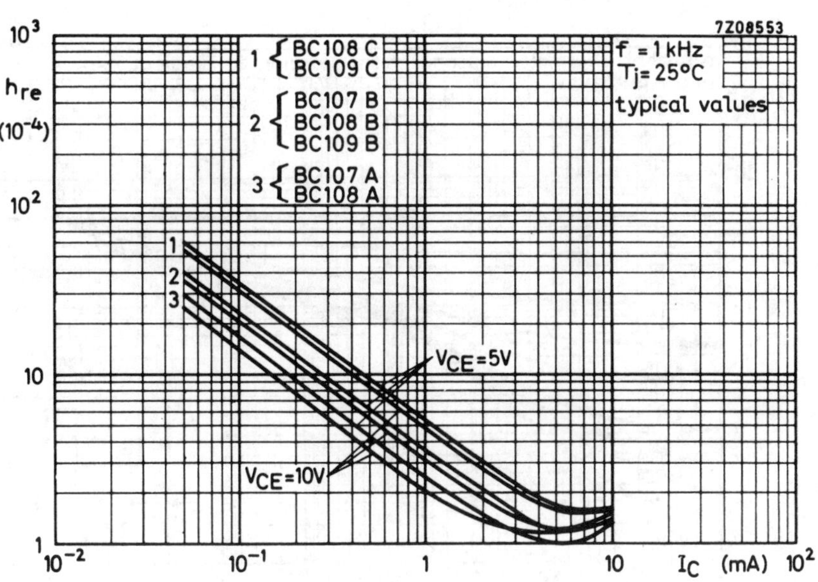
7Z08553
h_{re}
(10^{-4})
1 {BC108 C BC109 C
2 {BC107 B BC108 B BC109 B
3 {BC107 A BC108 A
f = 1 kHz
Tj = 25°C
typical values
VCE = 5V
VCE = 10V
I_C (mA)

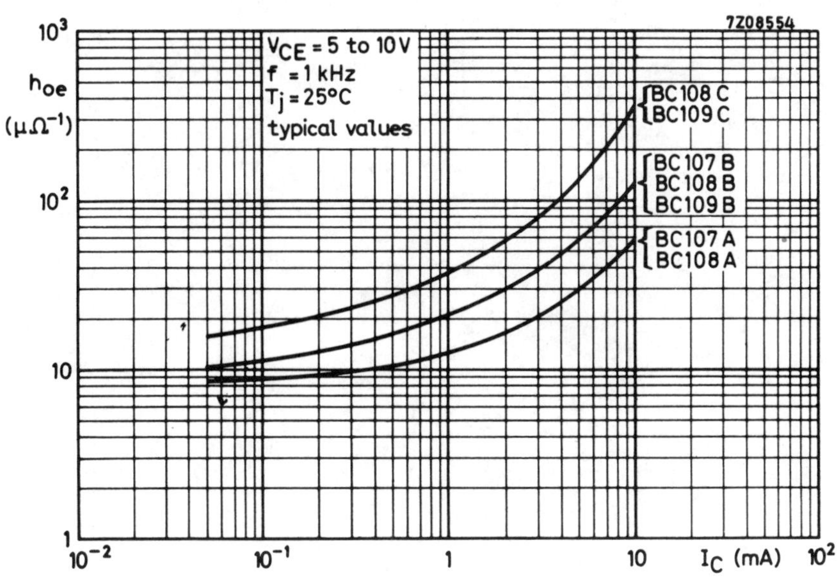
7Z08554
h_{oe}
$(\mu\Omega^{-1})$
VCE = 5 to 10 V
f = 1 kHz
Tj = 25°C
typical values
BC108 C
BC109 C
BC107 B
BC108 B
BC109 B
BC107 A
BC108 A
I_C (mA)

BC107 to 109

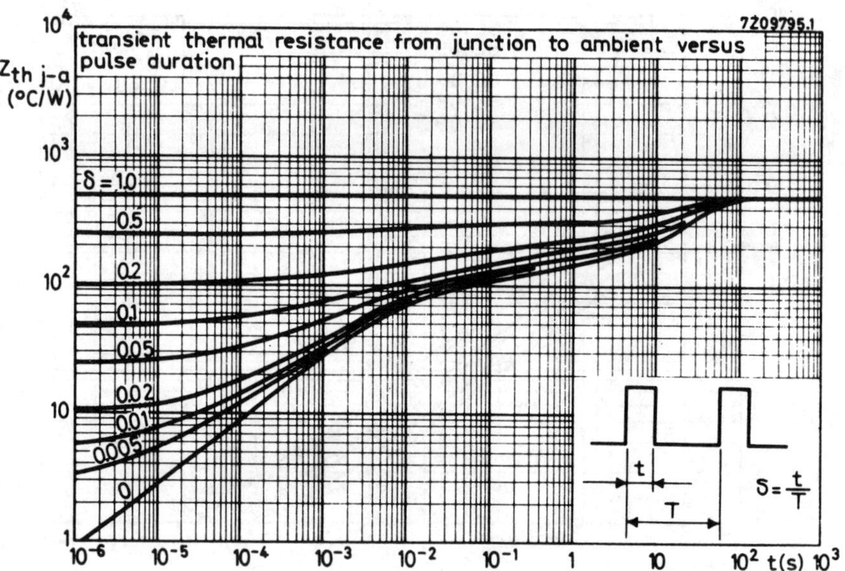
7Z09795.1
transient thermal resistance from junction to ambient versus pulse duration
$Z_{th\ j-a}$ (°C/W)
δ = 1.0
0.5
0.2
0.1
0.05
0.02
0.01
0.005
0
t
T
δ = t/T
t(s)

E.6 Texas high-power npn BJT type TIP31

TIP31 SERIES

NPN SINGLE-DIFFUSED MESA SILICON POWER TRANSISTORS

FOR POWER AMPLIFIER AND HIGH SPEED SWITCHING APPLICATIONS
DESIGNED FOR COMPLEMENTARY USE WITH TIP32 SERIES

- **40W at 25°C Case Temperature**
- **3A Rated Collector Current**
- **Minimum f_T of 3MHz at 10V, 500 mA**
- **Customer-specified selections available**
- **Also Available in Europe as BD241**

MECHANICAL DATA

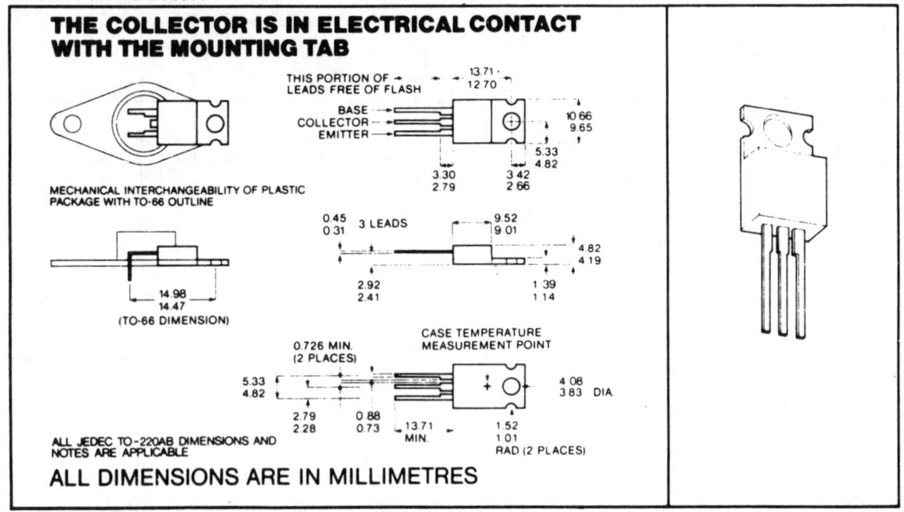

ABSOLUTE MAXIMUM RATINGS AT 25°C CASE TEMPERATURE (UNLESS OTHERWISE NOTED)

PARAMETER	TIP31	TIP31A	TIP31B	TIP31C	TIP31D	TIP31E	TIP31F	UNIT
Collector-Base Voltage	80	100	120	140	160	180	200	V
Collector-Emitter Voltage[1] @ 30mA	40	60	80	100	120	140	160	V

Emitter-Base Voltage	5V
Continuous Collector Current	3A
Peak Collector Current[2]	5A
Continuous Base Current	1A
Safe Operating Area	See Figure 5
Continuous Device Dissipation[3]	40W
Continuous Device Dissipation at (or Below) 25°C Free-Air Temperature[4]	2W
Unclamped Inductive Load Energy[5]	32 mJ
Operating Collector Junction Temperature Range	-65°C to 150°C
Storage Temperature Range	-65°C to 150°C
Lead Temperature 3.2 mm from Case for 10 Seconds	250°C

Notes
1. This value applies when the base-emitter diode is open circuited.
2. This value applies for $t_w \leq 0.3$ ms, Duty Cycle $\leq$ 10%.
3. Derate linearly to 150°C case temperature at the rate of 0.32 W/°C
4. Derate linearly to 150°C free-air temperature at the rate of 16 mW/°C
5. This rating is based on the capability of the transistor to operate safely in the circuit in Figure 2.

TIP31 SERIES
NPN SINGLE-DIFFUSED MESA SILICON POWER TRANSISTORS

electrical characteristics at 25°C case temperature

PARAMETER		TEST CONDITIONS AT 25°C	TIP31/31A		TIP31B/31C		TIP31D/31E 31F		UNIT
			MIN	MAX	MIN	MAX	MIN	MAX	
I_{CEO}	Collector Cutoff Current	V_{CE} = 30V I_B = 0		0.3					
		V_{CE} = 60V I_B = 0				0.3			mA
		V_{CE} = 90V I_B = 0						0.3	
I_{CES}	Collector Cutoff Current	V_{CE} = Rated BV_{CBO} V_{BE} = 0		0.2		0.2		0.2	mA
I_{EBO}	Emitter Cutoff Current	V_{EB} = 5V I_C = 0		1		1		1	mA
h_{FE}	Static Forward Current Transfer Ratio	V_{CE} = 4V I_C = 1A See Notes 6 & 7	25		25		25		
		V_{CE} = 4V I_C = 3A	10	50	10	50	5		
V_{BE}	Base-Emitter Voltage	V_{CE} = 4V I_C = 3A See Notes 6 & 7		1.8		1.8		1.8	V
$V_{CE(Sat)}$	Collector-Emitter Saturation Voltage	I_B = 375mA I_C = 3A		1.2		1.2			V
		I_B = 750mA I_C = 3A See Notes 6 & 7						2.5	
h_{fe}	Small-Signal Common-Emitter Forward Current Transfer Ratio	V_{CE} = 10V I_C = 0.5A f = 1KHz	20		20		20		
$\|h_{fe}\|$	Small-Signal Common-Emitter Forward Current Transfer Ratio	V_{CE} = 10V I_C = 0.5A f = 1MHz	3		3		3		

NOTES: 6. These parameters must be measured using pulse techniques. t_w = 300 µs, duty cycle ≤ 2%.
7. These parameters are measured with voltage sensing contacts separate from the current carrying contacts.

thermal characteristics

PARAMETER		MAX	UNIT
$R_{\theta JC}$	Junction-to-Case Thermal Resistance	3.125	°C/W
$R_{\theta JA}$	Junction-to-Free-Air Thermal Resistance	62.5	

switching characteristics at 25°C case temperature

PARAMETER		TEST CONDITIONS†	TYP	UNIT
t_{on}	Turn-On Time	I_C = 1 A, $I_{B(1)}$ = 100 mA, $I_{B(2)}$ = −100 mA,	0.5	µs
t_{off}	Turn-Off Time	$V_{BE(off)}$ = −4.3 V, R_L = 30 Ω, See Figure 1	2	

†Voltage and current values shown are nominal; exact values vary slightly with transistor parameters.

TIP31 SERIES
NPN SINGLE-DIFFUSED MESA SILICON POWER TRANSISTORS

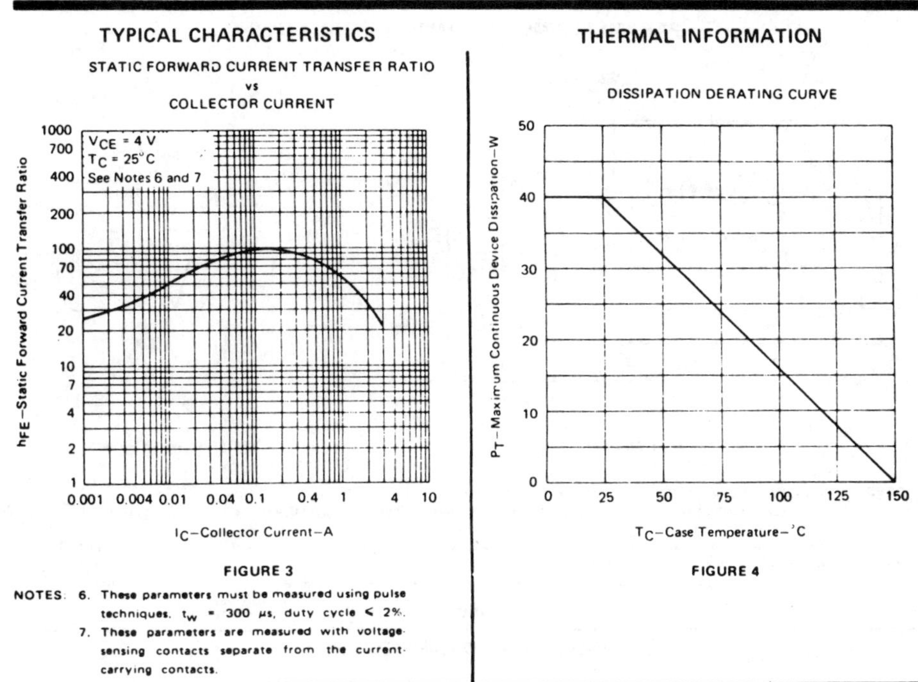

FIGURE 3

FIGURE 4

NOTES: 6. These parameters must be measured using pulse techniques, t_w = 300 μs, duty cycle ≤ 2%.

7. These parameters are measured with voltage-sensing contacts separate from the current-carrying contacts.

MAXIMUM SAFE OPERATION REGION T CASE ≤ 25 C

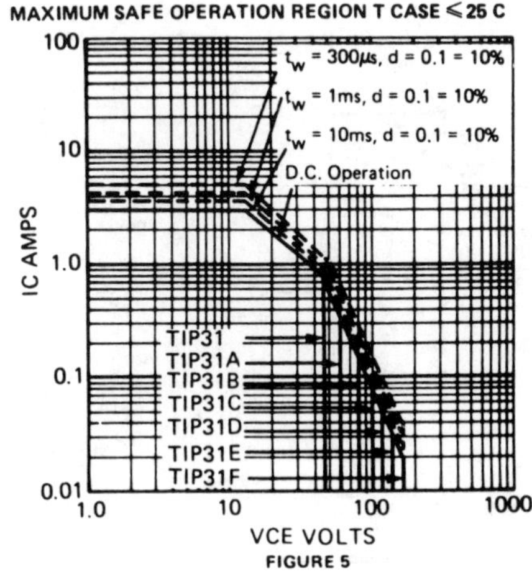

FIGURE 5

NOTE 8 This combination of maximum voltage and current may be achieved only when switching from saturation to cutoff with a clamped inductive load.

TIP31 SERIES
NPN SINGLE-DIFFUSED MESA SILICON POWER TRANSISTORS

PARAMETER MEASUREMENT INFORMATION

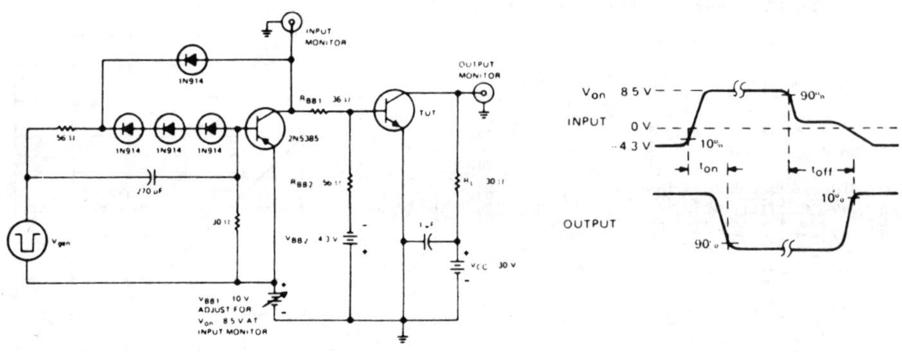

TEST CIRCUIT **VOLTAGE WAVEFORMS**

NOTES: A. V_{gen} is a −30-V pulse (from 0 V) into a 50 Ω termination.

B. The V_{gen} waveform is supplied by a generator with the following characteristics: $t_r \leqslant 15$ ns, $t_f \leqslant 15$ ns, $Z_{out} = 50\ \Omega$, $t_w = 20\ \mu s$, duty cycle $\leqslant 2\%$.

C. Waveforms are monitored on an oscilloscope with the following characteristics: $t_r \leqslant 15$ ns, $R_{in} \geqslant 10\ M\Omega$, $C_{in} \leqslant 11.5$ pF.

D. Resistors must be noninductive types.

E. The d-c power supplies may require additional bypassing in order to minimize ringing.

FIGURE 1

INDUCTIVE LOAD SWITCHING

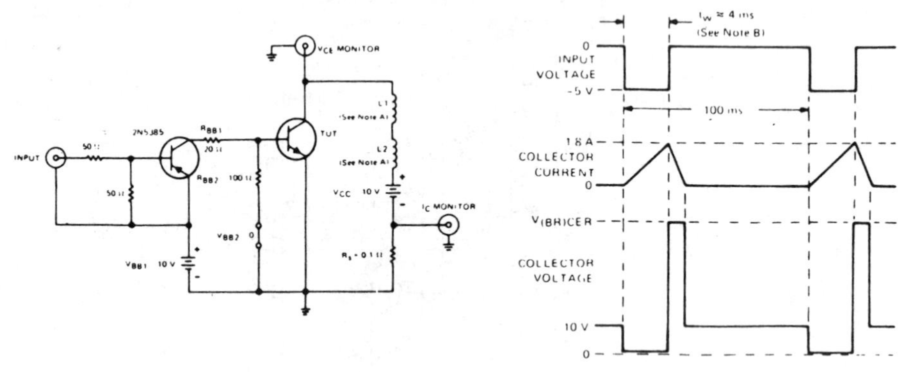

TEST CIRCUIT **VOLTAGE AND CURRENT WAVEFORMS**

NOTES: A. L1 and L2 are 10 mH, 0.11 Ω, Chicago Standard Transformer Corporation C-2688, or equivalent.

B. Input pulse width is increased until $I_{CM} = 1.8$ A.

FIGURE 2

E.7 **Siliconix low-power n-channel JFET type J201–4**

J201 SERIES

N-Channel JFETs

The J201 Series of popular, low-cost JFETs offers high performance in a wide range of applications. With features such as 100 pA gate leakage, −40 V breakdown voltage, and 5 nV/√Hz noise, these devices are especially characterized for sensitive amplifier stages. The J201 and J204 with low cut off voltages, are ideal for battery operated equipment and low current amplifiers. The J201 Series in the TO-92 package offers both value and compatibility with automated assembly.

PART NUMBER	$V_{GS(OFF)}$ MAX (V)	$V_{(BR)GSS}$ MIN (V)	g_{fs} MIN (mS)	I_{DSS} MAX (mA)
J201	−1.5	−40	0.5	1
J202	−4	−40	1	4.5
J203	−10	−40	1.5	20
J204	−2	−25	0.5	3

ABSOLUTE MAXIMUM RATINGS (T_A = 25 °C unless otherwise noted)

PARAMETERS/TEST CONDITIONS	SYMBOL	LIMIT J201-3	LIMIT J204	UNITS
Gate-Drain Voltage	V_{GD}	−40	−25	V
Gate-Source Voltage	V_{GS}	−40	−25	V
Gate Current	I_G	50		mA
Power Dissipation	P_D	360		mW
Power Derating		3.27		mW/°C
Operating Junction Temperature	T_J	−55 to 135		°C
Storage Temperature	T_{stg}	−55 to 150		°C
Lead Temperature (1/16" from case for 10 seconds)	T_L	300		°C

J201 SERIES

ELECTRICAL CHARACTERISTICS [1]			LIMITS					
				J201		J202		
PARAMETER	SYMBOL	TEST CONDITIONS	TYP [2]	MIN	MAX	MIN	MAX	UNIT
STATIC								
Gate-Source Breakdown Voltage	$V_{(BR)GSS}$	$I_G = -1\ \mu A$, $V_{DS} = 0$ V	-57	-40		-40		V
Gate-Source Cutoff Voltage	$V_{GS(OFF)}$	$V_{DS} = 20$ V, $I_D = 10$ nA		-0.3	-1.5	-0.8	-4	V
Saturation Drain Current [3]	I_{DSS}	$V_{DS} = 20$ V, $V_{GS} = 0$ V		0.2	1	0.9	4.5	mA
Gate Reverse Current	I_{GSS}	$V_{GS} = -20$ V, $V_{DS} = 0$ V	-2		-100		-100	pA
		$T_A = 125°C$	-1					nA
Gate Operating Current	I_G	$V_{DG} = 15$ V, $I_D = 0.1$ mA	-2					pA
Drain Cutoff Current	$I_{D(OFF)}$	$V_{DS} = 15$ V, $V_{GS} = -10$ V	2					pA
Gate-Source Forward Voltage	$V_{GS(F)}$	$I_G = 1$ mA, $V_{DS} = 0$ V	0.7					V
DYNAMIC								
Common-Source Forward Transconductance	g_{fs}	$V_{DS} = 20$ V, $V_{GS} = 0$ V, f = 1 kHz		0.5		1		mS
Common-Source Input Capacitance	C_{iss}	$V_{DS} = 20$ V, $V_{GS} = 0$ V, f = 1 MHz	4.5					pF
Common-Source Reverse Transfer Capacitance	C_{rss}		1.3					pF
Equivalent Input Noise Voltage	$\bar{e}_n$	$V_{DS} = 10$ V, $V_{GS} = 0$ V, f = 1 kHz	6					$nV/\sqrt{Hz}$

NOTES:
1. $T_A = 25°C$ unless otherwise noted.
2. For design aid only, not subject to production testing.
3. Pulse test; PW = 300 µs, duty cycle ≤ 3%.

J201 SERIES

ELECTRICAL CHARACTERISTICS [1]			LIMITS					
				J203		J204		
PARAMETER	SYMBOL	TEST CONDITIONS	TYP [2]	MIN	MAX	MIN	MAX	UNIT
STATIC								
Gate-Source Breakdown Voltage	$V_{(BR)GSS}$	$I_G = -1\ \mu A$, $V_{DS} = 0$ V	-57	-40		-25		V
Gate-Source Cutoff Voltage	$V_{GS(OFF)}$	$V_{DS} = 20$ V, $I_D = 10$ nA		-2	-10	-0.3	-2	V
Saturation Drain Current [3]	I_{DSS}	$V_{DS} = 20$ V, $V_{GS} = 0$ V		4	20	0.2	3	mA
Gate Reverse Current	I_{GSS}	$V_{GS} = -20$ V, $V_{DS} = 0$ V	-2		-100		-100	pA
		$T_A = 125°C$	-1					nA
Gate Operating Current	I_G	$V_{DG} = 15$ V, $I_D = 0.1$ mA	-2					pA
Drain Cutoff Current	$I_{D(OFF)}$	$V_{DS} = 15$ V, $V_{GS} = -10$ V	2					pA
Gate-Source Forward Voltage	$V_{GS(F)}$	$I_G = 1$ mA, $V_{DS} = 0$ V	0.7					V
DYNAMIC								
Common-Source Forward Transconductance	g_{fs}	$V_{DS} = 20$ V, $V_{GS} = 0$ V, f = 1 kHz		1.5		0.5		mS
Common-Source Input Capacitance	C_{iss}	$V_{DS} = 20$ V, $V_{GS} = 0$ V, f = 1 MHz	4.5					pF
Common-Source Reverse Transfer Capacitance	C_{rss}	$V_{DS} = 20$ V, $V_{GS} = 0$ V, f = 1 MHz	1.3					pF
Equivalent Input Noise Voltage	$\bar{e}_n$	$V_{DS} = 10$ V, $V_{GS} = 0$ V, f = 1 kHz	6					$nV/\sqrt{Hz}$

NOTES: 1. $T_A = 25\,°C$ unless otherwise noted.
2. For design aid only, not subject to production testing.
3. Pulse test; PW = 300 μs, duty cycle ≤ 3%.

N-Channel JFET

DESIGNED FOR:

- Small Signal Amplifiers
- Voltage Controlled Resistors
- Choppers

FEATURES

- Low Noise NF < 1 dB at 1 KHz
- Operation from Low Power Supply Voltages $V_{GS(off)}$ < 1 V (2N4338)
- High Off-Isolation as a Switch $I_{D(OFF)}$ < 50 pA
- High Input Impedance

TYPE	PACKAGE	DEVICE
Single	TO-92	• J201, J202, J203, J204 PN4302, PN4303, PN4304
	SOT-23	• SST201, SST202, SST203, SST204
	TO-18	• 2N4338, 2N4339, 2N4340, 2N4341 VCR4N
	TO-72	• 2N4867, 2N4868, 2N4869, 2N4867A, 2N4868A, 2N4869A
	Chip	• Available as above specifications

GEOMETRY DIAGRAM

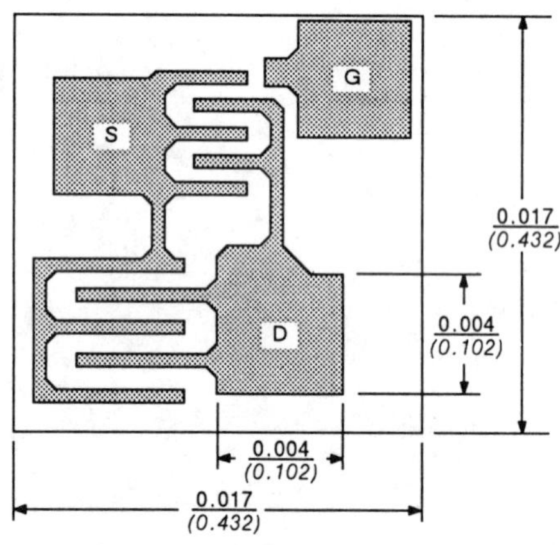

Gate also backside contact

TYPICAL CHARACTERISTICS

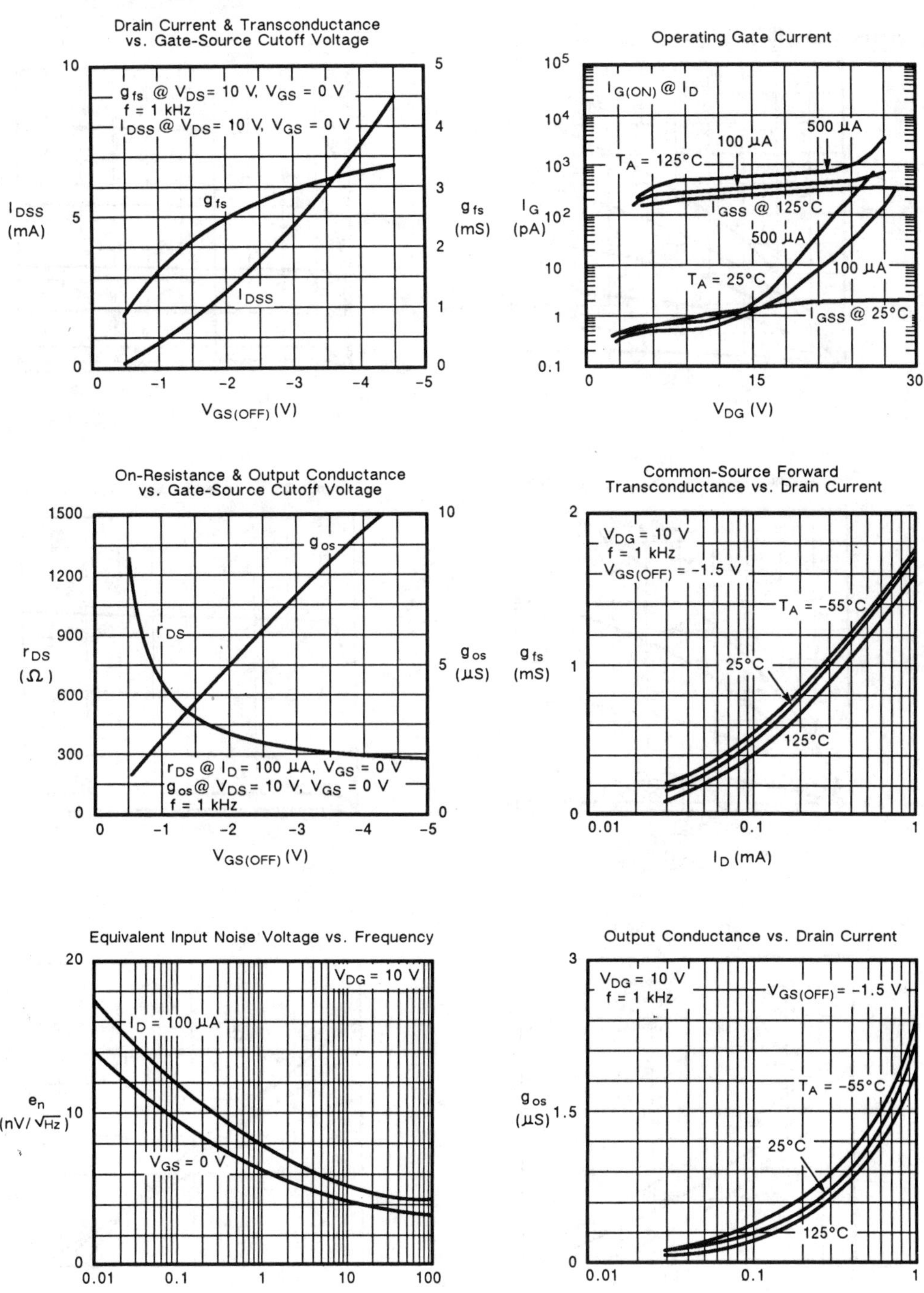

TYPICAL CHARACTERISTICS

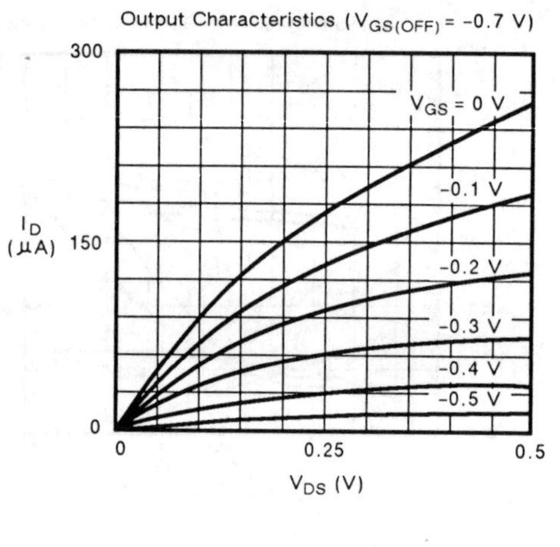

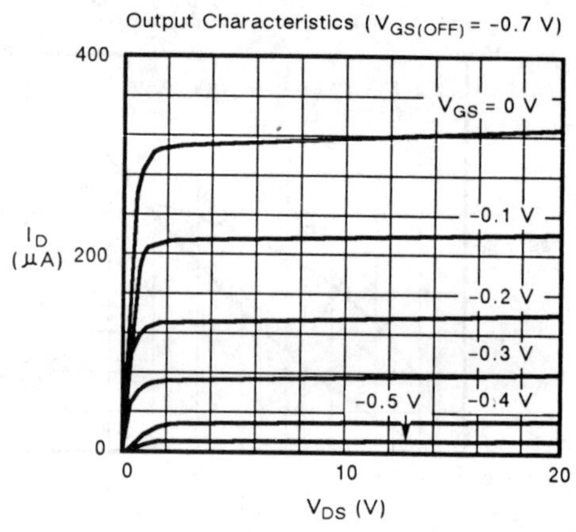

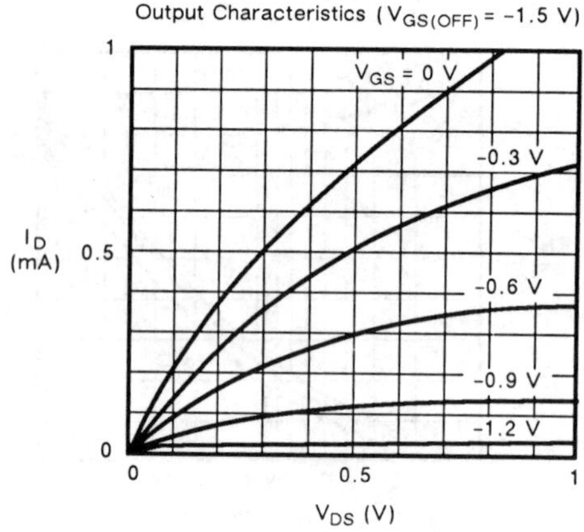

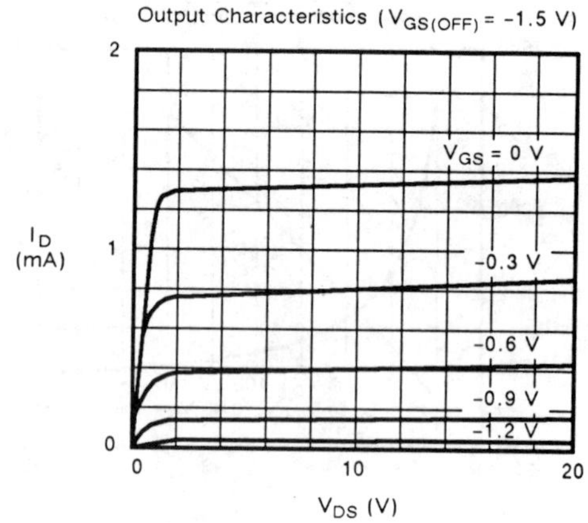

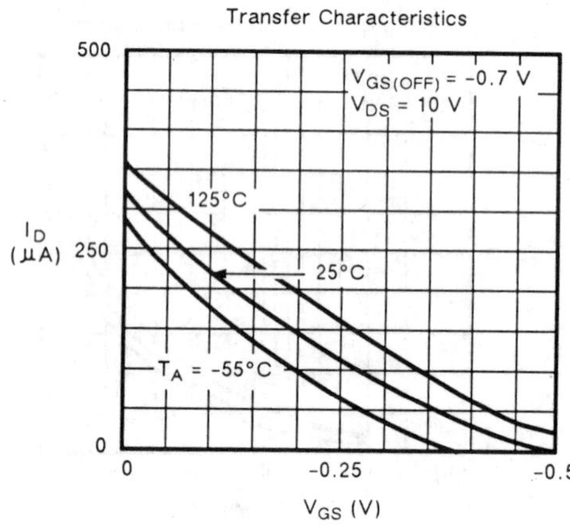

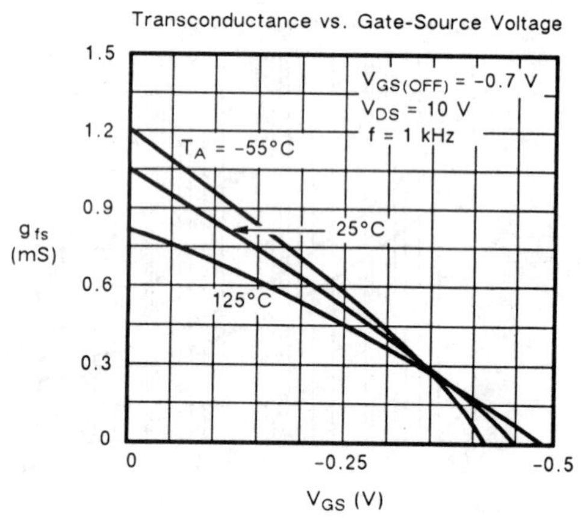

TYPICAL CHARACTERISTICS

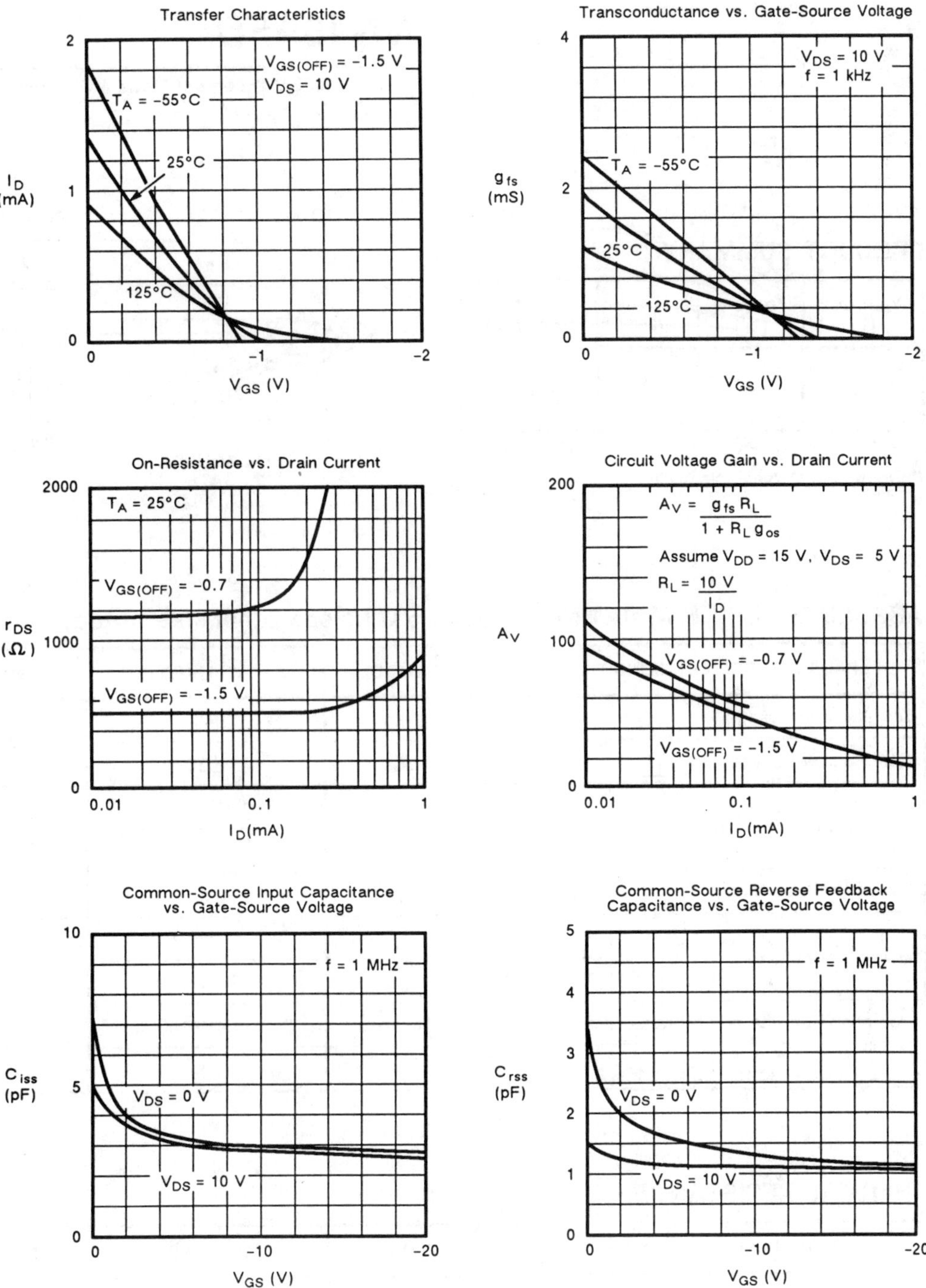

E.8 Siliconix medium-power n-channel VMOST type VN46AFD

VN46AFD

N-Channel Enhancement-Mode MOS Transistor

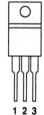

PRODUCT SUMMARY

$V_{(BR)DSS}$ (V)	$r_{DS(ON)}$ (Ω)	I_D (A)	PACKAGE
40	3	1.46	TO-220SD

Performance Curves: **VNDQ06**

TO-220SD

TOP VIEW

1 SOURCE
2 GATE
3 & TAB - DRAIN

ABSOLUTE MAXIMUM RATINGS (T_C = 25°C unless otherwise noted)

PARAMETERS/TEST CONDITIONS		SYMBOL	VN46AFD	UNITS
Drain-Source Voltage		V_{DS}	40	V
Gate-Source Voltage		V_{GS}	±30	
Continuous Drain Current	T_C = 25°C	I_D	1.46	A
	T_C = 100°C		0.92	
Pulsed Drain Current[1]		I_{DM}	3	
Power Dissipation	T_C = 25°C	P_D	15	W
	T_C = 100°C		6	
Operating Junction and Storage Temperature		T_j, T_{stg}	-55 to 150	°C
Lead Temperature (1/16" from case for 10 seconds)		T_L	300	

THERMAL RESISTANCE

THERMAL RESISTANCE	SYMBOL	VN46AFD	UNITS
Junction-to-Case	R_{thJC}	8.3	°C/W

[1]Pulse width limited by maximum junction temperature

VN46AFD

ELECTRICAL CHARACTERISTICS[1]			LIMITS			
				VN46AFD		
PARAMETER	SYMBOL	TEST CONDITIONS	TYP[2]	MIN	MAX	UNIT
STATIC						
Drain-Source Breakdown Voltage	$V_{(BR)DSS}$	V_{GS} = 0 V, I_D = 10 μA	70	40		V
Gate Threshold Voltage	$V_{GS(th)}$	V_{DS} = V_{GS}, I_D = 1 mA	1.5	0.8	2.5	
Gate-Body Leakage	I_{GSS}	V_{DS} = 0 V, V_{GS} = ±15 V	± 1		±100	nA
Zero Gate Voltage Drain Current	I_{DSS}	V_{DS} = 40 V, V_{GS} = 0 V	0.05		10	μA
		V_{DS} = 32 V, V_{GS} = 0 V, T_C = 125°C	0.3		500	
On-State Drain Current[3]	$I_{D(ON)}$	V_{DS} = 10 V, V_{GS} = 10 V	1.8	1		A
Drain-Source On-Resistance[3]	$r_{DS(ON)}$	V_{GS} = 5 V, I_D = 0.3 A	1.8		5	Ω
		V_{GS} = 10 V, I_D = 1 A	1.3		3	
		T_C = 125°C	2.6		6	
Forward Transconductance[3]	g_{FS}	V_{DS} = 10 V, I_D = 0.5 A	350	170		mS
Common Source Output Conductance[3]	g_{OS}	V_{DS} = 10 V, I_D = 0.1 A	1100			μS
DYNAMIC						
Input Capacitance	C_{iss}	V_{DS} = 25 V V_{GS} = 0 V f = 1 MHz	35		50	pF
Output Capacitance	C_{oss}		25		65	
Reverse Transfer Capacitance	C_{rss}		5		10	
SWITCHING						
Turn-On Time	t_{ON}	V_{DD} = 25 V, R_L = 23 Ω I_D = 1 A, V_{GEN} = 10 V R_G = 25 Ω (Switching time is essentially independent of operating temperature)	8		15	ns
Turn-Off Time	t_{OFF}		9.5		15	

NOTES: 1. T_C = 25 °C unless otherwise noted.
2. For design aid only, not subject to production testing.
3. Pulse test; PW = 300 μs, duty cycle ≤ 2%.

N-Channel Enhancement-Mode MOSFET

DESIGNED FOR:

- Switching
- Amplification

FEATURES

- Low $r_{DS(on)}$ < 3.5 Ω

TYPE	PACKAGE	DEVICE
Single	TO-205AD	• 2N6659, 2N6660 VN67AB
	TO-220SD	• VN40AFD, VN46AFD, VN66AFD, VN67AFD
	TO-220	• VN66AD, VN67AD
Quad	14-Pin Plastic	• VQ1004J
	14-Pin Dual-In-Line	• VQ1004P
	Chip	• Available as above specifications

GEOMETRY DIAGRAM

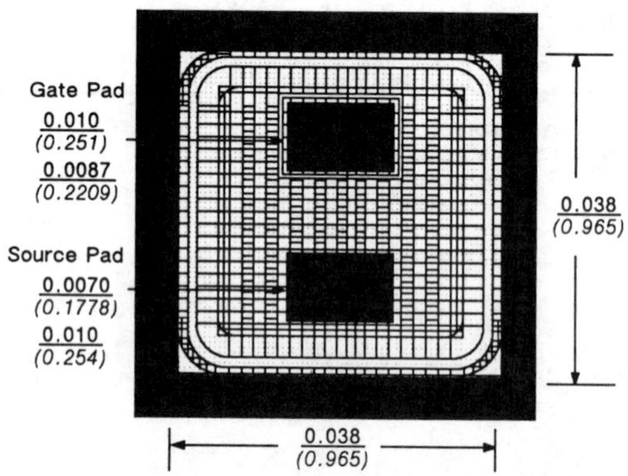

TYPICAL CHARACTERISTICS

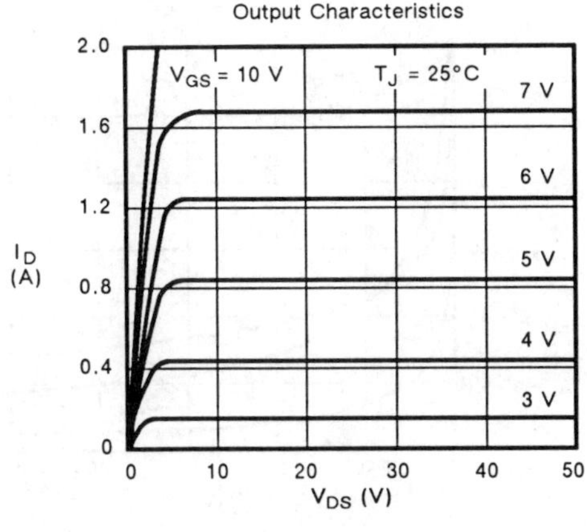

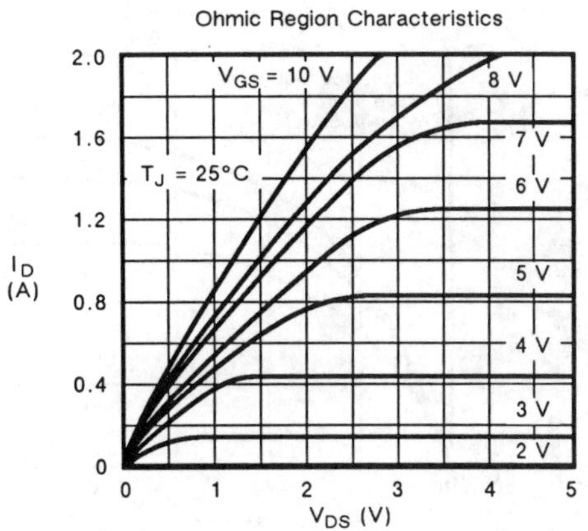

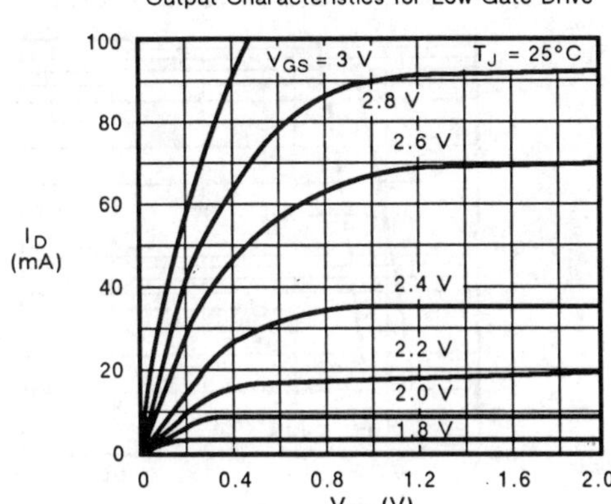

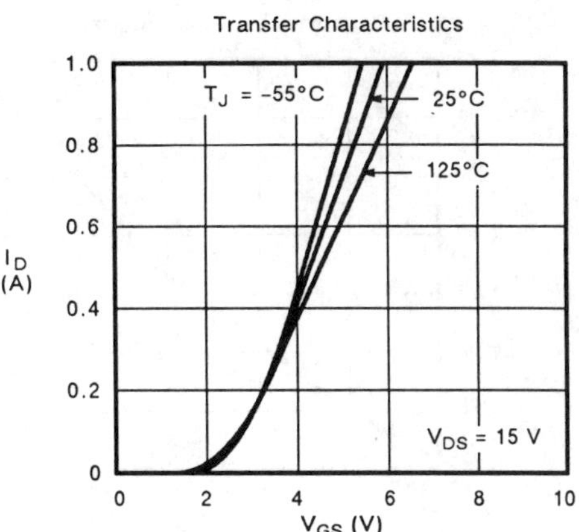

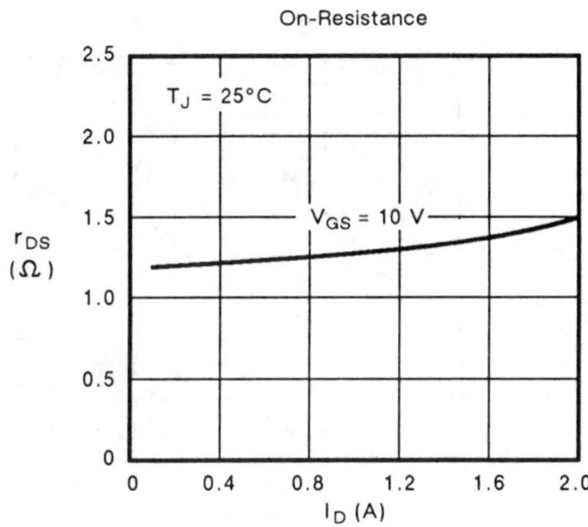

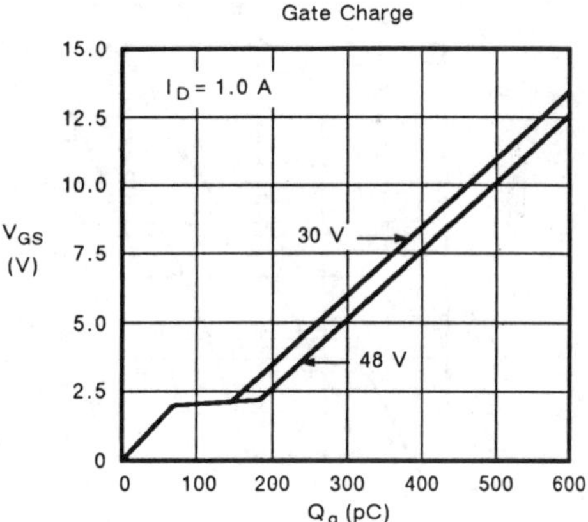

TYPICAL CHARACTERISTICS

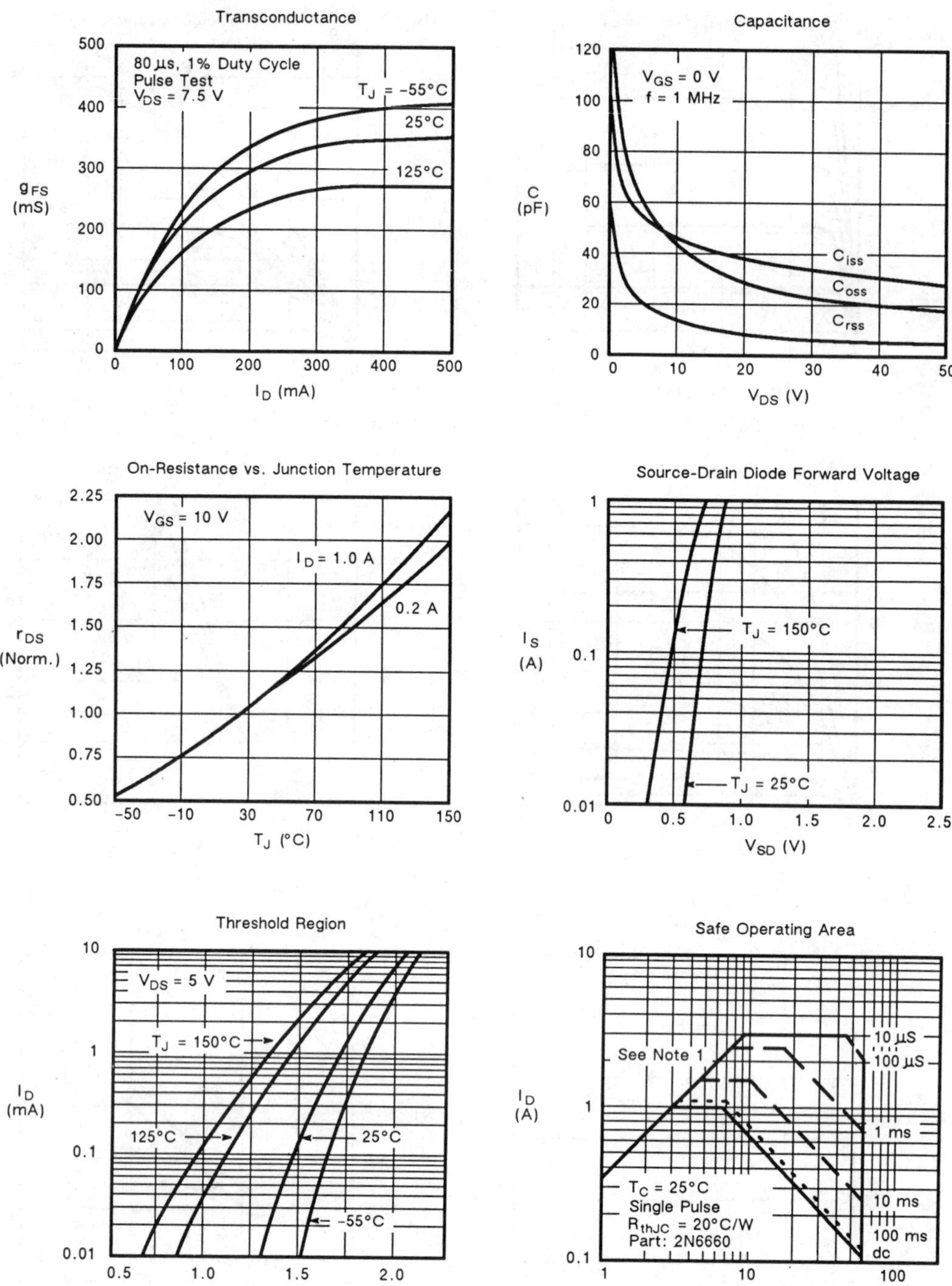

[1]Operation in this area may be limited by $r_{DS(ON)}$

TYPICAL CHARACTERISTICS

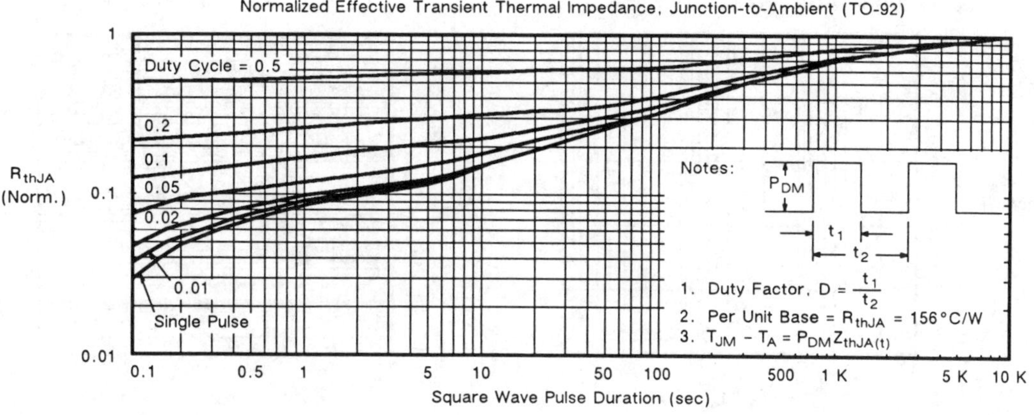

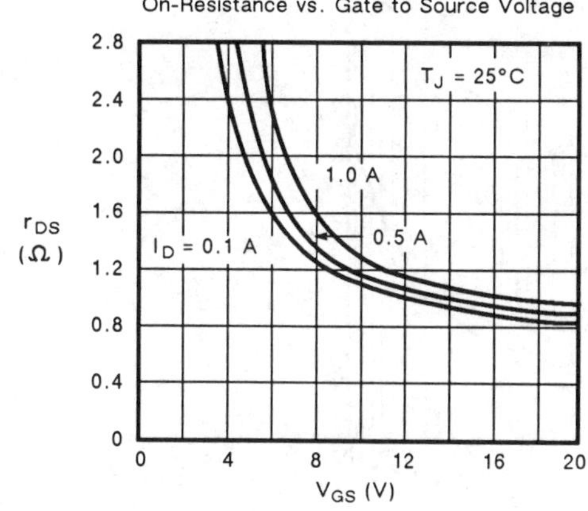

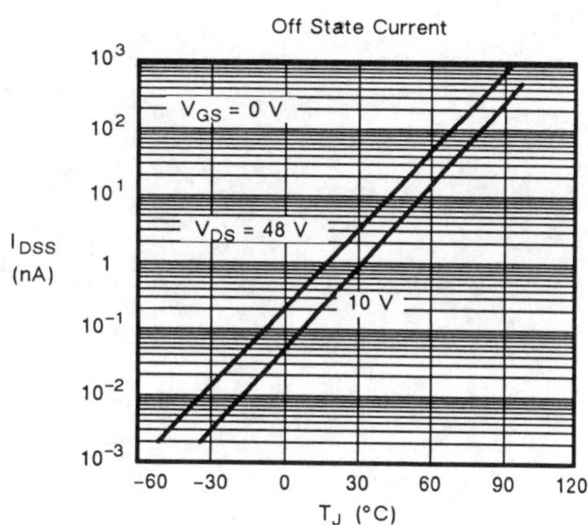

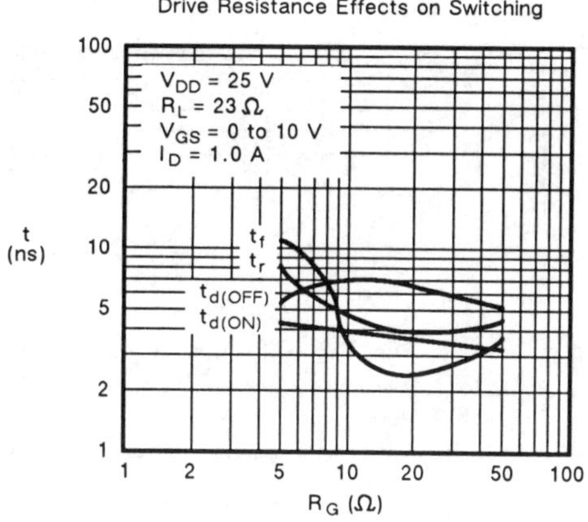

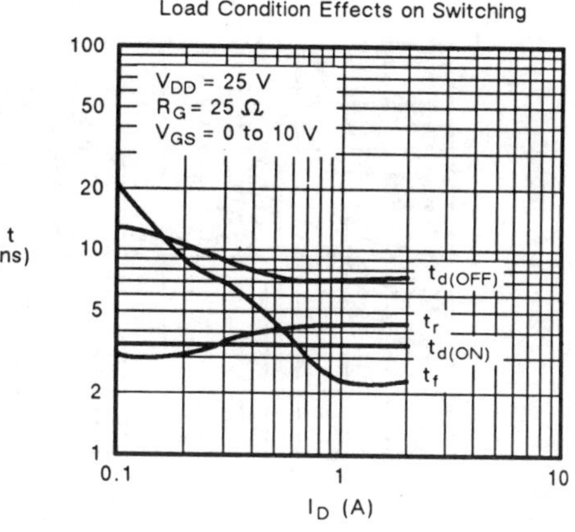

TYPICAL CHARACTERISTICS

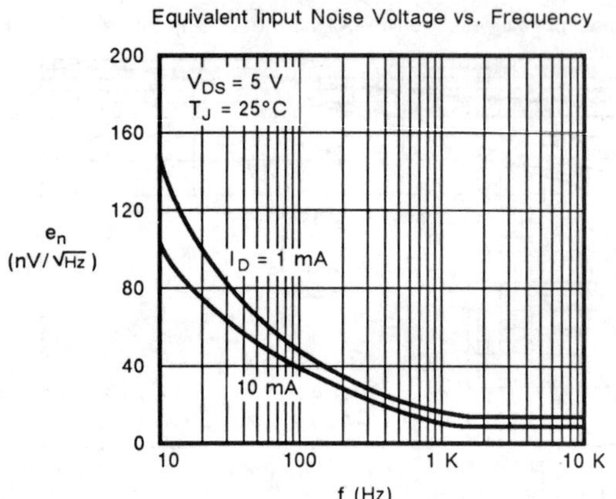

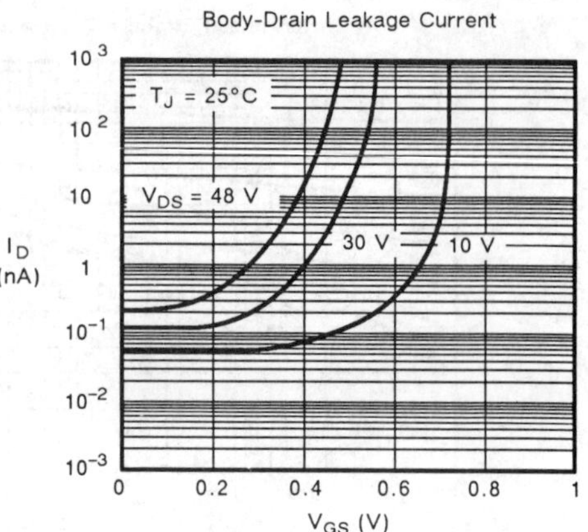

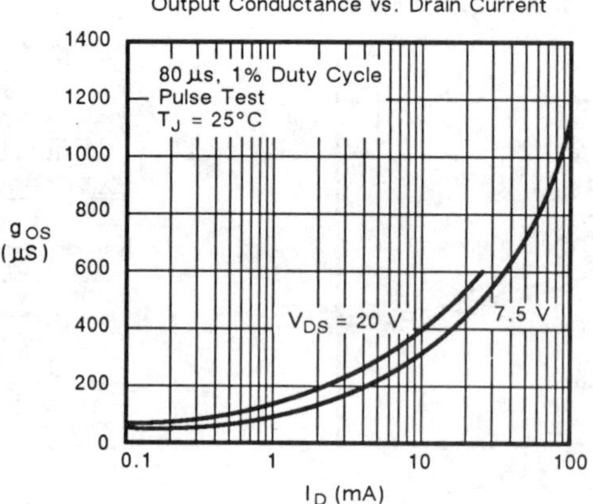

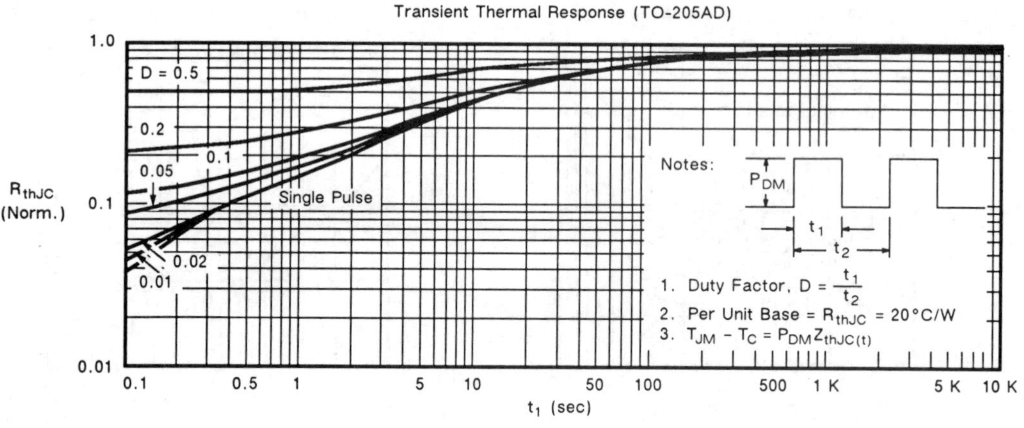

E.9 Philips general-purpose bipolar operational amplifier type 741

μA741/μA741C/SA741C
General Purpose Operational Amplifier

Product Specification

DESCRIPTION

The μA741 is a high performance operational amplifier with high open-loop gain, internal compensation, high common mode range and exceptional temperature stability. The μA741 is short-circuit-protected and allows for nulling of offset voltage.

FEATURES

- **Internal frequency compensation**
- **Short circuit protection**
- **Excellent temperature stability**
- **High input voltage range**

PIN CONFIGURATION

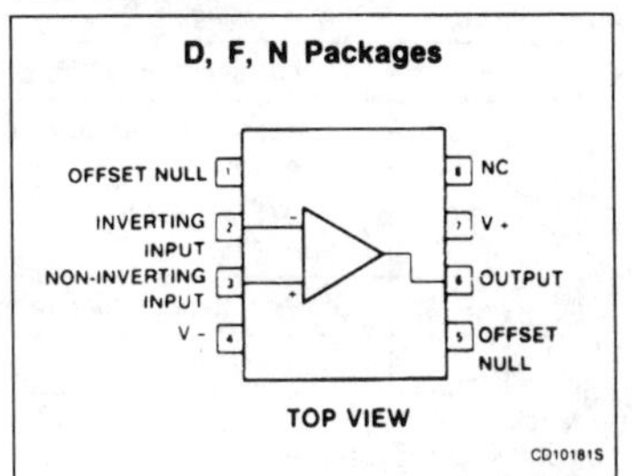

ORDERING INFORMATION

DESCRIPTION	TEMPERATURE RANGE	ORDER CODE
8-Pin Plastic DIP	-55°C to +125°C	μA741N
8-Pin Plastic DIP	0 to +70°C	μA741CN
8-Pin Plastic DIP	-40°C to +85°C	SA741CN
8-Pin Cerdip	-55°C to +125°C	μA741F
8-Pin Cerdip	0 to +70°C	μA741CF
8-Pin SO	0 to +70°C	μA741CD

EQUIVALENT SCHEMATIC

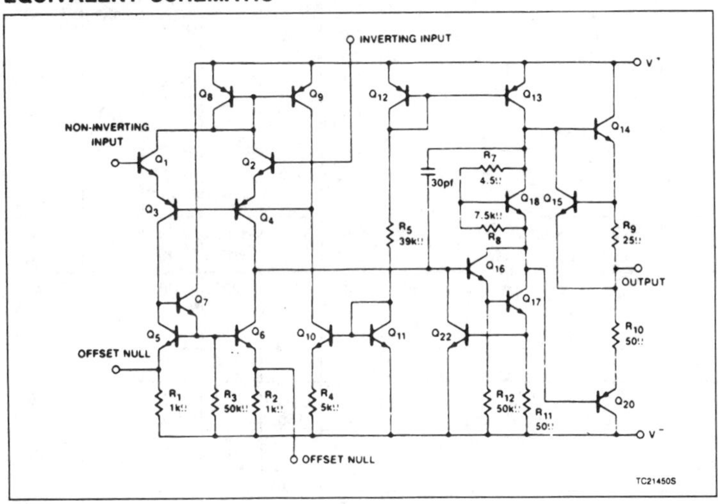

General Purpose Operational Amplifier μA741/μA741C/SA741C

ABSOLUTE MAXIMUM RATINGS

SYMBOL	PARAMETER	RATING	UNIT
V_S	Supply voltage		
	μA741C	±18	V
	μA741	±22	V
P_D	Internal power dissipation		
	D package	780	mW
	N package	1170	mW
	F package	800	mW
V_{IN}	Differential input voltage	±30	V
V_{IN}	Input voltage[1]	±15	V
I_{SC}	Output short-circuit duration	Continuous	
T_A	Operating temperature range		
	μA741C	0 to +70	°C
	SA741C	−40 to +85	°C
	μA741	−55 to +125	°C
T_{STG}	Storage temperature range	−65 to +150	°C
T_{SOLD}	Lead soldering temperature (10sec max)	300	°C

NOTE:
1. For supply voltages less than ±15V, the absolute maximum input voltage is equal to the supply voltage.

DC ELECTRICAL CHARACTERISTICS (μA741, μA741C) $T_A = 25°C$, $V_S = ±15V$, unless otherwise specified.

SYMBOL	PARAMETER	TEST CONDITIONS	μA741			μA741C			UNIT
			Min	Typ	Max	Min	Typ	Max	
V_{OS}	Offset voltage	$R_S = 10kΩ$		1.0	5.0		2.0	6.0	mV
		$R_S = 10kΩ$, over temp.		1.0	6.0			7.5	mV
$ΔV_{OS}/ΔT$				10			10		μV/°C
I_{OS}	Offset current			20	200		20	200	nA
		Over temp.						300	nA
		$T_A = +125°C$		7.0	200				nA
		$T_A = -55°C$		20	500				nA
$ΔI_{OS}/ΔT$				200			200		pA/°C
I_{BIAS}	Input bias current			80	500		80	500	nA
		Over temp.						800	nA
		$T_A = +125°C$		30	500				nA
		$T_A = -55°C$		300	1500				nA
$ΔI_B/ΔT$				1			1		nA/°C
V_{OUT}	Output voltage swing	$R_L = 10kΩ$	±12	±14		±12	±14		V
		$R_L = 2kΩ$, over temp.	±10	±13		±10	±13		V
A_{VOL}	Large-signal voltage gain	$R_L = 2kΩ$, $V_O = ±10V$	50	200		20	200		V/mV
		$R_L = 2kΩ$, $V_O = ±10V$, over temp.	25			15			V/mV
	Offset voltage adjustment range			±30			±30		mV
PSRR	Supply voltage rejection ratio	$R_S \leq 10kΩ$					10	150	μV/V
		$R_S \leq 10kΩ$, over temp.		10	150				μV/V
CMRR	Common-mode rejection ratio					70	90		dB
		Over temp.	70	90					dB
I_{CC}	Supply current			1.4	2.8		1.4	2.8	mA
		$T_A = +125°C$		1.5	2.5				mA
		$T_A = -55°C$		2.0	3.3				mA

General Purpose Operational Amplifier — μA741/μA741C/SA741C

DC ELECTRICAL CHARACTERISTICS (Continued) (μA741, μA741C) $T_A = 25°C$, $V_S = \pm 15V$, unless otherwise specified.

SYMBOL	PARAMETER	TEST CONDITIONS	μA741			μA741C			UNIT
			Min	Typ	Max	Min	Typ	Max	
V_{IN}	Input voltage range	(μA741, over temp.)	±12	±13		±12	±13		V
R_{IN}	Input resistance		0.3	2.0		0.3	2.0		MΩ
P_D	Power consumption			50	85		50	85	mW
		$T_A = +125°C$		45	75				mW
		$T_A = -55°C$		45	100				mW
R_{OUT}	Output resistance			75			75		Ω
I_{SC}	Output short-circuit current		10	25	60	10	25	60	mA

DC ELECTRICAL CHARACTERISTICS (SA741C) $T_A = 25°C$, $V_S = \pm 15V$, unless otherwise specified.

SYMBOL	PARAMETER	TEST CONDITIONS	SA741C			UNIT
			Min	Typ	Max	
V_{OS}	Offset voltage	$R_S = 10k\Omega$		2.0	6.0	mV
		$R_S = 10k\Omega$, over temp.			7.5	mV
$\Delta V_{OS}/\Delta T$				10		μV/°C
I_{OS}	Offset current			20	200	nA
		Over temp.			500	nA
$\Delta I_{OS}/\Delta T$				200		pA/°C
I_{BIAS}	Input bias current			80	500	nA
		Over temp.			1500	nA
$\Delta I_B/\Delta T$				1		nA/°C
V_{OUT}	Output voltage swing	$R_L = 10k\Omega$	±12	±14		V
		$R_L = 2k\Omega$, over temp.	±10	±13		V
A_{VOL}	Large-signal voltage gain	$R_L = 2k\Omega$, $V_O = \pm 10V$	20	200		V/mV
		$R_L = 2k\Omega$, $V_O = \pm 10V$, over temp.	15			V/mV
	Offset voltage adjustment range			±30		mV
PSRR	Supply voltage rejection ratio	$R_S \leqslant 10k\Omega$		10	150	μV/V
CMRR	Common mode rejection ration		70	90		dB
V_{IN}	Input voltage range	Over temp.	±12	±13		V
R_{IN}	Input resistance		0.3	2.0		MΩ
P_d	Power consumption			50	85	mW
R_{OUT}	Output resistance			75		Ω
I_{SC}	Output short-circuit current			25		mA

AC ELECTRICAL CHARACTERISTICS $T_A = 25°C$, $V_S = \pm 15V$, unless otherwise specified.

SYMBOL	PARAMETER	TEST CONDITIONS	μA741, μA741C			UNIT
			Min	Typ	Max	
R_{IN}	Parallel input resistance	Open-loop, f = 20Hz	0.3			MΩ
C_{IN}	Parallel input capacitance	Open-loop, f = 20Hz		1.4		pF
	Unity gain crossover frequency	Open-loop		1.0		MHz
	Transient response unity gain	$V_{IN} = 20mV$, $R_L = 2k\Omega$, $C_L \leqslant 100pF$				
t_R	Rise time			0.3		μs
	Overshoot			5.0		%
SR	Slew rate	$C \leqslant 100pF$, $R_L \geqslant 2k\Omega$, $V_{IN} = \pm 10V$		0.5		V/μs

General Purpose Operational Amplifier μA741/μA741C/SA741C

TYPICAL PERFORMANCE CHARACTERISTICS

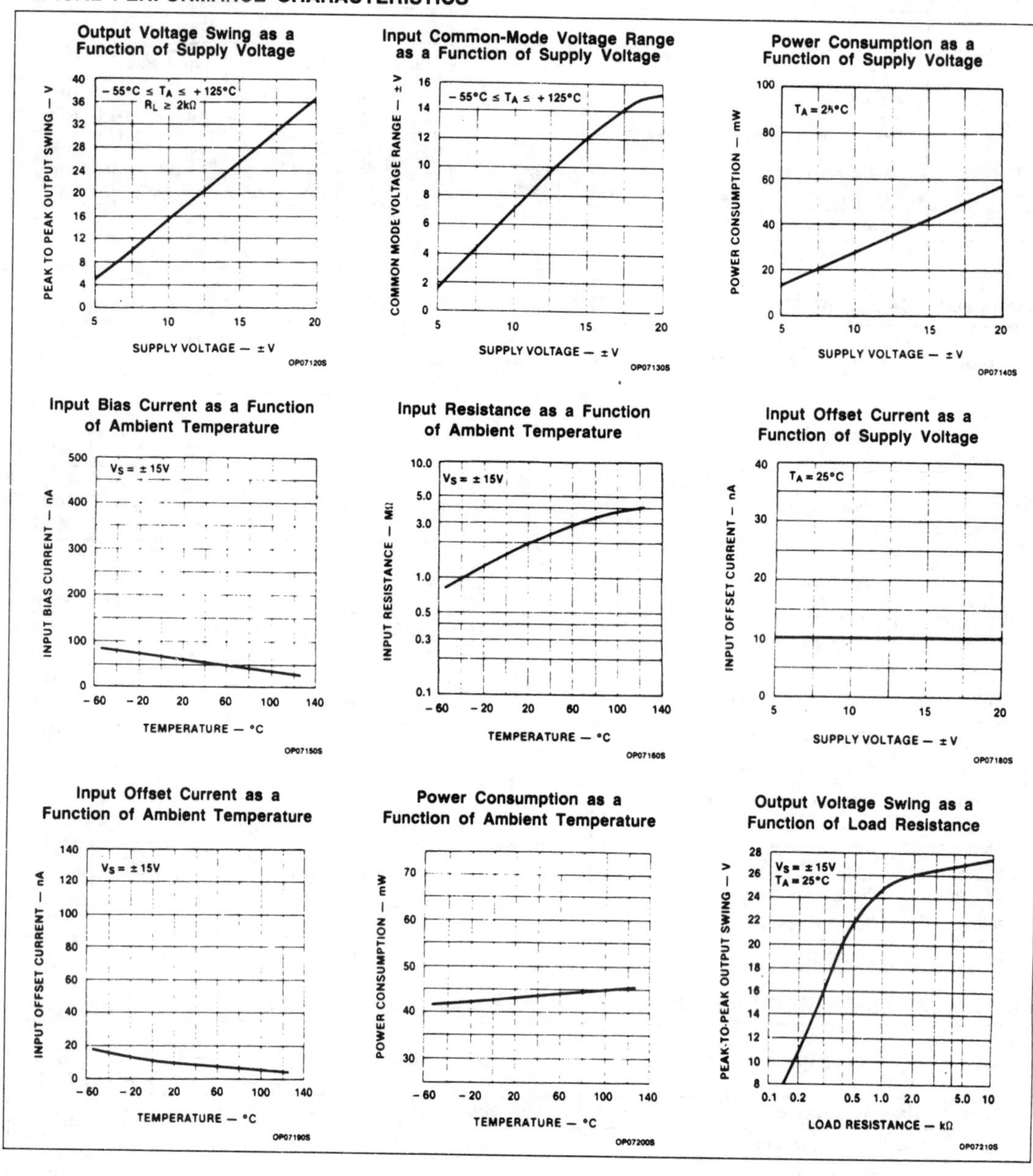

General Purpose Operational Amplifier μA741/μA741C/SA741C

TYPICAL PERFORMANCE CHARACTERISTICS (Continued)

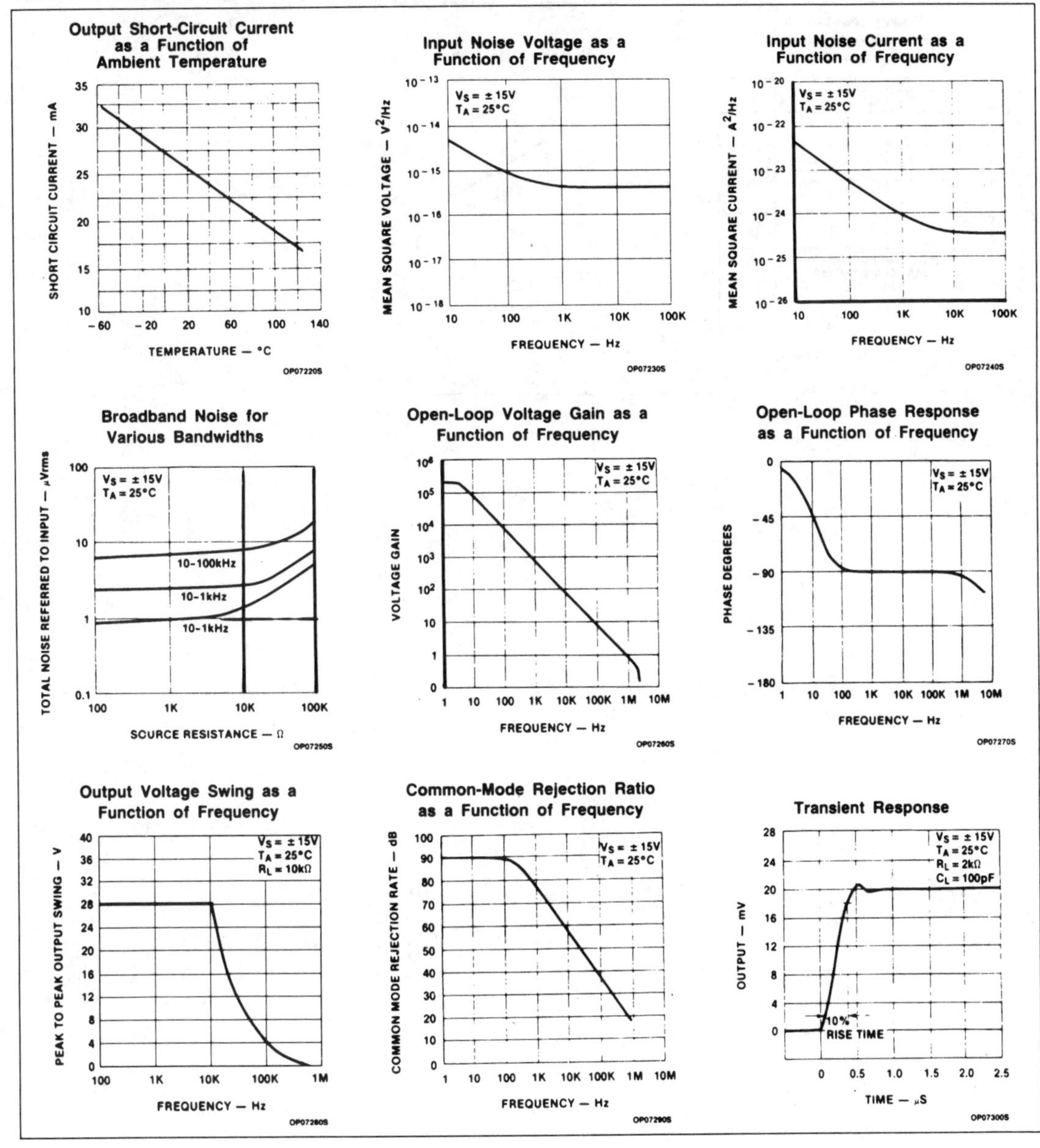

General Purpose Operational Amplifier μA741/μA741C/SA741C

TYPICAL PERFORMANCE CHARACTERISTICS (Continued)

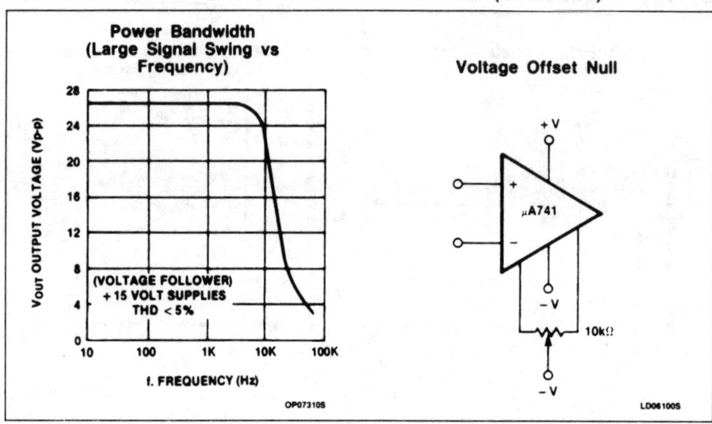

UK/US Differences in Terminology Spelling and Notation

UK	*US*
$C_{b'e}$	C_{π}
$C_{b'c}$	C_{μ}
g_{fe}	g_m
g_{fs}	g_m
$r_{bb'}$	r_b
$r_{b'e}$	r_{π}
$r_{b'c}$	r_{μ}
Analog(ue)	Analog
Colour	Color
Earth	Ground
Metallise	Metalize
Model	Equivalent circuit
Potential	Voltage
Q-point	Quiescent point

Index